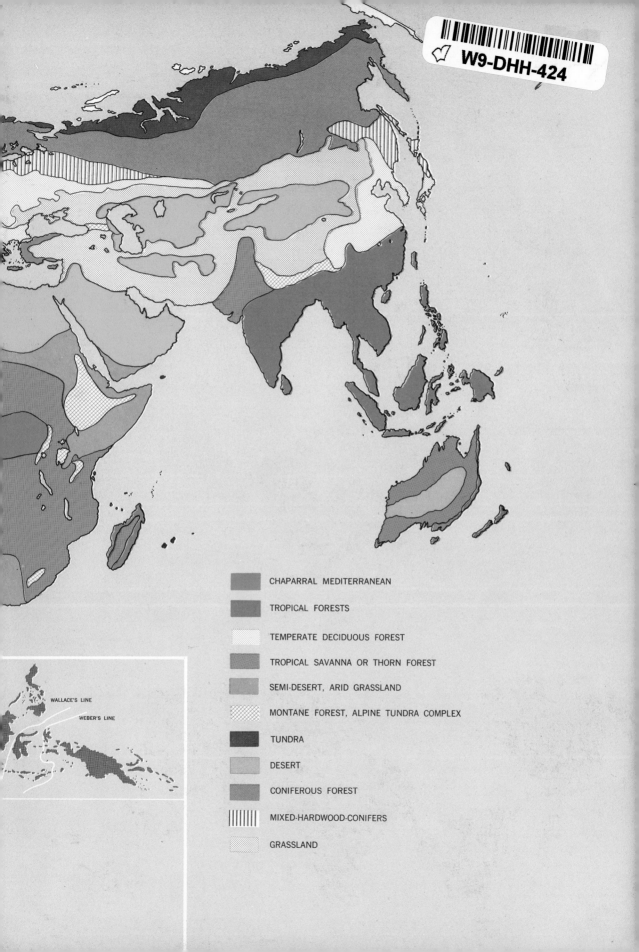

CHAPARRAL MEDITERRANEAN

TROPICAL FORESTS

TEMPERATE DECIDUOUS FOREST

TROPICAL SAVANNA OR THORN FOREST

SEMI-DESERT, ARID GRASSLAND

MONTANE FOREST, ALPINE TUNDRA COMPLEX

TUNDRA

DESERT

CONIFEROUS FOREST

MIXED-HARDWOOD-CONIFERS

GRASSLAND

WALLACE'S LINE

WEBER'S LINE

ECOLOGY

and FIELD BIOLOGY

HARPER & ROW, Publishers   *New York and London*

by *ROBERT LEO SMITH*

West Virginia University

Illustrated by

NED SMITH

ECOLOGY
and FIELD BIOLOGY

To my
Mother and Father
and especially
to Alice
my wife, who has carried most
of the burden and enjoyed little
of the pleasure of writing this book

Contents

Preface   vii

Part I   *Introduction*

1   The nature of field biology   3

Part II   *The ecosystem and the community*

2   The ecosystem and the community   11
3   Energy flow and material cycling   27
4   Environmental influences   60
5   Periodicity and biological clocks   98
6   Succession   127

Part III   *Aquatic and terrestrial habitats*

7   Water as a medium for life   157
8   Lakes and ponds   162
9   Bogs, swamps, and marshes   182
10   Flowing waters   192
11   Estuaries, tidal marshes, and swamps   210
12   The seashore   221
13   The soil   243
14   Life in the soil   261
15   The grasslands   275
16   Shrublands and the desert   289

Contents

17   The forest   301
18   The tundra   318
19   Distribution of communities   331

Part IV   Population ecology

20   Relations within a population   341
21   Relationships between populations   397

Part V   Natural selection and speciation

22   Natural selection: an introduction   427
23   The basis of natural selection   431
24   Species and how they arise   448

Part VI   The behavior of animals

25   Behavior: some basic considerations   485
26   Egocentric behavior   494
27   Social behavior   512

Bibliography   545

Suggested readings for chapters 1–27   573

General references

Aids to identification   585
Journals of interest to field biologists   589
General bibliographies   591

Appendixes

A   An annotated bibliography of statistical methods   593
B   Environmental measurements   596
C   Study of the plant community   610
D   Studying animal populations   636
E   Methods for studying animal behavior   662

Index   669

Preface

Prefaces are written to be read, although I suspect that more readers flip past them than read them. I once asked a class near the end of the semester how many had read the preface of the text we were using and not one of them had. Personally I read the preface first and perhaps several times later. In many books the preface is the most absorbing part, which may say a lot for the preface or very little for the book. But in technical and text books, the preface is about the only place where the author gives us any real glimpse of himself and of his reasons for writing the book, how he thinks it should be used, what problems he had, and who assisted him. So this preface is being written to be read before, I hope, the reader ventures much further.

The book is entitled *Ecology and Field Biology*. The term field biology is often associated with such semitaxonomic subjects as field zoology, field botany, and so on, in which collections are made one day and identifications the next; or in which a great effort is made to identify different organisms in their habitat. This is not the type of field biology I have in mind, in spite of the title. I like to think of it more as biology out in the field, in contrast to the purely laboratory-confined, molecular-orientated biology. And that basically is ecology. But to give the title the breadth it needs, both words are used.

Interest in field biology courses of some sort is growing in colleges and universities. In some, such a course is required. At one time, general biology courses were taught from a natural history point of view, but now all this has changed. General biology has gone molecular. In addition, so much new information in physiology has accumulated that this area tends to dominate much of the introductory biology course. Other relevant areas, such as ecology, natural selection, and evolution, are relegated to a few chapters at the end of many of the major biology texts and may never be presented in class. Then, too, biology instructors, perhaps reflecting an urban environment and culture, have left the woods and fields for the laboratory, where their closest associations with animal life below the human level are white mice, flour beetles, and fruit flies. And even these are being abandoned for test tubes. Under such a regime the student has been exposed to only one-half of biology. The other half, the natural history half, through necessity is often ignored. This second half, just as important as the first, must be picked up in another course.

Actually, natural history, field biology, or ecology, call it what you will, should be a part of the education not only of every biologist but also of every chemist, physicist, engineer, lawyer, teacher, agricultural and forestry student, and liberal arts students. It should, in sum, be a part of the liberal education. The reason is simple. As we become more and more engrossed in technology, in our own chrome-plated civilization, we tend to forget that man is a part of nature. His roots still cling to "mother earth," no matter how much concrete and steel separate man from the land. Human life on earth still depends upon the trapping of solar energy, upon the cycling of materials and water through the ecosystem. Many of the problems, social and political, that we face now and will have to face in the future are basically ecological ones: overpopulation, deterioration of our habitat, pollution of air and water, radioactive fallout, sprawling urbanization. Unless the technologist from whose hands comes "progress" and the man in the street, the voter who ultimately decides basic issues, appreciate the ecology of nature and man, we will do even more violence to ourselves and the world about us than we have done already. In the end, it is the ecological half of biology, rather than molecular biology, that holds the key to the future of man. In fact, ecology is emerging as the phase of biology that offers the major approach to the understanding of life.

But, back to the book. I have divided the text into six parts. Part I consists of only one chapter, a short one on the nature of field biology. Part II is basically functional ecology—how the community and the ecosystem operate. Chapters 2 and 3 are basic to the whole area of field biology and ecology, as is Chapter 6, especially for those who have "applied ecology" as a major interest. Part III is really an extension of Part II. It contains the habitat approach to ecology. The major units of both aquatic and terrestrial ecosystems are discussed. The aquatic ecosystems end with the edge of the sea, however; I did not venture into the ocean itself because of the great amount of additional space needed to do it justice. In Part III you will find amplified a number of principles that have been discussed briefly in Part II, and you will find as well the basic principles of limnology and soils. Part IV is population ecology. Here the major emphasis is on the relationship between individuals within the population and on the relationships between populations. Part II and Part IV taken together form the heart of ecology. Part V, really a continuation of population ecology, takes a look at how the individual populations arrived on the scene, their natural selection and evolution. The ecological aspects of natural selection are stressed. Part VI is animal behavior. Even though it has the term ethology attached to it, animal behavior is still in many respects within the realm of ecology; this in spite of the fact that some ethologists are sidling over to psychology and neurophysiology. But I have approached behavior chiefly as ecology, since the social behavior of animals is a part of their environment.

I have not attempted to separate basic and applied ecology. Just exactly where does one draw the line? Neither have I ignored man. Man as an influence on the ecosystem is considered along with the rest. There is some tendency among ecologists to stand off and look at things as if man didn't exist. In addition, I have paid some attention to the development of ecological principles, but rather than concentrate on the historical in one chapter, I have discussed it in appropriate places throughout the book.

This text is intended for a sophomore or junior course in field biology with the assumption that the student has had a full year in general biology, botany, or zoology, preferably the first. Such a course could be a terminal one in a liberal arts curriculum. Or it could serve as a background course for such advanced courses as plant ecology, vertebrate ecology, marine biology, fishery biology and wildlife, forest and range management, and agriculture. The grounding in ecology is essential to all these fields, which today are tending more and more to produce specialists so narrow that they do not understand and oftentimes do not even care what effects their work has on the environment and life of organisms, including man. At the same time, I hope that this book will also serve as a reference for specialists in the field, especially for the applied ecologists in forestry, wildlife, fisheries, and sanitary engineering, as well as for those interested in natural history as an avocation.

Field biology and ecology as it is taught in colleges and universities is still a fluid subject. It does not fit into any narrow compartment of subject material such as those in which general biology and introductory courses in zoology and botany find themselves. It goes by a variety of titles—field biology, natural history, general ecology, to mention a few. And the content and approach of such courses are nearly as varied as the instructors.

Only in a two-semester course could one cover all the material in this book. But I have not written it as a one-semester or a two-semester course. It was planned to give the instructor a great deal of flexibility in how he presents his course. The text should enable the instructor to put his own imprint on the course, to pick and choose among the material that best fits his interests, training, and local environmental situation. The student can then read whatever else he desires on his own.

However, in any course of this nature, there are some basic principles that should be put across. I would strongly recommend that a course include Chapters 2, 3, 4, 5, and 6. Once into these chapters, the instructor can venture into one or several of the habitat chapters. If the course is given in the fall, the instructor might want to start off with field work right away and wade into Part III, where he will find plenty of references back to Part II. In the spring, one could start out with Chapters 2, 3, 20, and 21, and then go back to 6 and on into Part III. In any event, I would suggest that the student read some of the habitat chapters, especially Chapters 7, 8, and 10, which contain some basic background on limnology, and Chapter 13 on the soil. If the instructor is more inclined toward the population approach to ecology, he could start off with Chapters 6, 20, and 21, work into 26 and 27, and end up with Chapters 2 and 3. This at least gives some idea of the flexibility and hints of the many ways that the chapters might be combined to serve a course. Each part must not be considered an entity in itself. There is a good deal of relationship and many cross references between parts and chapters.

Since the book covers field biology, I have emphasized the field aspects. The purely laboratory situation rarely enters the picture, and only where I feel it necessary. For this reason flour beetles and fruit flies are scarce in these pages, and not because I am unfamiliar with the literature or fail to recognize its importance. In the examples, I have selected, where possible, the more familiar plants and animals, because in my experience student interest is achieved most easily when examples are within the range of their experiences. For this reason the white-tailed deer, mule deer, cottontail rabbit, song sparrow, and cicadas figure large in these pages. I have attempted to keep a pretty good balance between plants and animals. Even ecologists seem to be developing into specialists these days. In fact some animal ecologists (I dislike this division of ecology into plant and animal) admit they know little about the literature of plant ecology, which is a sorry state of affairs.

The reader will soon note that I have tapped (in keeping with my interests) a source of material that rarely gets into ecology texts—the publications of various state game and fish departments. The wildlife and fishery biologists of these state organizations are doing some excellent ecological work that often goes unnoticed by most ecologists, primarily because not being in an "applied" area, ecologists rarely come in contact with the publications.

The problem of documentation in a textbook is often a difficult one. I have aimed at a rather complete documentation, but undoubtedly in the course of writing I have slipped up here and there. I also cite the sources for illustrations where appropriate and include these citations in the bibliography. I must admit that I have done this because I get rather exasperated when the authors of other books give a citation for an illustration as "after so and so, date" and go no further. I have the habit of looking up the original sources quite frequently and I hope the reader will do the same. At the risk of interrupting the student's reading, I have cited author and date in the body of the text. If the student, after reading, will turn to the Bibliography following the last chapter, Chapter 27, he will find the complete reference. Each appendix is also followed by its own bibliography. If a student will look up a few of these references, he will be likely to gain a better appreciation of the nature of original research. If there is some particular area in which the reader is interested, the bibliography will be the key that will further unlock the door to even more information.

One thing I avoided was padding the Bibliography. Usually only one or two sources are cited in any one instance. I note a trend toward this sort of padding these days. Important sources that are not cited I have included in the Suggested Readings list, which follows the Bibliography.

In the list of Suggested Readings, I have aimed chiefly at books. Articles and papers are included only when I feel that they have some significance and when they are not in the Bibliography. Frankly, the best source for additional material is the Bibliography, which gives the lists of papers and books cited throughout the text. This source material was sifted from thousands of references. Any point stressed in the text is elaborated in the original sources. Admittedly these are harder to read—often deadly dull—and some, unless one has access to a well-stocked university library, may be hard to locate.

Following the Suggested Readings list is a section entitled Aids to Identification, which lists sources the reader may refer to when he wishes to identify plants and animals encountered in the field. The sources are grouped, for convenience, under such headings as Lower Plants, and Grasses and Wildflowers.

I have also included a list of the English-language journals published that are of interest to field biologists, with a short description of each, so that the reader can tell if the journal will be useful to him.

And finally, there is a list of the bibliographies put out by various organizations to provide up-to-date listings of material published on subjects of interest to those concerned with ecology. The reader will of course be able to refer to these bibliographies in the future for information on articles and papers that will come out after this book is published.

A field biology course without field work is not complete. Without it the subject becomes purely academic. The appendixes of this book offer a wide variety of suggestions for field work, far more than can be completed by any one class or person. But out of all the suggestions and methods given, there should be some seeds of ideas on what to do. Personally I suggest that the bulk of the field work be concentrated around one community or ecosystem. Ponds are excellent; where these are lacking, a stream or grassland or woodland would be good substitutes, but they are a little more difficult to handle. At the same time, a few side trips to other ecosystems should be taken. On the other hand, perhaps a population or behavioral project might be more suitable, especially where the classes or laboratory sections are small.

In many recent publications there is a trend toward the photograph. Someone has predicted that photography would replace art in our books. In many it has. But in books like this the photograph—and I appreciate good photography—cannot show what a drawing can. An examination of the illustrations in this text vividly point out this fact. This text relies heavily on the excellent drawings done by Ned Smith (no relation). He is, to my mind, one of the top wildlife and outdoor illustrators working in this country today. He has done a superb job in translating my ideas into completed, finished drawings that are little masterpieces. He also offered numerous ideas and changes in layout and approach. The majority of illustrations are original in design, although the ideas may have come, in some cases, from a number of sources, all acknowledged. In most instances, the drawings have been done from actual specimens and field sketches, rather than from illustrations in other books.

Marston Bates once wrote that textbooks form a class of publications all by themselves—they are uniformly dull. But he added that there is no reason why they should be. I hope that this one isn't dull. I have written this book for the student—to be read. And I hope he or she will read those pages that must go unassigned for his own information and enjoyment.

ROBERT LEO SMITH

Acknowledgments

The author of a textbook depends upon a number of people, and among these some must be singled out. Dr. F. Reese Nevin, State University of New York, Plattsburg, encouraged me to undertake the writing of this book. Among those who read portions of an earlier draft of the text and offered their suggestions were: Professor Arnold Benson, West Virginia University, who read Chapters 3 and 7–11; Dr. Warren Chase, University of Michigan, Chapter 6; Dr. David E. Davis, Pennsylvania State University, Chapters 20 and 21; Dr. Willem van Eck, West Virginia University, Chapter 13; Drs. Robert and Millicent Ficken, University of Maryland, Chapters 25–27. Final reviewers were Dr. Henry J. Tompson, University of California at Los Angeles, Chapters 6–19; Dr. Harold A. Mooney, UCLA, Chapter 4; Dr. J. T. Enright, UCLA, Chapter 5; and Dr. Monte Lloyd, UCLA, Chapters 1, 2, 3, 20–24. For their pointed comments, helpful suggestions, and new insights, I am more than grateful. I incorporated many of the changes and additions they suggested. But any errors of fact and error of interpretation are my own.

For photographs and other illustrative material I am particularly indebted to Dr. George Ammann, Michigan Department of Conservation; George Harrison, Pennsylvania State Game Commission; Dr. L. W. Gysel, Michigan State University; Dr. Glenn Sanderson, Illinois Natural History Survey; Dr. Wendell Swank, Arizona Game and Fish Department. In addition I wish to thank the various publishers and authors who permitted us to redraw or adapt their illustrations. The bulk of the art work was done by Ned Smith, already mentioned above. I appreciate the constant encouragement and advice given me by James Cron, now a vice president of Harper & Row, as well as his patience in waiting for a manuscript that took the author longer than he planned. And the same can be added for Andrew Sinauer, the biology editor, who steered the manuscript through to publication. Finally I wish to acknowledge the aid and assistance of my wife, Alice, who in addition to typing most of the manuscript, patiently endured five years of book widowhood, while I spent evenings, weekends, and even vacations writing. Too often she had to take second place to a book. For her patience and understanding, I will always be grateful.

PART I

PART I Introduction

CHAPTER 1

*The nature
of
field biology*

This is an age of ferment and change. A little less than two score years ago Charles Lindbergh bravely crossed the Atlantic alone in a single-engine plane. Today we are orbiting men in space and have successfully sent rockets and cameras to the moon. In the early 1920s radio was just beginning to get its feet on the ground; today pictures along with voices are being transmitted around the world by way of communication satellites. We have probed the secrets of the atom and unleashed its awesome power. And in doing so we have changed the direction of world history and the destiny of mankind. A ferment has also developed in biology. The probing of the secrets of the cell, the discovery of the stuff of life, DNA, and advances in biochemistry have revolutionized biology—so much in fact that molecular biology has become the siren of the science, luring scholars away from the more organism-centered areas of the field.

A quarter of a century ago and earlier, the major introductory path to biology was through natural history, or as it was even more popularly known, nature study. This was a time when people were just awakening to the world of nature about them. Nature had ceased to be an enemy. The fields were cleared, the forest subdued, and there was even becoming a danger that many

3

of the common animals—gray squirrels, beaver, deer, wild turkeys, and ducks —were on the border of extinction. The conservation movement was building up full steam in the 1930s; and natural history, or nature study, was a part of nearly every school curriculum, even though it was, more often than not, poorly taught. Too often it consisted only of coloring bird pictures and writing paragraphs about them. But then at least we youngsters became aware that birds did exist, that they were colorful and interesting, and were something more than living targets for BB guns. It was an age when John Burroughs was popular, the Reed *Bird Guides* were the last word in field guides, and the Comstock *Handbook of Nature Study* was the bible of natural history. Today Peterson replaces Reed, Comstock is old fashioned and no longer popular, and John Burroughs' volumes collect dust on the shelves. In some ways I think this is too bad. It wouldn't hurt young people—or for that matter molecular biologists either—to read John Burroughs. And in this age of urbanization, Comstock's *Handbook* could tempt young students and their teachers back into the realities of the world of nature—away from the noise, the grime, the polluted air, and the sterile concrete of an urban world.

The point is that not too many years ago a biologist developed because he had a close contact with nature and an interest in life. Modern biologists are beginning to arrive on the scene through the doorways of chemistry, physics, and mathematics, disciplines not immediately related to the living environment. In fact too many such biologists couldn't care less about the woods and the fields. They look upon biology as beginning and ending with a group of chemical compounds, and they think that the answer to life lies within the realm of the physical sciences.

Part of the reason for the swing away from natural history lies in biology itself. For a long time traditional biology started and ended with the naming of organisms. Biology as taught in schools and colleges was an endless repetition of the study of types of organisms. It was largely descriptive, weak in quantitative data, and lacked the strong conceptual foundation that so marked physics, chemistry, and mathematics. Even at the popular level, the mass of amateur naturalists who started out watching birds or collecting insects rarely got beyond the identification stage. They made little or no attempt to understand the organism, to find how it really lived or what its function was in nature. Even professionals fell into this trap; or at least they confined their work to descriptive biology. As a result natural history, once a rigorous subject, lost its position among the sciences and became equated with emotionalism and superficiality. (Remember the cartoons of the effeminate little man with glasses running around with a butterfly net?)

But in spite of it all, natural history is still very much with us; but it has evolved into ecology, which is, as someone described it, natural history quantified. Where the old focal point was the kinds of organisms, the new focal point is the nature of living systems. Just as molecular biology attempts to probe the secrets of living systems at the cellular level, so the new ecology, or natural history, probes the secrets of living systems at the levels of the organism, the population, and the ecosystem.

The word ecology comes from the Greek *oikos*, meaning "household" or "home" or "place to live." Thus ecology deals with the organism and its place to live. Basically this is the organism's environment; so ecology might well be called environmental biology. That word environment, like sin, covers a multitude of things. For one thing the environment includes the surroundings of the animal; and the surroundings can be modified by the animal (or plant) itself. The environment also includes for the individual organism those of its own kind, as well as organisms of other kinds. There are relationships between individuals within a population and with individuals of different populations. Animals react in a social sort of way, involving various patterns of behavior. Since all organisms have become adapted to the environment and are always adjusting to a changing environment, natural selection and evolution become a part of ecology.

Because of its far-flung involvements with so many fields, ecology, or natural history, or field biology, call it what you will, is often regarded as a generality rather than a speciality. Indeed one ecologist, A. Macfadyen, in his book *Animal Ecology: Aims and Methods* (1957)* wrote:

The ecologist is something of a chartered libertine. He roams at will over the legitimate preserves of the plant and animal biologist, the taxonomist, the physiologist, the behaviourist, the meteorologist, the geologist, the physicist, the chemist, and even the sociologist; he poaches from all these and from other established and respected disciplines. It is indeed a major problem for the ecologist, in his own interest, to set bounds to his divagations.

This statement nicely emphasizes that ecology is a multidisciplinary science; and it has to be to reach the heart of the problems of environmental biology. Yet every ecologist is grounded in a speciality and comes into the field by one of many avenues: taxonomy, behavior, physiology, botany, zoology, pedology, meteorology, and so on.

Ecology had its beginning in *plant geography*. Humboldt, De Candolle, Engler, Gray, and Kerner described the distributions of plants and in so doing raised some questions that have not been answered yet. Out of the roots of plant geography grew another stem, *community ecology,* the study of groups of organisms (called *synecology* in some texts). Cowles, Clements, Tansley, and Braun-Blanquet are a few of the men who devised methods to study and define the composition, structure, and dynamics of a whole community, but their efforts were confined to plants. Victor Shelford in America and Charles Elton in England attempted to study both structural elements of the community—plants and animals—together.

Ecology also springs from another root, *natural history,* which began with the descriptive studies of organisms by the early naturalists. Such studies reach far back into antiquity. The history of birds and mammals as discussed by Audubon, Wilson, and Brewster is basically ecology. Out of such studies have grown investigations of the organism itself (called *autecology* in some books). Today this area is represented by ecological life history and behavior studies.

The consideration of populations of individual organisms is *population ecology,* which can rightly be considered to have begun with Malthus, who called attention to expanding populations and the limitations of the food supply. Later Pearl, Verhulst, and Lotka placed a mathematical foundation under population studies. The work of Malthus indirectly led into *evolutionary studies*

---

* Full information for sources may be found in the Bibliograpy following Chapter 27.

and the *new systematics,* for it was from Malthus' essay on populations that Darwin received the first inspiration for his theory of evolution. Out of the work of Darwin and the genetical theories of Mendel grew the field of *population genetics,* the study of evolution and adaptation. Seeking answers to these and other ecological questions, some biologists turned to the field of *behavior.*

Early investigation of the physical environment of organisms, stemming largely from the work of Liebig, led to *ecoclimatology* and *physiological ecology.* Out of aquatic biology, represented by the works of Thienemann, Lindeman, and Hutchinson, came studies of bioenergetics, trophic-dynamic aspects of the community, and biogeochemical cycles, or *ecosystem ecology.*

Today all these areas of study form one great trunk of modern biology—ecology, or environmental biology.

For many years ecology has been criticized for a lack of quantitative data and conceptual strength. This fault was due largely to an early concentration on purely descriptive work and an obsession for developing a new and unnecessary terminology, which (happily) is dying out. But modern ecology has shifted from description to a study of function. The day of simply listing species and describing situations in a general way is past. Now the ecologist or field biologist studies nutrient cycles, energy flow, the diversity of species, functional niches, population growth, social behavior, and so on. He draws upon chemistry, physics, and especially mathematics to develop new tools and methods to probe the ecosystem. The aquatic biologist, the marine and terrestrial ecologists, the population ecologists, and others who, walking separate ways, thought each had little in common with the other, are discovering that ecology does contain some basic concepts relevant to all.

These principles gradually unfold in the chapters to follow. As yet they have not been boldly elucidated or standardized as the kind of basic laws that one finds in genetics or mathematics. In time they undoubtedly will be; but as a sort of an introduction to the material to come, some of the principles might be stated as follows.

1. The ecosystem is the major ecological unit. It has both structure and function.

2. The structure is related to species diversity. The more complex the structure, the greater is the diversity of species.

3. The function of the ecosystem is related to the flow of energy and the cycling of materials through the structural members of the ecosystem.

4. The relative amount of energy needed to maintain an ecosystem depends upon its structure. The more complex and mature it is, the less energy it needs to maintain one unit of that structure, or complexity (Margalef, 1963).

5. Ecosystems tend toward maturity; and in doing so they pass from a less complex to a more complex state. This directional change is called *succession.* Early stages are characterized by an excess of potential energy and a relatively high energy flow per unit of biomass. In mature ecosystems, there is less waste and less accumulation of energy because the energy flows through more diverse channels.

6. When an ecosystem is exploited and that exploitation is maintained, then the maturity of the ecosystem declines.

7. The major functional unit of the ecosystem is the population. It occupies a certain functional niche, which is related to the population's role in energy flow and cycling of nutrients.

8. Relationships among populations create new functional niches, so that the accumulation of species in an ecosystem, and the increase in maturity, are to some extent self-reinforcing processes.

9. However, a functional niche within a given ecosystem cannot be simultaneously and indefinitely occupied by a self-maintaining population of more than one species.

10. Both the environment and the amount of energy fixation in any given ecosystem are limited. When a population reaches the limits imposed by the ecosystem, its numbers must stabilize or, failing this, decline (often sharply) from disease, strife, starvation, low reproduction, and so on.

11. Changes and fluctuations in the environment (exploitation and competition, among others) represent selective pressures upon the population to which it must adjust. Those organisms that cannot adjust disappear, perhaps decreasing for a time the maturity of the ecosystem.

12. The ecosystem has historical aspects. The present is related to the past, and the future is related to the present.

Today biologists seem to be gathering into two camps. In one are those who see all of biology as centered in the areas of chemistry and physics. They are drawing to them cellular physiologists, biochemists, and biophysicists. These are the molecular biologists concerned with the basic biochemical structure of life. In the other camp are the environmental biologists, who are attracting climatologists, ethologists, taxonomists, systematists, evolutionists, pedologists, and so on. In many ways this division is unfortunate, for each faction can offer much to the other. Many of the discoveries of molecular biology are relatively meaningless unless they can be viewed from the vantage point of the population and the ecosystem. And some of the problems at the population and ecosystem levels can be answered only with the help of molecular biology. In reality biology is a gradient from the molecular level to the cellular to the ecosystem, and each segment of the gradient blends into the others.

But molecular biology to the contrary, the fact still remains that the most important current level of biological study is the organism and its environment. This is being recognized even in nonbiological circles, as man's impact on his own environment is being felt more keenly day by day. Because radioactive fallout from the atmospheric testing of nuclear devices has appeared —and is dangerously high in places—in the food we eat, we have become conscious of nutrient cycles. Because of the losses of animal life from lethal concentrations in pesticides picked up through the food chain and because of the national attention called to this problem by Rachel Carson in her book *Silent Spring,* we have become increasingly aware of chemical poisons and other pollutants that are being cycled through the ecosystem. As urban developments eat away at the countryside, we are becoming more concerned about open spaces. At the same time human populations throughout the world are increasing at an accelerated rate. The population growth curve is following a pattern typical of other animal populations that have exceeded the limits of their environment and died off in great numbers from disease, strife, starvation, and lack of cover. As yet there is no convincing evidence that man is excused from the same ecological laws that govern other animal populations. He can exceed the limits of his environment; he can deplete and contaminate his own habitat.

There are other problems, all ecological. Agriculture and now forestry are concentrating upon monoculture—single-species ecosystems—in spite of the difficulties and dangers attendant on unnaturally simplified ecosystems that lack a diversity of species. Over much of the world, especially in the grasslands, we continue to disrupt the energy balance through overgrazing and end up with eroded mountain sides, silt-clogged streams and lakes, and a scarcity of water. This discourse could be continued, but enough has been written to press home the fact that the future of human life on earth demands more knowledge about the ecosystem than we yet possess. Man for the first time in the history of the earth has become completely the dominant organism, changing the earth and its vegetation almost at will, with little regard for the consequences. It is little wonder then that some of the most intellectually challenging problems in biology and in the affairs of men are found in the area of ecology.

PART II

PART **II**   *The ecosystem
and the community*

CHAPTER 2

*The ecosystem
and
the community*

From a distance the landscape is a mosaic of topograph-
ical and vegetational patterns (Fig. 2-1). There are ridges and valleys, rock
ledges, grasslands, old fields, forests, streams, and ponds. Each of these various
parts of the mosaic supports its own more or less distinct forms of life. Wood
thrushes sing in the shadows of the forest. Catbirds and cottontail rabbits
hide in the cover of brushy fields. Meadowlarks sing from high vantage points
in the haylands. Trout swim in the cool waters of the streams. In the ponds
sunfish guard their nests of eggs and turtles sun themselves on protruding
logs.

A closer look at any of these parts of the landscape mosaic reveals differences and similarities. The sun shining on the open pond warms the shallow
water and supplies energy for photosynthetic activity of microscopic plants.
These tiny plants in turn support a variety and abundance of minute animal
life. Both provide food for young sunfish, tadpoles, and aquatic insects. The
insects are eaten by adult sunfish, frogs, and birds. The sunfish and frogs
become food for bass and heron. Cattails, reeds, and waterlilies growing along
the pond shore furnish food and shelter for muskrats, nesting sites for ducks
and red-winged blackbirds, and support for aquatic insects, snails, and flatworms.

11

Figure 2-1 *The landscape is a mosaic of topographical and vegetational patterns—forest, grasslands, old fields, flowing water.* (Photo by author.)

If the water of the pond is drained, all pond life is destroyed. If the cattails and reeds are covered by fill, redwings, muskrats, and many aquatic insects disappear. If insect life is destroyed, the food supply of frogs and sunfish is eliminated, and this in turn affects the bass and heron. Remove the bass, and the sunfish population may become so large that the fishes' growth will be stunted. Thus all the organisms of the pond depend not only upon clean water but also, directly or indirectly, upon one another for their well-being and existence.

The forest on the slope is quite different from the pond, yet there are many similarities. Trees and other plants capture and channel energy from the sun to other members of the forest. Deer browse on leaves and twigs; and earthworms and other soil organisms consume fallen leaves. Insects feed on leaves and plant juices. Woodland mice eat seeds and insects, and they themselves in turn become food for weasels and hawks. The forest provides shelter for many forms of life and modifies the wind and temperature. The forest vegetation depends upon those organisms that break down organic matter and return the minerals back to the soil. When trees are cut or burned, the forest inhabitants disappear and are replaced by other organisms. If deer become too numerous, they overbrowse the forest and destroy young trees and food and shelter for other animals. Just as in the pond, all forest organisms depend, directly or indirectly, on each other for their existence.

Those organisms occupying the same area make up a *biotic community*, a naturally occurring assemblage of plants and animals that live in the same environment, are mutually sustaining and interdependent, and are constantly fixing, utilizing, and dissipating energy. The interacting populations are characterized by constant death and replacement and usually by immigration and emigration of individuals. The populations themselves are always fluctuating with seasonal and environmental changes.

The community depends upon and is influenced by the habitat, the specific set of conditions that surround the organisms, such as sunlight, soil, mineral elements, moisture, temperature, and topography. The biotic (living) and the abiotic (nonliving) interact, thus creating an ecological system, or *ecosystem*. All ecosystems, terrestrial or aquatic, have two basic components. One is the *autotrophic*, which fixes the energy of the sun and manufactures food from simple, inorganic substances; the other is the *heterotrophic*, which utilizes the food stored by the autotrophs, rearranges it, and finally decomposes the complex materials into simple, inorganic compounds again. These two functional components are arranged in strata, or layers, in the ecosystem. Autotrophic metabolism is greatest in the upper stratum, where the most light is available. In the forest this is in the canopy; in the pond it is in the sunlit surface waters where the small microscopic plants are concentrated. Heterotrophic activity is most intense where organic matter accumulates. In terrestrial ecosystems this is in the upper layer of the soil; in aquatic ecosystems it is in the bottom sediments.

Aside from function, the ecosystem also has structure; and of the structural components there are four. The first is the abiotic: the materials, elements, and compounds of the environment, such as soil, water, minerals, and moisture. Then there is the autotrophic element, the producers, chiefly green plants. The heterotrophic element consists of the larger consumers, who feed on green plants and other organisms; and the decomposers, or small consumers, chiefly bacteria and fungi, that break down the complex compounds of dead organic matter, utilize part of it, and in doing so release some of the simple substances back into the ecosystem again.

The producers and consumers in the ecosystem can be arranged into several feeding groups, each known as a *trophic* (feeding) *level* (see Chap. 3). Each trophic level contains at any one time a certain amount of living material composed of a number of kinds of organisms. This is the standing crop, most often expressed as the number per unit area or *biomass* (living weight) per unit area. The standing crop consists of a wide diversity and number of plants and animals, which collectively make up the species structure of the ecosystem.

The place where an organism lives and its surroundings, both living and nonliving, is its *habitat*. The wood thrush inhabits a deciduous forest; the wood sorrel grows in acid, humus-rich soil of the cool, deep woods. Even within a given community the distribution of certain organisms may be quite localized because of microdifferences in moisture, light, and other conditions. These localized areas are *microhabitats*. The idea of habitat can be extended to include the place occupied by the entire community. In this case the habitat would include only the physical environment.

More than just occupying space, each species and each individual in the community performs some function. What the organism does—or, to say it somewhat anthropomorphically, its occupation—in the community is called its *niche*. Some species occupy a very broad ecological niche. They may feed on many kinds of food, part plant, part animal; or if strictly herbivorous, they may feed on a wide variety of plants. Other organisms occupy highly specialized niches. The woodcock, for example, possesses a sensitive, flexible bill adapted for probing in the soft earth for earthworms, which make up the

13

bulk of the bird's diet. Organisms have arrived at their respective niches through long periods of evolution (see Chap. 24). Since no two species in the community occupy the same niche (this is discussed in Chap. 21), each more or less complements the other. This reaches a high refinement among the grazing animals of the African plains. Since each kind feeds on preferred food plants, between them they utilize all forms of vegetation from ephemeral annuals and herbs to acacia trees (Darling, 1960; Talbots, 1963*b*). Giraffes feed chiefly on trees, rhinos on brush, wildebeest on grass. Even among animals living on the same class of food, the diets are complementary. Red oats grass is the major forage species for the wildebeests, the topis, and the zebras. The wildebeests feed chiefly on the short, fresh leaves of this grass. Zebras feed on red oats grass when it is more mature, when leaves are over four inches long, but they avoid this grass when it is dry. The topis, however, prefer the dry red oats grass.

Just as ecosystems have some basic components, so are the niches they contain basic and repetitive. Through natural selection, different animals (although some may belong to the same genera) in widely separated ecosystems occupy similar niches and perform similar tasks. The mountain lion of North America, for example, feeds on the deer; the African lion feeds on plains antelope and the wildebeest. Animals that have the same occupation in different ecosystems are termed *ecological equivalents*.

Dominance and species diversity

The community is an aggregation of species. Among these only a comparatively few species are found in abundance, either in numbers or in biomass; the majority are comparatively rare (Preston, 1948; MacArthur, 1960). In virgin stands of mixed mesophytic forest in eastern Kentucky, for example, the canopy layer of the cove forest consisted of about 28 per cent beech, 12 per cent sugar maple, 14 per cent white oak, and 6 per cent yellow poplar and black oak; the remaining 15 species each ranged in abundance from 6 to 0.7 per cent (Braun, 1950). Birds, too, exhibit the same kind of commonness and rarity. One census in a spruce forest of northern Maine (Stewart and Aldrich, 1952) revealed that the magnolia warbler and bay-breasted warbler each had a density of 50 birds per 100 acres; the Cape May, the Blackburnian and the myrtle warblers were only half as abundant. Six species had densities ranging from 28 to 10, while the remaining 23 species had densities of 8 or less per 100 acres.

The common species often are considered as the *dominants*, since they are more abundant, contain more mass, or preempt more space. In some communities these dominants may exert some influence over the other organisms. In the forest, for example, certain trees of the upper canopy influence the amount of light and moisture reaching the ground and the type of shelter offered other plants and animals. They also affect the soil structure and its chemical composition and in turn the organisms that live in the forest soil.

Although the dominants do influence the physical conditions for many organisms, their influence on the actual distribution of associated species is open to question (Whittaker, 1962). For the most part the plant dominants are widely distributed and thus contain across their range a number of different ecotypes—ecological variants adapted to local conditions. Although they are very similar in appearance and although they have the same modifying influences over the internal environment of the community, their associated species may be quite different. In the southern Appalachians, beech forest and oak forest grow at several elevations. The dominants are the same at each elevation but the associated species in the understory are different. The American beech dominates certain communities at low elevations. A second beech community growing above 3000 feet (914 meters) elevation and separated by about 2000 feet (±600 meters) from the lowland population is floristically very different (Whittaker, 1956). On the other hand, some dominant species have a very narrow ecological tolerance, and in this case the associated organisms are the same from one place to another.

Occasionally an animal comprises the dominant mass of the community; this is the case for the coral reef, found in clear, warm waters of tropical and subtropical regions. Coral reefs are built up by anthozoan organisms related to jellyfish and sea anemones. These animals secrete hard, compact, stony skeletons, or cups, in which they live, one generation secreting new cups upon the old. In the chasms and crevices of coral ledges live protozoans, sponges, clams, starfish, octopuses, brilliantly colored fish, and myriads of other forms of life.

Dominance in a community may be the result of the coaction between two or more species, particularly between plants and animals. Prairie dogs can produce and maintain a short-grass stage in the mixed prairie, especially if they have some supplemental help in the form of grazing by cattle and buffalo (Koford, 1958). In earlier days the buffalo on the western plains preferred the taller grasses over the short-grass species. Consequently over an extensive area the short grass replaced the tall almost entirely (Larson, 1940). The activity of beavers, damming streams and cutting woody vegetation, will eliminate one community and develop and maintain another (Fig. 2-2).

Physical features also may directly control the community. Examples of this are mud flats along a river, rock outcrops on a mountain side, or a body of water or marine bottom where wind and water are controlling elements.

Species diversity

The diversity of species within a community reflects in part the diversity in the physical enviroment. The greater the variation in the environment, the more numerous are the species, since there are more microhabitats available and more niches to fill. Communities possessing a high number of different species usually have complex trophic structures.

Diversity is least in the simpler, less stable ecosystems (Fischer 1960; Elton, 1958), such as the tundra and agricultural ecosystems. In tropical regions where the climate is stable, many ecological communities have evolved to maturity. Within them has developed a large number of different species, none of them really abundant. Because each species occupies a rather specialized niche (think, for example, of the wide spectrum of grazing animals on the African plains), the

Figure 2-2 *A beaver dam across a small stream flooded out acres of forest and created a pond habitat.* (Photo by author.)

food demands of the population are more widely and evenly distributed. At higher latitudes, in areas of less stable and more severe climates, and in youthful landscapes, the trophic structure is simpler and the species are fewer, but they reach much higher population densities, as a rule.

Within any community the diversity is greatest in small organisms. There are many more kinds of insects than there are birds, more birds than mammals, and more small mammals than large ones, irrespective of their position in the food chain. Because they are small, these organisms have become adapted to the conditions afforded by the small, diversified microenvironments found within the community. Each species uses the environment in such a way that it is unavailable to the others (see Chap. 21—the competitive exclusion principle). The total number of individuals of all species together, however, is essentially constant.

The relative abundance of various species within a community depends in part on the species themselves. Some are strictly opportunistic (MacArthur, 1960), common when conditions are highly favorable and scarce when this is not so. No equilibrium is established within the population. Examples of this include diatom blooms in polluted water, many invertebrate populations, and plant populations in the very early stages of succession. Community structure is reflected best by those species that develop some sort of population equilibrium (see Chap. 20). Among these, relative abundance is important. Some are very common, some are very rare, and between the two is a whole range of intermediates. These latter species, appearing in moderate abundance, are more numerous than either extreme (Preston, 1948).

Community composition

The composition of any one community is determined in part by the species that happen to be distributed on the area and can grow and survive under prevailing conditions. Seeds of many plants may be carried by the wind and animals, but only those adapted to grow in the habitat where they are deposited will take root and thrive. The element of chance also is involved. One adapted species may colonize an area and prevent others equally as well adapted from entering. Wind direction and velocity, size of the seed crop, disease, insect and rodent damage all influence the establishment of vegetation. Thus the exact species that settle an area and the number of individual species that succeed are situations that seldom if ever are repeated in any two places at any two times. Nevertheless there is a certain pattern, with more or less similar groups recurring from place to place. Only a relatively small group of species are potential dominants, since a limited number are well adapted to the over-all climate and soils of the region they occupy.

Communities are often regarded, especially for practical reasons of description and study, as distinct natural units or associations, but more often than not community boundaries are hard to define. Some, such as a pond, a tidal beach, a grassy bald, islands of spruce and fir within a hardwood forest, old fields and burns, have sharply defined boundaries. Here the vegetational pattern is

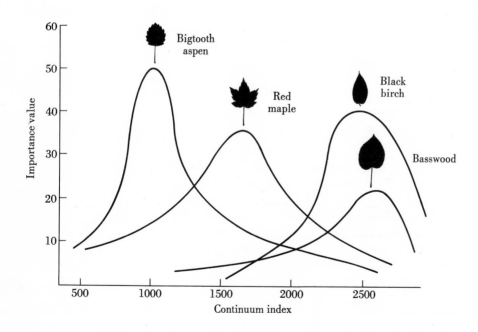

Figure 2-3 *Distribution of some forest-tree species on a continuum index.* (Adapted from Curtis and McIntosh, 1951.)

17

discontinuous. Most often, however, one community type blends into another. The species comprising the community do not necessarily associate only with one another but are found with other species where their distribution overlaps (Figs. 2-3 and 2-4). Some organisms will succeed only under certain environmental conditions and tend to be confined to certain habitats. Others tolerate a wider range of environmental conditions and are found over a wider area. Species shift in abundance and dominance, because of change in altitude, moisture, tempera- ture, and other physical conditions. One species may be dominant in one group, an associated species in another. This sequence of communities showing a gradual change in composition is called a *continuum* (Curtis, 1959). Each community

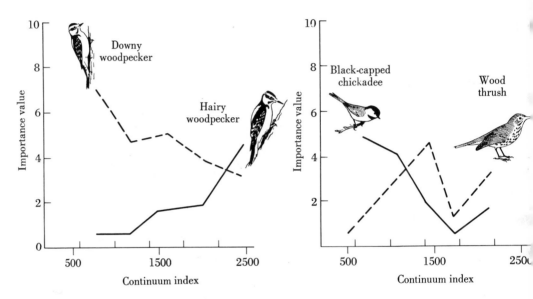

Figure 2-4 *Distribution of several bird species along a vegetational gradient.* (Adapted from Bond, 1957.)

is similar to, but slightly different from, its neighbor, the difference increasing roughly as the distance between them. Even when the dominant plants change completely, the community may integrate in the understory vegetation. The con- tinuum is much like a light spectrum. The end colors, red and blue, and other primary colors in the middle are distinguishable, but the boundaries grade con- tinuously in either direction. Eventually the continuum must end, when en- vironmental conditions favor a completely different group of organisms. A com- munity in such a gradient can be described as a discrete area or point in the continuum, the point being defined by some given criteria.

The distribution of species along an environmental gradient is not confined to plants alone. The same phenomena also have been found in the case of insects (Whittaker, 1952) and birds (Bond, 1957) (Fig. 2-4).

Involved in the above idea of a community are two opposing philosophies: the individualistic approach, advanced by H. A. Gleason (1926) and further ex- panded by such ecologists as Whittaker (1951, 1952, 1956), Curtis (1959) and

McIntosh (1958); and the organismic approach, developed by Clements (1916) and still advanced by his school of ecology.

The individualistic viewpoint emphasizes the species rather than the community as the essential unit in the analysis of interrelationships and distribution. The species respond independently to the physical and biotic environment; they are not bound together into groups of associates that must appear together. Instead, when the species populations along an environmental gradient, short or long, are plotted, the resulting graph appears similar to a normal curve (Fig. 2-3). The curves of many species overlap in a heterogeneous fashion. Thus the vegetation and its associated animal life exhibit a gradient or continuum from one extreme (for example, xeric conditions) to another (wet conditions). The community is regarded as a continuous variable.

The organismic viewpoint regards the community as a sort of superorganism, the highest stage in the organization of the living world—rising from cell to tissue, organs, organ systems, species, population, and community. The whole is more than the sum of its parts. Just as the tissues have certain characteristics and functions above and beyond those of the cells that comprise them, so does the community have characteristics and functions above and beyond the species and populations it embodies. The community acts as a unit in succession, in seasonal activity, in competition with other communities, in trophic functions.

The future may reveal that, like the Wise Men of Hindustan, each is partly right and each is partly wrong. The species that collectively make up the biotic community may respond individually to the environment; yet each community, in ways perhaps not clearly definable by human criteria, still operates as a functional unit, especially in regard to the flow of energy and the cycling of materials.

Ecotone

The place where two major communities meet and blend together is called an *ecotone* (Fig. 2-5). Organisms common to the communities on both sides, as well as a number of versatile species, tend to colonize such transition areas. Because of this, the variety and density of life often is greatest in such areas (Leopold, 1933). A breeding-bird census in Illinois showed 14 species in the forest interior and 22 on the forest edge (Johnston, 1947). A census on a 130-acre area in Pennsylvania showed that the greatest density of birds was in orchards, temporary thickets, slashings, and mixed conifers and hardwoods. Areas of uniform vegetation, such as large meadows or pure conifer stands, had low populations (Edeburn, 1947). If meadows were strip-cropped, the bird populations increased from 48 pairs per 100 acres in large meadows to 93 pairs in meadows broken by strips of grain, and from 10 pairs on large grain fields to 27 pairs per 100 acres on strip-cropped grain fields (Good and Dambach, 1943).

Stratification

All communities can be subdivided into more or less distinct layers, or strata, both on a vertical and a horizontal plane.

Stratification of terrestrial communities reflects largely the life forms of plants —the characteristic appearance of the vegetation, such as size, branching, and

19

Figure 2-5 An ecotone, or edge between forest and old field. (Photo by author.)

leaves. This is an expression of genetic characteristics, often modified by environment. The general appearance of a community and the stratification of animal life as well is determined largely by the life form of the dominant plants. Because of this, the life form has been widely used to describe the plant structure of a community. Among several classification systems proposed, the most widely used is that of Raunkaier, which is based largely on overwintering parts (Table 2-1).

A life-form classification is very useful for comparing communities. All species in a region or in a community can be grouped into several classes, and the ratio between them can be expressed as a percentage (Table 2-2), giving a biological spectrum of the area (Fig. 2-6). Hemicryptophytes, for instance, would be most abundant in grasslands and old fields, therophytes in the desert and weed communities. In woodlands of eastern North America geophytes, such as the dogtooth violet, are most characteristic of the forest in spring, while hemicryptophytes, such as asters, are common in autumn.

A useful classification system for aquatic communities has been developed by Dansereau (1945, 1959), which is well correlated with the horizontal zonation of communities along streams and the shores of lakes and ponds (Table 2-3). Vertical gradients in aquatic environments are aptly expressed as changes in the physical environment, involving light, temperature, and oxygen. These three govern to a large extent the distribution of life and biological activity in deep water (Fig. 8-1).

Each vertical layer in the community is inhabited by its own more or less characteristic organisms. Although considerable interchange takes place between several strata, many highly mobile animals confine themselves to only a few layers, particularly during the breeding season. Occupants of the vertical strata

TABLE 2-1. RAUNKAIER'S LIFE FORMS

NAME	DESCRIPTION
1. Therophytes	Annuals survive unfavorable periods as seeds. Complete life cycle from seed to seed in one season.
2. Geophytes (Cryptophytes)	Buds buried in the ground on a bulb or rhizome.
3. Hemicryptophytes	Perennial shoots or buds close to the surface of the ground; often they are covered with litter.
4. Chamaephytes	Perennial shoots or buds on the surface of the ground to about 25 cm above the surface.
5. Phanerophytes	Perennial buds carried well up in the air, over 25 cm. Trees, shrubs, and vines.
6. Epiphytes	Plants growing on other plants; roots up in the air.

may change during the day or the season. Such changes reflect daily and seasonal variations in humidity, temperature, light, acidity, oxygen content of water, and other conditions, or the different requirements of the organisms for the completion of their life cycles.

Horizontal stratification or zonation (Fig. 6-4) is caused primarily by differences in climatic or edaphic conditions, which retard or inhibit rooted vegetation. This type of stratification is most conspicious around ponds and bogs (see Chap. 9, Fig. 9-2).

Stratification increases the number and variety of places in which the organisms can live in a given area. Highly stratified communities generally contain a wider variety of animal life than those with only a few layers.

TABLE 2-2. AN EXAMPLE OF AN ANALYSIS OF LIFE-FORMS SPECTRA OF TWO PLANT COMMUNITIES: A NEW JERSEY PINE BARREN AND A MINNESOTA JACK PINE FOREST*

BASIS OF SPECTRUM	COMMUNITY	NUMBER OF SPECIES	PERCENTAGE				
			Ph	Ch	He	G	Th
Species list	New Jersey	19	84.2	0	10.5	5.2	0
	Minnesota	63	23.8	4.7	60.3	7.9	3.1
Cover	New Jersey	19	98.1	0	1.9	0	0
	Minnesota	63	11.8	2.5	55.6	28.7	1.4

* Stern and Buell, 1951.

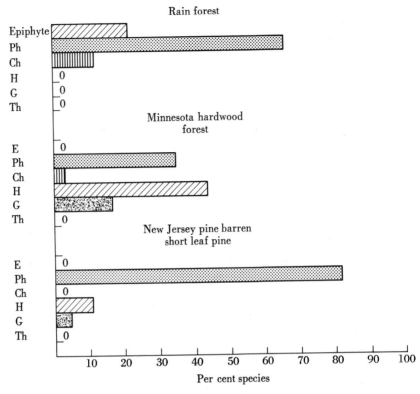

Figure 2-6 *Life-form spectra of a tropical rain forest* (adapted from Richard, 1952), *a Minnesota hardwood forest* (data from Buell and Wilbur, 1948), *and a New Jersey pine barren* (data from Stern and Buell, 1951).

Naming the community

Although the major current concept of the community is that of a continuum, the plant and animal life of any large area is so complex that it must be separated into subdivisions. Thus the aggregation of organisms in any given locality or habitat must be regarded as a unit if the community is to be studied, described, or compared with similar community stands in other habitats. To give order to the study of communities, some system of classification is needed, even though the communities of a region often cannot be placed in discrete units.

There are a number of approaches to community classification, each arbitrary and each suited to a particular need or viewpoint (Hanson, 1958). The most widely used classifications include physiognomy, species composition, dominance, and habitat.

Physiognomy, or general appearance, is a highly useful method of naming and delineating communities, particularly in surveying large areas, and as a basis for further subdivision of major types into their component communities. Since animal distribution is most closely correlated to the structure of vegetation

TABLE 2-3. LIFE FORMS OF AQUATIC PLANTS*

RELATION TO SUBSTRATUM			TYPE	EXAMPLE
Free (not rooted or anchored)			Natantia	*Lemma minor, Ceratophyllum demersum*
Rooted in soil	Emersed, at least in part	Broad leaved	Foliacea	*Sagittaria latifolia, Pontederia cordata*
		Narrow, tubular, or linear leaved	Junciformia	*Scirpus validus, Juncus nodosus*
		Floating leaved	Nymphoidea	*Nymphaea odorata, Nymphoides lacunosum*
	Submersed (at most a few floating leaves)	Long, leafy stems and/or leaves ribbonlike	Vittata	*Potamogeton richardsonii, Vallisneria americana*
		Leaves much reduced, crowded at base	Rosulata	*Isoetes braunii, Lobelia dortmanna*
		Annuals	Annua	*Najas flexilis, Potamogeton pusillus*
Adnate or epipyhtic			Adnata	*Podostemon cerato-phyllum, Fontinalis* spp.

* From Dansereau, 1945.

and not the species composition (cf., for birds, MacArthur and MacArthur, 1961), classification by physiognomy will relate both the animals and the vegetations of an area. Communities so classified are usually named after the dominant form of life, usually plant, such as the coniferous or deciduous forest, sagebrush, short-grass prairie, and tundra. A few are named after animals, such as the barnacle-blue mussel (*Balanus-Mytilus*) community of the tidal zone. One, of course, may grade into the other; so even here the classification may be based on arbitrary, although specific, criteria.

In areas where the habitat is well defined, physiography is used to classify and name communities. Examples of such are sand dunes, cliffs, tidal mud flats, lakes, ponds, and streams.

Finer subdivisions are often based on species composition, a system which works much better with plants alone than with animals or with both. Such a classification requires at first a detailed study of the individual community. Such a system also involves a number of concepts: frequency (the regularity with which a species is distributed throughout a community), dominance, constancy, presence, and fidelity (see Appendix C).

A group of stands in which more or less the same combination of species occurs can be classified as the same community type, named after the dominant organisms or the ones with the highest frequency. Examples of such are the *Quercus-Carya* association, or oak-hickory forest, the *Stipa-Bouteloua* association, or mixed prairie, and the animal-dominated *Balanus-Mytilus,* or barnacle-blue mussel, community of the tidal zone. European ecologists have developed the floristic classification with emphasis on dominance, constancy, and diagnostic species. They group communities into classes, orders, alliances, and associations (for a complete discussion on this, see Poore, 1962; Whittaker, 1962).

The floristic system is modified when the stands are treated as a continuum. The community complex of a major physiognomy is subdivided by species composition and correlated with an environmental gradient arbitrarily divided into five segments: wet, wet mesic, mesic, dry mesic, and dry (Curtis, 1959). Thus the deciduous forest in Wisconsin has been divided into southern and northern hardwoods and northern forest. These are further divided in a moisture gradient. The southern hardwoods for example include: the dry southern hardwoods with bur, black or white oak as the dominants; the dry mesic with red oak or basswood; the mesic with sugar maple and beech; the wet mesic with silver maple, elm, and ash; and the wet mesic with willow or cottonwood. Such a system recognizes the influences of habitat on community composition. Detailed studies on animal distribution may reveal similar influences of animal composition. A shift of species composition of birds occurs in the southern forests of Wisconsin (Bond, 1957). In the dry stands the most important species are the scarlet tanager, rose-breasted grosbeak, cardinal, blue jay, black-capped chickadee, downy woodpecker, and the red-headed woodpecker. In the dry-mesic segment, however, the wood thrush, least flycatcher, blue-gray gnatcatcher, redstart, yellow-throated vireo, veery, and ruby-throated hummingbird are the dominant species.

A large problem in community classification is to arrive at a system that will embrace animals as well as plants. Communities distinguished by plant composition indicate little about the animals of the community, since animal distribution cannot be correlated with plant species distribution. As a result animal and plant communities usually are studied separately, which unfortunately obscures the wholeness of the community and limits our understanding of its functions.

To escape this dilemma in part, the distribution of animals can be related to the life form of plants and types of vegetation. This results in a more inclusive classification, which embraces several plant communities but includes all animal life associated with them; this classification is called the *biome*. The biome is a broad ecological unit characterized by the distinctive life forms of the climax species, plant or animal. The biome is further subdivided into smaller units, distinguished by uniformity and distinctness in species composition of the climax and its successional stages (see Chap. 19). Thus the life form of plants is emphasized, rather than the taxonomic composition, which in the final analysis plays the most important role in dominance.

This brings up another concept: fidelity, or the "faithfulness" of a species to a community type. Species with low fidelity occur in a number of different communities and those with high fidelity in only a few. Seldom if ever are the latter found away from certain other plant and animal associates. The greater the ratio of the constant species to the total number of species, the more homogeneous is the community and the more sharply can it be delineated. Often, however, this simply reflects a group of species unable to grow successfully under a wide range of ecological conditions or with other species. Species, in general, can be grouped as *exclusive,* those completely or almost completely confined to one kind of community; *characteristic* (including the selective and preferential species of plant ecologists), those that are most closely identified with a certain community; and *ubiquitous* (or indifferent), those which have no particular affinity to any community. The characteristic species high in constancy and dominance are the ones that really characterize the community type.

Recognition of characteristic species often offers problems, and some decision is necessary as to how abundant or constant a species must be in order to be characteristic. This is a greater problem among animals than among plants, since dominance and comparative abundance of the latter offer a firmer base for a decision. To be characteristic, an animal species should be conspicious and occur in at least 50 per cent of all samples taken in the community (Thorson, in Hedgpeth, 1957). In a study of breeding birds in Ontario (Martin, 1960), a species was considered characteristic of a community type if at a population level of one to nine pairs per 100 acres (40 hectares), it was three times more abundant there than in any other community. Species with a population density of 10 to 100 pairs per 100 acres were considered characteristic if twice as abundant in one type of vegetation over another. If a species had a density of more than 100 pairs per 100 acres, a 50 per cent difference was considered adequate.

SUMMARY

However the community may be classified, or what methods may be employed to distinguish one community from another, the basic concept remains unchanged. A biotic community is a naturally occurring assemblage of plants and animals living in the same environment, mutually sustaining and interdependent, constantly fixing, utilizing, and dissipating energy. Interacting populations are characterized by constant death and replacement and usually by immigration and emigration of individuals.

The biotic community is a part of a larger whole, the ecosystem, in which the living and the nonliving interact to bring about the circulation, transformation, and accumulation of energy and matter. In the nonliving this is accomplished by the physical processes of evaporation, precipitation, erosion, and deposition, and the gaseous cycles. In the living it is accomplished by two components, the autotrophic, which fixes energy by photosynthesis, and the heterotrophic, which utilizes and circulates energy and matter through herbivory, predation in the broadest sense, and decomposition.

Each organism in the community occupies a particular functional niche, at which it arrived by a long process of natural selection and evolution. The more niches there are to occupy, the more complex the community, the greater the diversity of species, and the more stable the ecosystem.

Among these species a few may exert a dominant role over the rest of the community. Usually plants govern its development and influence the total species composition. The make-up of any one community is determined in part by the species that happen to be distributed on the area and can grow and survive under the prevailing conditions. Thus an element of chance is involved. The exact species that settle on an area and the number that survive are rarely repeated in any two places at a time, but there is a certain recurring pattern of more or less similar groups. Rarely can different groups of communities be sharply delimited, for they blend together to form a sequence of communities gradually changing in composition, known as a continuum. A place where two major communities meet and blend together is called an ecotone.

All communities exhibit some form of layering or stratification, which largely reflects the life form of the plants and which influences the nature and distribution of animal life in the community. Communities most highly stratified offer the richest variety of animal life, for they contain a greater assortment of microhabitats and available niches.

CHAPTER 3

Energy flow
and
material cycling

The existence of the living world, including human life, depends upon the flow of energy and the circulation of materials through the ecosystem. Both influence the abundance of organisms, the rate at which they live, and the complexity of the community. Energy and materials flow through the community together; one cannot very well be separated from the other. But the flow of energy is one way; once used by the community, it is lost. Material on the other hand recirculates. An atom of carbon or calcium may pass between the living and the nonliving many times, or it may even be exchanged between ecosystems. This one-way passage of energy and the round trip of materials are the cogs on which the living world turns.

Energy flow

Energy exists in two forms, potential and kinetic. Potential energy is energy at rest, capable of performing work. Kinetic energy is the energy of motion and results in work, performed at the expense of potential energy.

The behavior of energy is described by two laws of thermodynamics. One law, the first, states that the amount of energy in the universe is constant. It may change form, pass from one place to another, or act upon matter in various ways, but regardless of what transformation or transfers take place, no gain or loss in total energy is involved. Energy simply is transferred from one type to another, never created or destroyed. If wood is burned, kinetic energy is released. The amount of kinetic energy released equals the potential energy present prior to burning:

$$C + O_2 \longrightarrow CO_2 + \text{energy (heat and light)}$$

Energy was neither lost nor gained. On the other hand energy may be paid into a reaction. Even here the first law holds true. During photosynthesis, more energy is stored than went into the reaction:

$$12H_2O + 6CO_2 + \text{energy from sunlight} \longrightarrow C_6H_{12}O_6 + 6H_2O + 6O_2$$

Here the extra energy is acquired from sunlight, but again there is no gain or loss of total energy involved.

The familiar formula for photosynthesis hides the actual story. Photosynthesis is a photolytic process:

$$CO_2 + 2H_2O + \text{light and chlorophyll} \longrightarrow CH_2O + O_2 + H_2O$$

The oxygen released comes from the water molecule, not from the carbon dioxide. Diagrammatically it can be shown as

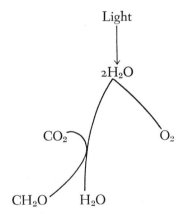

The resulting water molecules are not the same as those split in the photolysis.

Although the total amount of energy involved in any reaction, such as that of burning wood, does not increase or decrease, much of the energy does become useless for further transfer. This phenomenon involves the second law of thermodynamics. It states that when energy is transferred or transformed, part of the energy assumes a form that cannot be passed on any further. When coal is burned in a boiler to produce steam, some of the energy creates steam and part is dispersed as heat to the surrounding air. The same thing happens to energy in the community. As energy is transferred from one organism to another as food, a large part of that energy is degraded as heat, and the remainder is stored as living tissue.

If energy is not cyclic, there must be some continuing energy source for the community. This source is the sun. Approximately 57 per cent of the sun's energy is absorbed in the atmosphere and scattered in space. Some 36 per cent is expended to heat water and land areas and to evaporate water. Fortunately energy released from decay prevents much dissipation of heat into the ground. Approximately 8 per cent of light energy strikes plants. Of this 10 to 15 per cent is reflected, 5 per cent is transmitted, and 80 to 85 per cent absorbed. Most of the absorbed energy is lost as heat in the evaporation of water. An average of only 2 per cent (0.5 to 3.5 per cent) of the total light energy striking a leaf, and this is restricted largely to the red end of the spectrum, is used in photosynthesis.

Food chains

Green plants alone are able to trap the sun's energy, which they use to reduce the carbon that forms the fuels of life—carbohydrates, fats, and proteins. Since virtually all other living organisms depend upon green plants for their energy, the efficiency of plants on any one given area in capturing solar energy sets the upper limits to long-term energy flow and biological activity in the community.

The energy stored by plants is passed along through the community in a series of steps of eating and being eaten, known as a *food chain*. Food chains are descriptive. When worked out diagrammatically, they consist of a series of arrows, each pointing from one species to another, for which it is a source of food. In Fig. 3-1, for example, the marsh vegetation is eaten by the grasshopper, the grasshopper is consumed by the shrew, the shrew by the marsh hawk or the owl. Thus we have a relationship that can be written as follows:

Marsh grass ⟶ grasshopper ⟶ shrew ⟶ marsh hawk

But as the diagram indicates, no one organism lives wholly on another; the resources are shared, especially at the beginning of the chain. The marsh plants are eaten by a variety of birds, mammals, and fish; and some of the animals are consumed by several predators. Thus food chains become interlinked to form a *food web*. Now, if all the organisms that obtained their food in the same number of steps (for example, the grasshopper, the snails, and the fish) are superimposed, the structure can be collapsed into a series of single points, representing the functional *trophic levels* of the community. Thus each step in the food chain represents a trophic level. Animals at the lower level, such as the grasshopper and snail, may occupy a single trophic level. But most of the animals at the higher levels participate simultaneously in several trophic levels, as do the voles and the song sparrow.

At each step in the food chain a considerable portion of the potential energy is lost as heat. As a result, organisms in each trophic level pass on less energy than received. This limits the number of steps in any food chain to four or five. The longer the food chain, the less energy there is available for the final members.

The trophic levels

Producers. The first trophic level, represented by green plants, consists of *producers*. Plants are capable of fixing light energy and manufacturing food from simple inorganic substances. The producers are the base upon which the heterotrophic component of the community rests.

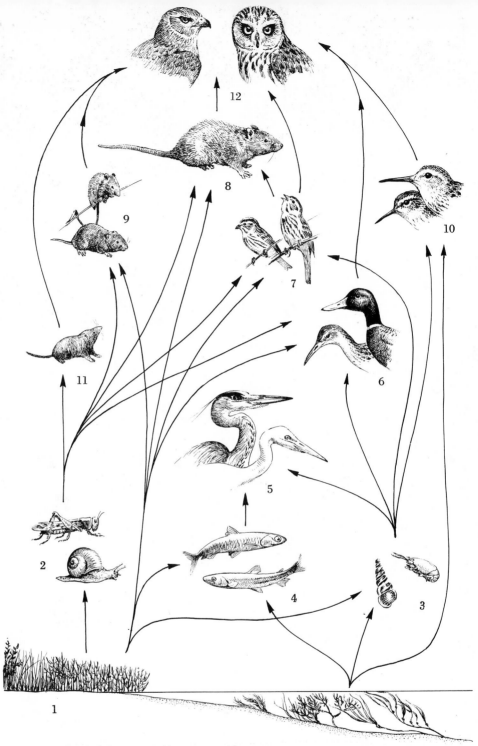

Figure 3-1 *A midwinter food web in a Salicornia salt marsh (San Francisco Bay area). Producer organisms (1), terrestrial and salt marsh plants, are consumed by herbaceous terrestrial invertebrates, represented by the grasshopper and snail (2). The marine plants are consumed by herbivorous marine and intertidal invertebrates (3). Fish, represented by smelt and anchovy (4), feed on vegetative matter from both ecosystems. The fish in turn are eaten by first-level carnivores, represented by the great blue heron and common egret (5). Continuing through the web, we have the following omnivores: clapper rail and mallard duck (6); savanna and song sparrows (7); Norway rat (8); California vole and salt-marsh harvest mouse (9); the least and western sandpipers (10). The vagrant shrew (11) is a first-level carnivore, while the top carnivores (second level) are the marsh hawk and short-eared owl (12). (Food web adapted from Johnston, 1956.)*

Herbivores. *Herbivores* are the plant feeders, capable of converting energy stored in plant tissue into animal tissue. Their role is essential in the community, for without them the higher trophic levels could not exist. The English ecologist, Charles Elton, in his classic little book, *Animal Ecology,* suggested that the term "key industry" be used to denote those animals that both feed upon plants and are so abundant that many other animals depend upon them.

Only the herbivores are adapted to live on a diet high in cellulose. Modification in the structure of the teeth, complicated stomachs, long intestines, a well-developed caecum, and symbiotic flora and fauna enable these animals to use plant tissues. For example ruminants, such as the deer, have a four-compartment stomach. As they graze, these animals chew their food hurriedly. The material consumed descends to the first and second stomachs (the rumen and reticulum), where it is softened to a pulp by the addition of water, kneaded by muscular action, and fermented by bacteria. At leisure the animals regurgitate the food, chew it more thoroughly, and swallow it again. This time the mass bypasses the first and second stomachs and enters the third stomach, the omasum, and the fourth, the abomasum.

The digestive process relies heavily on bacterial fermentation in the rumen, reticulum, and omasum. The bacteria attack the cellulose and break it down into fatty acids, which are digested and absorbed on the spot. With the cell walls gone, fats, starches, and proteins in the plant cells are released for further digestion. In addition the bacteria also synthesize B-complex vitamins and essential amino acids.

The chief herbivores on land are insects, rodents, and hoofed animals. In lakes and seas minute crustaceans "graze" on diatoms, the major plant producers in marine and aquatic communities.

Carnivores. Herbivores in turn are the energy source for the *carnivores,* the flesh eaters. Those organisms that feed directly upon the herbivores are termed first-level carnivores or second-level consumers. Usually they are larger and stronger than their prey and more or less solitary in habit. First-level carnivores represent an energy source for the second-level carnivores. Still higher categories of carnivorous animals feeding on secondary carnivores may exist in some communities. As the trophic level of carnivores increases, their numbers decrease and their fierceness, agility, and size increase. Finally, the energy stored at the top carnivore level is utilized by the decomposers.

As a group the carnivores are well adapted for a diet of flesh. Hawks and owls have sharp talons for holding prey and hooked beaks for tearing flesh. Mammalian carnivores have canine teeth for biting and piercing. Cheek teeth are reduced, but many forms have sharp-crested shearing or carnasial teeth.

Omnivores. Not all consumers can be fitted neatly in each trophic level, for many consumers do not confine their feeding to one level alone. The red fox feeds on berries, small rodents, and even dead animals. Thus it occupies herbivorous and carnivorous levels, as well as acting as a scavenger. Some fish feed on both plant and animal matter. The basically herbivorous white-footed mouse also feeds on insects, small birds, and bird eggs. Many species, including the white-footed mouse, are cannibalistic. They eat the flesh of their own kind not only in an extreme food shortage, as one might like to believe, but frequently as a way of supplementing their diet. The food habits of many animals vary

31

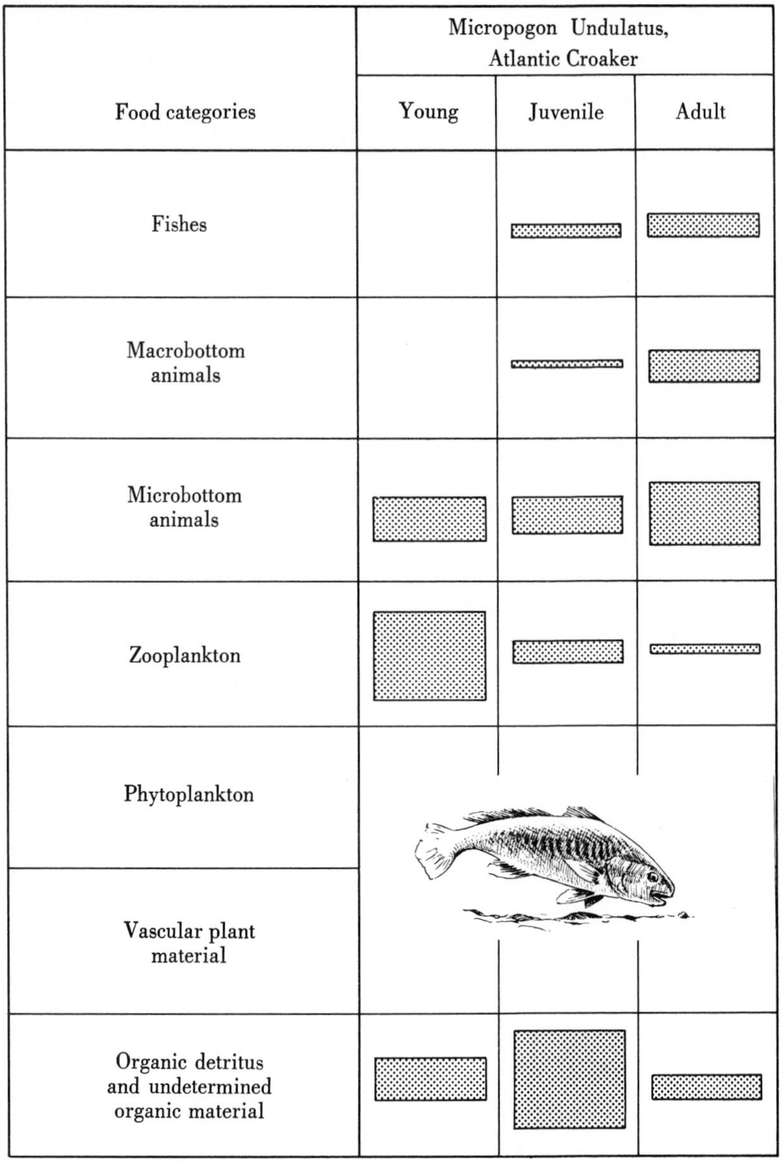

Food categories	Micropogon Undulatus, Atlantic Croaker		
	Young	Juvenile	Adult
Fishes		▒▒▒▒▒▒	▒▒▒▒
Macrobottom animals		∿∿∿∿∿	▒▒▒
Microbottom animals	▒▒▒▒	▒▒▒▒	▒▒▒▒▒
Zooplankton	▒▒▒▒▒	▒▒▒▒	∿∿∿∿
Phytoplankton			
Vascular plant material			
Organic detritus and undetermined organic material	▒▒▒▒	▒▒▒▒▒	▒▒▒

Figure 3-2 *Trophic spectra for young, juvenile, and adult stages of the Atlantic croaker from Lake Pontchartrain. The young fish subsist chiefly on zooplankton, the juveniles on organic detritus, the adults on bottom animals and fish.* (Graph after Darnell, 1961.)

with the seasons, with stages in the life cycle, and with the size and growth of the organism (Fig. 3-2). Consumers that belong to more than one trophic level or feeding group are called *omnivores*.

Decomposers. *Decomposers* make up the final feeding group. They are chiefly microorganisms (bacteria, yeast, and fungi), which break down the remains and wastes of organisms into simpler substances. Decomposers render organic matter soluble and break it down chemically. This material is then utilized by *transformers,* bacteria that change organic compounds into inorganic forms used by photosynthetic plants. Decomposers that work on plant material are functional herbivores, those that break down animal tissue are functional carnivores.

Others.   Several other feeding groups are also involved in energy transfer. *Parasites* are one; most parasites spend a considerable part of their life cycle living on, or in, and drawing their nourishment from, their hosts without actually killing them. Other parasites, the *parasitoides,* draw nourishment from the host until the host dies. At this point the parasitoid transforms into another stage of its life cycle, becoming independent of the host. Functionally, parasites are specialized carnivores, or in the case of plant parasites, herbivores. *Scavengers* are animals that eat dead plant and animal material. Among these are termites and various beetles that feed in dead and decaying wood, and crabs and other marine invertebrates that feed on plant particles in water. Botflies, dermestid beetles, vultures, and gulls are only several of many animals that feed on animal remains. Depending on what they eat, the scavengers are either herbivores or carnivores. *Saprophytes* are plant counterparts of scavengers. They draw their nourishment from dead plant and animal material, chiefly the former. Since they do not require sunlight as an energy source, they can live in deep shade or dark caves. Examples of saprophytes are fungi, Indian pipe, and beech drops. The majority of these are herbivorous; others, such as the entomophagous fungi, feed on animal matter.

Major food chains

All food chains, directly or indirectly, relate back to living plants. In some marine communities and perhaps fresh water communities, the bulk of plants produced may be consumed by the grazers, but in terrestrial communities this is rarely the case. Part of the plant energy is fed into the grazers and then passed on to higher trophic levels, but the remainder is consumed by detritus-feeding animals, such as soil mites and millipedes, and by bacteria and fungi of decay (Fig. 3-3).

The amount of energy shunted down the two routes varies among communities. In an intertidal salt marsh, less than 10 per cent of living plant material is consumed by herbivores and 90 per cent goes the way of the detritus feeders and decomposers (Teal, 1962). In fact most of the organisms of the intertidal salt marshes obtain the bulk of their energy from dead plant material. Fifty per cent of the energy fixed annually in a Scots pine plantation is utilized by decomposers (Fig. 3-3). The remainder is removed as yield or is stored in tree trunks (Ovington, 1961). Only about 7 per cent of the annual crop of leaves produced by a European deciduous forest is consumed by leaf-eating insects (Bray, 1961). The remainder of the leaves are utilized by dead plant consumers. In some communities, particularly undergrazed grasslands, unconsumed organic matter may accumulate and the materials remain out of circulation for some time, especially when conditions are not favorable for microbial action (see Chap. 15). The decomposer or detritus food chain receives additional materials from the waste products and dead bodies of both the herbivores and carnivores.

There are a number of supplementary food chains in the community, including the parasitic, saprophytic, and scavenger. Parasitic food chains are highly complicated, because of the life cycle of the parasites. Some parasites are passed from one host to another by predators in the food chain (see Fig. 21-2). External or ectoparasites may transfer from one host to another. Other parasites are transmitted by insects from one host to another through the blood stream or plant fluids. Food chains also exist among parasites themselves. Fleas that parasitize mammals and birds are in turn parasitized by a protozoan *Leptomonas*. Chalcid wasps lay eggs in the ichneumon or tachinid fly grub, which in turn is parasitic on other insect larvae. In these parasitic food chains, the members, starting with

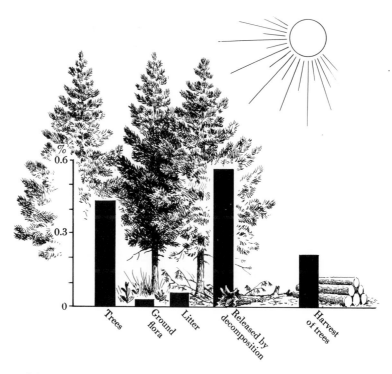

Figure 3-3 *The fate of the 1.3 per cent of solar energy assimilated as net production by a Scots pine plantation 23 years old.* (Adapted from Ovington, 1962.)

the host, become progressively smaller and more numerous with each level in the chain.

Food chains involving saprophytes and scavengers may take two directions, toward the carnivores or toward microorganisms. The role of these feeding groups in the final dissipation of energy has already been mentioned. But they also are food to numerous other animals as well. Slugs eat the larvae of certain Diptera and Coleptera, which live in the heads of fungi and feed on the soft material. Mammals, particularly the red squirrel and chipmunks, eat woodland fungi. Dead plant remains are food sources for springtails and mites, which in turn are eaten by carnivorous insects and spiders. These in turn are energy sources for insectivorous birds and small mammals. Blowflies lay their eggs in dead animals and within 24 hours the maggot larvae hatch. Unable to eat solid tissue, they reduce the flesh to a fetid mass by enzymatic action, in which they feed on the protein material. These insects are food for other organisms.

Energy flow and energy budgets

Net production. The flow of energy through the community starts with the fixation of sunlight by plants, a process which in itself demands the expenditure of energy. Plants get a start by living first on the food stored in the seed until its production machinery is working. Once started, the green plant then begins to accumulate energy. Energy accumulated by plants is called *production,* or more specifically *primary production,* since it is the first and basic form of energy storage. The rate at which it accumulates is known as *primary productivity.* All of the sun's energy that is assimilated—i.e., total photosynthesis—is *gross primary production.* Since plants, like other organisms, must overcome the tendency of energy to disperse, free energy (that available to do work) must be expended for production as well as for reproduction and maintenance. The energy required for this is provided by a reverse of the photosynthetic process, or respiration. The energy remaining after respiration and stored as organic matter is *net primary production,* or plant growth.

Since productivity is a rate, it must be measured in some sort of units. The basic unit of energy used in ecological work is the calorie, usually the large, or kilocalorie, the amount of heat needed to raise one liter (or kilogram) of water one degree centigrade. The small calorie, heat needed to raise one gram of water one degree centigrade, is used when small organisms or small quantities of energy are involved. But for most purposes the large calorie, abbreviated kcal, is used. If the caloric value of plants or any material is uniform, units of weight may be used instead (for example, see Table 3-1). If these units are to be used to estimate efficiencies and other ratios, the same unit must be used for both the numerator and the denominator of the ratio. Only calories can be compared with calories, gram dry weight with gram dry weight, and so on.

When it comes to storing energy, photosynthesis is not very efficient in converting the sun's energy into organic matter. In the first place the usable spectrum, 4000 to 7000 Angstroms, represents only about one-half of the total energy. For productive vegetation about 1 to 3 per cent of annual incident radiation is converted into food energy. Highest short-term efficiency measured over a period of weeks may amount up to 9 per cent (Wassink, 1959). The net primary production of a 55-year-old Scots pine plantation amounted to a little over 422×10^{10} cal per hectare, equivalent to a mean annual transformation of solar energy of about 8×10^{10} cal, of which three-quarters can be attributed to the trees (Ovington, 1959). Since the average annual income of solar radiation to the pine plantation is somewhere around 770×10^{10} cal per hectare of land, the annual efficiency of the Scots pine is 1.3 per cent, or about 2.5 per cent based on usable light energy. The annual net production of dry matter for tropical forests has been estimated at about 40×10^{3} cal per hectare, equivalent to an annual fixation of about 18×10^{10} cal per hectare (Ogawa et al., 1961). The annual incident radiation within the range for photosynthesis is about 600×10^{10} cal per hectare, making the photosynthetic efficiency about 3 per cent. Sugar-cane fields in Java have an efficiency of around 1.9 per cent (Hellmers and Bonner, 1959).

Net primary production accumulates over a period of time as plant biomass. **35**

Part of this accumulation is turned over seasonally through decomposition. Part is retained over a longer period of time as living material. The amount of this accumulated organic matter found on a given area at a given time is the standing-crop biomass, which can vary seasonally and even daily. In grassland and old-field ecosystems much of the net production is turned over every year. The standing crop of living material in an old field in Michigan amounted to some 4×10^3 kilograms (kg) per hectare in late summer compared to 80 kg per hectare in early spring. But at this time the standing crop in dead matter was nearly 3×10^3 kg per hectare (Golley, 1960). A similar situation existed in a salt marsh where the standing crop in autumn was 9×10^3 kg per hectare; in winter it was just one-third of this (Teal, 1962). In the forest a considerably greater portion of the net production is tied up as wood. Tree-trunk biomass over a wide variety of species at age 50 ranges from 100 to 300×10^3 kg per hectare dry weight, equivalent to 2 to 6×10^3 kg per hectare mean annual increment on the trunks (Ovington, 1962*b*). Roots account for another part of a steadily accumulating standing crop. On the other hand, a considerable portion of net production is lost through decomposition each year. Leaf fall in woodland ecosystems varies from 1.5 to 2.5×10^3 kg per hectare each year. Annual turnover in a Scots pine plantation amounts to around 8×10^3 kg per hectare, while in an evergreen gallery forest the turnover, which involves almost if not all the litter, is about 25×10^3 kg per hectare.

Annual net production in woodlands increases with age up to a certain point and then declines. Mean annual net primary production of a Scots pine plantation was a little over 12×10^3 kg per hectare at 30 years of age; it then declined slightly (Ovington, 1961). The plantation, however, achieved maximum production at the age of 20, when it amounted to 22×10^3 kg per hectare. Woodlands apparently achieve their maximum annual production in the pole stage, when the dominance of the trees is the greatest and the understory is at a minimum. The understory makes its greatest contribution during the juvenile and mature stages of the forest. The fate of the net production on a Scots pine plantation is illustrated, as has been shown, in Fig. 3-3. As age increases, more and more of the production is needed for maintenance and very little gross production is left for growth.

Net and gross production vary among different plant communities. Variations in the ranges of net production for different species and ecosystems, stated as thousands of kilograms per hectare per year, are given in Table 3-1 and need no elaboration here. The most productive ecosystems are coral reefs, estuaries, and some intensive year-long agricultural fields, while parts of the open oceans and deserts are very low, anywhere from 0.5 to 1.0 grams per square meter per day. Somewhere between are forests, grassland, and agriculture, with production ranging from 1 gram per square meter per day to 20 grams. The maximum rate that any extensive ecosystem can reach and hold probably is no higher than 25 grams per square meter per day (Odum, 1959).

Consumer production. Net production is energy available to the heterotrophic component of the ecosystem. Theoretically at least, all of it is available to the grazers and even to the decomposers; but it is used this way only under the most ideal conditions. The net production of any given community may be dispersed to another food chain either by migration out of the area or by some other means such as winds and currents. For example, about 45 per cent of the net production of a salt marsh is lost to estuarine waters (Teal, 1962). Much of the living material is physically unavailable to the grazers—they cannot reach the plants. Living organic matter, as long as it is alive, is unavailable to decomposers and detritus feeders; and dead material may not be relished by the grazers. A considerable portion of the plant material may pass through the animal body undigested. The grasshopper assimilates only about 30 per cent of the grass it consumes, leaving 70 per cent available to the detritus-decomposer food chain

TABLE 3-1. NET ORGANIC PRODUCTION OF SOME SELECTED ECOSYSTEMS

ECOSYSTEM	NET PRODUCTION, IN THOUSANDS OF KILO-GRAMS PER HECTARE PER YEAR	AUTHORITY
Alpine Meadow (exclusive of roots)	.0002–.0011	Billings and Bliss, 1959
Rhododendron maximum shrub community	2	Whittaker, 1961
Old field, 1 year after abandonment— South Carolina	5	Odum, 1960
Birch woods, England	8	Ovington and Madgwick, 1959
Mixed shrub community	10	Whittaker, 1961
Scots Pine, 35 years old	12	Ovington, 1957
Corn, Wisconsin, (weeds excluded)	15	Transeau, 1926
Evergreen gallery forest, Thailand	25	Ogawa et al., 1961
Silver Springs, Florida	65	Odum, 1957
Coral Reef, Eniwetok Atoll	81	Odum and Odum, 1955

(Smalley, 1960). Mice, on the other hand, assimilate around 85 to 90 per cent of what they consume (Golley, 1960; Smith, 1962).

Energy, once consumed by an animal, either is diverted to maintenance, growth, and reproduction or is passed from the body. The bulk of the energy consumed goes into maintenance. This includes energy used in the nutritive process, involving both the capture or harvesting of the food as well as its digestion; muscular work expended in the animal's daily routine of living; maintenance of bodily homeostasis; and replacement of protoplasm—that is, keeping up with the wear and tear on the body. Energy used for maintenance is lost through respiration and is unavailable to the ecosystem. Maintenance costs, highest in the small, active, warm-blooded animals, are fixed or irreducible; any

37

energy left over goes into production, including new tissue, fat tissue, and new individuals. The percentage of energy converted to production is greatest when the birth rate of the population and the growth rate of individuals are the highest. This usually coincides—for obvious reasons—with the time when net production also is the highest. Unused energy passes through the body as feces, as urea and other nitrogenous wastes, and as fermentation gases (Fig. 3-4).

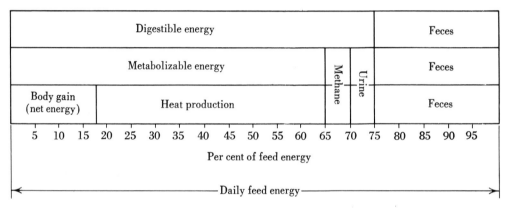

Figure 3-4 *Relative values of the end products of energy metabolism in the white-tailed deer. Note the small amount of net energy gained (body weight) in relation to that lost as heat, gas, urine, and feces. The deer is a first-level consumer, or herbivore. (After Cowan, 1962.)*

The energy budget of an animal population on any trophic level may be summarized by the formula

$$E = R + P$$

in which E is the total energy flow, R is the total cost of maintenance, and P is the total production for a given period of time. For animals, this formula might be modified to read

$$E = I + F$$

in which I is energy consumed and F is energy lost in feces.

Efficiency of production. The rate of energy consumption and the rate of assimilation are one thing; the efficiency of energy utilization is another, and it has an important bearing on how much energy one trophic level in the food chain passes on to the next. Efficiency is the ratio of useful output of energy in relation to input. There are all sorts of ways to look at efficiencies, but the most valuable from the functional viewpoint is food-chain efficiency, or the efficiency of transfer of ingested energy. It represents the ratio of the calories assimilated by the carnivore level to the calories assimilated by the herbivore level:

$$\text{Food-chain efficiency} = \frac{\text{calories assimilated by carnivores}}{\text{calories assimilated by herbivores}}$$

Other efficiencies useful to know are those concerned with processes taking place within a population. Two of these are:

$$\text{Growth efficiency} = \frac{\text{potential energy used in growth}}{\text{ingested potential energy}}$$

$$\text{Assimilation efficiency} = \frac{\text{potential energy ingested} - \text{feces energy}}{\text{potential energy ingested}}$$

These efficiencies vary between species and trophic levels. Growth efficiencies among large animals appear to be less than among small animals. Assimilation efficiencies seem to be higher among carnivores than herbivores, since meat is more nutritious and easily digested than plant food; but the maintenance costs of carnivores also must be higher.

Body size. Body size imposes a limit on energy flow through a given population. There is no linear correlation between energy flow and body weight or surface area per se, but there is a correlation with the metabolically effective body weight. Thus an increase of 100 per cent in body weight means a 70 per cent increase in metabolic weight. As the body size increases, the neuroendocrine system, which controls metabolism, increases proportionally with body surface rather than with weight. Thus metabolic rate per gram of weight rises exponentially as the weight of the individual declines.

Size acts in still another way. It has considerable influence on the direction a food chain takes, since there are upper and lower limits to the size of food an animal can capture. Some animals are too fleet to be caught; others are large enough to defend themselves successfully. Some foods are too small to be collected economically, since it takes too long to secure enough to meet the animal's metabolic needs. Thus the size of a carnivore's prey is determined by the upper limit by the predator's strength and on the lower limit by the animal's opportunity to secure enough prey to meet its needs.

There are exceptions, of course. Spiders and snakes by injecting poisons kill prey much larger than themselves. Wolves hunting in packs can kill an elk or a caribou. The idea that food chains involve animals of progressively larger sizes is true only in a very general way. In the parasitic chain the opposite situation exists. The larger animals are at the base and, as the number of links increases, the size of the parasites becomes smaller. The only animal that can deal with food of any size is man.

Size of the standing crop. The size of the standing crop influences the capacity to produce. A pond with too few fish, or a forest with too few trees, does not have the capacity to utilize the energy available. On the other hand, too many fish or too many trees means less energy available to each individual.

This lowers the efficiency of use. The size and composition of the standing crop vary with the region. It may consist of many species, as in a coral reef, or few, as in the tundra. This has a considerable influence on the storage and transfer of energy through the community.

A large standing crop, however, is not synonymous with productivity. Instead, a reverse may be true. Production of bottom fauna in a pond amounted to nearly 17 times the standing crop when fish were present. In the absence of fish, the production rate of fish food decreased and finally stopped with a larger standing crop. Thus the standing crop of bottom fauna in the presence of fish was depressed, but production increased. In ponds with fish, the annual production amounted to 811 pounds of fish food and 181 pounds of fish per acre. This represents an efficiency of 18 per cent in energy conversion from bottom fauna to fish (Hayne and Ball, 1956).

Ecological pyramids. The number of organisms involved in the amount of energy passing through the food chain becomes smaller with each successive link. The relationship between successive links can be shown graphically by ecological pyramids. The use of ecological pyramids was advanced by C. E. Elton (1927), who pointed out the great difference in the numbers of organisms involved in each step of the food chain. The animals at the lower end of the food chain are the most abundant. Successive links of carnivores decrease rapidly in number until there are very few carnivores at the top. This concept is known as the pyramid of numbers (Fig. 3-5 a). The pyramid of numbers often is confused with a similar one in which organisms are grouped into size categories and then arranged in order of abundance. Here the smaller organisms again are the most abundant; but such a pyramid does not indicate the relationship of one group to another.

The pyramid of numbers ignores the biomass of organisms. Although the numbers of a certain organism may be greater, their total weight, or biomass, may not be equal to that of the larger organisms. Neither does the pyramid of numbers indicate the energy transferred or the use of energy by the groups involved. And since the abundance of members varies so widely, it is difficult to show the whole community on the same numerical scale.

More informative is the pyramid of biomass (Fig. 3-5 b). This indicates, by weight or other means of measuring living material, the total bulk of organisms or fixed energy present at any one time. Since some energy and material is lost in each successive link, the total mass supported at each level is limited by the rate at which energy is being stored below. This usually results in a gradually sloping pyramid for most communities, particularly in terrestrial and shallow-water situations where the producers are large and long lived. Occasionally the pyramid of biomass may be inverted, if the rate of turnover of producer organisms is very large. This happens at times in open- or deep-water communities where there are rapid turnovers of minute producer organisms.

A third type of relationship is that of energy, the most certain of all to be a pyramid, but data for its construction is difficult to obtain. This pyramid indicates not only the amount of energy flow at each level but, more important, the actual role the various organisms assume in the transfer of energy (Fig. 3-5 c). The base upon which the energy pyramid is constructed is the amount of

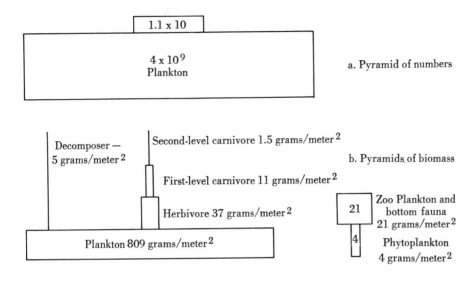

a. Pyramid of numbers

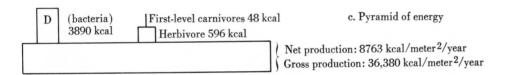

b. Pyramids of biomass

Second-level carnivore 1.5 grams/meter^2

First-level carnivore 11 grams/meter^2

Herbivore 37 grams/meter^2

Decomposer — 5 grams/meter^2

Plankton 809 grams/meter^2

Zoo Plankton and bottom fauna 21 grams/meter^2

Phytoplankton 4 grams/meter^2

c. Pyramid of energy

D (bacteria) 3890 kcal

First-level carnivores 48 kcal

Herbivore 596 kcal

Net production: 8763 kcal/meter^2/year
Gross production: 36,380 kcal/meter^2/year

Figure 3-5 *Ecological pyramids.* (a) *Pyramid of numbers;* (b) *pyramid of biomass;* (c) *pyramid of energy.* (Data from W. E. Pequegnat, 1961; H. E. Odum, 1957; H. W. Harvey, 1950; J. M. Teal, 1962.)

organisms produced per unit time or, stated differently, the rate at which food material passes through the food chain. Some organisms may have a small biomass, but the total energy they assimilate and pass on may be considerably greater than that of organisms with a much larger biomass. On a biomass pyramid these organisms would appear much less important in the community than they really are.

Energy pyramids are always sloping, since less energy is transferred from each level than was paid into it. This is in accord with the second law of thermo-dynamics. In instances where producers have less bulk than consumers, par-ticularly in open-water communities, the energy they store and pass on must be greater than that of the next level. Otherwise the biomass that producers support could not be greater than the producers themselves. This high energy flow is maintained by a rapid turnover of individual plankton, rather than an increase of total mass.

41

Flow of energy through a natural food chain

Quantitative descriptions of energy flow through any food chain are rather difficult to obtain, but one that has been rather carefully worked out (Golley, 1960) involves old-field vegetation, the meadow mouse, and the least weasel (Fig. 3-6). The mouse was almost exclusively herbivorous and the weasel lived

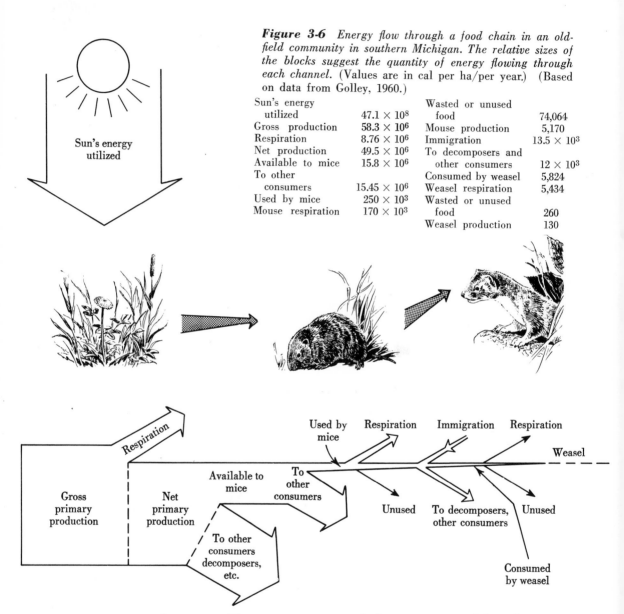

Figure 3-6 *Energy flow through a food chain in an old-field community in southern Michigan. The relative sizes of the blocks suggest the quantity of energy flowing through each channel.* (Values are in cal per ha/per year.) (Based on data from Golley, 1960.)

Sun's energy utilized	47.1×10^8	Wasted or unused food	74,064
Gross production	58.3×10^6	Mouse production	5,170
Respiration	8.76×10^6	Immigration	13.5×10^3
Net production	49.5×10^6	To decomposers and other consumers	12×10^3
Available to mice	15.8×10^6	Consumed by weasel	5,824
To other consumers	15.45×10^6	Weasel respiration	5,434
Used by mice	250×10^3	Wasted or unused food	260
Mouse respiration	170×10^3	Weasel production	130

mainly on mice. The vegetation converted about 1 per cent of the solar energy into net production, or plant tissue. The mice consumed about 2 per cent of the plant food available to them and the weasels about 31 per cent of the mice. Of the energy assimilated, plants lost about 15 per cent through respiration, the mice 68 per cent, and the weasel 93 per cent. The weasels used so much of their assimilated energy in maintenance that a carnivore preying on the weasel could not exist.

In a more general sense, in the transformation of energy through the ecosystem, the energy is reduced in magnitude by 100 from primary producers to plant consumers and by 10 for each step thereafter. Thus if an average of 1000 kcal of light energy per square meter per day were fixed by green plants, about 10 kcal would be converted to herbivore tissue, 1.0 kcal as first-level carnivore production and 0.1 kcal for the second-level carnivore. The amount of food available

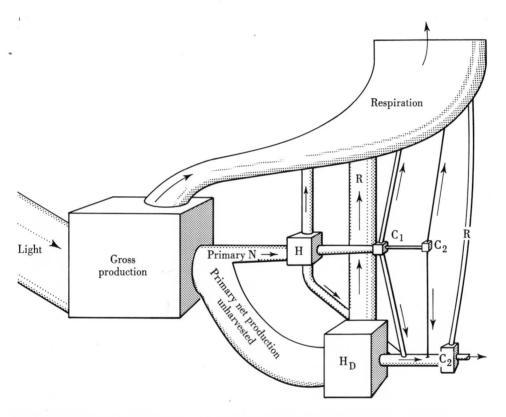

Figure 3-7 *A generalized diagram showing energy flow through the ecosystem. There are two major pathways, through the herbivore chain and through the decomposer chain. N = net production; H = herbivore; H_D = herbivore decomposers; C = carnivores; R = respiration.*

to second- and third-level carnivores is so small that few organisms could be supported if they depended on that source alone. For all practical purposes each food chain has from three to four links, rarely five. The fifth link is distinctly a luxury item in the ecosystem (see Fig. 3-7).

The degradation of energy through successive trophic levels has broad implications for man. Too often we regard energy flow and food chains as something that belongs out in a woods or a lake, something that involves creatures of the wild, but not man. But man is as much a part of the energy flow through the ecosystems as the mouse and the weasel or the herring and the sharks. We too depend upon plants to fix the energy we need to keep life going, even though we may tap it from a can or a deep freeze. Energy in food chains diverted through man is lost in about the same ratio as it passes from plant——→beef——→ man as it does when passing from plant——→mouse——→weasel. Man, being omnivorous, can support a much higher population if he becomes also a herbivore —this is possible through the cooking of plants to make them digestible. In countries of burgeoning populations, man does exist on the herbivore level. People over most of the world cannot afford the luxury of losing the energy involved in converting plant tissue to beef and pork. Such a diet is impossible; there would be too little energy to go around. As the world population continues to climb, more and more of mankind will be forced to live on the trophic level next to plant, for the shorter the food chain, the more energy there will be to go around.

Community energy budgets

Since energy flow involves both inputs and outputs, the efficiency of an ecosystem can be estimated by measuring the quantity of energy entering the community through various trophic levels and the amount leaving. Thus a balance sheet for energy and production with debit and credit sides (Table 3-2) can be drawn up for a community.

Few communities have been studied intensively enough to present such a broad picture, but there are some available. One is a salt marsh, an autotrophic community (Teal, 1962), and the other a cold spring, a heterotrophic community (Teal, 1957), since the major energy source was plant material fallen into the water.

Of the energy transformed by organisms in the spring, 76 per cent entered as leaves, fruit, and branches of terrestrial vegetation. Photosynthesis accounted for 23 per cent and 1 per cent came from immigrating caddisfly larvae. Of this total input, 71 per cent was dissipated as heat, 1 per cent lost through the emigration of adult insects, and 28 per cent was deposited in the community. In the salt marsh the producers themselves were the most important consumers, for plant respiration accounts for 70 per cent of gross production, an unusually high figure, Scots pine, for example, utilizes only about 10 per cent in respiration. Plants are followed by the bacteria, which utilize only one-seventh as much as the producers. Primary and secondary consumers come in a poor third, using only one-seventh as much energy as the bacteria.

Methods of estimating production

Estimating the rates of energy fixation in an ecosystem is difficult and the task of measuring all aspects of the energy flow is enormous. Several major techniques for determining primary productivity are in current use. All estimate energy fixation indirectly by relating the amount of materials, oxygen, or carbon dioxide released or used.

Light and dark bottle

The light and dark bottle method, commonly used in aquatic environments, is based on the assumption that the amount of oxygen produced is proportional

TABLE 3-2 COMMUNITY ENERGY BALANCE SHEETS FOR AN
AUTOTROPHIC AND HETEROTROPHIC COMMUNITY

AUTOTROPHIC COMMUNITY: THE SALT MARSH (Teal, 1962)

Input as light	600,000 kcal/m²/year
Loss in photosynthesis	563,620, or 93.9 per cent
Gross production	36,380, or 6.1 per cent of light
Producer respiration	28,175, or 77 per cent of gross production
Net production	8,205 kcal/m²/year
Bacterial respiration	3,890, or 47 per cent of net production
First-level consumer respiration	596, or 7 per cent of net production
Second-level consumer respiration	48, or 0.6 per cent of net production
Total energy dissipation by consumers	4,534, or 55 per cent of net production
Export	3,671, or 45 per cent of net production

HETEROTROPHIC COMMUNITY: TEMPERATE COLD SPRING (Teal, 1957)

Organic debris	2,350 kcal/m²/year, or 76.1 per cent of available energy
Gross photosynthetic production	710 kcal/m²/year, or 23.0 per cent of available energy
Immigration of caddis larvae	18 kcal/m²/year, or 0.6 per cent of available energy
Decrease in standing crop	8 kcal/m²/year, or 0.3 per cent of available energy
Total energy dissipation to heat	2,185 kcal/m²/year, or 71 per cent of available energy
Deposition	868 kcal/m²/year, or 28 per cent of available energy
Emigration of adult insects	33 kcal/m²/year, or 1 per cent of available energy

to gross production—since one molecule of O_2 is produced for each atom of carbon fixed. Two bottles containing a given concentration of phytoplankton are suspended at the level from which the samples were obtained. One bottle is black, to exclude light; the other is clear. In the light bottle a quantity of oxygen proportional to the total organic matter fixed (gross production) is produced by photosynthesis. At the same time some of the oxygen is being utilized in respiration. The amount of oxygen left is proportional to the amount of fixed organic matter remaining after respiration (net production). The quantity of oxygen in the light bottle indicates net photosynthesis, or net primary production. In the dark bottle, oxygen is being utilized but is not being produced. Thus the quantity of oxygen utilized, obtained by subtracting from the quantity of oxygen at the start (determined by control bottles) the amount left at the end of the run (usually 24 hours) gives a measure of respiration. The amount of oxygen in the light bottle added to the amount used in the dark provides an estimate of total photosynthesis, or gross production.

In a modification of this method, the whole aquatic ecosystem becomes the light and dark bottle, with the daytime representing the light bottle, the nighttime the dark. The oxygen content of the water is taken every two or three hours during a 24-hour period. From this, the rise and fall of oxygen during the day and night can be plotted as a diurnal curve (Odum, 1956). This method, adaptable to the study of flowing water communities, takes into account the photosynthesis of bottom plants, as well as the oxygen exchanged between air and water and between water and bottom mud.

Still another modification of the light and dark bottle method suited for terrestrial communities involves the amount of carbon dioxide produced. A plastic bag or bell jar is placed over a sample of the community. Air is drawn through the enclosure and passed over a carbon-dioxide absorbent. A similar sample is covered by a dark jar or bag. The amount of carbon dioxide produced under the dark jar is a measure of respiration; under the light jar the quantity of carbon dioxide would be equivalent to photosynthesis minus respiration. The two results added together indicate gross production.

Chlorophyll

An estimate of production of some ecosystems can be obtained from chlorophyll and light data. This technique evolved from the discoveries by plant physiologists that a close relationship exists between chlorophyll and photosynthesis at any given light intensity. This relationship remains constant for different species of plants and thus communities, even though the chlorophyll content of organisms varies widely, as a result of nutritional status and duration and intensity of the light to which the plant is exposed.

This method, best adapted to aquatic ecosystems, involves the determination of chlorophyll *a* content of the plant per gram or per square meter, which under reasonably favorable conditions is the same. Also obtained is the total daily solar radiation reaching the surface, the extinction coefficient of visible light in the water, and the photosynthesis of the population at light saturation. For example, marine phytoplankton assimilated, at light saturation, 3.7 grams of carbon per hour for each gram of chlorophyll (Ryther and Yentsch, 1957). From such information, total daily production within a body of water can be estimated.

The chlorophyll method is well suited for survey work of aquatic ecosystems. It eliminates the need to enclose a sample of the community in artificial containers, or to make time studies of photosynthesis. Chlorophyll *a* can be easily extracted with acetone and quantitatively determined by means of a spectrophotometer. Light data can be obtained from tables of average solar radiation. Light extinction can be determined by photometer or by using visibility disks to give the total productive area in the aquatic ecosystem. Since the total quantity of chlorophyll per square meter tends to increase and decrease according to the amount of photosynthesis, it indicates the food-manufacturing potential at a given time. The amount of other pigments also can be used to estimate the biomass of the producers.

The harvest methods

The harvest method is used to determine the production of cultivated land and range, where production starts from zero at seeding or planting time, becomes maximum at harvest, and is subject to little utilization by consumers. This method involves the weighing of samples removed at intervals through the season to obtain a measure of growth, in order to get net production. Also giving an estimate of net production is the determination of the disappearance of raw materials, particularly nitrogen and phosphorus. This is a useful method in communities where materials accumulate over winter or are supplied annually. The rate of decrease of the constituents would be a measure of productivity.

Radioactive tracers

The most recent method of determining production involves the measurement of the rate of uptake of radioactive carbon (C^{14}) by plants. This is the most sensitive technique now available to measure net photosynthesis under field conditions.

Basically the method involves the addition of a quantity of radioactive carbon as a carbonate ($C^{14}O_3$) to a sample of water containing its natural phytoplankton population. After a short period of time, to allow photosynthesis to take place, the plankton material is strained from the water, washed, and dried. Then radioactivity counts are taken, and from them calculations are made to estimate the amount of CO_2 fixed in photosynthesis. This estimate is based on the assumption that the ratio of activity of $C^{14}O_3$ added to the activity of phytoplankton is proportionate to the ratio of the total carbon available to that assimilated.

Radioactive phosphorus, P^{32}, also has been used, but since phosphorus tends to be absorbed by sediments and organisms more rapidly than it is assimilated by organisms, estimates obtained from phosphorus are inaccurate. This method is much more useful for determining the direction of energy flow than for estimating the fixation of energy. This has been done rather successfully for an old-field ecosystem by Odum and Kuenzler (1963). These investigators labeled three dominant species of plants, *Heterotheca, Rumex,* and *Sorgum,* by spraying a solution of phosphorus-32 on the crowns of the plants; each of the three was isolated in separate quadrants. The solution was soon absorbed and incorporated into the plant biomass. If an animal ate the plant, it in turn became radioactive. These investigators found that two animals—the cricket, *Oecanthus,* and the ant, *Dorymyrmex*—were actively feeding on the plants. Radiation showed up in these two in one to two weeks, while in other grazing herbivores, including the grasshopper, it appeared later, from two to five weeks. Among the predators, such as the spider, the radioactive tracer did not reach its maximum level until four weeks after the initial labelling. Late, too, in showing any concentration of phosphorus-32 were the detritus or litter feeders, the snails. Thus radioactive tracers not only aid in the separation of animals of the community into their appropriate trophic levels but also enable the determination of habitat niches. In the above experiment, for example, Odum and Kuenzler found that the most common grazing herbivores in the old-field community fed freely on several dominant species of plants without any marked preference, while some of the rarer species were quite selective.

Consumer production

Estimating consumer production also has its problems and difficulties. Methods involve the determination of food consumption, energy assimilation, heat production and maintenance, and growth.

The first step involves some estimation of food consumption. This can be determined in the laboratory or estimated in the field. Laboratory determinations involve feeding the animal a known quantity of its natural foods, allowing it to eat over a period of time, usually 24 hours, then removing the food and weighing the remains. The amount of food consumed equals the amount fed minus the amount removed. The caloric value of the food consumed can be determined by burning a sample in the calorimeter or by obtaining the caloric value for the foods involved from a table—if one exists. If the activity periods of the animal and the weight of the food its stomach will hold are known, then consumption can be rather accurately determined by multiplying the activity periods by the mean weight of observed stomach contents from a sample of animals from the population. Activity periods are used, since most animal activity usually is concerned with feeding.

Once consumed, the food must be assimilated. Assimilation can be determined by subtracting the energy voided in feces from energy consumed. The assimilation of natural foods by animals is still largely unknown.

The energy assimilated is used for maintenance and growth. Energy used for maintenance is lost. The cost of maintenance can be determined by confining the animal to a calorimeter and measuring the heat production directly, or the energy used in maintenance can be determined indirectly by placing the animal in a respirometer and measuring the oxygen consumed or the carbon dioxide produced. These results are then converted to calories of heat. But to do this one must know the respiratory quotient, the ratio of the volume of carbon dioxide produced to the oxygen consumed. The respiratory quotient varies with the type of food utilized in the body. To estimate accurately the heat production of a population from laboratory determinations, one must also know the daily activity periods, the weight distribution of the population, and the environmental temperature.

Production or storage of energy is estimated by observing the growth or weight increase, obtained by weighing individuals fed on a natural diet in the laboratory or by weighing animals each successive time they are caught in the field. An indirect and usually more useful method is based on the age distribution of a population, the growth curve for the species, and the caloric value of the animal tissue. Growth curves must be obtained for each population under investigation and for each season under study. Once a growth curve is available and the age distribution of the population is known, the weight of the tissue produced in a given period can be estimated for each age category. The weight gain is then converted to caloric equivalents.

Biogeochemical cycles

Living organisms require at least 30 to 40 elements for their growth and development. Most important of these are carbon, hydrogen, oxygen, phosphorus, potassium, nitrogen, sulphur, calcium, iron, magnesium, boron, zinc, chlorine, molybdenum, cobalt, iodine, and fluorine. These materials flow from the nonliving to the living and back to the nonliving again, in a more or less circular path known as the *biogeochemical cycle* (*bio* for living, *geo* for water, rocks, and soil, and *chemical* for the processes involved). Some of the materials are

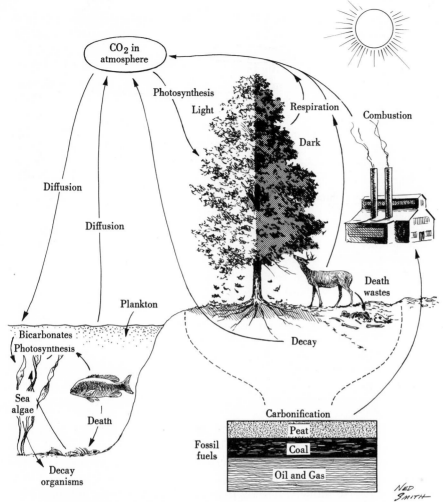

Figure 3-8 *The carbon cycle in the ecosystem. See text for details.*

returned as fast as they are removed; some are stored in short-term nutrient pools; others may be tied up chemically or buried deep in the earth for long periods of time in long-term nutrient pools before being released and made available to the biotic world.

Basically there are two types of biogeochemical cycles, the gaseous and the sedimentary. Both involve biological and nonbiological agents and both are more or less tied to another cycle, that of water.

Gaseous cycles

Carbon cycle

Carbon is a basic constituent of all organic compounds. Since energy transfers occur as the consumption and storage of carbohydrates and fats, carbon moves through the ecosystem with the flow of energy. The source of nearly all carbon found in living organisms is carbon dioxide, free in the atmosphere and dissolved in the waters of the earth (Fig. 3-8). The first step in the utilization of CO_2 by living organisms is photosynthesis by green plants. Carbon, together with oxygen and hydrogen, in the presence of sunlight, is converted to simple carbohydrates. These in turn are synthesized by plants into complex fats and polysaccharides. The polysaccharides and fats stored in plant tissues are eaten by animals, who digest and resynthesize these carbon compounds into others. Meat-eating animals feed on the herbivores, and the carbon compounds again are redigested and resynthesized into other forms. Some of the carbon is returned to the atmosphere directly, since CO_2 is a by-product of respiration of both plants and animals. The carbon locked up in the animal wastes and in protoplasm of plants and animals is released eventually by organisms of decay. Bacteria and fungi attack and feed upon plant and animal remains, break down the complex organism compounds into simpler substances, which are then available for another cycle. After their work, most of the organic carbon is CO_2 once again.

Part of the organic carbon becomes incorporated in the earth's crust as coal, gas, petroleum, limestone, and coral reefs. Such deposits are removed from circulation for long periods of time, often permanently. Some of them are liberated by our industrial and agricultural use of these products; and some CO_2 is released from limestone through weathering. But the circulation of carbon through the ecosystem depends upon living organisms.

Nitrogen cycle

Although nitrogen makes up the greatest part of the atmosphere, green plants obtain their nitrogen from the soil solution in the form of ammonia (NH_3) or nitrates (NO_3) (Fig. 3-9). The most important source of nitrogen from green plants is the nitrogen-fixing bacteria. These live in the root nodules of plants, particularly legumes, and, independently, in the soil. Bacteria, of the genus *Rhizobia,* take nitrogen directly from the air as they grow and multiply in the root nodules of legumes. This nitrogen is available to plants and aids their growth. Some of it is secreted into the soil and becomes available to other plants. Considerable quantities of nitrogen also are added to the soil by free-living, nitrogen-fixing bacteria, particularly species of *Azotobacter* and *Clostridium.* Some blue-green algae, especially species of *Anabaena* and *Nostoc,* perform the same nitrogen-fixing role in aquatic situations.

Nitrogen is excreted as ammonia, urea, uric acid, or other nitrogenous compounds. The breakdown of dead tissue by decay bacteria releases ammonia from proteins and other nitrogenous compounds. Nitrifying bacteria oxidize ammonia into nitrites (NO_2) and still other bacteria oxidize nitrites to nitrates (NO_3). These inorganic nitrogen compounds are usable directly from the soil by green plants.

Oxygen cycle

Oxygen, free in the atmosphere and dissolved in water, is a by-product of photosynthesis. Plants and animals utilize oxygen in respiration and return it to the atmosphere and water in the form of carbon dioxide. The carbon dioxide is utilized by green plants as an essential raw material for carbohydrate synthesis.

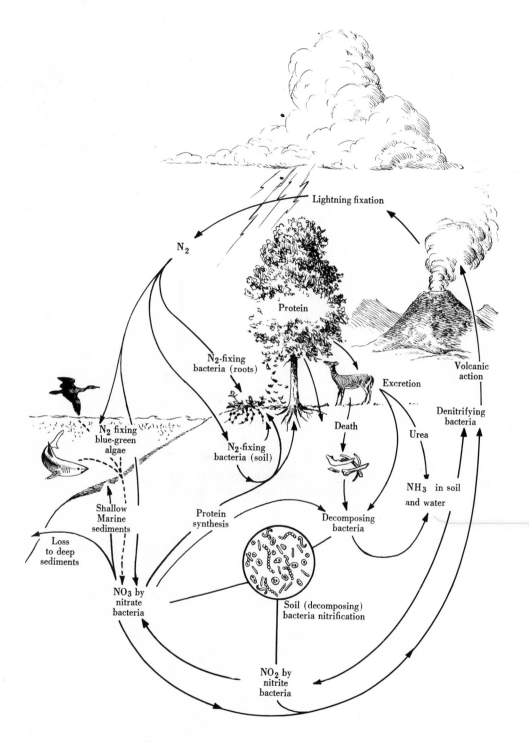

Figure 3-9 *The nitrogen cycle in the ecosystem.*

In such a simple yet vital cycle, oxygen is replenished and maintained in the ecosystem.

Water cycle

The interchange of water between air, land, and sea and between living organisms and their environment is accomplished through the water cycle. The water cycle (Fig. 3-10) involves evaporation, transpiration, cloud formation,

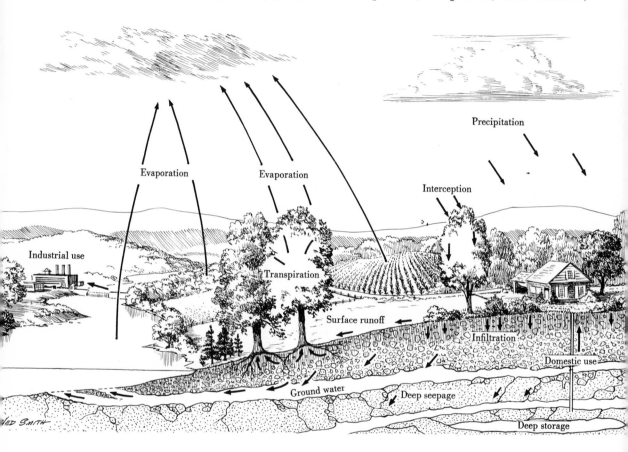

Figure 3-10 *The water cycle.*

precipitation, surface-water runoff, and percolation. Of these, the key process is evaporation, since it maintains the humidity of the atmosphere and feeds back the moisture necessary for cloud formation and precipitation.

Taking the earth as a whole, the cycling of water is a closed system. No more is coming in than is going out. Outputs are controlled by the net amounts of solar energy, by the amount of water available for vaporization, and by the limitations of the soil storage capacity, which involves, among other things, topography, exposure to wind, shading, and so on. Since the actual evaporation of water from land surfaces with vegetation passes partly through the stomata of leaves, the combined water losses are referred to as *evapotranspiration*. The

it of water lost annually through this process from various types
aces and vegetation varies from about 25 to 75 per cent of the pre-
vith the highest percentage always associated with forest cover. The
water available for vaporization are determined by the amounts sup-
ecipitation and condensation, the latter being rather negligible.
nfall input and evaporation output lies the precarious water balance
and soil ecosystem. In this system the soil is the only retention me-
which water may be temporarily stored. Inputs in excess of the
city or the infiltration rates of the soil will run off through and over

Sedimentary cycles

lements required by living organisms are obtained initially from
urces. Available forms occur as salts dissolved in soil water or in
s, and seas. The mineral cycle varies from one element to another;
ly it consists of two phases, the salt-solution phase and the rock
ral salts come directly from the earth's crust by weathering (see
The soluble salts then enter the water cycle. With water they move
soil to streams and lakes and eventually reach the seas, where
indefinitely. Other salts are returned to the earth's crust through
sedimentation. They become incorporated into salt beds, silts, and limestones
where, after weathering, they again enter the cycle.

Plants and many animals obtain their mineral needs from mineral solutions
in their environments. Other animals acquire the bulk of their mineral needs
from the plants and animals they consume. After death of living organisms, the
minerals are returned to soil and water through the action of decay organisms.

The three most important roles in all these nutrient cycles are played at one
end by green plants and at the other end by decay organisms, and on the return
trip by air and water. Without these, there could be no cyclic flow of nutrients.

Other nutrient cycles

Constantly, nutrients are being removed or added by natural and artificial
processes (Fig. 3-11). In woodland, shrub, and grassland ecosystems, nutrients
are returned anually to the soil by leaves, litter, roots, animal excreta, and bodies
of the dead. Released to the soil by decomposition, these nutrients again are
taken up first by plants and then by animals. In fresh waters and the sea, the
remains of plants and animals drift to the bottom, where decomposition takes
place. The nutrients again are recirculated to the upper layers by the annual
overturns (see Chap. 8) and by upwellings from the deep.

The nutrient cycle, however, is not a closed circuit within an ecosystem.
Nutrients are continuously being imported, as well as being carried out of the
ecosystems. Appreciable quantities of plant nutrients are carried in by rain and
snow (Emanuelsson, Eriksson, and Egner, 1954). In Western Europe, at least,
the weight of nutrients supplied by this source is roughly equivalent to the
quantity removed in timber harvest (Neuwirth, 1957). A small quantity of the
nutrients carried to the forest by rain and snow is absorbed directly through
the leaves, but this hardly offsets the quantity leached out. Rain water dripping

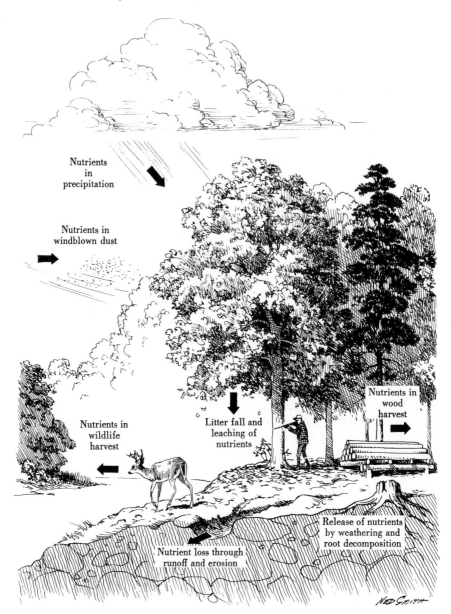

Nutrients
in
precipitation

Nutrients in
windblown dust

Nutrients in
wood
harvest

Nutrients in
wildlife
harvest

Litter fall and
leaching of
nutrients

Release of nutrients
by weathering and
root decomposition

Nutrient loss through
runoff and erosion

NED SMITH

Figure 3-11 Nutrient cycle in a forest ecosystem. Input includes nutrients carried in by precipitation and windblown dust, through litter fall, and through the release of nutrients by weathering and root decomposition. Outgo is through wood harvest, wildlife harvest, runoff, erosion, and leaching.

down from the canopy is richer in calcium, sodium, potassium, phosphorus, iron, manganese, and silica than rain water collected in the open at the same time, although less rain water reaches the forest floor (Tamm, 1951; Madgwick and Ovington, 1959). In fact rain water collected on the woodland floor may be ten times as rich in potassium as that collected in the open (Madgwick and Ovington, 1959). These nutrients "leached" from the foliage in time are absorbed by the surface roots and translocated to the canopy again. Such little nutrient cycles take only a few days.

These little nutrient cycles can be followed by means of radioactive tracers. By inoculating white oak trees with 20 microcuries of cesium-134, Witherspoon and others (1962) were able to follow the gains, losses, and transfers of this radioisotope. About 40 per cent of the cesium-134 inoculated into the oaks in April moved into the leaves by early June (Fig. 3-12). When the first rains fell after inoculation, leaching of radiocesium from the leaves began. By September this loss amounted to 15 per cent of the maximum concentration in the leaves. Seventy per cent of this rain-water loss reached mineral soil; the remaining 30 per cent found its way into the litter and understory. When the leaves fell in autumn, they carried with them two times as much radiocesium as was leached from the crown by rain. Over the winter, one-half of this was leached out to mineral soil. Of the radiocesium in the soil, 92 per cent still remained in the upper four inches nearly two years after the inoculation. Eighty per cent of the cesium was confined to an area within the crown perimeter and 19 per cent was located in a small area around the trunk. This suggests that cesium distribution in the soil was greatly influenced by leaching from rainfall and stem flow (see Chap. 18).

In addition to nutrients added by precipitation and by foliar leaching are those added by extraneous material, such as dust and pollen filtered out of the air by the forest canopy.

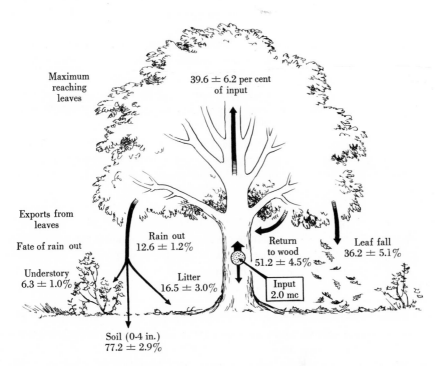

Figure 3-12 *The cycle of cesium-134 in white oak as an example of nutrient cycling through plants. The figures are the average of 12 trees at the end of the 1960 growing season. (After Witherspoon et al., 1962.)*

The gain of nutrients to the ecosystem from precipitation, extraneous material, and mineral weathering is offset by losses. Water draining away from forests carries away more mineral matter than is supplied by precipitation (Viro, 1953), although some of these nutrients may be geological in origin, rather than leached from the soil. Considerable quantities of nutrients in the forest are tied up in the trees and the humus layer. Fifty-five-year-old Scots pine, planted on the open heaths of Britain, accumulated 52 kg of sodium per hectare, 305 kg of potassium, 643 kg of calcium, 142 kg of magnesium, 86 kg of phosphorus, and 1062 kg of nitrogen (Ovington, 1959). When trees, or any vegetation, are harvested, appreciable amounts of nutrients are removed. Intensive forestry and agriculture on some soils may so reduce the nutrient reserves that the soil becomes impoverished. Removal of animals through hunting and trapping also drains away nutrients from the ecosystem, although normally this is not serious; but the drain through the removal of domestic grazing animals may be very great. The ecosystem can remain productive only if the nutrients withdrawn are balanced by an inflow of replacements.

Phosphorus cycle

Of all the nutrients in the sedimentary cycle, one of the most important ecologically is phosphorus; it is the one most likely to be deficient, and so limits the biological productivity of some areas. Phosphorus is indispensible to life, for it is involved in the metabolic processes of energy transfer and in encoding information in the genes.

The main reservoirs or pools of phosphorus are rock and natural phosphate deposits, from which it is released by weathering, by leaching, and by mining for agricultural purposes. Some of it passes through the terrestrial and freshwater ecosystems by the way of plants, grazers, predators, and parasites; and it is returned to the ecosystem by death and decay. But much of it escapes to the sea, where the phosphorus is deposited partly in shallow sediments and partly in the deep. Some of the latter may be recirculated by upwelling, which brings the phosphates from unlighted depths to the photosynthetic zone. Here it is taken up rather rapidly, often in as short a time as five minutes, by all forms of phytoplankton. This phosphorus then is either redeposited as sediment, at times within three days, or ingested by the grazing zooplankton. These zooplankton in turn may excrete as much phosphorus daily as is stored in their bodies (Pomeroy et al., 1963). In doing so, they are instrumental in keeping the phosphorus cycle going. More than half of this excreted phosphorus is in the phosphate form and the remainder is in organic compounds. Whether these organic compounds can be utilized directly by the phytoplankton or whether they must be further degraded by bacteria is still unknown. But if it must be broken down, then bacteria would also play a major role in the phosphorus cycle of the sea. Some of the phosphorus eventually is returned to land through the harvest of fish and through the guano deposits of fish-eating birds. The activity of phytoplankton, however, seems to be inadequate to keep phosphorus in circulation. More, apparently, is being lost to the depths of the sea than is being added to terrestrial and aquatic ecosystems (Hutchinson, 1957).

Phosphorus, like other elements, may take diverse pathways through an ecosystem. Its movements through the several levels can be followed by the use of phosphorus-32 as a tracer. By adding carefully regulated amounts of phosphorus-32, Ball and Hooper (1963) followed the movements of this element through a trout-stream ecosystem. The uptake was rather rapid, the material traveling from 453 to 11,263 yards downstream, depending upon conditions, before being finally removed. Microscopic plants (periphyton) growing on the rocks and other substrate, and three species of larger plants, *Potamogeton*, the alga *Chara,* and water moss *Fontanalis,* were responsible for most of the uptake. Maximum amounts of radioactive phosphorus appeared in plant tissues shortly after the material passed through the area; and the rate of loss was the greatest shortly thereafter. Losses decreased with time for almost 15 to 20 days, when equilibrium was achieved. This suggested that the plants were recycling phosphorus. Concentration of phosphorus in consumer organisms reflected differences in both metabolic turnover rates and in food relationships. Small filter feeders, especially the black fly larvae, reached the highest level of concentration in the shortest time, followed by the animals that scraped periphyton from the rocks. At the same time these organisms lost phosphorus-32 quite rapidly. The material persisted longer in such omnivorous feeders as the scud and the caddisfly, and even longer in the large detritus feeders such as the burrowing mayfly. Phosphorus-32 appeared the latest and was retained the longest in the invertebrate and vertebrate predators. The investigators found considerable variation in the uptake and retention of phosphorus-32 by different plants and animals from year to year. This suggested that the major differences in the cycling of radioactivity was related to the way phosphorus-32 distributed itself between soluble and particulate phases in the stream water.

In the intertidal salt marshes of southeastern United States, the ribbed mussel *Modiolus dimissus* plays a major role in the turnover of phosphorus through the ecosystem (Kuenzler, 1961). To obtain its food, which consists of small organisms as well as particles rich in phosphorus suspended in the tidal waters, the mussels must filter great quantities of sea water. Some of the particles they ingest, but most are rejected and deposited as sediments on the intertidal mud. These particles, rich in phosphorus, are then retained in the salt marsh instead of being carried out to sea. Each day the mussels remove from the water one-third of the phosphorus found in suspended matter. Or to state it a little more precisely, every 2.6 days the mussels remove as much phosphorus as is found on the average in the particles in the water. The particulate matter deposited on the mud is utilized by the deposit feeders, that release the phosphate back to the ecosystem. Thus the ribbed mussel, although of little economic importance to man and relatively unimportant as an energy consumer in the salt marsh, plays a major role in the cycling and retention of phosphates in the salt marsh. The worth of an animal cannot always be measured in terms of economic values or ignored because it contributes little to energy flow. It may serve some other important ecological function in the community that remains to be discovered.

Cycling of radioactive materials

In recent years man has been adding new radioactive materials into the biogeochemical cycle, whose long-range effects are still unknown. These radioactive materials result from chain reactions in nuclear-weapons testing and in nuclear reactors. When the uranium atom is split or fissioned into smaller parts, it produces, in addition to tremendous quantities of energy, a number of new elements, or fission products, including strontium, cesium, barium, and iodine. Some of these fission products last only a few seconds; others can remain active for several thousand years. Although they are not essential for life, these radioactive elements enter the food chain and become incorporated in the living organisms. In the same atomic reaction some particles with no electrical charges, called neurons, get in the way of high-energy particles. Nonfission products are the result, and they include the radioisotopes of such biologically important elements as carbon, zinc, iron, and phosphorus, which are useful in tracer studies. Both fission and nonfission products are released to the atmosphere by nuclear testing and, unless carefully handled, by wastes from nuclear reactors. Later these return to the earth along with rain, dust, and other material as atomic fallout. In the case of large-weapons testing in the atmosphere, this fallout can be worldwide. Once they reach the earth the isotopes enter the food chain and become concentrated in organisms in amounts that exceed by many times the quantities in the surrounding environment. This, in effect, produces local radiation fields in the tissues of plants and animals.

One of the most important radioactive materials released into the biogeochemical cycle is strontium-90. A common component of atomic fallout and atomic wastes, it loses its radioactivity slowly (half life 28 years). Ecologically it behaves like calcium and follows it in the cycling of materials. Strontium-90 is rapidly absorbed by plants through the foliage and the roots; and when taken in with food by animals and man, it becomes concentrated in the bone and other areas of calcium deposition.

Strontium-90 enters animal tissue most easily through the grazing food chain, especially in regions with high rainfall and with low levels of calcium and other mineral nutrients in the soil. Sheep grazing on the English moors, where soils are acid and the rainfall high, have a higher concentration of strontium-90 than sheep grazing in drier, more fertile areas. A more striking example involves the lichen⟶caribou⟶man food chain in the arctic regions of the world. The Far North has been subject to rather heavy atomic fallout and a dominant plant, the lichen, absorbs virtually 100 per cent of the radioactive particles falling upon it. From lichens, the main contaminants, strontium-90 and cesium-137, travel up the food chain from caribou and reindeer to carnivores and man. Humans who depend upon caribou and reindeer for their protein already have accumulated from one-third to one-half of the permissible amounts (Palmer et al., 1963). In other words the radiocontamination of the lichen-caribou-man food chain has already reached a level where it may affect genetically and physically both caribou, their carnivores, and man. Elsewhere in the world the problem is not as great, but it still exists. There has been a small but steady accumulation of strontium-90 in the bones of children and adults in North America and Europe. These examples serve as warnings of what can happen if we fail to use care and restraint in the exploitation of atomic energy, even for peaceful purposes. The same can be said for other pollutants, such as poisonous atmospheric gases and especially pesticides, which also become concentrated as they pass through the food chain.

SUMMARY

Two basic functional characteristics of the ecosystem are the flow of energy and the cycling of materials, both carried through the food chain. The energy of sunlight is fixed by the autotrophic component of the ecosystem, the green plants, as primary production. This energy is then available to the heterotrophic component of the ecosystem, of which the herbivores or plant eaters are the primary consumers. The herbivores in turn are a source of food for the carnivores. At each step or transfer of energy in the food chain, a considerable amount of potential energy is lost as heat, until ultimately the amount of available energy is so small that few organisms can be supported at that source alone. The animals high on the chain often utilize several sources of energy, including plants, and thus in their feeding habits become omnivores. All food chains eventually end with the decomposers, chiefly organisms that reduce the remains of plants and animals into simple substances. Energy flow in the ecosystem may take two routes: one goes through the grazing food chain, the other through the detritus food chain, in which the bulk of production is utilized as dead organic matter by the decomposers.

The loss of energy at each transfer limits the number of trophic levels, or steps, in the food chain to four or five. At each level the biomass usually declines; so if the total weight of individuals at each successive trophic level is plotted, a sloping pyramid is formed. In certain aquatic situations, however, where there is a rapid turnover of small aquatic consumers, the pyramid of biomass may be inverted. Energy, however, always decreases from one trophic level to another and is always pyramidal.

Materials flow from the living to the nonliving and back to the living again in a perpetual cycle through the ecosystem. There are two kinds of cycles: the gaseous, represented by the carbon, oxygen, and nitrogen cycles, and the sedimentary, represented by the phosphorus cycle. The sedimentary cycle usually involves two phases, salt solution and rock. Minerals become available through the weathering of the earth's crust, enter the water cycle as salt solutions, take diverse pathways through the ecosystem, and ultimately return to the sea or back to the earth's crust through sedimentation. Important roles in the mineral cycle are played at one end by green plants, which take up the materials, at the other end by decomposers, which release the materials for reuse, and by air and water, in which the return trips are made. Thus the whole chain of life depends upon the continual fixation and transfer of energy and the never-ending odyssey of materials through the ecosystem.

CHAPTER 4

Environmental influences

In 1840 a German organic chemist, the foremost of his day, Justus von Liebig, published a book, *Organic Chemistry and Its Application to Agriculture and Physiology*. He described in it his analyses of surface soil and plants; and he set forth this simple statement, revolutionary for his day: "The crops on a field diminish or increase in exact proportion to the diminution or increase of the mineral substances conveyed to it in manure." Essentially what he said was that each plant requires certain kinds and quantities of nutrients or food materials. If one of these food substances is absent, the plant dies. And if it is present in minimal quantities only, the growth of the plant will be minimal. This became known as the *law of the minimum*.

Continued investigation down through the years disclosed that not only nutrients but other environmental conditions, such as moisture and temperature, also affected the growth of plants. Later, animals were found to be limited by food, water, temperature, and humidity. Eventually the law of the minimum was extended to cover all environmental requirements of both plants and animals.

Later studies of environmental influences on plants and animals showed that not only does too little of a substance or condition limit the presence or success of an organism, but also too much. Organisms, then, live within a range between too much and too little, the limits of tolerance. This concept of maximum substances or conditions limiting the presence or success of organisms was incorporated by V. E. Shelford in 1913 into the *law of tolerance* (Fig. 4-1).

Modern ecologists, however, recognize that organisms actually are limited by a number of conditions, and often by an interaction between them. An organism,

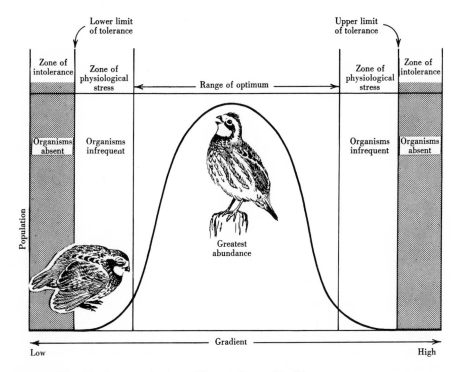

Figure 4-1   *The law of tolerance, illustrated graphically.*

for example, may have a wide range of tolerance for one substance or condition and a narrow range for another, and thus be limited by the item for which it possesses a narrow range of tolerance. It follows then that an organism that exhibits a wide range of tolerance for all environmental influences would be widely distributed. In some cases when one condition is not optimum for the species, the limits of tolerance are reduced in others. On the other hand some organisms may utilize an item in surplus as a substitute for another that is deficient. Some plants respond to sodium when the potassium supply is inadequate (Reitemeier, 1957). The maximum and minimum levels of tolerance for all environmental conditions of a species vary seasonally and geographically. Examples of the extensions of this law will be found in the following discussion of some of the items important to organisms.

Elements and nutrients

The elements and nutrients so necessary for the growth and reproduction of plants and animals and for the maintenance of the community move, as already outlined (Chap. 3), through the biogeochemical cycles—passing from the living to the nonliving and back to the living again. The kind and quantity of nutrients available to and passed along in the biogeochemical cycle have a great influence on the proper functioning of living systems.

Elements provided through the gaseous cycle (Chap. 3) are oxygen, nitrogen, carbon, and hydrogen.

Oxygen is rarely inadequate for life in terrestrial habitats, except at high altitudes (Chap. 18), deep in the soil, and in soils saturated with water. But oxygen may be limited in aquatic communities. Here the supply comes from diffusion of atmospheric oxygen into the water and from photosynthesis. The total quantity of oxygen that water can hold at saturation varies with temperature, salinity, and pressure. It is depleted by the respiration of aquatic plants and animals. Oxygen content in aquatic environments fluctuates daily from a low at night, when respiration is greatest, to a high at midday when photosynthesis is the highest.

Unlike oxygen, carbon dioxide, which makes up only 0.03 per cent of the atmosphere, seems to be limited in terrestrial environments. At least plant physiologists have demonstrated that the rate of photosynthesis increases if a greater quantity of carbon dioxide is available (see Bonner, 1962). The amount of carbon dioxide in natural waters is highly variable, for it occurs in free and combined states. The proportion of the two has a great influence on the hydrogen ion concentration (pH) in aquatic mediums and in the soil. Carbon dioxide combines with water to form a weak carbonic acid, H_2CO_3, which dissociates:

$$CO_2 + H_2O \rightleftharpoons H_2CO_3 \rightleftharpoons H^+ + HCO_3^- \rightleftharpoons H^+ + CO_3^=$$

CO_2 in solution and H_2CO_3 make up free carbon dioxide, while the bicarbonate (HCO_3^-) and the carbonate ($CO_3^=$) ions are the combined forms. The bicarbonate and carbonate ions are very important in buffering or resisting a change in pH. This is significant in ecological systems, since an increase in pH lowers the availability of most nutrients to plants. Like oxygen, carbon dioxide shows daily fluctuations, but the curves are opposite to those of oxygen. The CO_2 concentration is lowest around midday and highest at night, when only respiration is taking place.

Nitrogen makes up 78 per cent of the atmosphere, but it is available to most plants only in a fixed form, such as in nitrites and nitrates (the exceptions are nitrogen-fixing bacteria and blue-green algae; see Chap. 3, Nitrogen Cycle). Most of the nitrogen in the soil is found in organic matter. Nitrogenous compounds leached from the soil and transported by drainage water seem to be the most important source of nitrogen for aquatic communities. During the summer the nitrogen supply in these may be utilized completely by phytoplankton, and nitrates may disappear from the surface water. As a result phytoplankton growth, or "bloom," is reduced greatly in late summer. Nitrates build up again in winter. A similar depletion of nitrogen also may occur in terrestrial communities.

All life processes depend upon nitrogen. It is the building block of protein and a part of enzymes. Nitrogen is needed in abundant supply for reproduction, growth, and respiration. Even chlorophyll is a nitrogenous compound.

Macronutrients

Oxygen, carbon, and nitrogen are considered the energy elements and are needed in relatively large quantities. Other elements and compounds moving through the ecosystems in the sedimentary cycles are needed in smaller amounts. These are the macronutrients and micronutrients. The macronutrients include calcium, magnesium, phosphorus, potassium, and sulphur.

Two elements needed in appreciable quantities are *calcium* and *magnesium*. Magnesium is an integral part of chlorophyll, without which no ecosystem could function; and the element is active in the enzyme systems of plants and animals. In plants calcium is especially important in combining with pectin to form calcium pectate, a cementing material laid down between cells. Plant roots need an available supply of this element at the growing root tips in order to develop normally. In animals, calcium is essential for proper acid-base relationships, for clotting of blood, for alternate contraction and relaxation of the heart muscles, and for the control of fluid passage through the cells. It gives rigidity to the skeleton of vertebrates, and it is the principal component in the exoskeleton of insects and the shells of mollusks and arthropods. A number of mollusks and bivalves are restricted to hard water because of insufficient calcium to harden the shells. A few thin-shelled species are adapted to live in soft water. Hard water contains 53 parts per million (ppm) of calcium and 34 ppm of magnesium or more; soft water contains 50 ppm of calcium and 14 ppm of magnesium or less.

Phosphorus not only is involved in photosynthesis, but also plays a major role in energy transfer within the plant and animal body. It is a major component of the cell nuclear material, where it is involved in cellular organization (DNA) and in the transfer of hereditary material. The lack of phosphorus probably is more closely associated with poor plant growth than is any other element. When the supply of phosphorus is low, growth is arrested, maturity delayed, and roots stunted.

Potassium is utilized in large quantities by plants; and if it is readily available and abundant and growing conditions are favorable, the uptake in crop plants at least may be above that of their average total requirements (Reitemeier, 1957). The formation of sugar and starches in plants, the synthesis of proteins, normal cell division and growth, and carbohydrate metabolisms in animals all depend upon an adequate supply of potassium.

Sulphur, like nitrogen, is a basic constituent of protein, and many plants may utilize as much of this element as they do phosphorus. Sulphur, supplied by soil organic matter and rain water, is sufficient to meet plant needs. Considerable quantities are released to the atmosphere in industrial areas and carried to the soil by rain water. Excessive sulphur can be toxic to plants. Exposure for only an hour to air containing one part per million of sulphur dioxide is sufficient to kill vegetation. For this reason countrysides near smelters are often denuded of vegetation. Plants, especially in arid and semiarid country, also are affected by high concentrations of soluble sulphates in soils, which limit the uptake of calcium.

Micronutrients

Organisms also require other elements, but in such small quantities, often measured in fractions of an ounce rather than in pounds, that they are called trace elements, or micronutrients. These include copper, zinc, boron, manganese, molybdenum, cobalt, vanadium, sodium, chlorine, and iron. Some are essential to all organisms; others appear to be essential only to animals. If micronutrients are lacking, plants and animals fail as completely as if they lacked nitrogen, calcium, or any other major element.

Sodium and *chlorine* are on the borderline between micro- and macronutrients. They are required in minute quantities by plants but in much greater quantities by animals. Chlorine was proved to be a plant nutrient in 1954; and sodium can substitute for potassium to satisfy the plant's need for that element. Both sodium and chlorine are indispensable for vertebrate animals. Obtained from salt, these elements are important for the maintenance of acid-base balance of the body, the total osmotic pressure of extracellular fluids, and for the formation and flow of gastric and intestinal secretions.

Iron, manganese, and *zinc* usually are abundant in the soil, but they may be unavailable to plants. Zinc and manganese, for example, may exist as insoluble compounds in the soil when the pH is around 7. Zinc is needed in the formation of auxins in plant growth substances, is a component of several plant enzyme systems, and is associated with water relations in plants. Iron and manganese are involved in the production of chlorophyll. Iron is a part of complex protein compounds that act as activators and carriers of oxygen and as transporters of electrons.

Boron and *cobalt* are two micronutrients whose deficiency effects, the one in plants and the other in animals, are notable. Some fifteen functions have been ascribed to boron, including pollen germination, cell division, carbohydrate metabolism, water metabolism, maintenance of conductive tissue, and translocation of sugar in plants. Plants with boron deficiency are stunted both in leaves and roots. This condition is most common in the croplands of eastern and central North America, where vegetation is continuously being removed. Without cobalt, an element not required by plants, animals become anemic and waste away. Deficiency of cobalt is most pronounced in ruminants such as deer, cattle, and sheep, since they require the element for the synthesis of vitamin B_{12}. The quantity of cobalt required is very small. An acre of grassland carrying seven sheep must supply only 0.01 ounce a year.

In addition to producing deficiency symptoms when inadequate, some micronutrients can be toxic when they are in excess. Among these are *copper* and *molybdenum*. Molybdenum acts as a catalyst in the conversion of gaseous nitrogen into a usable form by free-living, nitrogen-fixing bacteria and blue-green algae. But high concentrations of molybdenum cause "teart disease" in ruminants such as cattle and deer. This disease is characterized by diarrhea, debilitation of the animal, and permanent fading of the hair color. Copper, concentrated in the chloroplasts, affects the photosynthetic rate, is involved in oxidation-reduction reactions, and acts as an enzyme activator. But in excess, it interferes with phosphorus uptake in plants, depresses iron concentration in the leaves, and reduces growth. In animals copper deficiency results in low hemoglobin content in the blood, causing a type of anemia. Early stages of copper deficiency usually show up as reduced reproductive efficiency. Later it may retard growth, cause abnormal bone formation and coarse and depigmented hair.

Nutrients and animal life

Since all animals depend directly or indirectly on plants for food, the nutrient content of plants affects the well-being of animals. Plants growing on nutrient-deficient soil pass on the deficiency to animals. The healthiest animals come from areas of most fertile soils. Studies of soil-wildlife relationships in Missouri show that in a sample of 8000 raccoons, the largest came from areas with the richest soils. Among males, average weight ranged from 12 pounds in lowest-fertility areas to 18.5 pounds in highest-fertility areas. The difference between females was even greater, being from 8.6 to 17.6 pounds (Nagel, 1943).

Size of deer, antler development, and reproductive success all are related to nutrition (Fig. 4-2). Only deer obtaining high-quality food grow large antlers; deer on diets low in energy, calcium, phosphorus, and protein are stunted in

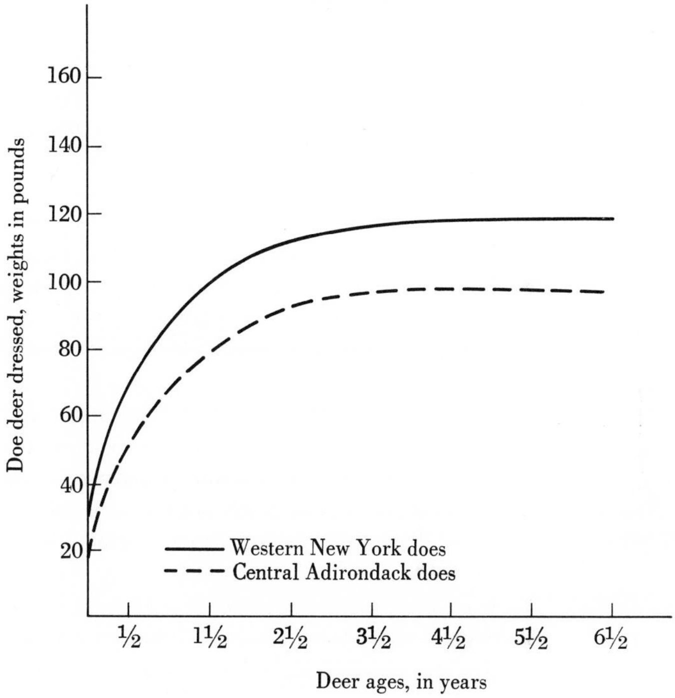

Figure 4-2 The differences in the dressed weights of doe deer from a good range in western New York to a poor range in the central Adirondacks. (After Severinghaus and Gottlieb, 1959.)

growth and the bucks develop only thin spike antlers (French et al., 1955). Reproductive success of does is best on range where food is both abundant and nutritious. On the best range in New York State, 1.71 fawns on the average were born for each doe, while in poor range, average fawn production was only 1.06 for each doe (Cheatum and Severinghaus, 1950). A higher proportion of well-fed young does, including fawns, conceive than those occupying range where food is low in quality and quantity (Taber, 1953).

Deer appear to be able to select the most nutritious forage available, especially that with greater amounts of calcium, phosphorus, and ether extract. When deer had a free choice of food, they selected forages that gave them 12 per cent more extract, 38 per cent more calcium, and 34 per cent more phosphorus (French et al., 1955). Mule deer concentrate on vegetation growing in pockets of deep soil scattered through regions of poor soil (Taber and Dasmann, 1958). This preference is due more to improved palatability rather than to any recognition by deer that the plants have a greater nutritive value.

The limiting influence of nutrients on production is emphasized when fertilizer is applied to trees and ponds. Responses of trees to application of a complete fertilizer (containing nitrogen, phosphorus, and potassium) often is surprising. Fertilization of ponds and small lakes is followed by an increased concentration of phytoplankton and consequently an increase in the photosynthetic rate. Fish in such waters grow faster, because of improved food supply. When fertilizer was applied to a 120-acre unstratified lake on Kodiak Island, Alaska, the rate of photosynthesis in a 10-day period after fertilization was increased by a factor of 2.5 to 7, in comparison with a 10-day period before fertilization (Nelson and Edmondson, 1955).

Temperature

The ability to withstand extremes in temperature varies widely among plants and animals; but there are temperatures above and below which no life can exist. Fifty-two degrees centigrade is about as high a temperature as any animal can withstand and still grow and multiply. Among plants, however, some hot-spring algae live in water as warm as 77°C (158°F) and some arctic algae can complete their life cycles in places where temperatures barely rise above 0°C (32°F).

An animal's response to wide ranges in temperature is influenced by its physiology. Since invertebrates, fish, amphibians, and reptiles have no internal mechanism for temperature regulation, their body temperatures vary with external conditions. Such animals are called *poikilothermal*. These animals are active during the warm seasons; during winter, most of them are dormant, except for fish and social insects such as the honeybee. By constant vibration of heavy wing muscles, the bees are able to maintain temperatures within the hive a few degrees above the air outside. Most poikilothermal animals become inactive when the temperature of their surroundings goes below 8°C (43°F) or rises to 42°C (108°F).

Birds and mammals can, within limits, maintain constant body temperatures, regardless of temperature variations of air and water. Such animals are termed *homeothermal*. Their life processes are adjusted to function at the animal's normal temperature, averaging a little less than 38°C (100°F) in mammals and three to four degrees higher in birds. If its temperature control fails, the animal dies. Thus while these animals cannot withstand serious temperature changes within the body, they are active during all seasons of the year and are independent of temperature change in the external environment.

All living organisms apparently have a temperature range outside of which they fail to grow or reproduce. Within the favorable range, organisms have an optimum or preferred temperature, at which they best maintain themselves. The optimum temperature may vary within the life cycle or with the process involved. Optimum temperature for photosynthesis is lower than that for respiration. If the temperature goes much above the optimum for photosynthesis, the plant may not be able to balance energy fixation with respiration. The seeds of many plants will not germinate, and the eggs and pupae of some insects will not hatch or develop normally until chilled. Brook trout grow best at 13° to 16°C, but the eggs develop best at 8°C.

Temperature influences the speed and success of development of poikilothermic animals. In general complete development of eggs and larvae is more rapid in warm temperatures. Trout eggs, for example, develop four times faster at 15°C than at 5°C. Similar examples can be found among insects. The chironomid fly, *Metriocnemus hirticollis,* requires 26 days at 20°C for the development of a full generation, 94 days at 10°C, 153 days at 6.5°C, and 243 days at 2°C (Andrewartha and Birch, 1954).

Environmental temperatures fluctuate both daily and seasonally. Temperatures of any one area will vary from sunlight to shade and from daylight to dark. Surface temperatures of soil may be 30°C higher in the sunlight than in the shade and up to 17°C higher during the day than during the night. On the desert this spread may be as high as 40°C. Temperatures on tidal flats exposed to the sun may rise to 38°C; in a few hours these same flats are covered by water at 10°C. Seasonal fluctuations may be just as extreme. In North Dakota, where the annual mean temperature is between 5°C and 9°C (36° to 44°F), yearly temperatures fluctuate from a low of −43°C (−56°F) in winter to 49°C (120°F) in summer. In the mountainous eastern state of West Virginia, where the mean annual temperature is 12°C (54°F), temperatures range from −37°C to 44°C (−34 to 108°F).

Organisms that inhabit these areas are adapted to meet in one way or another temperature extremes. Animals of the desert country seek cool underground or shaded retreats during the day and are active only at night and during the morning and evening hours. Voles and shrews avoid the cold surface air in winter by remaining in tunnels beneath the snow. Plants of temperate regions go into winter dormancy; life is maintained in perennating buds and seeds. Many species of insects, as well as certain crustaceans, mites, and snails, enter *diapause,* a state of dormancy and arrested growth. Eggs, embryonic larvae, or pupal stages may be involved. In addition to tiding the animal over unfavorable periods, diapause also synchronizes the life cycle of a species with the weather and ensures that active stages will coincide with the climatic conditions and food supply that favor rapid development and high survival.

Some poikilothermic animals become dormant during periods of temperature extremes. Amphibians and turtles bury themselves in the mud of pond bottoms; snakes seek burrows and dens in rocky hill sides. There they remain in a state of suspended animation until the temperature warms again. Winter dormancy is called *hibernation;* summer dormancy is *estivation.*

Hibernation

Hibernation and estivation are not confined to poikilothermic animals alone. The phenomena also occur among a few homeothermic animals, particularly bats, ground squirrels, woodchucks, and jumping mice. Like dormancy in "cold-blooded" animals, hibernation in homeothermic animals is characterized by a reduction in the general metabolism to a degree never found in the deepest everyday sleep. But there is a difference. When reptiles and amphibians are exposed to cold, the animal cools because it has no way by which to stay warm. As the

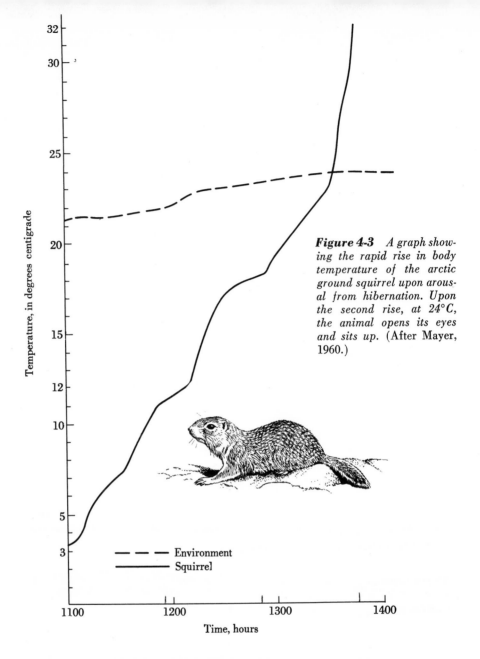

Figure 4-3 *A graph showing the rapid rise in body temperature of the arctic ground squirrel upon arousal from hibernation. Upon the second rise, at 24°C, the animal opens its eyes and sits up. (After Mayer, 1960.)*

Temperature, in degrees centigrade

– – – Environment
——— Squirrel

Time, hours

poikilotherm's system becomes cooler, the heart rate and metabolic rate decline. But when a mammal enters hibernation, the heart rate and metabolic rate decline, and *then* the body temperature drops.

The onset of dormancy in warm-blooded animals may take place with one decline in temperature, as in the hamster and pocket mouse, or it may come in a series of steps, as it does in the groundhog and ground squirrel. The temperature of the California ground squirrel drops a number of degrees, remains at this point for a while, then rises to the normal body temperature again (Strumwasser, 1960). The next day, when the animal again enters hibernation, its body temperature drops even lower. This continues daily, until the body temperature is just a few degrees above the environment. This apparently conditions the body and brain to lower temperatures. After a few such fitful

Figure 4-4 *A black bear that has just been aroused from its winter's sleep. The bear is not a true hibernator.* (Photo courtesy of the Pennsylvania Game Commission.)

starts at complete dormancy, the animal finally curls up to sleep in its retreat. In this state of suspended animation, only the vital life of the animal continues, maintained by shallow breathing, slow circulation, and a continual digestive absorption of stored fat. The reduced metabolism is characterized by great differences in body temperature, pulse rate, and breathing. The breathing rate, rapid in small mammals, is reduced to less than one a minute, and these breaths usually occur in a series of two or three gasps with long intervals between. The body temperature in the ground squirrel drops from 18.5°C to 4.2°C. The heart rate is reduced to two to three beats a minute, although the blood pressure remains relatively high. The optimum environmental temperature for hibernators is 4.5°C (40°F); the body temperature passively follows the fluctuation in environmental temperatures between 3.3°C to 12.8°C. If the environmental temperature reaches the freezing point of water, the metabolic rate of the hibernating animal increases. This increase may be able to keep the body temperature above freezing without the animal awakening. Mammalian hibernators, however, do not remain in a state of complete inertia all during the period of dormancy. They awake from time to time, eat a little, void, and return to their deep sleep.

Arousal from hibernation is explosive and certainly the most dramatic aspect of the hibernation cycle (Fig. 4-3). As the animal starts to come out of the sleep, its body temperature rises rapidly, perhaps from 4°C to 17.5°C in an hour and a half (Mayer, 1960). In the case of the ground squirrel, when the anterior part of the body has reached about 36.5°C, the temperature of the hind parts rises rapidly, due to dilatation of the blood vessels. The animal's hair is erect and its body shakes. At around 16°C, the animal tries to right itself, and at 17.5°C the shivering stops and the squirrel moves its tail. At 24°C the animal opens its eyes and suddenly sits up. At this time the temperature rises rapidly again. When the body temperature reaches 24 to 25.4°C, about three hours from the time of initial arousal, the ground squirrel is sitting up and flicking its tail. The animal is warm and active again.

The black bear (Fig. 4-4) and skunk are not true hibernators; in both, neither body temperature nor pulse are lowered significantly and breathing is more frequent. During warm spells both will leave their dens and move about. Rarely are adult skunks inactive for over a month nor the young for more than four months. During these deep sleeps the animals may lose from 15 to 40 per cent of body weight (Hock, 1960).

Most aquatic cold-blooded animals remain active throughout periods of temperature extremes, but metabolism in general may be lowered greatly. Experiments have shown that largemouth bass, acclimatized to 5°C, are slow to respond even to a slight current and are somewhat hampered in their maintenance or equilibrium. Food consumption, activity, and cruising speed all decreased with lowered temperatures (Fig. 4-5). Bass did not eat at all when the weekly mean temperature was 5°C; at 12°C, each bass fingerling consumed on the average 1.6 minnow per week, and at 20°C, an average of 4.1 minnows (Johnson and Charlton, 1960). Cruising speed of bass rose steadily from 5°C to a maximum at 25°C. Lowered activity at low temperatures, as well as lower metabolism, conserved oxygen, the concentration of which often drops dangerously low in ponds during winter (see Chap. 8). In fact the oxygen requirement of bass at 5°C is only about 10 per cent of that at 29°C (Johnson and Charlton, 1960).

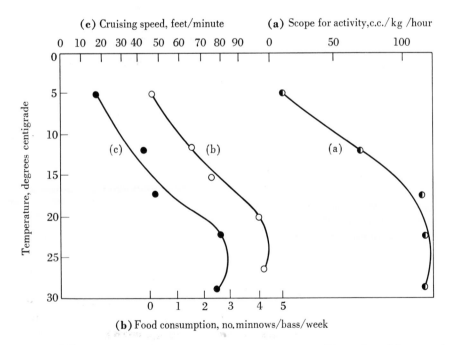

Figure 4-5 *The scope of activity* (a), *food consumption* (b), *and cruising speed* (c) *of the large mouthed bass at several experimental temperatures. Scope for activity is the difference between standard oxygen uptake and active oxygen uptake.* (After Johnson and Charlton, 1960.)

Poikilotherms are at a disadvantage at high temperatures too. Increased metabolic activity increases oxygen consumption; and oxygen concentrations in heavily vegetated areas may be severely reduced during the night by respiration of plants. When water becomes too warm (28 to 30°C), largemouth bass either retreat to cooler water or remain in the shade of overhanging trees and refuse to eat. During this period of high body temperature, hemoglobin content increases in gills, the operculum pulse rate quickens, and the lactic-acid level, which increases the oxygen-combining power of blood, rises. By such physiological adaptability, the bass is able to cling to a precarious existence during periods of temperature stress (Denyes and Joseph, 1956).

Acclimatization

Within the same species and often within the individual, the range of temperature tolerance varies. The limits of temperature tolerance depend in part on the condition of the animal and the temperature of its immediate environment. Poikilothermic animals are, within limits, able to adjust to higher and lower temperatures. If an organism lives at the higher end of the tolerable range, the animal acclimatizes itself sufficiently so that the lethal temperature will be somewhat higher; but its lower limit will be higher than if it were living within the cooler range of tolerable temperatures. The reverse is true of animals living in cooler environments. Since acclimatization takes place from one season to the next, a population is able to adjust to the prevailing temperatures each season. The brook trout exhibits a seasonal change in selected temperature from 12°C in summer and fall to 8°C from November to January (Sullivan and Fisher, 1953). On the other hand, experimental work indicates that when warm-water species of fish are acclimatized to a constant temperature level, the fish lose their ability to select their optimum temperature and show reduced precision in their reactions to high temperatures. Where such natural acclimatizations occur, the fish may become insensitive to high temperatures and high mortality may take place (see Norris, 1963).

Acclimatization to changing temperatures by warm-blooded animals depends upon their ability to regulate the gradient between body and air temperatures. This they accomplish mainly by changes in insulation, by production of heat, and by changing the body temperature.

Resisting temperature extremes by varying the body temperature is not a method commonly employed by birds and mammals, since body temperatures are about the same for all species in all climates (Morrison and Ryser, 1952; Irving, 1960). Mean body temperatures differ about as much among species of the arctic as they do among those of the temperate and tropical regions.

Change in insulation is the major means by which warm-blooded animals adapt to seasonal changes of temperatures. The degree of insulation is varied by changes in the thickness and type of fur, the degree of vascularization of the skin and limbs, and by posture and behavior. Insulation value of fur varies with or is correlated with the thickness of fur; in small mammals, there is a further correlation of fur thickness with body size (Scholander, Walters, Hock, and Irving, 1950). Fur of small mammals is short and light; if it were heavy, the animals would have a difficult time moving about. Consequently in cold weather they must huddle together or remain in warm nests to conserve heat. Among mammals larger than a fox, there is no relationship between fur thickness and size. Arctic mammals have a thick underfur overlaid by a heavy fleece, a coat which provides excellent insulation. In summer the transfer of heat away from the body is increased when the heavy fur is shed. Arctic birds have longer feathers than birds of the temperate regions, and at the base of these feathers there is dense down as well (Irving, 1960). With numerous air spaces between them, feathers are excellent insulators; the bird can increase their effectiveness by erecting them. This increases the layer of warm air between the surface of the feathers and the surface of the skin. A heavy layer of fat, too, is an excellent insulator and is especially well developed in arctic marine mammals, such as the seals, walrus, and whales. Insulation can be controlled to some degree by posture and behavior. To conserve heat, the animals may curl up or wrap a furry tail about them. They may lose heat by stretching out and exposing thinly furred areas to the air.

Vascularization is another device among animals for conserving or getting rid of heat (Scholander, 1955). Many animals have extensive areas in the extremities where the arterial system joins the venous. The arteries carrying warm blood transfer the heat back to the returning venous blood, thus cooling extremities (Irving and Krogh, 1954). This is especially important among arctic animals. Seals, for example, have such a thick layer of fat and a pelage so dense that body heat can be dissipated only from the flippers, which are well supplied with sweat glands and are black in color. (Black bodies not only absorb all frequencies of radiation impinging upon them; they also emit all wave lengths back to the atmosphere.) This they accomplish by waving the flippers in the air and by swimming in cold water (Bartholomew and Wilke, 1956). Similar cooling is necessary among arctic animals to *prevent* excessive heat loss through the extremities, for legs and feet are exposed and the feet are in contact with the cold ground. If the extremities were too warm, the snow would melt and subsequently freeze; if they were too cold, the interior of the extremities would drop below the freezing point. Circulation in the extremities is poor, which tends to cool the feet and check heat loss. In addition, fat of low melting point is selectively deposited in those parts of the extremities subject to excessive cooling (Irving, 1960). Tissue temperature in arctic gulls declines rapidly along the tibia under the covering of feathers. The temperature change takes place here; the heat from the warm arterial blood is transferred to the cool venous blood returning from the foot (Irving, 1960).

Within limits, warm-blooded animals can maintain their basal heat production by changing insulation. But with declining temperatures there is a point beyond which insulation is no longer effective and body heat must be maintained by increased metabolism. The temperature at which this takes place is called the *critical temperature,* and it varies greatly between tropical and arctic animals (Scholander, Hock, Walters, Johnson, and Irving, 1950). Tropical birds and mammals exposed to temperatures below 23.5 to 29.5°C increase their heat production. If the air temperature is lowered to 10°C, the tropical animal must triple its heat production; and if lowered to freezing, the animal is no longer able to produce heat as rapidly as it is being lost. Arctic small mammals, on the other hand, do not increase their heat production until the air temperature has fallen to −29°C. Large arctic mammals can sustain the coldest weather without heat beyond that produced by normal basal metabolism. Eskimo dogs and arctic foxes can sleep outdoors at temperatures of −40°C without stress. This is not due to any difference in metabolism itself but to effective insulation.

The adjustment of animals to changes of temperature, which has just been discussed, has been viewed from the point of the species. The individual animal may also act to acclimatize itself to temperature changes. At high temperatures the animal may reduce its basal metabolism and transfer heat to the periphery of the body by increased blood flow to the skin. Panting or sweating increases evaporative cooling, as does wetting the skin and fur. Individuals of some species can acclimatize to cold temperatures by increasing their metabolism for a limited period of time. Warm-acclimated animals exposed to cold increase heat production by shivering and other physical means. Animals acclimatized to cold temperatures increase heat by chemical thermogenesis—they have a higher metabolic rate at the critical point than animals not adjusted to the cold. This may be due to an increased activity of the thyroid gland (Fisher, 1958).

Temperature and distribution

Since the optimum temperature for the completion of the several stages of the life cycle of many organisms varies, temperature imposes a restriction on the distribution of species. Optimal temperatures for some species are so different from those of others that the animals cannot inhabit the same area. Some organisms, particularly plants that are growing under suboptimal temperatures, cannot compete with the surrounding growth, a situation which would not exist under optimal conditions.

Generally the range of many species is limited by the lowest critical temperature in the most vulnerable stage of its life cycle, usually the reproductive stages. Although the Atlantic lobster will live in water with a temperature range of 0 to 17°C, it will breed only in water warmer than 11°C. The lobster may live and grow in colder water but a breeding population never becomes established there.

A classic example of temperature limitation on animal distribution is found among four species of ranid frogs (Moore, 1949). The wood frog breeds in late March, when water temperature is about 10°C. Its eggs can develop at temperatures as low as 2.5°C. Larval stages transform in about 60 days. This frog ranges into Alaska and Labrador, further north than any other North American amphibian or reptile. The meadow frog breeds in late April, when water temperatures are about 15°C, and the larvae require around 90 days to develop. As a result the northern limit of its range is southern Canada. The southernmost species of the three, the green frog, does not breed until the water is about 25°C, and the eggs will develop at 33°C, a lethal temperature for the others. Its eggs, however, will not develop at all until the temperature exceeds 11°C. The range of the green frog extends only slightly above the northern boundary of the United States.

Some plants, such as blueberries, will not fruit or flower successfully unless chilled. Other plants may grow in a region during the summer, but are unable to reproduce or grow to normal size, since their tender twigs freeze back in

73

winter. These plants are restricted in their natural range to areas where temperatures are favorable.

Moisture

Maintenance of a water balance between an organism and its surroundings is not a serious problem in aquatic environments, except where water levels fluctuate and where waters are salty. Aquatic organisms maintain their water balance by regulating osmotic pressure. Fresh-water organisms live in an environment where the surrounding water has a lower salt concentration than their bodies. The problem here is to rid the body of excess water taken in through the permeable membranes. Protozoans dispose of excess water through the contractile vacuole. Other organisms have either flame cells, nephridia, or kidneys. Fresh-water fish maintain their salt concentration by salt absorption through special cells in the gills. Marine forms, however, live in a medium which has a higher salt concentration than they possess. Water tends to leave the body and salts enter. Marine teleost fish swallow sea water and absorb it with the salt into the gut. Excess salts are then removed through special cells in the gills. Marine fish discharge little water as urine. Sharks and other elasmobranch fish retain urea in the body to maintain a slightly higher concentration of salt in the body than surrounding sea water. Pelagic sea birds are able to utilize sea water, for they possess special salt-secreting glands located on the surface of the cranium (Schmidt-Neilson, 1960). Gulls, petrels, and other sea birds excrete from these glands fluids in excess of 5 per cent salt. Petrels and other tube-nosed swimmers forceably eject the fluid through their nostrils; in other species, the salt solution drips out of the internal or external nares. A gull given one-tenth of its weight in sea water excreted 90 per cent of the salt through the salt gland within three hours.

Plants of the salt marshes live in a physiological desert. Although they are surrounded by an abundance of water, the plants grow in a physiologically dry substrate, since the higher osmotic pressure outside their roots limits the water they can absorb. An increase in sodium and chlorine uptake is compensated for by a corresponding dilution of the internal solution, with the water stored in the tissues. In addition these plants exhibit a high internal osmotic pressure, many times that of fresh-water and terrestrial plants, possess salt-secreting glands and heavy cutin on the leaves, and are succulent (see Chapman, 1960).

Precipitation

Rainfall is not uniformly distributed. Mean annual precipitation is influenced by topography and mass air movements (Fig. 4-6). Mountains along the east and west coasts of North America interfere with the even sweep of the winds off the oceans across the continent and intercept the moisture they contain. This causes excessive moisture on the windward side of the mountains and local and regional rain shadows on the leeward side (see Chap. 16).

Seasonal distribution of rainfall is more important to organisms than average annual precipitation (Fig. 4-7). A world of difference exists between a region

Mean annual precipitation, in inches

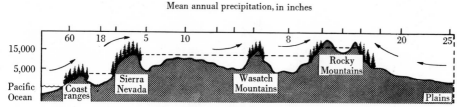

Profile showing Pacific forests

Mean annual precipitation, in inches

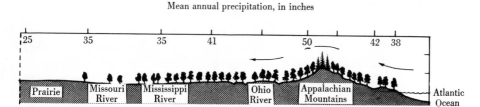

Profile showing Atlantic forests

Figure 4-6 *The influence of moist air currents on forest distribution in the East and in the West along the thirty-ninth parallel of north latitude.* (Adapted from *Climate and Man*, 1941, U.S. Department of Agriculture Yearbook of Agriculture, p. 494.)

receiving 50 inches of rain rather evenly distributed throughout the year and a region in which nearly all of the 50 inches falls during a several-month period. In this latter situation, so characteristic of tropical and subtropical climates, organisms must face a long period of drought. An alternation of wet and dry seasons influences the reproductive and activity cycles of organisms as much as light and temperature in the temperate regions.

Over three-fourths of the precipitation that falls on the land surface is drawn back into the water cycle before it reaches the ocean (see Chap. 3). Evaporation of water, the process in which more water molecules leave the surface than enter it, is governed by the *vapor-pressure deficit* of the atmosphere. This is the difference between the partial pressure of water at saturation and the prevailing vapor pressure of the air. Or, to put it more simply, it is the amount of water vapor necessary under existing conditions to saturate a particular volume of air. If the vapor pressure of water at the surface of soil or plants and animals is greater than that of the air, water evaporates. The opposite process is *condensation*.

The moisture content of the air is usually expressed as *relative humidity*. This is the amount of moisture in the air, expressed as a percentage, compared to the amount of water that could be held at saturation at the existing temperature. As the air warms up, its relative humidity drops (providing there is no accompanying increase in the total moisture content of the air), since warm air can hold more moisture than cool air. As the relative humidity drops, the vapor-pressure deficit increases and increased evaporation takes place. Fluctuations in relative humidity take place during a 24-hour period. Generally it is lower by day and

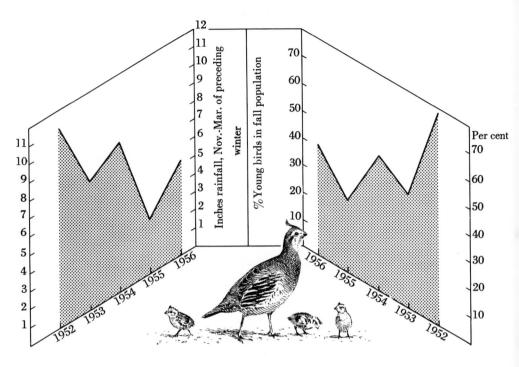

Figure 4-7 *The relationship of winter rainfall to age composition of a Gambel's quail population in southern Arizona the following year.* (After Sowls, 1960.)

higher by night. It decreases as distance above ground increases and is greater under a canopy of vegetation than in the open. This relationship is diagrammed in the illustration of forest community (Fig. 17-1).

Temperature and wind both exert a considerable influence on evaporation rates. An increase in air temperature causes convection currents. This sets up an air turbulence which mixes surface layers with drier air above. Wind movements associated with cyclonic disturbances also mix moisture-laden air with drier air above. As a result, the vapor pressure of the air is lowered and evaporation from the surface increases.

Rain that falls on land must enter the substrate if it is to be available to terrestrial plants over a period of time. Infiltration of water into soil is influenced by texture, plant cover, and activity of man. Considerable quantities of water run off the surface into streams, never to enter the ground. This occurs especially on surfaces poorly protected by vegetation or disturbed by tillage, logging roads and trails, and overgrazing. Water entering the soil will seep down to an impervious layer of clay or rock to form *ground water*. A part of the water is retained in the soil. That portion of water held by capillary forces between the ground-soil particles is *capillary water*. Another portion of water adheres as a thin film to soil particles. This is *hydroscopic water* and is unavailable to plants. The maximum amount of water that a soil can hold after gravitational water is drained away is called *field capacity*.

The capacity of soils to retain and store water varies considerably. Since sandy soils have few fine clay or silt particles filling the pore space, they have less surface area on which the water can cling; and the pores are so large that the weight of the water forces it to run down and out of the soil. Fine-textured soils retain water for a longer time in rather large quantities. Since the surface area on which the water can cling is greater and the size of the pores is smaller, water is slowly discharged into the subsoil. Sandy soils may store 10 to 15 per cent of their weight in water, clay 50 to 70 per cent. Water retention is increased by the humus, or organic-matter, content of the soil. Humus may retain 100 to 200 per cent of its own weight in water. For each one inch of humus, about 0.8 inches of water is stored for as long as two days after a rain and is slowly discharged into streams.

The amount of humus in the soil depends upon vegetation and management. In precolonial days the original forest soil in the northern hardwoods region contained an estimated 137,000 pounds of humus per acre. A well-managed farm soil may contain 60,000 to 80,000 pounds. Soils of low fertility contain only 20,000 to 30,000 pounds per acre. Forest soil with humus 4 inches deep may retain as much as 1.60 inches of water; but the water storage capacity of cropland is one third of this or less. Water storage capacity may be reduced further by impervious surfaces created by poor soil management. In fact up to 72 per cent of the water may be lost as runoff. Thus the management of the land affects, often drastically, the moisture retention capacity of a soil.

Meeting moisture problems

Both excessive and deficient moisture can be detrimental to organisms, but many are adapted to meet moisture extremes in one way or another. Since many invertebrates and amphibians must avoid dry air to prevent desiccation, they are found in moist or aquatic situations and are active chiefly at night when humidity is the highest. Many invertebrates are quite sensitive to moisture variations and will leave an area of low humidity to go to one where the moisture is more favorable for the animal at the time. A reverse movement to a drier situation occurs among animals that are sensitive to high humidity. The reaction, however, of animals to moisture is influenced by the condition of the animal, the temperature, light intensity, and the like.

Survival during long periods of dry weather or existence in arid regions is achieved by organisms in various ways. Some plants of the dry country are small annuals that complete their life cycles in a very short time during and immediately after the rainy period, before the soil dries out. They survive the dry period as seeds. Other plants of arid regions may be succulents. They have reduced intercellular space and enlarged vacuoles, in which water accumulates during the rainy season. At this time the plants swell rapidly, then gradually shrivel during the dry season as they draw on the stored water. Cacti, an example of succulent desert plants, also have shallow root systems, which enable them to absorb the maximum amount of water during the rainy season; and the stomata are closed during the day and open at night in order to reduce transpiration. Other plants either have deep root systems that can tap deep moisture supplies or go dormant during the dry season. Mesquite, for example, has a root system that penetrates up to 175 feet deep (Phillips, 1963). The creosote bush has evergreen leaves that are heavily waxed and resistant to desiccation. Plants in regions with higher moisture reduce transpiration and survive the physiologically dry period of winter by shedding leaves. Waxy secretion on buds and twigs also help reduce water loss. Plants react to dry conditions by rolling, curling, or folding the leaf to reduce the unit area exposed.

Desert animals confine their activities to the period between sunset and sunrise when humidity is highest and the temperatures coolest. Desert amphibians burrow into beds of temporary streams, where moisture is high, and stay there during the day or remain there during extensive dry spells. Desert mammals, such as the kangaroo rats, and many insects that live in dry situations conserve metabolic water. They live on the moisture obtained from their food and from the breakdown of carbohydrates in the digestion of food (see Chap. 16). Water loss is further prevented by dry integument, by dry feces—characteristic of desert rodents and pronghorn antelope—and by crystalline urine in reptiles, birds, and insects. Large desert mammals, such as the camel, can use water effectively for evaporative cooling through the skin and respiratory system, since their low surface area to body-size ratio and lower internal heat production result in slower accumulation of heat. The camel not only excretes highly concentrated urine but can withstand dehydration up to 25 per cent of body weight, and it loses water from body tissues rather than the blood (Schmidt-Neilsen, 1959). The camel's body temperature is labile, dropping to 33.8°C over night and rising to 40.6°C by day, at which point the animal begins to sweat. The camel accumulates its fat in the hump rather than over the body. This speeds heat flow away from the body, and its thick coat prevents the flow of heat inward to the body.

Many animals go into a dormant state during dry periods. A flatworm, *Phagocytes vernalis,* which occupies ponds that dry up during the summer, encysts. As the water warms, this flatworm reacts by detaching small pieces from the posterior end of its body, until the entire animal is reduced to a number of fragments. Each fragment rounds up and secretes a layer of slime, which hardens into a cyst highly resistant to drying. These cysts remain in the debris of the pond bottom until the ponds fill again, when they hatch. Other aquatic or semiaquatic organisms retreat deep into the soil until they reach ground-water level. Still others spend the dry season in estivation. Many insects undergo diapause, just as they do when confronted with unfavorable temperature.

Moisture also influences the speed of development and even fecundity of some insects. If the air is too dry, the eggs of some locusts and other insects may become quiescent. There is an optimum humidity at which nymphs develop fastest. Some insects lay more eggs at certain relative humidities than above or below this point.

Too much water may be as detrimental as too little. High water tables result in shallow-rooted trees that are easily toppled by the wind and are sensitive to drought and frost. Terrestrial plants subject to prolonged flooding, particularly during the growing season, will die from the lack of oxygen about the roots. This happens frequently to trees in areas flooded by beaver. Heavy rain and prolonged wet spells cause widespread death among mammals and birds from drowning, exposure, and chilling. Excessive moisture and cloudy weather kill insect nymphs, inhibit insect pollination, and spread parasitic fungi, bacteria, and viruses among both plants and animals.

Interaction of temperature and moisture

A close interaction exists between temperature and moisture in terrestrial environments; and the two determine in a large measure the climate of a region and the distribution of vegetation. Low-moisture conditions are more extreme when temperatures are high or low. Moisture in turn influences the effects of temperature, a fact observable to everyone. Cold is more penetrating when the air is moist, and high temperatures are more noticeable when relative humidity is high.

Mean monthly temperatures and relative humidities or precipitation can be plotted on a graph to form a climatograph, which gives a composite picture of the climate of an area (Fig. 4-8 above and below). The mean monthly temperature and the mean monthly rainfall or relative humidity are plotted on the vertical and horizontal axes respectively as a single dot. Twelve dots for the year connected together form an irregular polygon, which can be compared with another for similarity or difference in fit. By use of this, climates can be compared much more easily than they can by tables. Such climatographs are useful to contrast or compare one region or one year with another. Often this is done to determine the suitability of an area for the introduction of exotic animals, particularly game birds.

East-west zonation of vegetation follows a pattern of moisture distribution more than that of temperature. If temperature alone controlled plant distribution in North America, the vegetation zones would be in broad belts running east and west. Only in the far north do the vegetation zones (tundra and the coniferous forest) stretch in these directions. Below this, vegetation is controlled by precipitation and evaporation, the latter influenced considerably by temperature. Since available moisture becomes less from east to west, vegetation follows a similar pattern, with belts running north and south. Humid regions along both coasts support natural forest vegetation. This zone is broadest in the east. West of this eastern forest region is a subhumid zone, where precipitation is less and evaporation is higher. Here the ratio of precipitation to evaporation is about 60 to 80 per cent, and the land supports a tall-grass prairie. Beyond this is semiarid country, where the precipitation-evaporation ratio is 20 to 40 per cent; it supports a short-grass prairie. To the west of this and on the lee of the mountains is the desert.

In mountainous country, both east and west, vegetation zones reflect climatic changes on an altitudinal gradient (Fig. 4-9). These belts often duplicate the pattern of latitudinal vegetation distribution. In general the belts include the land about the mountain base that has a climate characteristic of the region. Next is a higher montane level, which has greater humidity and temperatures that decrease as altitude increases. Here the forest vegetation changes from deciduous to coniferous. Beyond this is a subalpine zone that includes coniferous trees adapted to a more rigorous climate than the montane species. Above this is the alpine or tundra zone, where the climate is cold and cloudy. Here trees are replaced by grasses, sedges, and small tufted plants. Between the alpine and the subalpine lies the krummholz, a land of stunted trees. On the very top of the highest mountains is a land of perpetual ice and snow.

79

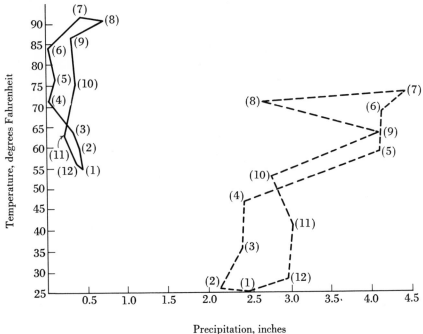

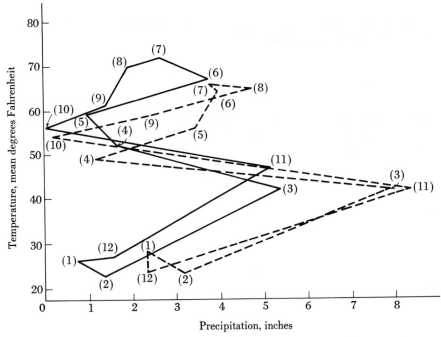

Figure 4-8 *Temperature-moisture climatographs. (above) A climatograph comparing two very different regions, the desert and the eastern deciduous forest. Note how the hot, dry climate differs graphically from the cool, temperate, moist climate of the east. These 12-sided polygons give a picture of temperature and moisture conditions and permit the comparison of one set of conditions with another. (Data: mean temperature and precipitation, 1941–1950, for Yuma, Arizona, and Albany, New York.) (below) A climatograph comparing conditions on the rain-shadow side and the high-rainfall side in the Appalachian Mountains of West Virginia.*

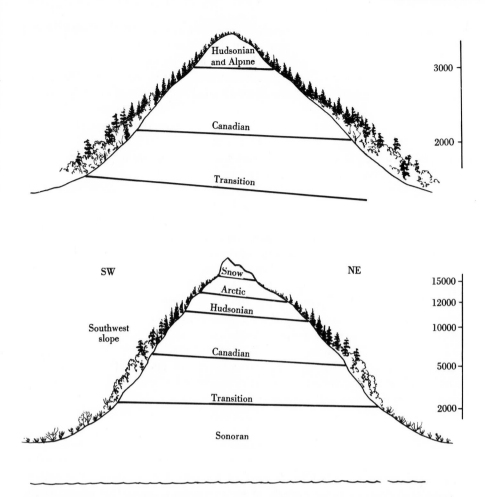

Figure 4-9 *Altitudinal zonation in mountains. (above). Eastern Mountains, as represented by Mount Marcy, in the Adirondacks. The forest on the lower slope is Transition, consisting chiefly of northern hardwoods. The forest on the middle slope is Canadian, with paper birch, red spruce, and balsam. The upper slopes is Hudsonian and Alpine, characterized by dwarf spruce and willows and heaths. In the southern Appalachians, the northern hardwoods are replaced by oaks and hickory; the northern hardwoods replace the spruce, and the spruce replaces the willows and stunted spruce. (below). A generalized Western mountain. The Sonoran zone is characterized by grassland and shrubby vegetation—chaparral, juniper, etc.; the Transition by oaks and, higher up, lodgepole pine. The Canadian zone contains lodgepole pine, Englemann spruce, red fir, silver fir; the Hudsonian, mountain hemlock, western white pine; the Arctic-Alpine, willows, etc. Note that the life zones extend higher on the southwest slope than on the northeast slope. Elevations are approximate only.*

Wind

The wind is a powerful agent influencing the growth and distribution of many organisms and molding the character of the community.

Drying action of high, warm winds in the winter when soil moisture is low or unavailable creates physiological drought. The wind removes humid air about the leaves and increases transpiration. Losing more water than they are able to absorb, evergreens in particular dry out and their foliage turns brown.

Plants which normally grow tall become low and spreading when high winds are frequent and regular, a situation characteristic of the timberline. Here, on high wind-swept ridges, cushion plants with small, uniform, crowded branches are most common. Because of constant desiccation, cells of plants growing in these places never expand to normal size, and all organs are dwarfed. Terminal branch shoots are killed back by desiccation, by blasting by ice particles, and, along the ocean, by the effects of salt spray. As a result the terminals are replaced by strong laterals, which form a mat close to the ground.

Strong and persistent winds blowing from a constant direction bend the branches of trees around to the windward side until, like a weathervane, they point out the direction of the prevailing wind (Fig. 4-10). Often the wind may kill all the twig-forming buds, so that no limbs develop on the windward surface.

Shallow-rooted trees and trees with brittle woods, such as the willows, cottonwoods, and maples, are thrown or broken by strong winds. Windthrow is most prevalent among trees growing in dense stands that, through logging or natural damage, are suddenly exposed to the full force of the wind. Hurricanes and other violent windstorms sweeping over forested areas may uproot and break trees across a considerable expanse of land.

Hurricanes and strong storms cause deaths among animals also, and often carry individuals far from their normal environment and set them down elsewhere. Winds are an important means of dispersal for seeds and small animals such as spiders, mites, and even snails.

Light

Light is a part of the radiant energy of the sun that penetrates the earth's atmosphere. Solar radiation consists of electromagnetic waves that extend from very short, or high-frequency, wave lengths to very long, low-frequency wave lengths. The visible segment of these wave lengths, all that can be perceived by the human eye, is known as light; it ranges in wave lengths from 0.3 microns to 0.7 microns (3000 to 7000 Angstrom units). These frequencies are known as violet, indigo, blue, green, yellow, orange, and red. Photochemical activity is greatest at the violet end. High-frequency short-wave radiations from 0.3 microns downward are ultraviolet rays, X rays, and gamma rays. These are capable of penetrating matter, producing ionization. From the upper visible limit of the human eye, 0.7 microns, upward to about 1000 microns is heat-radiating infrared radiation; in the vicinity of 1000 microns, infrared is replaced by radio waves.

The influence of light depends upon its intensity, quality, and duration. The photosynthetic rate of a plant leaf increases linearly with increasing light intensity up to the point of light saturation, usually one tenth to two tenths of full sunlight; after this point the rate remains the same. The efficiency of the photosynthetic process, however, declines steadily with increasing light intensity. Thus, a leaf exposed to full sunlight is not very efficient at utilizing light energy; at the best it utilizes about five per cent. At low light intensity the photosynthetic rate is lower, but efficiency increases and may approach that of 20 per cent

Figure 4-10 *Like weathervanes, these spruces point out the direction of the prevailing wind.* (Photo by Bill Jones.)

(Bonner, 1962). This fact, however, must not be interpreted as meaning that expected plant yields decrease under high light intensity. Actually the reverse is true; the greater the light intensity, the higher the yield, since more light reaches the lower leaves and even the lower layers of chlorophyll within the leaf.

The light intensity at which plants can no longer carry on sufficient photosynthesis to maintain themselves is called the *compensation intensity*. This is the point at which photosynthesis balances respiration, where plants are just able to replace material lost in respiration night and day. Few green plants can live where light intensity is less than 1 per cent full sunlight, or about 100 foot-candles.

Some plants are more shade-tolerant than others. Sugar maple, white cedar, and hemlock successfully exist under a dense forest canopy at low light intensities, but they do not attain normal growth there. In aquatic situations, light penetration is influenced by turbidity either from debris or from phytoplankton growth. Light stimulates the development of a dense phytoplankton growth at the surface, which prevents the light from reaching deeper water. This limits the growth of rooted aquatics.

Visible light that penetrates water becomes limited more and more to a narrow band of blue light at wave lengths of about 0.5 microns as the water depth increases from 0.1 meters to 100 meters. This is in part the reason why water of deep, clear lakes looks blue. Eventually blue light is filtered out and the remaining green light is poorly absorbed by chlorophyll. Depths at which green light occurs are occupied by red algae, since these plants possess supplementary pigments that enable them to utilize the energy of green light.

Light influences the reproductive and activity cycles of both plants and animals. This is discussed in detail in Chap. 5. But it should be noted here that light plays a limiting role in plant distribution. Many plants will not flower until a critical day length is reached. If the period is reached so late that seeds cannot develop before frost, then the plant will be unable to establish itself successfully in that area. Germination of many seeds is influenced by long days; in some, long days inhibit and short days stimulate germination.

Radiation

A new dimension has been added to ecological influences in the nuclear age: high-energy radiation. The sources come from fallout, from atomic blasts, radioactive wastes, and nuclear reactors.

What is involved here is high-energy, short wave length radiations, known as ionizing radiations. They are so called because the radiations are able to remove electrons from some atoms and attract them to other atoms, producing positive and negative ion pairs. Of ionizing radiations ecologically important, two, alpha and beta, are corpuscular. They are streams of atomic or subatomic particles that have a definite mass, and travel only a short distance through the air and water. Once stopped, they transfer their energy to the object they strike, producing locally a large amount of ionization. They have their greatest effect when ingested, absorbed, or internally deposited. The other form is ionizing electromagnetic or gamma radiation, which has a short wave length, travels a great distance, and penetrates matter easily. This is the form of radiation produced by nuclear reactions. The effects of electromagnetic radiation depend upon the number and energy of the rays and the distance of the organism from the source. Since this radiation is penetrating, it can produce its effects without being taken inside.

Increasing attention is being given to the effects of gamma radiation on ecosystems. When an unshielded nuclear reactor was built in a forested valley near Atlanta, Georgia, a group of biologists under Robert B. Platt took advantage of the situation to observe the effects of radiation on the forest ecosystem. After measuring the amounts of radiation at increasing distances from the site, they revisited the area to follow the changes taking place. Gamma radiation and neutrons (large, uncharged particles that, although they themselves do not emit radiation, cause ionization by bumping atoms out of normal position) devastated the vegetation, killing pines several hundred feet away, reducing the reproductive capacity of more distant plants, and altering the normal sequence of succession.

At the Brookhaven National Laboratory on Long Island, additional studies were made on the effects of ionizing radiation on two ecosystems, an oak-pine forest and an old field (Woodwell, 1962; Sparrow and Woodwell, 1963). A source of gamma radiation was suspended in a tower in such a manner that it could be raised or lowered into a lead container by a winch, from a safe distance. The container shielded the source and allowed movement into the area. The radioactive source for the forest was cesium-137 and for the old field, cobalt-60. Both produced daily exposure rates that ranged from several thousand roentgens per day (Table 4-1) at a distance of a few meters to two roentgens at

TABLE 4-1. RADIOACTIVE ISOTOPE TERMINOLOGY USED IN TEXT

Roentgen	Amount of radioactive isotopes required to produce 1.61×10^{12} ion pairs per gram of air. It corresponds to the absorption of 84 ergs of energy per gram of air.
Radiation dose (rad)	100 ergs of energy absorbed per gram of body tissue.

130 meters. The highest exposures available, continued daily through the winter and into the spring, devastated both communities, but there was a wide difference in the resistance of the vegetation.

None of the higher plants of the forest community survived 360 roentgens per day. Most trees of all species were killed by 60 roentgens per day over a six-month period; and major damage from chronic exposure at 20 to 30 roentgens per day appeared in a couple of weeks. Pitch pine was the most sensitive to radiation. Growth was inhibited by 1 or 2 roentgens per day, and the trees were killed by 20 to 30 roentgens, about one-half the exposure that caused comparable damage to oaks. In Georgia, Platt (1963) found that loblolly pine that received doses of 2000 or more rads turned brown and in a few weeks were dead. As pines at a greater distance from the reactor accumulated 7000 rads, they too died, within 90 to 120 days. At the end of two years all pines within 2000 feet of the reactor were dead, yet the hardwoods were not noticeably affected.

On the other hand, an old-field community, dominated by pig weed and crab grass, exposed to the same amount of radiation, was five times as hardy as pine. The basic plant population was essentially unaltered at exposures of less than 300 roentgens per day, although growth, form, and reproductive capacity were affected by daily exposures of 100 to 300 roentgens. Of the old-field plants the common groundsel was the most resistant, surviving exposures of more than 10,000 roentgens. At Brookhaven, mosses and lichens survived total exposures of more than 200,000 roentgens (Woodwell, 1962). In Georgia a rock outcrop community, dominated largely by annuals, was significantly changed in structure at total chronic exposures in the range of 20,000 to 40,000 roentgens over four months at the rate of 170 to 310 roentgens per day (McCormick, 1963). The more radiosensitive species were selectively eliminated, while the more radio-resistant species expanded, partly because of the stimulatory effect on plants that comes from irradiated seeds.

Approximately 6 months after irradiation of the oak-pine forest and old field started at Brookhaven, the differences in the radiosensitivity of the plants and the decreasing exposure rates with an increasing distance from the source produced a zonation of vegetation (Woodwell, 1962). This included a zone of total kill of all higher plants, a zone of sedge, a heath-shrub zone dominated by huckleberry—a most radio-resistant species—an oak zone, and an oak-pine forest. In the old-field ecosystem, the zones included, in order, total kill, groundsel, crab grass, panic grass, and pigweed.

When plants are injured by radiation, insects can intensify the damage, for they, especially the herbivorous ones, are well adapted to survive widespread radiation disturbances. At Brookhaven the leaftiers, leaf rollers, leaf beetles, and loopers were more resistant than their white-oak host. Without any apparent increase in absolute numbers, they ate most of the remaining foliage on the trees (Woodwell, 1962). Bark lice and pine wood borers increased, while other insect populations were depressed. Thus changes in host-parasite and predator-prey relationships can greatly heighten the damage already caused by radiation.

These radiation studies indicate that earlier successional stages of terrestrial communities are far more resistant to ionizing radiation than are the later stages. Most resistant are the mosses and lichens. Thus the same levels of radiation lethal to man can destroy complex ecosystems and replace them with simple ecosystems of radio-resistant plants and animals, the latter mainly insects.

Radiation damage is closely correlated with the amount of energy absorbed by the chromosomes (Sparrow and Woodwell, 1963). Large chromosomes are more susceptible to damage than small ones, and organisms with few chromosomes are more subject to damage than those with many. Thus polyploidy—the occurrence of extra sets of chromosomes in the nucleus—adds resistance to radiation damage. The amount of energy absorbed is also influenced by the period of exposure. Slowly dividing cells, irradiated over an extended period of time, are subject to greater total exposure before the next division than those rapidly dividing. Tissues rapidly dividing can replace damaged cells with undamaged ones. But the reproductive stages are highly susceptible to radiation damage. Dose rates far below those required for severe inhibition of growth or for lethal effects will cause the complete failure of sexual reproduction. This is because of the high nuclear volume of the chromosomes, their reduced number after meiosis, the subsequent slow rate of nuclear development, and the increase of any aberrations through meiotic pairing. On the other hand dormant seeds are highly resistant. The seeds of pitch pine, one of the most susceptible of plants, will withstand a radiation dosage of 12,000 roentgens, while the tree itself will succumb to 27 roentgens per day.

The life form of the plant, independent of the chromosome size and number, influences the radiosensitivity of the organisms. Since perennial grasses and ferns have some shoot meristems at and below ground level, they are partially or completely shielded from radiation (see Chappel, 1963). Hemicryptophytes and cryptophytes can survive intensities of radiation that are lethal for plants with a similar nuclear volume and chromosome number but whose shoots are more fully exposed.

Of all the animal groups, mammals are the most sensitive to radiation, succumbing to exposures of 200 to 1000 roentgens; this contrasts sharply with insects, which can tolerate exposures from 1000 to 10,000 roentgens, depending upon the species. Thus intense radiation could easily turn an ecosystem over to the insects. A study of the reaction of mammals to intense radiation averaging 4308 rads—80 times the lethal dose of 50—delivered over a 5-day period eliminated an introduced population of cotton rats (Schnell, 1963). On the other hand an environmental dose of 5369 rads delivered over a 15-day period resulted in the disappearance of 38 per cent of the resident individuals of two species of *Peromyscus*. The white-footed mice living in an open field all disappeared, but some of the beach mice, a deep-burrowing species, and some of the woodland white-footed mice survived. These latter two received considerable shielding by the habitat, which reduced radiation 88 per cent for the mice. Surviving white-footed mice in the woodland showed 0 to 5 per cent graying of the pelage several weeks after exposure; beach mice living in an open field where the radiation was 15 times a lethal dose showed 53 to 100 per cent pelage graying. Behavioral changes, too, took place. Irradiated cotton rats living free in the field showed a lack of aggressiveness and alertness, impairment of motor reflexes and equilibrium, and a general reduction of activity, with loss of appetite. Rats acting in this manner were never again recaptured.

Nestling bluebirds, more resistant to gamma radiation than chickens, die when exposed to 3000 roentgens (Willard, 1963). The estimated lethal dose (50 for a 6-day old nestling) was about 2500 roentgens; however, birds receiving a sublethal dose were so severely stunted that their chances of survival were poor. All nestlings that survived irradiation developed normal fledgling behavior and attempted to leave the nest, even though growth and feather development was stunted. Nestlings that received 800 to 900 roentgens when 2 days old were able to leave the nest with normal nestmates; but since they were weakened and possessed subnormal flying ability, their survival was doubtful. Nestlings receiving 1500 roentgens were able to crawl out of the nest box but were unable to fly even when they attempted to do so. Thus even though the nestling birds received sublethal doses that affected growing tissues, the radiation did not impair the brain centers responsible for inherent behavior.

Microclimates

When the weather report states that the temperature is 75°F and the sky is clear, the information may reflect the general weather conditions for the day. But on the surface of the ground in and beneath the vegetation, on slopes and cliff tops, in crannies and pockets, the climate is quite different. Heat, moisture, air movement, and light all vary radically from one part of the community to another to create a whole range of "little" or "micro" climates.

On a summer afternoon the temperature under calm, clear skies may be 82° at six feet, the standard level of temperature recording. But on or near the ground—at the two-inch level—the temperature may be 10° higher; and at sunrise when the temperature for the 24-hour period is the lowest, the temperature may be 5° lower than at the standard level (Biel, 1961). Thus in the middle eastern part of the United States, the temperature near the ground may correspond to the temperature at the six-foot level in Florida, 700 miles to the south; and at sunrise the temperature may correspond to the six-foot-level temperature in southern Canada. Even greater extremes occur above and below the ground surface. In New Jersey, March temperatures about the stolons of clover plants one-half inch above the surface of the ground may be 72°F (21°C), while three inches below the surface the temperature about the roots is 30°F (−1°C) (Biel, 1961). The temperature range for a vertical distance of three and one half inches is 40°F (20°C). Under such climatic extremes most organisms exist.

The chief reason for the great differences between the ground level and six feet high is solar radiation. During the day the soil, the active surface, absorbs solar radiation, which comes in short waves as light, and radiates it back as long waves to heat a thin layer of air above (Fig. 4-11). Since air flow at ground level is almost nonexistent, the heat radiated from the surface remains close to the ground. Temperatures decrease sharply in the air above this layer and in the soil below. The heat absorbed by the ground during the day is reradiated by the ground at night. This heat is partly absorbed by the water vapor in the air above. The drier the air, the greater is the outgoing heat and the stronger is the cooling of the surface of the ground and the vegetation. Eventually the ground and the vegetation are cooled to the dewpoint, and water vapor in the air may condense as dew. After a heavy dew a thin layer of chilled air lies over the surface, the result of rapid absorption of heat in the evaporation of dew.

By altering wind movement, evaporation, moisture, and soil temperatures, vegetation influences or moderates the microclimate of an area, especially near the ground. Temperatures at the ground level under the shade are lower than those in places exposed to the sun and wind. Average maximum soil temperatures at the one-inch level below the surface in a northern hardwoods forest and an aspen-birch forest in New York State were 60°F (15.5°C) from mid-May to late June and 68°F (20°C) (absolute maximum 78°F) from early July to mid-August (Spaeth and Diebolt, 1938). Mean differences between maximum temperatures for the forest and adjacent fields ranged from 9° to 24°F. Maximum soil temperatures at one inch in open chestnut-oak forests were 66°F (19°C) from mid-May to late June and 75°F (24°C) (absolute maximum, 93°F) from July to mid-August. On fair summer days a dense forest cover reduces the daily range of temperatures at one inch by 20° to 30°F, compared with the temperature in the soils of bare fields.

Vegetation also reduces the steepness of the temperature gradient and influences the height of the active surface, the area which intercepts the maximum quantity of solar insolation. In absence of or in the presence of very thin vegetation, temperature increases sharply near the soil; but as the plant cover increases in height and density, the leaves of the plants intercept more solar radiation (Fig. 4-12). The plant crowns then become the active surface and raise it above

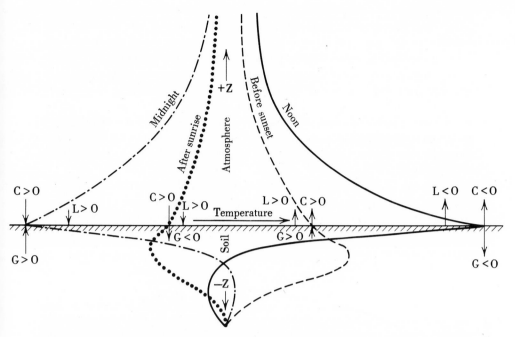

Figure 4-11 *Idealized temperature profiles in the ground and air for various times of the day, and the transport of heat by convection, C; by conduction, G; and by latent heat of evaporation or condensation, L.* (From D. M. Gates, 1962, *Energy Exchange in the Biosphere*, Harper and Row, New York.)

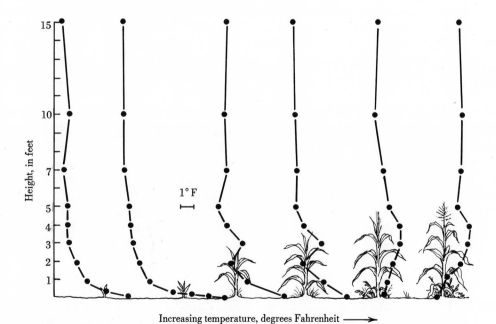

Figure 4-12 *Vertical temperature gradients at midday in a cornfield from the time of seeding stage to the time of harvest. Note the increasing height of the active surface.* (Adapted from Wolfe et al., 1949.)

the ground. As a result temperatures are highest just above the dense crown surface and lowest at the surface of the ground. Maximum absorption of solar radiation in tall grass occurs just below the upper surface of the vegetation, while in the short grass, maximum temperatures are at the ground level (Waterhouse, 1955). As the grasses grow taller the level of maximum temperature falls into and rises with the upper level of the grass stalks until the temperature eventually reaches an approximate equilibrium with the air above. (Among broad-leafed plants daily maximums occur on the upper leaf surfaces.) At night minimum temperatures are some distance above the ground since the air is cooled above the tops of plants and the dense stalks prevent the chilled air from settling to the ground.

Within dense vegetation air movements are reduced to convection and diffusion (Fig. 4-13). In dense grass and low plant cover, complete calm exists at ground level. This calm is an outstanding feature of the microclimate near the

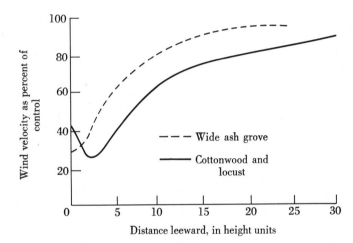

Figure 4-13 *Comparative wind velocity at 16 inches above the ground to the leeward of open ash grove and a cottonwood and locust shelterbelt. The curve for the ash grove illustrates the loss of effectiveness when a stand of trees is open, allowing the wind to sweep under the crowns. Zero is the lee face of the barrier.* (After Stoeckeler, 1962.)

ground, since it influences both temperature and humidity and creates a favorable environment for insects and other animals.

Vegetation also deflects wind flow up and over its top (Fig. 4-14). If the vegetation is narrow, such as is a windbreak or a hedgerow, the microclimate on the leeward side may be greatly affected. Deflection of wind produces an area of eddies immediately behind the vegetation, in which the wind speed is low and small particles such as seeds are deposited. Beyond this is an area of turbulence, in which the climate tends to be colder and drier than normal. If some wind passes through the barrier and some goes over it, no turbulence develops, but the mean temperature behind the barrier is high in the morning and lower in the afternoon.

Humidity differs greatly from the ground up. Since evaporation takes place at the surface of the soil or at the active surface of plant cover, the vapor content (absolute humidity) decreases rapidly from a maximum at the bottom to atmospheric equilibrium above. Relative humidity increases above the surface, since actual vapor content increases only slowly during the day while the capacity of the heated air over the surface to hold moisture increases rather rapidly. During the night little difference exists above and on the ground. Within the growing vegetation, however, relative humidity is much higher than above the plant cover. In fact near-saturation conditions may exist.

Soil properties, too, enter the microclimatic picture. In a soil that conducts heat well, considerable heat energy will be transferred to the substratum, from which it radiates to the surface at night. On such soils, surface temperatures are lower by day and higher by night than the surface temperatures of poorly conducting soils. This influences the occurrences of frosts. Moist soils are better conductors of heat than dry soils. Light-colored sandy soils increase reflection and reduce the rate at which heat energy is absorbed. Dark soils, on the other hand, absorb more heat.

North and south slopes

The microclimatic variations throughout a given area, then, result from differences in slope, soil, and vegetation. The greatest microclimatic differences exist between north and south slopes. South-facing slopes receive the most solar energy, which is maximal when the slope grade equals the sun's angle from the zenith point. North-facing slopes receive the least energy, especially when the slope grade equals or exceeds the angle of sun-ray inflection. At latitude North 41° (about central New Jersey and southern Pennsylvania) midday insolation on a 20° slope is, on the average, 40 per cent greater on south slopes than on north during all seasons. This has a marked effect on the moisture and heat budget of the two sites. High temperatures and associated low vapor pressures induce evapo-transpiration of moisture from the soil and plants. The evaporation rate often is 50 per cent higher, the average temperature higher, the soil moisture lower, and the extremes more variable on south slopes. Thus the microclimate ranges from warm, xeric conditions with wide extremes on the south slope to cooler, less variable, more mesic conditions on the north slope. Xeric conditions are most highly developed on the top of south slopes where air movement is the greatest, while the most mesic conditions are at the bottom of the north slopes (Fig. 4-15 above and below). In the central and southern Appalachians, north slopes are steeper and include many minor microreliefs—small depressions and benches created largely by the upheaved roots of thrown trees. South slopes are longer and less steep, because of long-term downward movement of the soil. The whole north-south slope complex is the result of a long chain of interactions: the solar radiation influences moisture regimes, the moisture regime influences the species of trees and other plants occupying the slopes. The species of trees in turn influence mineral recycling, which is reflected in the nature and chemistry of the surface soil and the nature of the herbaceous ground cover.

Tree cover on the north-facing and south-facing slopes of the New Jersey hills does not reflect the microclimates of the two slopes as well as the herbaceous layer, according to Cantlon (1953), but differences do show up. In New Jersey yellow poplar does not occupy the south slope nor black oak the north. Flowering dogwood grows on both slopes, but is most abundant on the north. Rhododendron, spicebush, and maple-leaf viburnum occupy the north slopes. Ferns and mosses characterize the ground layer of the north slopes; grasses and sedges, the south.

The differences apparent between the north and south slopes in the New

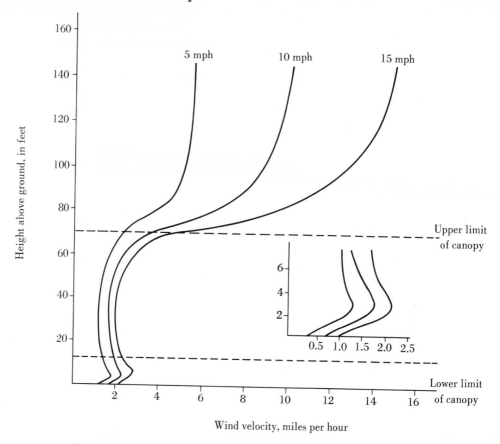

Figure 4-14 *Comparative wind velocities. (above) Distribution of wind velocities with height as affected by the timber canopy of coniferous forests for wind velocities of 5, 10, and 15 miles per hour measured 142 feet above the ground. (After Fons, 1940.) (right) The average wind velocity during a June day (based on 1938, 1939, 1940 dates) inside a coniferous forest with a cedar understory in northern Idaho. Note decrease in velocity near the ground. (After Gisborne, 1941.)*

Jersey hills are much more pronounced in the mountains of the central Appalachians. In this latter region the land is strongly dissected by a dendritic drainage pattern, the slopes are extreme—ranging up to 85 and 90 per cent—and the valleys are very narrow. In places, particularly in the Cumberland Plateau, the hills arise abruptly from narrow stream bottoms and the ridges drop off sharply. In these situations the plant communities of the north and south slopes often are sharply defined at the ridge top, the xeric south-slope vegetation meeting the more mesic vegetation of the upper north slope (Fig. 4-16).

The lower north slopes of the Cumberland Plateau support a forest dominated by beech, sugar maple, and yellow poplar, with black birch, basswood, black walnut, and butternut as associates. This gradually gives way to a red oak–white oak–basswood forest on the upper slopes. The umbrella tree and the redbud are characteristic of the understory.

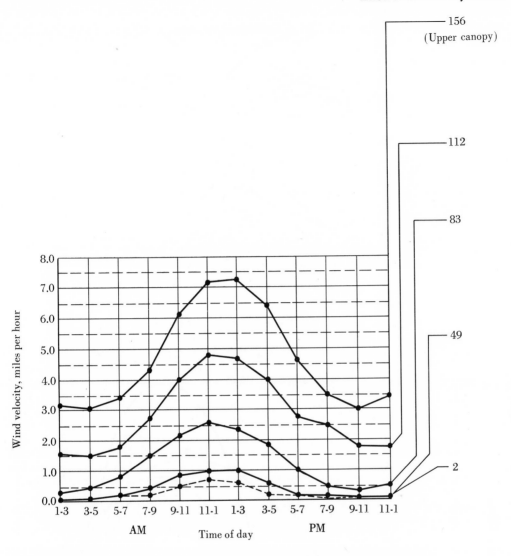

The lower south slope that lies within the shelter and shadow of the north slope is very similar to the lower and middle north slope and often contains the most abundant hemlock stands. This bottom slope forest soon changes to oak forest on the middle south slope, where black oak and scarlet oak are dominant. The upper south slope supports a forest of chestnut oak, pitch pine, and shortleaf pine. The characteristic understory tree is sourwood. Flowering dogwood and sassafras are common to both slopes, but dogwood is the most abundant on the north and sassafras on the south. Red maple, an irregular understory tree on the north slope, is abundant on the south. Red oak, occurring in all strata, is most abundant on the north slope, while black locust and shadbush are generally distributed on the south slope.

Even more pronounced differences exist underfoot in the herbaceous layer. Forty-eight species of herbs and ferns are exclusive to the north slopes in the

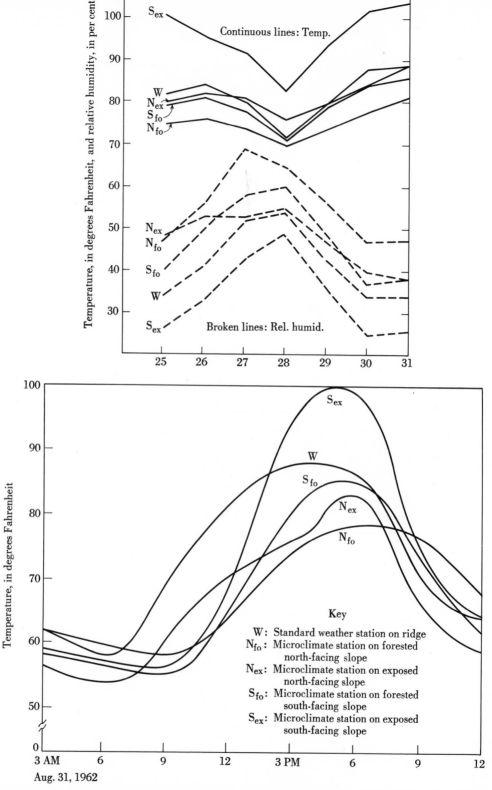

Figure 4-15 *Daily maximum temperature, minimum relative humidity, as recorded by four weather stations measuring microclimate and a single standard weather station during a week in August, 1962. Note extremes recorded at exposed sites (Sex), differences in readings of microclimate stations, standard station. (below) Temperatures recorded at the five stations in August on a sunny day. Temperatures recorded at the exposed site showed the greatest variation. Contrast this with the forested north-facing slope. (Data courtesy W. A. van Eck.)*

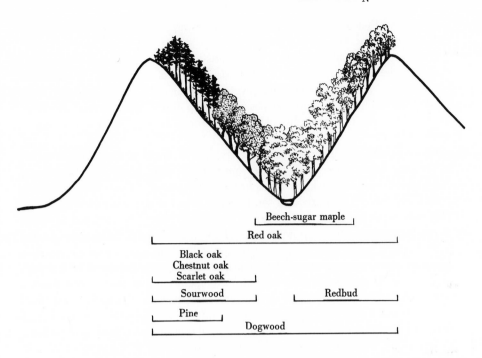

N

Beech-sugar maple
|_____ Red oak _____|

Black oak
Chestnut oak
Scarlet oak

|_____ Sourwood _____| |_____ Redbud _____|

|__ Pine __|
|_____ Dogwood _____|

Tree distribution, Cumberland mts.

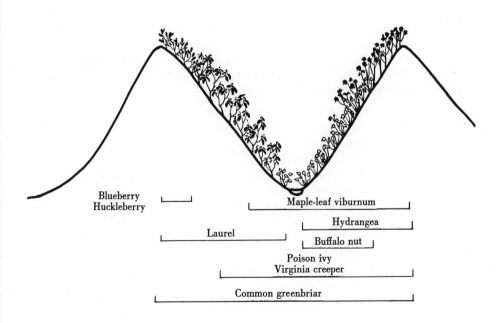

Blueberry
Huckleberry |____| |__ Maple-leaf viburnum __|

                              |_____ Hydrangea _____|
|_____ Laurel _____|
                              |__ Buffalo nut __|

                   Poison ivy
                   Virginia creeper

|_____ Common greenbriar _____|

Shrub distribution, Cumberland mts.

Figure 4-16 *The influence of microclimate on the distribution of trees and shrubs on north-facing and south-facing slopes in the Cumberland Plateau of southwestern West Virginia. (Original data: author.)*

Cumberland Plateau, while 61 are exclusive to the south slope (Smith and van Eck, unpublished data).

Similar vegetational changes are characteristic of north-facing and south-facing slopes in the chaparral of the North Coast Range of California. South slopes —warm, dry, and thin soiled—are covered with chamise, buckbush, and yerba santa. The cool, moist, north slopes with deep fertile soil support deerbush, eastwood manzanita, interior live oak, and California laurel (Taber and Dasmann, 1958).

Being mobile, few if any animals are typical of north or south slopes, as far as we now know. Deer tend to use south slopes more heavily in winter and early spring and north slopes more heavily in summer (Taber and Dasmann, 1958). Studies of the north- and south-facing slopes of ant mounds in Denmark (Haarlov, 1960) suggest that some soil invertebrates may be confined to either of the two slopes. The steep north sides of the mounds were completely covered with *Festuca ovina*; the gentle south slopes had an open cover of *Achillea* but were dominated by moss. Similar to the large slopes, the south-facing sides of the mounds had the highest maximum temperature and the greatest fluctuations. The soil fauna common to the north slopes were *Pyemotidae* spp. and *Tectocepheus alatus*; common to the south slopes were *Speleorchestes termitophilus* and *Passalogetes perforatus*. Of these only the mite *Passalogetes* was confined to one slope, the south, alone. This species, intolerant of humidity, can exist only in a dry habitat.

Valleys and frost pockets

The widest climatic extremes occur in valleys and pockets, areas of convex slopes, and low concave surfaces. These places have much lower temperatures at night, especially in winter, and much higher temperatures during the day, especially in summer, and a higher relative humidity. Protected from the circulating influences of the wind, the air becomes stagnant. It is heated by insolation and cooled by terrestrial radiation, in sharp contrast to the wind-exposed, well-mixed air layers of the upper slopes. In the evening cool air from the uplands flows down the slope into the pockets and valleys to form a lake of cool air. Often when the warm air in the valley comes in contact with the inflowing cold air, the moisture in the warm air may condense as valley fog.

A similar phenomenon takes place on small concave surfaces. Like the larger valley, these concave surfaces radiate heat rapidly on still, cold nights and cold air flows in from surrounding higher levels. On such sites the air temperature near the ground may be 15° lower than the surrounding terrain. This results in a temperature inversion, since the temperature increases with height above the ground. Since low ground temperatures in these areas tend to result in late spring frosts, early fall frosts, and a subsequent short growing season, these depressions are called frost pockets. These pockets need not be deep. Minimum temperatures in small depressions only three to four feet deep were equivalent to those of a nearby valley 200 feet below the general level of the land (Spurr, 1957). Such variations in temperature due to local microrelief can strongly influence the distribution and growth of plants. Tree growth is inhibited; and since the low surfaces more often than not accumulate water as well as cold air, such sites may contain plants of a more northern distribution. Frost pockets may also develop in small forest clearings. The surface of the tree crowns channels cold air into the clearings as terrestrial radiation cools the layer of air just above.

SUMMARY

The physical and chemical conditions of the environment influence the well-being and distribution of plants and animals and the functions of the ecosystem. The kind and quantity of elements and nutrients available for circulation in the biogeochemical cycle affect the growth and reproduction of plants and animals that vary in their requirements and tolerances for different elements. Some, the macronutrients, are required in relatively large quantities by all living organisms. Others, the trace elements, or micronutrients, are needed in lesser and often only minute quantities; yet without them plants and animals will fail, as if they lacked one of the major nutrients. Organisms live within a rather limited range of environmental temperatures and moisture conditions, outside of which they fail to reproduce or grow. To meet fluctuations in temperature and moisture extremes, many animals and plants have evolved a number of adaptations, such as dormancy, hibernation, seeds, and cysts, that get them through the unfavorable periods. Temperature and moisture, acting together, determine in a large measure the climate of a region and the distribution of plant and animal life. Wind increases evaporation and is a major agent in the dispersal of plants and animals. Light is essential to plants; without either, the ecosystems could not function. Light also influences the reproductive and activity cycles of plants and animals. Gamma radiation is a new ecological influence of the nuclear age. Not only can it kill off animal life; it can destroy complex ecosystems as well and convert the areas into simple ecosystems, dominated by radio-resistant plants and animals, the latter chiefly insects. Not only do all of the above environmental conditions influence life over a region, they also influence the distribution of life on a much smaller scale. Organisms occupying the same general habitat may be living under completely different conditions because of variations in the microclimate or microenvironment. Most pronounced are the environmental differences between ground level and the upper strata, and between north-facing and south-facing slopes. On a small scale or a large one, life is greatly influenced by the abundance and scarcity of nutrients and by the physical and chemical nature of the environment in which it exists.

Periodicity and biological clocks

One aspect of communities with which everyone is familiar is rhythmicity, the recurrence of daily and seasonal changes. Dawn ends the darkness and bird song signals its arrival. Butterflies, dragonflies, and bees become conspicuous; hawks seek out prey, and chipmunks and tree squirrels become active. At dusk, light fades and daytime animals retire, the blooms of waterlilies and other flowers fold, and animals of the night appear. The fox, the raccoon, the flying squirrel, the owls, and the moths take over niches occupied by others during the day. As the seasons progress, day length changes and with it other conspicuous activities. Spring brings the migrant birds and initiates the reproductive cycles of many animals and plants. In fall the trees of temperate regions become dormant, insects and herbaceous plants disappear, the summer-resident birds return south and winter visitors arrive. On the ocean shore the tide rises and falls about 50 minutes later each day and affects all life on the edge of the sea.

Underlying these rhythmicities are the movements of the earth relative to the sun and the moon. The earth's rotation on its axis results in the alternation of night and day. The tilt of the earth's axis, along with its annual revolution around the sun, produces the seasons. The tides result from an interaction of lunar and solar gravational forces, modified by the influences of ocean basins and local topography. The rotational periods of the earth and the moon usually produce successive high tides at intervals of 12.4 hours and extreme or "spring" tides at intervals of about 14 to 15 days (see Chap. 12).

Daily periodicity: the circadian rhythms

Since life evolved under the influences of daily and seasonal environmental changes, it is natural that plants and animals would have some rhythm or pattern to their lives that would synchronize them with fluctuations in the environment. For years biologists have been intrigued over the means by which organisms kept their activities in rhythm with the 24-hour day, including such phenomena as the daily pattern of leaf and petal movements in plants, the emergence of insects from pupal cases, the sleep and wakefulness of animals (Fig. 5-1). At one time biologists thought that these rhythmicities were entirely exogenous, that is, that the organisms responded only to external stimuli such

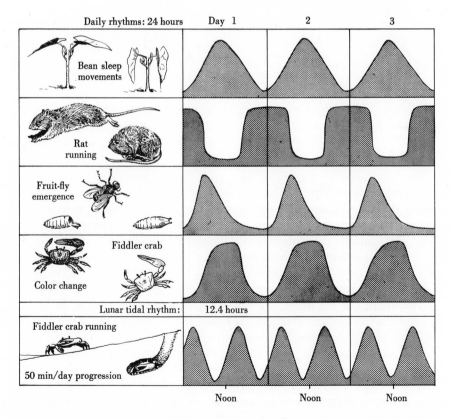

Figure 5-1 *Examples of rhythmic phenomena experimentally demonstrated to persist under constant conditions in the laboratory, illustrating diagrammatically the natural phase relationships to external physical cycles.* (Redrawn by permission from F. A. Brown, 1959, Living Clocks, *Science, 130* (3388) : 1537.)

as light intensity, humidity, temperature, and tides. Laboratory investigations, however, indicate that this is not the complete answer.

At dusk in the forests of North America a small squirrel with silky fur and large, black eyes emerges from a tree hole. With a leap the squirrel sails downward in a long sloping glide, maintaining itself in flight with broad membranes stretched between its outspread legs. Using its tail as a rudder and brake, it makes a short, graceful, upward swoop that lands it on the trunk of another tree. This is the flying squirrel, perhaps the commonest of all our tree squirrels. But because of its nocturnal habits, this mammal is seldom seen by most people. Unless it is disturbed, the flying squirrel does not come out by day. It emerges into the forest world with the coming of darkness; it returns to its nest with the first light of dawn.

If the flying squirrel is brought indoors and kept under artificial conditions of night and day, the animal will confine its periods of activity to darkness,

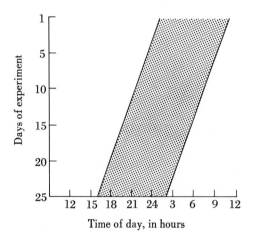

Figure 5-2 *Drift in the phase of the activity rhythm of a flying squirrel held in continuous darkness at 20°C for 25 days.* (Adapted by permission from P. J. DeCoursey, 1960, *Cold Spring Harbor Symposia on Quantitative Biology,* 25:51.)

its periods of inactivity to light. Whether the conditions under which the animal lives are 12 hours of darkness and 12 hours of light, or 8 hours of darkness and 16 hours of light, the onset of activity always begins shortly after dark. The squirrel's day-to-day activity forms a 24-hour period. This correlation of the onset of activity with the time of sunset suggests that light has a regulatory effect on the activity of the squirrel.

But the photoperiodism (response to changing light and darkness) exhibited by the squirrel is not quite so simple. There is more to it than the animal becoming active because darkness has come. If the squirrel is kept in constant darkness, it still maintains a relatively constant rhythm of activity from day to day (DeCoursey, 1961). But in the absence of any external time cues, the squirrel's activity rhythm deviates from the 24-hour periodicity exhibited under light and dark conditions. The daily cycle under constant darkness varies from 22 hours, 58 minutes, to 24 hours, 21 minutes, the average being less than 24 hours (most frequent 23:50 and 23:59) (DeCoursey, 1961). The length of the period maintained under a given set of conditions is an individual characteristic. Because of the deviation of the average cycle length from 24 hours, each individual squirrel gradually drifts out of phase with the day-night changes of the external world (Fig. 5-2). If the same animals are held under continuous light, a very abnormal condition for a nocturnal animal, the activity cycle is lengthened, probably because the animal, attempting to avoid running in the light, delays the beginning of its activity as much as it can.

In the open sea lives *Gonyaulax polyedra,* a photosynthetic dinoflagellate that emits light especially when disturbed by waves and by the wakes of boats. Its bioluminescence is maximum during the night. When cultures of *Gonyaulax* are held in the laboratory under alternating light and dark periods of 12 hours each, emission of light is 40 to 60 times greater during the dark period than during the light (Fig. 5-3) (Sweeney and Hastings, 1957). When these same light-dark cultures are held under continuous dim light, the rhythm of luminescence persists (Fig. 5-4), but if the cultures are placed in constant bright light or constant darkness, the rhythm is damped (Fig. 5-5). The rhythm, however, is not dependent upon prior exposure to light and dark conditions. Cultures

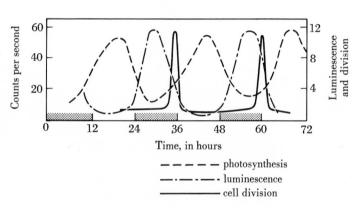

Figure 5-3 Diurnal rhythms of luminescence, photosynthesis, and cell division in cultures of Gonyaulax polyedra *held in light and dark periods of 12 hours each at 25°C. (Redrawn by permission from Hastings, 1959,* Annual Review of Microbiology, *13:299.)*

grown in bright light for one year showed diurnal rhythms when the same cultures were placed in constant dim or darkness (Sweeney and Hastings, 1958).

Not only does *Gonyaulax* possess a diurnal rhythm of bioluminescence; it also shows similar rhythms in cell division and photosynthesis (Hastings, 1959). Obviously the maximum for the phases of these different rhythms occurs at a different time of day (Fig. 5-3). Cultures maintained in alternating light and dark conditions reached their maximum cell divisions just at the end of the dark period, and their maximum photosynthetic activity ($C^{14}O_2$ incorporation) occurred at the eighth hour of the light period. These two rhythms also persisted when the cells were held under constant conditions of dim or darkness. Like the squirrel, *Gonyaulax* also showed a drift in the phase of the rhythm away from the 24-hour period of the solar day. Depending upon conditions, this period varies from 23 to 27 hours.

Night-blooming jessamine is a semitropical shrub of the Caribbean islands. Its abundant small, yellow flowers open at night and emit a powerful fragrance, which attracts night-flying insects that pollinate the plants. Both the opening and closing of the flowers and the emission of the odor continue to occur in a rhythmic manner in constant light as well as in constant darkness (Overland, 1960).

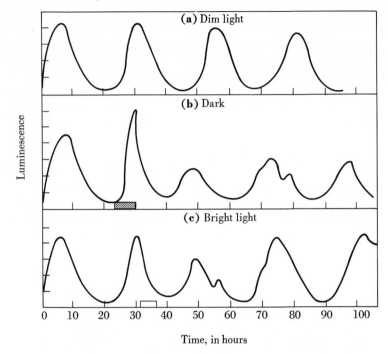

Figure 5-4 *Phase shift in the rhythm of luminescence in* Gonyaulax. *The cultures, maintained at first under light-dark conditions, were placed under constant light (100 foot-candles) at a constant temperature (23.5°C) at the end of a 12-hour period. Two days later measurements of luminescence were begun. (a) Rhythm of luminescence from a culture maintained in constant dim light. (b) Culture was transferred to darkness for six hours, then returned to dim light at 200 foot-candles. Note the phase shift in relation to the timing of the dark period, compared to control A. (c) Culture was transferred to bright light (1400 foot-candles) for six hours, then returned to constant dim light (100 foot-candles). Again a phase shift occurred. (Redrawn by permission from Hastings and Sweeney, 1958, Biological Bulletin, 115:446, Marine Biol. Lab., Woods Hole, Mass.)*

There are other examples of rhythms that persist under constant laboratory conditions: the opening of flowers in *Kalanchoe* (Bünsow, 1953), the leaf motions of *Phaseolus* (Bünning, 1935*b*), the emergence of insects from their pupal cases (Pittendrigh, 1954), the discharge of sporangenia by certain fungi (Uebelmesser, 1954).

The flying squirrel, the dinoflagellate *Gonyaulax,* the night-blooming jessamine,

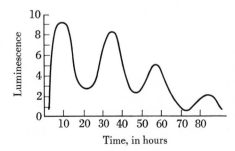

Figure 5-5 *Rhythm of luminescence in* Gonyaulax polyedra *from cultures held first in light-dark conditions, then left in the dark. Note how the circadian rhythm of luminescence damps out in constant darkness. (Redrawn by permission from Hastings and Sweeney, 1958, Biological Bulletin, 115:447, Marine Biological Lab., Woods Hole, Mass.)*

and the rest all have a characteristic in common. They possess a rhythm of activity that under field conditions exhibits a periodicity of 24 hours. Moreover, when these organisms are brought into the laboratory and held under constant conditions of light, darkness, and temperature, away from any external time cues, they still exhibit a rhythm of activity of approximately 24 hours. Because these rhythms approximate but seldom match the periods of the earth's rotation, they are called *circadian* (from the Latin *circa*, about, and *dies*, day). The period (the number of hours from the beginning of activity one day to the beginning of the activity on the next) of the circadian rhythm is referred to as "free-running," in contrast to a period synchronized to an environmental rhythm. The circadian rhythms apparently are internally driven, or endogenous, are temperature independent, and are innate, not learned from or impressed by the environment.

The innate character of the circadian rhythm is demonstrated by observations of several animals. When fruit flies, *Drosophila*, are kept under constant conditions from the larval stage on, they will still emerge from the pupae with a regular circadian rhythm (Bünning, 1935*a*). In fact *Drosophila* reared for 15 generations under continuous dim light still retained their capacity to emerge from the pupae according to a circadian rhythm (Bünning, 1935*a*). Eggs of chickens and lizards kept under constant conditions produce animals that later show regular circadian cycles (Aschoff and Meyer Lohmann, 1954).

Thus many plants and animals are influenced by two periodicities, the internal circadian rhythm of approximately 24 hours and the external environmental rhythm, usually a precise 24-hour rhythm. If the activity rhythm of the organism is to be brought into phase, or synchrony, with the external one, then some environmental "time-setter" must adjust the endogenous rhythm with that of the outside world. The most obvious time keepers, cues, synchronizers, or *Zeitgebers* (Aschoff, 1958) are temperature and light. Of the two, light is the master *Zeitgeber*. It brings the circadian rhythm of many organisms into phase with the 24-hour photoperiod of the external environment.

Although one might have difficulty proving in the field the role of light in synchronizing the circadian rhythm with the environment, it can be demonstrated in the laboratory (see Bruce, 1960). If an animal or plant is kept under constant conditions, such as continuous darkness or continuous light, the circadian rhythm drifts out of phase with natural light and dark and eventually may fade away. The length of time required for this to happen depends upon the organism and the conditions of light and darkness. The activity rhythm of rodents may continue for several months in constant darkness. Other rhythms, such as the leaf movements of plants, may fade much more quickly, while the circadian rhythms in *Gonyaulax* cultures have persisted in dim light for three years (Hastings, 1959). Once a rhythm has faded, a new one can be started by some exposure to light or dark. This may be the interruption of continuous darkness by a short flash of light, the interruption of continuous light by darkness, the change from continuous darkness to continuous light, or vice versa. With some organisms, a change in temperature may start a new rhythm.

The classical experiment involving light as a synchronizer was conducted with *Drosophila* (Pittendrigh, 1954). In their natural habitat, the fruit flies emerge from their pupal cases at about dawn. When fruit flies are allowed to lay their eggs in the laboratory and the eggs are left to develop, all under continuous darkness,

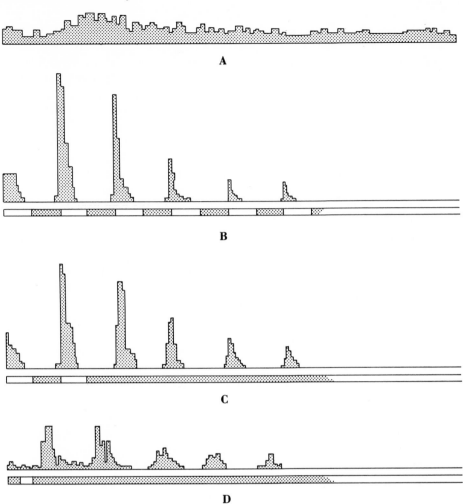

Figure 5-6 *Daily rhythm of emergence from pupae by* Drosophila. *(A) From cultures held under continuous darkness emergence is random. (B) From cultures held under light-dark conditions at 21°C. (C) From cultures held under light-dark conditions and then transferred to constant darkness at 21°C. Note that the rhythm tied to the original dawn is maintained in darkness. (D) From cultures held in continuous darkness and then exposed to a single light stimulus of four hours; see text.* (From Pittendrigh, 1954, *Proc. Nat. Acad. Sci.*, 40:1020, 1023.)

the flies emerge from the pupal cases at random through the day. But if larvae hatched from such eggs are subjected to only a single flash of light during the period of controlled darkness, the height of emergence of adult flies from pupal cases will take place at approximately the same hour of day that they were previously exposed as larvae to the flash of light (Fig. 5-6). A single flash of light during the larval period is sufficient to establish a rhythm of emergence of adult flies.

If *Gonyaulax* cells, whose rhythm of luminescence is in phase with a particular light-dark cycle, are exposed to a new schedule, in which the light-dark periods begin at a different hour of the solar day, the cells will shift the rhythm of luminescence to synchronize with the new light-dark period. The phase of the new rhythm relates to the time when the previous light-dark period occurred (Fig. 5-7) (Sweeney and Hastings, 1958). But exposure to a complete cycle of light and dark is not necessary. In one experiment cultures in phase with a particular light-dark regime were transferred first to constant dim light and a constant temperature. Later some cultures were exposed to a period of bright light, others to a period of darkness. When they were returned to a constant dim light, the *Gonyaulax* cells showed a marked shift in the phase of their rhythm to coincide with the time in the 24-hour day that they were exposed to light or dark (Fig. 5-4). Such a phase shift brings the endogenous rhythm of the organism into synchrony with, or entrains it to, the new light-dark cycle (Sweeney and Hastings, 1958).

The activity rhythm of some vertebrates shows a similar entrainment to light-dark cycles. The flying squirrel, both in its natural environment and in artificial day-night schedules, synchronizes its daily cycle of activity to a specific phase of the light-dark cycle. This was demonstrated in a series of experiments by DeCoursey (1960a, 1961). Flying squirrels were held in constant darkness until their circadian rhythms of activity were no longer in phase with the natural environment. Then they were subjected to a light-dark cycle that was out of phase with their free-running period. If the light period fell in the animals' subjective night, it caused a delay in the subsequent onset of activity. Synchronization took place in a series of stepwise delays, until the animals' rhythms were stabilized with the light-dark change (Fig. 5-8). If the light period fell at the subjective dawn or at the end of the dark period (when the animals' activity period was about to end), it caused an advance of activity

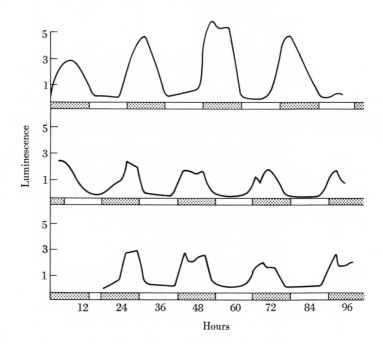

Figure 5-7 The effect of change in solar time at which the light-dark periods occur on the luminescence of culture of Gonyaulax. *The upper curve is the pattern of luminescence in a light-dark culture held on the schedule indicated. The lower two graphs indicate the effect of imposing upon cultures a light-dark schedule in which the light-dark periods were at a different time of day from the control. (Redrawn by permission from Hastings and Sweeney, 1958,* Biological Bulletin, *115:443.)*

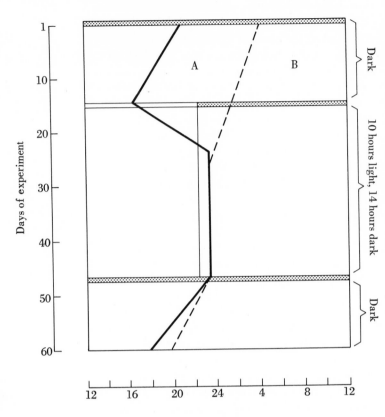

Figure 5-8 *Diagrammatic representation of the synchronization for flying squirrels with circadian rhythm in constant darkness of less than 24 hours to a cycle of 10 hours of light, 14 hours of darkness. In squirrel A, the rephasing light fell during its subjective night, synchronization was accomplished by a stepwise delay, and the onset of activity was stabilized shortly after light-dark change. In squirrel B, the light fell in the subjective day, and the free-running period continued unchanged until the onset drifted up against the "dusk" light change. This prevented it from drifting forward by a delaying action of light. When returned to constant darkness, the onset of activity continued a forward drift. (Redrawn from P. J. DeCoursey, 1960, Cold Spring Harbor Symposia on Experimental Biology, 25: 52.)*

toward the dusk period. And if the light fell in the animals' inactive day phase, it had no effect. Like *Gonyaulax*, the flying squirrels do not need to be exposed to a whole light-dark cycle to bring about a shift in the phase of the activity rhythm. A single 10-minute light period is sufficient to cause a phase shift in the locomotory activity, provided it is given during the squirrel's light-sensitive period (DeCoursey, 1960*b*).

The chaffinch, a bird active during the day, responds more rapidly to changes in the light-dark cycle. Birds held in 12 hours of light and 12 hours of dark were active during the light period (Fig. 5-9 a and b). After they were entrained to this light-dark cycle, the birds were placed in a constant dim light of 0.4 lux. The birds were active for a shorter length of time than they were before, their circadian activity rhythm (measured from the beginning of one period of activity to the beginning of another) was slightly more than 24 hours and drifted out of phase with the original 12:12-hour cycle (Aschoff and Wever, 1962; Aschoff, 1965). On the thirty-third day the birds were exposed to a new cycle of 12 hours of light, 12 of darkness. To this the birds became entrained immediately. Fifteen days later the same birds were placed under continuous light of 120 lux. The birds became active earlier each "day" and were active for a longer length of time; but their free-running period was somewhat shorter than 24 hours (Fig. 5-9 a). This latter phenomenon has resulted in a circadian

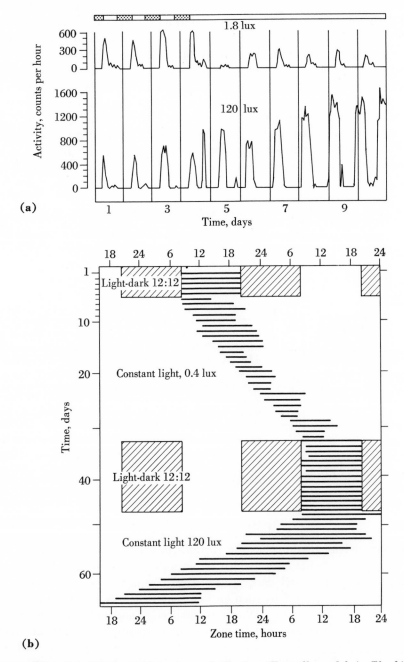

(a)

(b)

Figure 5-9 *(a) Activity rhythm of two chaffinches* (Fringilla coelebs). *The birds were kept three days in an artificial light-dark cycle and thereafter in continuous illumination, one in light with an intensity of 1.8 lux and the other in light of 120 lux. Ordinate, perch-hopping activity recorded by means of print-out counters. (b) Activity rhythm of a chaffinch in a light-dark cycle of 12 hours of light and 12 hours of darkness and in continuous illumination with an intensity of 0.4 lux and of 120 lux. Note how rapidly the birds became entrained to the light-dark cycle, and the direction of phase drift in the two illuminations.* (Redrawn by permission from J. Aschoff, 1965, Circadian rhythms in man, *Science, 148*:1428.)

rule that with increasing intensities of illumination the circadian rhythm is shortened in diurnal animals, lengthened in nocturnal (see Aschoff, 1962).

For the circadian rhythm to function as a time-measuring device, it must be and is temperature independent; that is, it is unaffected by a normal range of temperatures. However, a 24-hour temperature cycle can entrain the circadian activity rhythm of some organisms. One is the lizard *Lacerta sicula*. When this animal was kept in a constant light and a sinusoidal 24-hour temperature cycle, its activity cycle became entrained to the one of temperature (Fig. 5-10). The phase of the entrained rhythm depended upon the free-running period that the individual animal exhibited under the constant conditions in which it was held immediately before or after exposure to the temperature cycle (Hoffman, 1963).

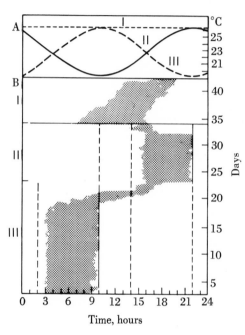

Figure 5-10 *Activity rhythm of a lizard* (Lacerta sicula) *held in constant conditions and in a 24-hour temperature cycle. (A) The temperature regimes under which the lizard was held; I, constant temperature; II, III, 24-hour temperature cycles. (B) Activity cycles of the lizard held under the three temperature regimes. The Roman numerals I, II, and III correspond to the temperature cycles in A. The broken vertical lines indicate the time of minimum temperatures; the solid line the maximum temperature. I: activity in constant temperature. Note the drift to the left. This drift was halted when the lizard was placed in temperature regime II. After a short stepwise rephasing to the right, the onset of activity became synchronized with the temperature minimum and was prevented from drifting forward by the delaying action of the temperature maximum. When the temperature cycle was reversed, in III, the lizard again became synchronized by a longer series of stepwise advances until the forward advance was stopped by the minimum temperatures. (Adapted from Hoffman, 1963.)*

Light and dark may be the *Zeitgebers* that control the phase of an organism's circadian activity rhythm, but the rhythms may relate more directly to other aspects of the environment, which, ecologically, are more significant to the organism than light and dark per se. The transition from day to night, for example, is accompanied by such environmental changes as a rise in humidity and a drop in temperature. Woodlice, centipedes, and millipedes, which lose water rapidly when exposed to dry air, spend the day in a fairly constant environment of darkness and dampness under stones, logs, and leaves. At dusk they emerge, when the humidity of the air is more favorable. In general, these animals show an increased tendency to escape from light as the length of time they spend in darkness increases. On the other hand, their intensity of response to low humidity decreases with darkness. Thus they come out at night into places too dry for them during the day; and as light comes they quickly retreat to their dark hiding places (Cloudsley-Thompson, 1956, 1960). Among some animals the biotic rather than the physical aspects of the environment may relate to the activity rhythm. Deer undisturbed by man may be active by day, but when they are hunted and disturbed they become strongly nocturnal. Predators must relate their feeding activity to the activity rhythm of the prey. Moths and bees must visit flowers when they are open and provide a source of food. And the flowers must have a rhythm of opening and closing that coincides with the time when the insects that pollinate them are flying. The entrainment of the phase of its activity rhythm to a natural light-dark cycle means more to an organism than simply an adjustment to a precise 24-hour period. More important, the entrainment serves to time the activities of plants and animals to a day-night cycle in a manner that is appropriate to the ecology of the species.

The possession of a circadian rhythm that can be entrained to environmental rhythms provides plants and animals with a biological clock, which probably is an integral part of cellular structure. With this, organisms can not only determine the time of day, they can also use the clock for time measurement. The clock, as already suggested, is not simply an hourglass or stop watch. It does not start on some given signal, such as dawn, run until stopped by another signal, such as darkness, and then start up again on another. The clock runs, or oscillates, continuously, but it must be regulated or reset by environmental signals. It is this latter characteristic of the clock that makes the 24-hour photoperiod possible. The environmental rhythm of daylight and dark is the signal by which the biological clock is set to the correct local time each day.

Time memory is another phenomenon in which the circadian rhythm is involved. Bees use the endogenous rhythm as an "alarm clock" to indicate successful feeding times at distant points. Sixty years ago the Swiss naturalist August Forel observed that bees visited his breakfast table every morning and fed on sweets. Each day they returned at the same time, even if no food were available. Other students of bees found that these insects visited buckwheat fields only in the morning hours when the blossoms secreted nectar. This activity has been verified experimentally. Honeybees trained to come to feeding stations baited with sugar water at one or two arbitrarily selected times of day will return at approximately the same time for a few following days, even if no food is provided. Thus bees can fix in their internal clock the time of day when feeding is successful. Bees retain this 24-hour time sense even when moved under constant light conditions from one time belt to another. Renner (1960) trained bees in Paris to feed from 8:15 to 10:15 P.M. French Daylight Time. These same bees were flown overnight to New York. In a test at New York the bees came to the feeding place at about 3 P.M., Eastern Daylight Time, or 24 hours after the last feeding in Paris. No bees appeared between 8:15 to 10:15 P.M., EDT. Since the above experiment was carried out in closed chambers with constant light and temperature, a similar experiment was carried out under field conditions. Bees on Long Island were trained to feed between 12:45 and 2:24 P.M., EST. After training was complete, the bees were flown to California. Here they sought food at 10 A.M., Pacific Standard Time, again 24 hours after their last feeding.

Celestial orientation

Some organisms, particularly arthropods, birds, and fish, utilize their time-sense ability as an aid to find their way from one area or region to another.

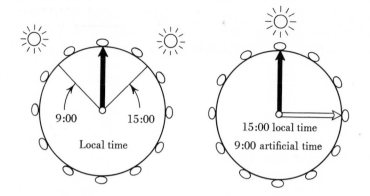

Figure 5-11 *Change of direction by a starling trained to feed from a dish oriented to the south. After the bird was held in an artificial day six hours behind local time for a period of 12 to 18 days, it was tested under natural sun at a time when its height was the same as to be expected under artificial condition. The orientation of the bird changed 90° clockwise from the training direction.* (Adapted from Hoffman, 1954).

To orient themselves, the animals use the sun (or in some cases the moon and the stars) as a compass. To do this, they utilize both their biological clock and observations on the azimuthal position of the sun in relation to an established direction. The azimuth is the angle between a fixed line on the earth's surface and a projection of the sun's direction on the suface. Using the sun as a reference point involves some problems for the animals since the sun moves. The target angle changes throughout the day. If the animal is to use the sun as a reference, it must be able to correct for the movement. This the animal seems to accomplish.

Hoffman (1959) trained starlings during natural daylight to a certain direction of the compass by feeding the birds at that position. Then he exposed the starlings to an artificial day-night cycle that began and ended six hours behind the natural one. The birds then searched for food 90 degrees to the right of the training direction (Fig. 5-11). Thus the birds were able to adjust for a change in time and sought the food by allowing for the change in the position of the sun. The birds continued to choose the direction they maintained in the artificial day, even when held under constant light and nearly constant temperature. This same ability also exists in fish (Braemer, 1959; Hasler, 1960), turtles (Carr, 1962), and lizards (Fischer, 1960), as well as in such invertebrates as bees (von Frisch, 1954), wolf spiders (Papi, 1955), and sand hoppers (Papi, Serretti, and Parrini, 1957).

For animals that migrate over great distances, the use of the sun compass must be further refined to compensate for the changes in azimuthal speed of the sun, which varies during the day according to the season and latitude. As the migrating animals pass rapidly from one region to another, they encounter changing day lengths with an increasing azimuthal angle speed around noon; and some eventually reach regions where the sun culminates in the north instead of the south. Exactly how the animals correct for these changes is unknown, but they may take into account the height of the sun and the rate of azimuthal change, together with a sense of time to estimate longitude (Matthews, 1955). How animals are able to navigate still remains unexplained; but one thing is fairly clear, the biological clock is involved.

Tidal rhythms

There are other environmental periodicities in addition to light and temperature with which the circadian rhythms of organisms can be synchronized. Some organisms that inhabit the intertidal zones of the sea show rhythms in their behavior that coincide with the cycles of high and low tide.

The European shore crab, *Carcinus maenas,* moves freely about in the littoral zone (see Chap. 12) at high tide. At low tide, the crab remains hidden under the rocks; but if the low tide comes at night, the crab moves about on shore.

The intertidal zone of the sandy beaches of southern California is inhabited by a small sand-beach amphipod, *Synchelidium,* which migrates up and down the shore with the changing tides. In the landward movement during rising tide, the amphipods are swept forward by the advancing waves and they bury

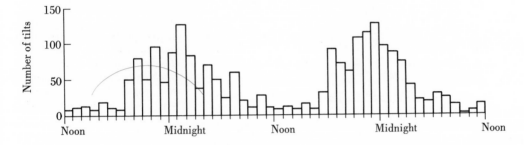

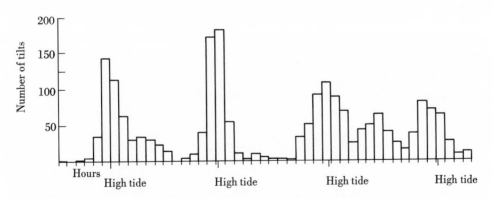

Figure 5-12 *Total activity for 15 European shore crabs,* Carcinus maenas, *collected on successive days over a semilunar period and each tested for 48 hours. Upper histogram shows total activity during each hour of the 48-hour periods, irrespective of times of high tide. Lower histogram shows total activity per hour plotted around the times of the four high tides, which occurred during each 48-hour period, irrespective of the time of day they occurred. (Redrawn from Naylor, 1958,* Jour. Experimental Biology, *35:606.)*

111

themselves in the sand. As the tide begins to ebb, the *Synchelidium* begin to swim in the water, which allows them to follow the waves back down the beach and avoid being stranded on the exposed sand.

When both of these animals are brought into the laboratory and held under constant conditions of light and temperature, their tidal rhythms persist for several days.

The crabs, freshly collected and held in the laboratory, showed bursts of intense activity around the time of high tide on the beach (Fig. 5-12) (Naylor, 1958). Even more interesting was the fact that the peaks of activity were greatest when the high tide outside occurred at night, while the lesser activity took place when high tide occurred during the day. When, during the period of observations, both high tides took place during the day and the low tide was at night,

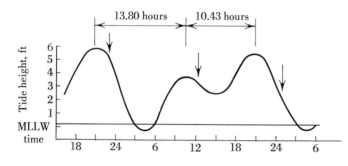

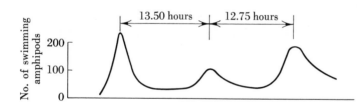

Figure 5-13 *Tidal rhythms of freshly collected amphipods based on counts of swimming amphipods during laboratory observations. Maximum activity took place shortly after the peak of high tide. Note how closely the peak of activity was synchronized with the irregular tidal rhythm. MLLW: mean lower low water.* (Adapted from Enright, 1963.)

a third nocturnal peak in locomotory activity appeared during low tide. This pattern suggests that two rhythms were involved, a tidal one with a periodicity of 12.4 hours superimposed on a normal 24-hour periodicity (Fig. 5-12). In fact when the crabs were held under a prolonged light-dark period in absence of tidal influences, the activity of the species showed a weak synchronization with light.

More complicated is the rhythmic activity of the *Synchelidium*. When this amphipod was brought into the laboratory and held under constant conditions, it showed two activity peaks (Fig. 5-13), one corresponding to each tidal crest (Enright, 1963). The fact that the tidal crests on the southern California coast are irregular and sometimes depart from the 12.4-hour tidal periodicity by as much as 3 hours makes this synchronization a rather remarkable one. The circadian or free-running rhythm in the laboratory is about 26 hours. Within three days the rhythm is completely damped. This tidal periodicity is also shared by three other intertidal crustaceans, the anomuran decapod *Emerita analoga,* the mystid *Archaeomysis maculata,* and the sand-beach isopod *Excirolana chiltoni.*

Since the timing and the intensity of the swimming activity of these crustaceans in the laboratory so closely followed the irregular tidal crests, the rhythm
had to be entrained in the field by some direct influence of the tides. What
the *Zeitgeber* might be was for a time unknown. Recent experimental work by
Enright (1965) with the isopod *Excirolana chiltoni* suggests that mechanical
stimulation, or the swirling of the animal by wave agitation, was the external
synchronizer for the entrainment of the crustacean's endogenous rhythm with
the tidal cycle. Mechanical stimulation was effective when a number of other
environmental cycles, including light-and-dark and submergence-and-exposure,
failed.

The survival advantage of such a rhythm is obvious. It is critical for these
animals to avoid being marooned on the beach between tides, for they would
die from desiccation. If the crustaceans, buried in the sand at high tide, began
to swim actively a few hours after the tide crested, they could follow the waves
back down the beach.

Lunar and semilunar reproductive cycles

Reproduction in some marine organisms is restricted to the time of spring
tides or to a period that bears some relation to these tides. These rhythmic
phenomena occur once every lunar cycle of 28 to 30 days or in some instances
once every semilunar cycle of 14 to 15 days. These rhythms assure that the
eggs and sperm of marine species are available at the same time and in the
same place.

Among some species these periodicities are so exact that they can be predicted far ahead of time. The grunion, a small, edible fish of California waters
that swarms in from the open sea to sandy beaches to lay its eggs, has a semilunar cycle. From February to September, grunion appear on the beaches at the
time of fortnightly high tides. The fish quickly dig pits in the sand, deposit
eggs and sperm in them, and return to the sea with the next wave that covers
them. The new generation develops in the warm, moist sand over a period
of about two weeks. Actually the time of development is about 10 days; but
since the eggs require mechanical agitation before hatching can take place,
young usually emerge at the time of the following high tide, every 12 to 14 days.

Another organism influenced by lunar periodicity is the Atlantic species of
Palolo worm, which lives in the crevices and burrows of rock and corals at
depths ranging up to 150 fathoms. The worms swarm by the millions on the
surface of the seas in summer, with most intense swarming taking place in
July. At this time the posterior half of the worms, laden with eggs and sperm,
swims to the top and releases the reproductive cells on the surface of the ocean.
Most swarms occur within five days of the third quarter of the moon and most
of the worms rupture at dawn (Clark, 1938).

That the phases of these endogenous rhythms may be controlled by moonlight has been suggested by the behavior of two marine organisms in the
laboratory. One of the marine polychaete worms, *Platynereis dumerili*, when
sexually mature, swarms for a few hours at the surface of the sea, spawns, and
dies. Maximum swarming of the Mediterranean population takes place between
the last and the first quarter of the moon (the Atlantic population swarms

113

fortnightly). Very few appear around the full moon. The other organism, the brown marine alga *Dictyota dichotoma,* releases eggs and sperm fortnightly in synchrony with the phases of the moon.

When these two, the worm and the alga, were held under natural-light conditions in the laboratory, they swarmed or released eggs and sperm as they would in the sea—in relation to the phases of the moon (Bünning and Müller, 1961).

By the use of artificial moonlight (illumination at night in the range of moonlight intensity—about 3 lux), several biologists have been able to demonstrate the correlation of swarming to the phases of the moon. When Hauenchild (1960) exposed *Platynereis* to constant artificial illumination, swarming was random throughout the lunar month. But if cultures of the worm were exposed to a 30-day illumination regime involving 24 days of 12 hours light and 12 hours dark each, followed by a 6-day period of constant illumination, maximum swarming occurred in relation to the time of the end of constant illumination. This induced periodicity was carried over through one more swarming without the use of any exogenous timer.

This relationship of reproduction to lunar rhythm is even more pronounced in the brown alga *Dictyota dichotoma.* The maximum discharge of eggs takes place 9 days after exposure to moonlight (Bünning and Müller, 1961). When this alga was held under a constant period of 14 hours of light and 10 hours of darkness, it continued to liberate eggs every 16 days. When artificial moonlight was offered during the dark periods even for one night, the next period of spawning appeared 9 days after the "moonlight," followed by another endogenous cycle of 15 to 16 days. Thus the phasing of the rhythm appears to be determined by moonlight.

To such marine organisms as these, this endogenous rhythm assures that reproductive activities, especially the release of eggs and sperm, will take place at the same time and in the same place, even if the moon should remain hidden for several months behind an overcast sky. In addition, the lunar cycle can adjust reproductive activities to spring tides and neap tides and restrict reproduction to certain times of the year and even to some restricted time of day.

Annual rhythms

As the seasons turn, the daily periods of daylight and darkness change. The activities of plants and animals are geared to this seasonal rhythm of night and day. The flying squirrel starts its daily activity with nightfall and maintains this relation through the year. As the short days of winter turn to the longer days of spring, the squirrel begins its activity a little later each day (Fig. 5-14). The commencement of bird song follows the dawn, but not until the light reaches a certain intensity, which varies with the species (Fig. 5-15).

The song of birds is associated with the reproductive cycle, which also follows a seasonal pattern. For most birds the height of the breeding season is spring; for the deer the mating season is the fall. Brook trout spawn in the fall; bass and bluegills in late spring and summer. The trilliums and violets bloom in the short days of early spring before the forest leaves are out and

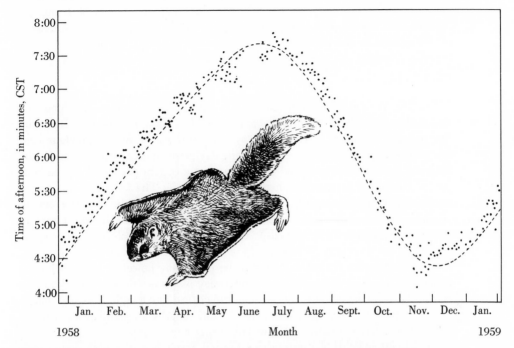

Figure 5-14 *Onset of running-wheel activity for one flying squirrel in natural daylight conditions throughout the year. The graph is the time of local sunset through the year. The open circles indicate the beginning of activity in clear-to-partly-cloudy skies; the solid indicate activity with 80 per cent of the sky overcast.* (With permission from DeCoursey, 1960, *Cold Spring Harbor Symposia in Quantitative Biology*, 25:50.)

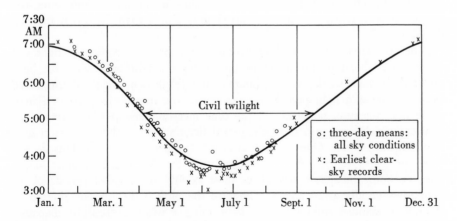

Figure 5-15 *Daybreak song of the cardinal from February 26, 1944, to April 20, 1948, in relation to the beginning of civil twilight.* (From Leopold and Eynon, 1961.)

while an abundance of sunlight reaches the forest floor. Asters and goldenrods flower in the shortening days of fall. Most animals and plants of temperate regions have reproductive periods that closely follow the changing day lengths of the seasons, or the photoperiod.

Photoperiodism in plants and animals

Based on photoperiodic responses, plants can be classed as short-day, long-day, and day-neutral. Day-neutral plants are those whose flowering is not affected by day length but rather is controlled by age, number of nodes, previous cold treatment, and the like. Short-day and long-day plants both are influenced by the length of day. When the period of light reaches a certain portion of the 24-hour day, it inhibits or promotes a photoperiodic response. The length of this period so decisive to the response is called the critical day length. It varies among organisms but usually falls somewhere between 10 and 14 hours. Throughout the year plants (and animals) "compare" this time scale with the actual length of day or night. As soon as the actual length of day or night is greater or smaller than the critical day length, the plant may flower or cease to flower, expand its leaves, lengthen its shoots. Short-day plants are those whose flowering is stimulated by day lengths shorter than the critical day length. Long-day plants are those whose flowering is stimulated by day lengths longer than a particular value. These latter usually bloom in late spring and summer.

In the cotton fields of the southern United States lives the pink cotton bollworm, the larva of a tiny moth. Except for a few hours directly after hatching, the larva spends its life in the flower buds or bolls of cotton. At the fourth larval instar stage, the insect goes into *diapause,* a stage of arrested growth over winter. The onset of diapause comes in late August; but not until near the autumnal equinox, September 21, when the night becomes equal to or longer than the day, does the number of diapausing larvae sharply increase. By the end of October virtually all the larvae are in diapause. Through the winter, the larvae remain in this state of arrested development; then in late winter, as the days begin to lengthen, the insect comes out of diapause and continues its growth. The emergence from diapause reaches its maximum just after the spring equinox, when the days are just slightly longer than those that induced diapause.

When the larvae of the pink bollworm were exposed to regimes of light and dark in the laboratory, the insect would go into diapause only when the light phase of the 24-hour day was 13 hours or less (Adkisson, 1964). If the larvae were exposed to a light period of 13.25 hours, the insect was prevented from going into diapause. So precise is the time measurement in the insect that a quarter-hour difference in the light period determines whether the insect goes into diapause or not. Once growth is arrested, the exogenous rhythms do not cease but continue through the diapause until the day length becomes longer than 13 hours. Diapause terminates most rapidly under photoperiods of 14 hours, less rapidly at 16 and 12. Thus to the pink bollworm, the shortening days of late summer and fall forecast the coming of winter and call for diapause; and the lengthening days of late winter and early spring are the signals for the insect to resume development, pupate, emerge as an adult, and reproduce more of its own kind.

116

That increasing day length increases gonadal development and spring migratory behavior in birds was experimentally demonstrated some 40 years ago when Rowan (1925, 1929) forced juncos into the reproductive stage out of season by artificial increases in day length. Results of subsequent experimental work with a number of species have shown that the reproductive cycle is under the control of an exogenous seasonal rhythm of changing day lengths and an endogenous physiological response timed by a circadian rhythm.

After the breeding season, the gonads of birds studied to date have been found to regress spontaneously. This is the *refractory* period, a time when light cannot induce gonadal activity, the duration of which is regulated by day length (see Farner, 1959, 1964; Wolfson, 1959, 1960). Short days hasten the termination of the refractory period; long days prolong it. Birds held on long days beginning in the fall fail to show any response to day length in the spring. During the period of refraction, the sensitivity of birds to light is restored; they are being "prepared" to respond to some subsequent photoperiod treatment. Since long days inhibit the refractory or preparatory period, the short days actually regulate the appearance of migratory and reproductive behavior half a year later. After the refractory phase is completed, in about six weeks of short days and long nights, the *progressive* phase begins, in late fall and winter. During this period the birds fatten, they migrate, and their reproductive organs increase in size. This process can be speeded up by exposing the bird to a long-day photoperiod. Completion of the progressive stage brings the bird into the *reproductive* stage.

A similar photoperiodic response exists in the cyprinid fish, the minnows. The annual sexual cycle among the minnows consists of a sexually inactive period, followed by the reproductive period (Harrington, 1959). Underlying this is an intrinsic sexual rhythm that consists of a long responsive period, alternating with a shorter refractory period. Long days occurring within the responsive period start the prespawning period, characterized by mating and territorial behavior. The prespawning period ends with the laying of the first eggs. The subsequent spawning period is consummatory and ends sometime before the days shorten to the critical length that initiated the prespawning activity. Following this is the refractory, or postspawning period, in which light fails to stimulate gonadal development. The prespawning period, from about mid-November to mid-July, is the phase in which the annual sexual period is timed.

The food-storing behavior of the flying squirrel in fall appears to be photoperiodically controlled (Muul, 1965). Squirrels held in the laboratory under seasonal photoperiods and controlled constant temperature exhibited an intensity of food storing similar to that of animals held under natural conditions. Squirrels exposed to seasonal temperatures and a controlled photoperiod of 15 hours of daylight showed no intense food-storage activity through the winter. When the light was reduced to 12 hours in March, there was a marked rise in food storage. Another group was held under constant temperature and a controlled photoperiod of 15 hours of daylight, which was reduced to 13 hours in mid-December. Within a week this group increased food-storage activity sharply and continued it from January through March. In still another experiment, the squirrels were subjected in mid-October to a photoperiod typical of mid-November. The intensity of food storage increased more rapidly than normal and reached an equivalent of that of mid-November under natural conditions. Further de-

117

creases in the length of day increased the performance of squirrels. By the beginning of November, when the squirrels were subject to a photoperiod equivalent to that of late December, the storage peak was maximum. Immediately a long day of 15 hours of light and 9 hours of dark, equivalent to midsummer conditions, was imposed on the squirrels. Some squirrels showed a sudden decrease in storage intensity; others showed a gradual decrease. But among the squirrels held under natural conditions, storage of food was still increasing (Fig. 5-16). These experiments demonstrate that the food-storage activity of the flying squirrel is photoperiodically controlled. Such a control synchronizes exploratory and storing behavior with a ripening of the mast crop—nuts and acorns—and prevents a premature harvest.

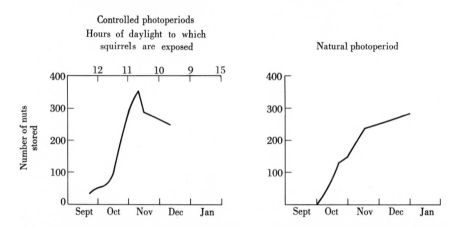

Figure 5-16 *Food-storage activity of flying squirrels held under controlled photoperiod compared to natural photoperiod.* (Redrawn by permission from L. Muul. 1965. *Natural History Magazine,* 64(3): 26.)

The lives of other mammals undoubtedly are under a similar photoperiodic control. The growth of antlers and the rise and decline of sexual activity in the white-tailed deer follow a seasonal rhythm (Fig. 5-17). Mating occurs in the fall, the fawns are born in the spring when the food supply is abundant for mother and young.

Physiological mechanisms: the Bünning model

The photoperiodic responses of plants and animals are not dependent upon the length of day as such, nor even on the length of night. Instead, what seems to be involved is a circadian rhythm of sensitivity to light as the inducing or inhibiting agent. Current experimental evidence suggests that a time-measuring process starts at the beginning of the light period or the beginning of the dark. This induces, after a certain length of time from the beginning of light or dark, a sensitive stage that responds specifically to light.

When plants are held under short-day and long-night conditions, the short-day plants are stimulated to flower, and the long-day plants are inhibited. When day length is increased, flowering is inhibited in the short-day and stimulated in

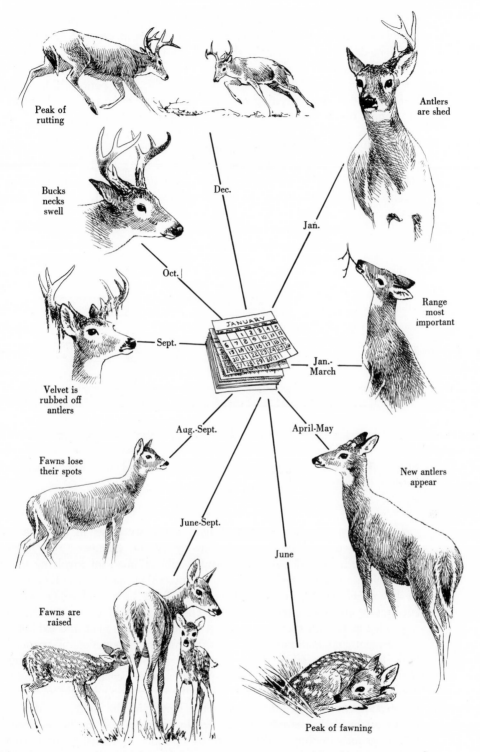

Peak of
rutting

Antlers
are shed

Bucks
necks
swell

Dec.

Jan.

Oct.

Sept.

Range
most
important

Velvet is
rubbed off
antlers

Jan.-
March

Aug.-Sept.

April-May

Fawns lose
their spots

New antlers
appear

June-Sept.

June

Fawns are
raised

Peak of fawning

Figure 5-17 *The seasonal cycle of the white-tailed deer, which begins with the breeding season in the fall. The annual breeding cycle of the white-tailed deer is attuned to the decreasing day length of fall.*

119

the long-day plants (Fig. 5-18). If the dark period of the short-day and long-day plant is interrupted, each reacts as if it had been exposed to a long day. The long-day plant flowers; the short-day plant does not.

Similar response occurs in animals. The diapause of insects, a short-day phenomenon, is inhibited by light breaks in the dark period (Bünning and Jaerrens, 1960). The breeding period of the ferret can be initiated by exposing the animal to 12 hours of light each day for a month if one hour of light is given from midnight to one o'clock (Hart, 1951). This contrasts with 18 hours of light required daily if the animal is exposed to light in a continuous period. In fact, 6 hours of light are sufficient to bring the ferret into breeding condition if the cycle includes 4 hours of continuous light and 20 hours of darkness interrupted between the seventeenth and nineteenth hours (Hammond, 1953).

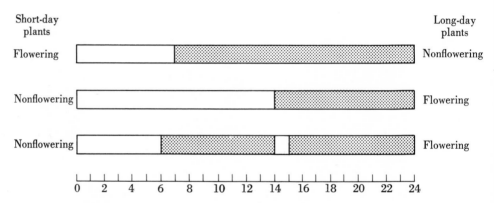

Figure 5-18 *The time of flowering in long-day and short-day plants, as influenced by photoperiod.*

That such a circadian rhythm of light sensitivity exists in birds has been demonstrated in a series of experiments by W. H. Hamner (1963). House finches were held under six experimental light regimes, all involving 6 hours of daylight: short-day cycles of 24 hours (6L/18D), 48 hours (6L/42D), and 72 hours (6L/66D); and long-day cycles of 12 hours (6L/6D), 36 hours (6L/30D), and 60 hours (6L/54D). The finches held under the first three responded as though they had received a short-day treatment and exhibited no enlargement and maturation of the testes and no production of sperm. The birds held on the other three treatments responded as if under long-day conditions. The testes enlarged and spermatogenesis began. Since all the birds were subject to the same length of light but to varying lengths of darkness, the experiments showed that neither the length of the light period nor the length of the dark was critical. The results indicate that the house finch has an endogenous rhythm with a periodicity of about 24 hours. During the long dark period the birds endogenously reached light-sensitive states about 24 hours apart. When light is given at the proper phase of the rhythm, gonadal enlargement and maturation take place, but when light is given at the light-

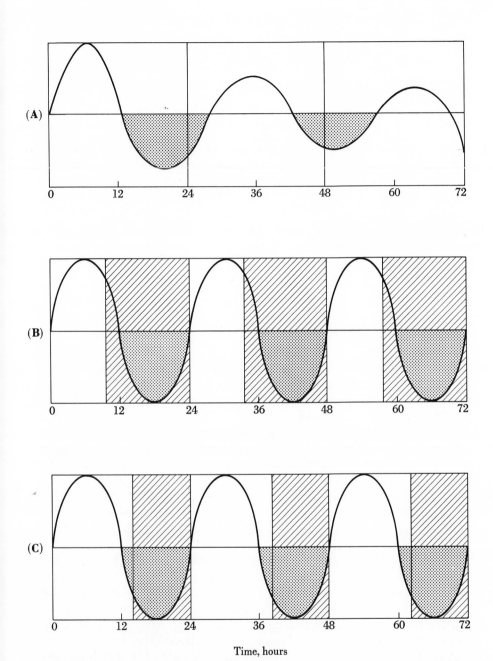

Figure 5-19 *The Bünning model. Oscillations of the clock cause an alternation of half cycles with quantitatively different sensitivities to light (white versus black). (A) The free-running clock in continuous light or continuous darkness tends to drift out of phase with the 24-hour photoperiod. (B) The short day. (C) The long day. Short-day conditions allow the dark to fall into the white half-cycle; in the long day, the light falls into the black half-cycle. (Redrawn by permission from Bünning, 1960, Cold Spring Harbor Symposia in Quantitative Biology, 25:253.)*

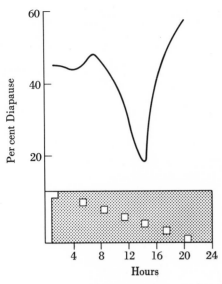

Figure 5-20 *Effects of light offered in the first half and second half cycle of about 12 hours each in* Pieris brassicae. *Additional light of one hour promotes diapause in this cabbage butterfly if offered during the first half of the cycle, but inhibits diapause during the second half of the cycle. Diapause is a short-day response.* (Adapted from Bünning and Joerrens, 1960.)

insensitive phase of the rhythm, no response occurred. Thus photoperiod-controlled reproductive cycles of birds are timed by a circadian rhythm of light sensitivity.

How this rhythm of light sensitivity in plants and animals might function is suggested in a hypothesis advanced by Dr. Edwin Bünning of Germany to explain the short-day and long-day reactions of plants. According to the Bünning model (Fig. 5-19), the circadian rhythm of light sensitivity goes through at least two half cycles of more or less opposite sensitivity to light: a tension or photophil phase, in which development is favored by light, and a relaxation or scotophil phase, in which development is inhibited. Each phase of the rhythm is about 12 hours long, but to function, the light phase must precede the dark. Short-day plants are considered scotophil in the second half of the cycle; if exposed to light at that time, their flowering is inhibited (Fig. 5-18). In the same half cycle, long-day plants are photophil; their flowering is stimulated. In addition, light sensitivity itself is rhythmic and seems to fluctuate in half cycles within the light and dark periods. There is a time of maximum sensitivity during the dark (Fig. 5-20), which in some organisms is about 14 to 16 hours from the beginning of the main light period. In the flying squirrel the sensitive periods are at the beginning of the subjective night and at subjective dawn (DeCoursey, 1960). Light exerts its maximum effect in the pink bollworm either 10 hours after dark or 10 hours before dawn (Adkisson, 1964). Additional light offered a few hours after the beginning of the light period has a stimulatory effect on the flowering of short-day plants (Bünning, 1964). Among many organisms the beginning of the previous light period may have a stronger influence on the timing of the point of maximum sensitivity than the beginning of the dark. At any rate both light and dark periods of a certain duration are required for a proper response. These rhythms in light sensitivity are endogenous. Light controls or sets the biological clock, and the clock in turn controls the light sensitivity of the organism. The responses of the organism are mediated by hormones. Exactly how the hormonal systems function in periodism is the subject of much current research. A discussion of this is beyond the scope of this book. It lies instead in works on endocrinology.

Some other aspects of periodicity

Seasonal periodicities in addition to activity also exist in the lives of plants and animals. Annual coloration of leaves in fall is a seasonal response brought on within the leaf by chemical changes. Animal coloration is influenced by photo-period. The summer coat of the snowshoe hare is brown; in winter it is white. The white hair makes the animal inconspicuous against the snow and may aid the hare to escape detection by predators (Fig. 5-21). Seasonal changes in light indirectly affect the food habits of animals, since the availability is directly related to the activity and reproductive cycle of prey species, and the flowering and fruiting of plants (Fig. 5-22).

The endogenous rhythms considered so far are ones that are correlated with the environment; there are also endogenous rhythms that are not so synchronized. Often these are temperature dependent and speed up their frequencies with in-creasing temperatures. Among such rhythms are the beating of the heart, the respiratory rate, and the transmission of nervous impulses. The timing of these rhythms involves internal feedback. The respiratory rate, for example, increases

Figure 5-21 *The white color of the snowshoe hare in winter and the brown color in summer are regulated by changing day length. As the nights lengthen and the days shorten, the pelage changes from brown to white, regardless of snow conditions or temperature.* (Photo courtesy Pennsylvania Game Commission.)

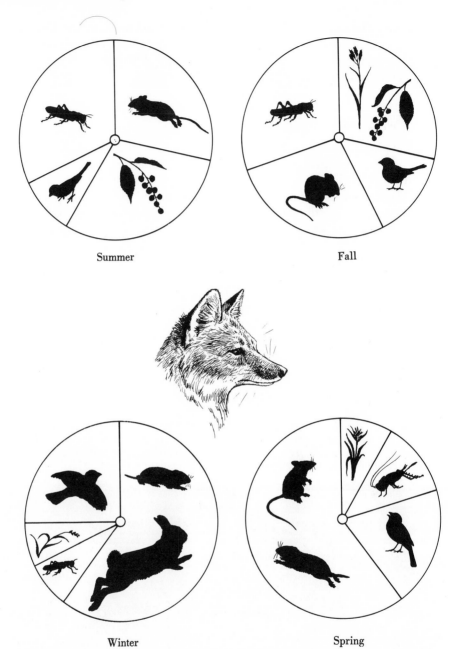

Figure 5-22 *The food habits of many animals, such as the red fox, are influenced by seasonal periodicities. The timing of flowering and the onset of breeding activities of animals influence the availability of foods through the year. Note the prominence of fruits and insects in summer and fall, and rodents in fall and winter. (Based on data from Scott, 1955.)*

as the level of the carbon-dioxide content of the blood increases, the information being fed to the lungs by way of the central nervous system.

Circadian rhythms in man

This discussion of circadian rhythms and periodicity in plants and animals brings up the question: What about man? Man, in common with other animals, possesses his circadian rhythms (see Aschoff, 1965; Sollberger, 1965). Some of these endogenous rhythms are influenced by man's activities and the imposition of his will. Others show up as truly circadian, the peak coming about once every 24 hours. Volunteer subjects kept without timepieces, in complete isolation from the outside world but allowed to set their own rhythms of eating and sleeping, of lights on and lights off, showed circadian rhythms in the calcium and potassium contents and volume of urine excretion, in body temperature, and in sleep and wakefulness. These rhythms ranged from 23.6 hours to 25.8 hours, with an average period of about 25 hours. In absence of any time cues, these rhythms showed a steady drift against clock time. Since man is a diurnal animal, the peaks of many of his endogenous rhythms come during the day. If his activity cycle is shifted to night, man in general is less efficient and may suffer psychologically and physiologically. He will live in a conflict situation between two tendencies in the circadian rhythm: to remain in phase with the normal environment as entrained by social *Zeitgebers* or to shift to a new work-rest cycle. The arrival of the jet and space age throw new complications into the system. Space travel can require days and weeks of short work-rest schedules under abnormal day-night situations within one 24-hour period, when astronauts pass from dark to light on every orbit of the earth. Jet trips around the world mean that the traveler for a few days will be out of rhythm with local time. A jet trip from New York to Paris or Paris to New York will put the passenger out of phase with local time by about six hours. Entrainment to new local time requires about two to three days, during which the traveler may experience periods of sleeplessness and hunger out of phase with local social environment. As man shortens travel time between distant points in the world and as he invades outer space, he will have to take his endogenous circadian rhythms into account.

SUMMARY

An almost universal feature of plants and animals is an internal physiological or biological clock, whose basic structure is probably chemical and is involved in the makeup of the cell. It is free running under constant conditions, with an oscillation or fluctuation that has its own inherent frequency. For most organisms, the inherited clock deviates more or less from 24 hours. Under natural conditions this clock is set or entrained to 24 hours by external time cues, or *Zeitgebers,* which synchronize the activity of plants and animals with the environment. Since the most dependable external time setter is light and dark—day and night—most of the selected species studied so far are entrained to a 24-hour photoperiod. The onset and cessation of activity are usually synchronized with dark and dawn, the response depending upon whether the organisms are diurnal (light active) or nocturnal (dark active). The biological clock is useful not only as a means to synchronize the daily activities of plants and animals with night and day, consistent with the ecology of the species, but also to time the activities with the seasons of the year. The possession of a self-sustained rhythm with approximately the same frequency as that of environmental rhythms enables organisms to "predict" such advance situations as the coming of spring. It brings plants and animals into a reproductive state at a time of year when the probability for the survival of offspring is the highest; it synchronizes within a population such activities as mating and migration, dormancy and flowering. The acquisition and refinement of a physiological timekeeper, geared to *Zeitgebers* that provide organisms with distinct and species-specific or population-specific synchronization with the environment, are a result of natural selection. The secrets of the clock, an understanding of how it works and where it resides in the organism, have yet to be discovered.

CHAPTER 6

Succession

$\mathbf{A}$bandoned cropland is a common sight in agricultural regions, particularly in areas once covered with forests. No longer tended, the lands grow up in grasses, goldenrod, and other herbaceous plants. Only the most unobservant would fail to notice that in a few years these same weedy fields are invaded by "brush"—blackberries, sumac, and hawthorns, followed by fire cherry, pine, and aspen. Many years later this abandoned cropland supports a forest of maple, hickory, oaks, or pines. Thus over a period of years, one community replaced another until a relatively stable forest finally occupies the area (Fig. 6-1 a and b).

The changes involved in the return of the forest were not haphazard, but orderly, and barring disturbance by man or natural events, the reappearance of the forest was predictable. This orderly and progressive replacement of one community by another until a relatively stable community occupies the area is called *ecological succession*. The whole series of communities, from grass to shrub to forest, that terminate in a final stable community is called a *sere*, and each of the changes that take place is a *seral stage*. Each seral stage is a community, although temporary, with its own characteristics, and it may remain for a very short time or for many years. Some stages may be completely missed or

A

B

C

D

Figure 6-1 *Successional changes in an old field over 20 years. (A) The field as it appeared in 1942, when it was moderately grazed. (B) The same area as it appeared in 1963. (C) A close view of the rail fence in the left background of A. (D) The same area 20 years later. The rail fence has rotted away and white pine and aspen grow in the area. (Photos by the author.)*

bypassed. This happens when old fields grow up immediately into forest trees, but even in these situations the young trees form a sort of shrub community.

The succession that took place on the old field is called *secondary*, since it proceeded from a state in which other organisms already were present. Secondary succession arises on areas disturbed by man, animals, or natural forces such as fires, wind storms, and floods. Its development may be controlled or influenced by the activities of man or animals, domestic or wild. Succession that takes place

128

on areas devoid or unchanged by organisms is called *primary* (Fig. 6-2).

The nature of succession

The idea of vegetational change is not recent. The fact that one aggregation of plants eventually is replaced by another has been noted for many years (see Spurr, 1952). Back in 1863 Anton Kerner described in a fascinating book, *Plant Life of the Danube Basin,* the formation of meadow from swamp, forest regeneration, and the forest edge, and he explained the "genetical relationship of plant formations," as he called succession. Within the pages of this old book lay the field of plant sociology in an embryonic state. In America, Thoreau knew about succession and wrote about it. Then in 1899 Cowles published his classic description of plant succession on the sand dunes of Lake Michigan. Sixteen years later, the pioneer plant ecologist, Frederick Clements, published a book, *Plant Succession,* which became the foundation of a system of studying and describing plant communities that colors ecological thinking today.

Succession is characterized by progressive changes in species structure, in organic structure, and in energy flow. It involves a gradual and continuous replacement of one kind of plant and animal by another, until the community itself is replaced by another that is more complex. In the early stages of succession, dominants may replace one another from year to year, and the number of species and often individuals increases. If the density of species is plotted against time, a sort of step diagram results. Later, changes in species structure take place more gradually. Since some have wider tolerances or occupy more generalized niches, they may persist over a longer period of time (Fig. 6-3). At the same time species diversity increases, initially at least, and then becomes stabilized in terms of functional groups (such as herbivores); or it may decline in older stages, as it does in the conifer plantation. This, however, does not mean

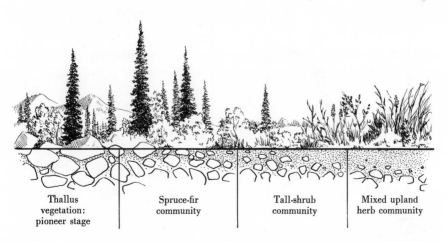

| Thallus vegetation: pioneer stage | Spruce-fir community | Tall-shrub community | Mixed upland herb community |

Figure 6-2 *Primary succession in the subalpine zone in the Wasatch Mountains, Utah. Here the early stage includes the trees, while the climax is a mixed herb community. Note the changes in soil depth from a rocky surface with fine soil only in crevices to a well-defined solum essentially free from rocks. (Based on data from Ellison, 1954.)*

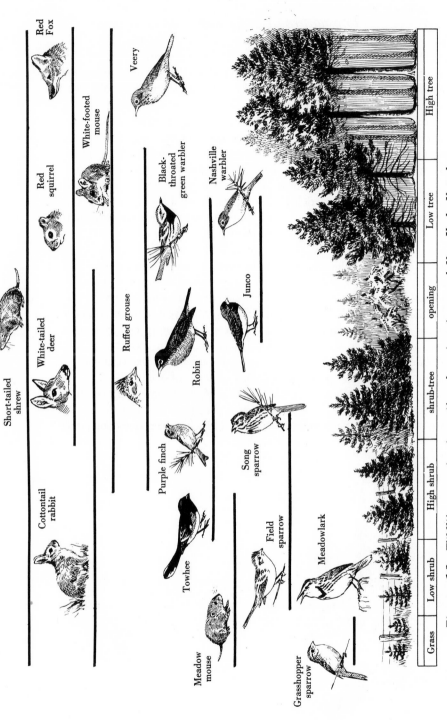

Figure 6-3 *Wildlife succession in conifer plantations in central New York. Note how some species appear and others disappear as vegetation density and height changes. Other species are common to all stages.*

Grass	Low shrub	High shrub	shrub-tree	opening	Low tree	High tree

Red Fox

Veery

White-footed mouse

Red squirrel

Black-throated green warbler

Nashville warbler

Short-tailed shrew

White-tailed deer

Ruffed grouse

Robin

Junco

Cottontail rabbit

Purple finch

Song sparrow

Towhee

Field sparrow

Meadowlark

Meadow mouse

Grasshopper sparrow

that the species diversity in any one taxonomic group increases with succession, although this occasionally happens (for example, the predominance of warblers in a coniferous forest community). Some insect groups, such as the grasshoppers, exhibit their largest species diversity as a taxonomic unit in the earlier stages. The increase in functional species diversity in later stages reflects an increase in niches brought about by increased stratification and zonation.

Accompanying these changes in species structure and diversity is an increase in biomass and organic-matter accumulation. The fertility of the soil and water increases, more elements are utilized, autotrophs increase both in coverage and mass and in turn are able to support a greater biomass of heterotrophs. The increases in the amount and the change in organic structure bring such a change in the environmental biochemical conditions that species better adapted to the changing environment replace those already on the site.

The change in species structure and organic accumulation is not necessarily accompanied by an increase in production, as is often inferred. On primary sites gross production necessarily increases during the early phases of succession, but gross production increases little in secondary succession. Production in early seral stages in Georgia was 1 to 3 grams per square meter per day, approximately the same as that for wheat, corn, oats, and natural grassland (Odum, 1960). Succession apparently consists of a series of temporary steady states of production, each associated with a major life form. This new steady state appears to be maintained at each stage, even though the species composition is gradually changing. The reason apparently is that maximum productivity of broadleaf plants is achieved when the leaf surface area exposed to incoming light is about four to five times that of the surface area of the ground. Any increase beyond this does not appear to increase photosynthetic rates, in part because of shading. As succession progresses, net community production decreases and community respiration increases. In other words, the ratio of production to respiration starts out as $P > R$ and eventually arrives at equilibrium, $P = R$.

Aquatic succession

The development of a pond into a mesic forest can be observed in a limited area, often about one pond alone. The first step in succession is the *pioneer stage,* characterized by a bottom barren of plant life. Such a stage can be found in newly formed, man-made ponds and lakes. The earliest forms of life to colonize the area are plankton, which may become so dense as to cloud the water. This plankton consists of microscopic algae and animal life, which upon death settle to the bottom to form a layer of muck.

If the plankton growth becomes rich enough, the pond may support other forms of life—bluegills, green sunfish, and largemouth bass, and small caddisflies that build cases of sand and feed on microorganisms living on the bottom.

The developing layer of loose, oozy material on the pond bottom creates a substrate for rooted aquatics, such as the branching green alga, *Chara,* the pondweeds and waterweeds (Fig. 6-4). These plants bind the loose bottom sediment into a firmer matrix and add materially to the deposition of bottom organic matter. Organisms common to the barren pond bottom cannot exist in the changed conditions of the submerged vegetation stage. The caddisflies of

131

the pioneering stage are replaced by other species able to creep over submerged vegetation and build cases from plant material. Dragonflies, mayflies, and small crustaceans appear.

Rapid addition of organic matter on the bottom reduces water depth and provides nutrients for more demanding plants. Floating aquatics, roots embedded in the bottom muck and leaves floating on the water's surface, invade the pond. Since these plants shut out the light from the pond depths, they tend to eliminate the submerged aquatic growth. This is the *floating-aquatics stage*, one in which living space is increased and diversified. Hydras, frogs, diving beetles, and a host of new insects capable of utilizing the undersurfaces of floating leaves appear.

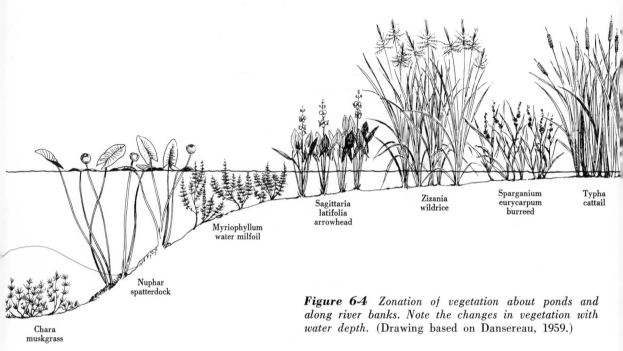

Sagittaria latifolia arrowhead

Myriophyllum water milfoil

Zizania wildrice

Sparganium eurycarpum burreed

Typha cattail

Nuphar spatterdock

Chara muskgrass

Figure 6-4 Zonation of vegetation about ponds and along river banks. Note the changes in vegetation with water depth. (Drawing based on Dansereau, 1959.)

Seasonal fluctuations in water levels alternately expose and cover the increasingly shallow bottom about the edge of the pond. Lacking the bouyancy and protection of water, the weak and soft-tissued floating plants cannot exist in the changing environment. Emergent plants—the cattails, sedges, bulrushes, and arrowheads, firmly anchored in the bottom muck by spreading fibrous roots and rhizomes—occupy the area. Since the leaves rise above and lack the protection of water, they possess flexible leaves and wandlike stems that bend easily before the wind and water. Animals of the floating stage are replaced by those that inhabit the jungle of emergent plant stems. Gill-breathing snails give way to the lung breathers. Different species of mayflies and dragonflies spend their nymphal stages on submerged stems and climb to the surface when they are ready to emerge as adults. Red-winged blackbirds, ducks, and muskrats become common to the area. As the oxygen supply of the water decreases, because of the increasing quantities removed through respiration by organisms of decay breaking down the accumulating organic matter, only animals with low oxygen requirements can exist. Bullheads replace sunfish and annelid worms colonize the bottom muck.

Since the dense root system and the annual deposition of leaf growth add great quantities of organic matter to the bottom, the substrate builds up rapidly after the emergents have appeared. Much of the old open-water area now is covered by sedges, cattails, and associated plants to form a *marsh*. As the bottom rises above the ground water level, the remnant of the open pond dries up in summer. It has now become a *temporary pond,* which contains only those organisms that can withstand drying in summer and freezing in winter.

Drainage improves as the land builds higher. The emergents disappear, the soil lies exposed above the water table, and organic matter, exposed to the air, decomposes more rapidly. Meadow grasses, accompanied by land animals, invade to form a marsh meadow in forested regions and a prairie in the grass country. In forested areas and in certain topographical situations between the prairie and the forest, alders, willows, and buttonbushes colonize the site. If the marsh is invaded directly by woody plants, the marsh-meadow stage never develops. Shrubs give way to trees—aspen, elm, red and silver maples, and white pine. Root systems, limited by high water tables, spread horizontally instead of vertically in the soil. The substrate is rapidly but unevenly built up by the accumulation of fallen trunks and by upturned roots and soil. As the forest floor becomes drier and the crown closes, seedlings of intolerant forest trees are unable to develop; but seedlings of sugar maple, beech, hemlock, spruce, and cedar, able to grow in low light intensities, dominate the understory and subsequently replace the intolerant trees. Since these trees tolerate the environmental conditions they create, the forest cover becomes stabilized.

Terrestrial succession

A similar sequence takes place on dry areas. Barren areas, whether they are natural primary sites, such as rock and sand dunes, or disturbed areas, such as abandoned cultivated fields or roadbanks, are a sort of natural vacuum eventually to be filled by living organisms. The plants and animals that colonize such sites comprise the pioneer communities. On primary sites no soil exists initially and successive communities can become more complex only as soils develop. Bare, disturbed areas, the secondary sites, have some sort of soil present already. Both, however, are characterized by full exposure to the sun, violent fluctuations in temperature, and rapid changes in moisture conditions.

Primary succession

Rocks and cliffs are common terrestrial primary sites. Bare rocks, on fully exposed cliffs and slopes, are colonized by crustose lichens, such as the widespread gray-green *Parmelia conspersa* and the black moss, *Grimmia. Cladonia* lichens may invade mats of black moss, followed by the hair-cap moss *Polytrichium,* or even vascular plants and grass (Oosting and Anderson, 1937, 1939). As yet there is no evidence that lichens either modify the rock or aid in the accumulation of fine soil or organic matter that can be colonized by other plants. As long as conditions are such that soil or organic debris cannot accumulate from some external source, crustose lichens and a few mosses persist indefinitely.

Wherever some soil has accumulated in crevices, recesses, and depressions, plants can take root. Usually these are a chance assortment of adapted species from the surrounding countryside plus a few distinctive rock species. From such areas a thin soil mat may spread outward and eventually cover the bare rock surface, but on more exposed sites the destructive forces of wind and water tear away the soil and plant cover and expose bare rock again. In soil pockets and crevices where the soil is deeper, woody plants become established.

The sand dune is another severe primary site. A product of pulverized rock, sand is deposited by wind and water. Where deposits are extensive, as along the shores of lakes and oceans and on inland sand barrens, sand particles may be piled up in long windward slopes to form dunes (Fig. 6-5) that move before the wind and often cover forests and buildings in their path, until stabilized by plants. With high surface temperatures by day and cold temperatures at night, dunes are rigorous environments for life to colonize. Grasses are the most successful pioneer and binding plants. When these, and such associated plants as beach pea, have stabilized the dunes, at least partly, mat-forming shrubs invade the area.

From this point, the vegetation may pass from pine to oak, or to oak directly, without an intervening pine stage. The low fertility of the dunes favors plants with low nutrient requirements. Since these plants are inefficient in cycling nutrients, especially calcium, soil fertility remains low. Because of this infertility and the low moisture reserves in the sand, oak is rarely replaced by more mesophytic and more nutrient-demanding trees (Olson, 1958). Only on the more favorable leeward slopes and in depressions where the microclimate is more moderate and where moisture can accumulate does succession lead to a mesophytic growth of such trees as sugar maple, basswood, and red oak. Because these trees recycle nutrients more efficiently, effectively shade the soil, and add to litter accumulation, they aid in the rapid improvement of nutrient and moisture conditions. On such sites a mesophytic forest may become established without going through the pine and oak stages (Olson, 1958).

Deposits left by receding glaciers also are often nutrient-poor sites. In Alaska, newly exposed raw glacial till is invaded first by mountain avens (*Dryas*), whose feathery seeds are carried to the site by the wind (Lawrence, 1958). Tolerant of adverse environmental conditions present there, the avens seeds germinate quickly to form a horizontal evergreen mat, green in spring and red bronze in fall. This mat reduces soil erosion and begins to build up organic matter. Mountain avens is followed closely by Sitka alder, a rapidly growing, upright shrub, capable of reproducing abundantly by seven years of age. Willow and cottonwood seedlings also appear, but on the nitrogen-impoverished soil they grow only as prostrate plants with yellowish leaves. But the alders, and to some extent the avens, possess in their roots large nodules of nitrogen-fixing bacteria, and nitrogen compounds fixed in alder roots leak out into the soil. Alder leaves, in which nitrogen constitutes up to three per cent of their dry weight, add considerably more of this nutrient to the soil. In fact alder thickets five years old and five feet tall add to the soil each autumn 140 pounds of nitrogen per acre, an amount which increases as the thicket grows older. Since the rate of nitrogen accumulation is high and the cool, moist climate prevents the utilization of nitrogen faster than it is fixed, nitrogen is stored in the young soil, more than a ton an acre in the

Figure 6-5 *Sand dunes along the northeastern Atlantic coast. (above) A dune colonized by vegetation. Note the heavier plant growth on the lee side. Beach grass dominates, with beach plum growing on the lower slope. (below) A closer view of beach grass and beach wormwood.* (Photos by author.)

upper 18 inches of leaf mold and soil in 70 years following the ice recession. As a result cottonwoods and alders are stimulated to vigorous, upright growth.

As the alder thicket matures and can grow no taller, cottonwoods and hemlocks rapidly emerge and eventually shade out the alder. One hundred and seventy years, more or less, after the ice has melted, the alder is gone, incorporated into the forest floor. The nitrogen reserves are depleted and a carpet of moss and deep litter covers the forest floor.

Secondary succession

Secondary succession is most commonly encountered on abandoned farm land and noncultivated ruderal sites such as fills, spoil banks, railroad grades, roadsides, all artifically disturbed and frequently subject to erosion and settling movements.

The species most likely to colonize such places are the so-called "weeds," a catch-all name that means something a little different to nearly everyone, depending upon his personal interests. Although virtually undefinable, weeds usually have two characteristics in common. They invade areas modified by human action; in fact a few are confined to such artificially modified habitats. And they are exotics, not natives, to the region. Once native species invade the area, these "weed" plants eventually disappear.

Annual, biennial, or perennial, all plants that settle initially on disturbed areas possess a great tolerance for soil disturbance and partial defoliation. Their seeds remain viable for a long time and may remain in the soil for a number of years until the conditions are right for germination. Some weeds require an open seedbed and exposed mineral soil for germination. Their rapid and successful colonization is aided by an efficient means of dispersal. Some have seeds that are light and carried by the wind; others spread by underground rhizomes. Vigorous, these pioneer plants grow rapidly under favorable conditions; in less favorable habitat they will set seed even when small (Sorensen, 1954).

In spite of this, these plants cannot maintain their dominance very long—three to four years at the most—if all disturbance ceases. Short life cycles, advantageous at first, are not adaptable to conditions imposed by incoming plants with long life cycles, ones that begin growth earlier in the spring and persist throughout the summer.

The species composition of pioneering communities is highly variable. Infinite combinations exist, depending upon the seed source, the cultural practices prior to abandonment of the land, and moisture and soil conditions. Broad differences exist between the first-year communities that spring up in small grain fields and those that appear in cultivated row-crop fields. Since land in row crops has large areas of exposed soil, the number of annuals and biennials, such as ragweed, all of which do well in the hot weather of midsummer, is high. In absence of cultivation, herbs are able to establish themselves in small grain fields unseeded to grass. In these the number of annuals and biennials is greatest the last year of use and decreases rapidly thereafter (Fig. 6-6) (Beckwith, 1954). Moist soils rich in plant nutrients support such plants as burdock, catnip, and nettle, while poorer, drier soils grow shepherd's-purse, chicory, and ragweed. On railroad grades and yards, fresh cinders, high in sulphur compounds and other toxic materials, compose a substrate suggestive of the saline soils of the western plains (Curtis, 1959). Here western plants carried eastward on rail cars

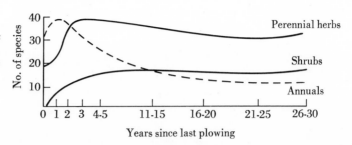

Figure 6-6 *The succession of vegetation on cultivated fields. Note the early rise and rapid decline of annuals.* (After Beckwith, 1954.)

may become established, among them western wheatgrass and sunflowers. In addition there is a wide assortment of exotic weeds.

Strip-mine spoil banks, common throughout eastern coal regions, are extreme environments because of acidic conditions and long steep slopes (Fig. 6-7) and are difficult sites for seedling establishment. Here wind-disseminated woody species, particularly aspen and fire cherry, are the dominant pioneer species, rather than herbs and grasses (Bramble et al., 1955). In West Virginia and Illinois, however, wind-disseminated grasses and herbs, such as broomsedge, cinquefoil, goldenrods, panic grass, and poverty grass also become established on the spoils. Because of the extreme variability of spoil material, populations of pioneering species tend to be clumped with considerable bare area between. The percentage of plant cover increases with alkalinity (Brown and Tryon, 1960). West Virginia spoils with a pH of 2.5 to 3.9 had very little herbaceous cover and few natural woody seedlings. As the pH increases, the number of woody seedlings and the amount of herbaceous cover increase. The greatest herbaceous cover exists at a pH of 7.5 to 7.9.

Thus succession, whether primary or secondary, starts with the colonization of the area by pioneer species—plants able to grow on a substrate low in nutrients and organic matter in an excessively wet or excessively dry environment, as well as able to withstand very bright sunlight and, on land, wide variations of surface temperature. The number of plants colonizing and surviving on the site are few at first, but as conditions improve, more of them occupy the area. Through the deposition of organic matter and shading of the surface, they reduce the surface evaporation and modify the environment enough to permit more demanding plants to invade the area. Better adapted to utilize the nutrients available, the new arrivals eventually take over and crowd out the pioneers by shading and by vigorous growth. The pioneer plants are restricted to the least-modified environment until they are finally eliminated. The new stand thickens, more organic matter is added to the soil, and environmental conditions continue to change. Eventually the stage is set for other plants and animals to invade and colonize the area and for a different community to develop (see Johnson and Odum, 1956; Pearson, 1959; Hirth, 1959). Thus one community replaces another until a stable community occupies the site.

Although succession has been described as a series of discrete steps leading to a final stage, the change is gradual, continuous, often variable, and in part controlled by the community itself. Stages may be skipped, telescoped, or extended. Often a seral stage may be prolonged by soil conditions or by a temporary climatic

Figure 6-7 *Strip-mine spoils. (above) Spoil banks and cut from a coal stripping operation in rolling topography. Note the slow invasion of plants. (right) Strip mining in steep, mountainous country. The overburden is rolled down the mountain side to cover the forest. This destroys existing forest vegetation and creates a site so severe that plants have difficulty colonizing it.* ((above) Courtesy Soil Conservation Service; (right) Courtesy James Brown.)

condition, such as drought; or succession may be accelerated by the omission of a stage, or by the combination of two or more stages into one. Under certain conditions succession may regress. Man, fire, floods, and the deposition of soil may alter conditions and set succession back to an earlier stage. In the prairie grasslands the constant burrowing of rodents and ants creates new bare areas, which are invaded by annuals. As the mounds and disturbed areas "mature," annuals are replaced first by plants with more exacting needs, then finally by climax species. This microsuccession is an excellent example of "gap-phase" replacement. While the grassland community as a whole is relatively stable, it may be undergoing violent fluctuations from disturbance on very small areas within.

In certain topographical situations, a seral stage may be destroyed by the vegetation itself and succession turned backward at an angle from its original direction. Sphagnum moss growing on poorly drained sites in Alaskan spruce forests becomes so soggy that soil aeration is impared, trees die, and logs and stumps become buried under a blanket of peat. As the forest dies, the sphagnum moss of the forest is replaced by sphagnum of the open. Seeds of hemlock and spruce may sprout in the mat, but they soon die for lack of nutrients and root aeration. The result is the famous northern muskeg.

Cyclic replacement

To determine whether a particular stage of vegetation is successional or not may be a problem. Succession may be confused with another type of vegetational and habitat change that occurs in cycles. Each successive community or phase is related to the other by orderly changes in an upgrade and downgrade series. These phasic cycles were first recognized and described in the Scottish heaths (Watt, 1947). Here Scotch heather represents the peak of the upgrade series. After its death, a lichen, *Cladonia silvatica,* becomes dominant and covers the dead heather stems. Eventually the lichen disintegrates to expose bare

Figure 6-8 Cyclic replacement in an old-field community. Moss—dock— lichen—bare ground. See text for details.

soil, the last of the downgrade series. The bare soil is colonized by bearberry, to initiate the upgrade series. Then heather reclaims the area and dominates again. There are other shorter phasic cycles, one involving heather, lichen, and bearberry and another involving heather, lichen, bare soil, and back to heather.

A similar cycle, frequently initiated by ants or ground squirrels, occurs in old-field communities in Michigan (Evans and Cain, 1952). Here bare areas at the bottom of the downgrade series are invaded by mosses, to start the upgrade series (Fig. 6-8). The mosses are invaded by Canada bluegrass and dock. The accumulation of dead culms and stems of these plants is covered by lichens of several species. Together the organic debris and the lichens crowd out the grass. Rain, frost, and wind destroy the lichens, and bare soil is exposed and left open to invasion by mosses again.

The climax

Eventually succession slows down and an equilibrium or steady state with the environment is more or less achieved. Theoretically, at least, this last stage is mature, self-maintaining, self-reproducing through developmental stages, and permanent; the vegetation is tolerant of the environmental conditions imposed by itself. This terminal community is characterized by an equilibrium between production and respiration, a wide diversity of species, a well-developed spatial structure, and complex food chains. This final stable community of the sere is the climax community, and the vegetation supporting it, the climax vegetation.

The composition, species structure, and balance of a climax community is determined by the total environment of the ecosystem and not by one aspect, such as climate alone (Whittaker, 1953; McIntosh, 1958; Sellack, 1960). Involved are the characteristics of each species population and their biotic interrelations, availability of flora and fauna to colonize the area, the chance dispersion of seeds and animals, and the soils and climate. Thus the mosaic of vegetation will change as the environment changes; and the climax community represents a pattern of populations that corresponds with and changes with the pattern of environmental gradients. The more diverse the environment, the more diverse the vegetational patterns. This basically is the polyclimax theory: that succession takes place toward a final stage, but this final stage will vary with specific environmental and biotic conditions.

The polyclimax concept differs considerably from the long-held monoclimax theory, developed largely by Clements. This theory recognizes only one climax, determined solely by climate, no matter how great the environmental conditions are at the start. All seral communities in a given region, if allowed sufficient time, will ultimately converge to a single climax. The whole landscape would be clothed with uniform plant and animal community. All communities other than the climax are related to the climax by successional development and are recognized as subclimax, postclimax, disclimax, and so on.

For all practical purposes the climax is rarely if ever attained. In fact there is considerable question if any such thing as climax really exists. True, the late stages in succession are relatively stable; they do exist for some time, and the trend, regardless of whether it started out from xeric or wet sites, is toward

140

a mesophytic condition. But, that succession ends here is not a proved fact. Even in the so-called climax communities, stability is never really achieved. Self-destructive biological changes are continually taking place, even though slowly. Trees grow old and die and may be replaced by new trees of a different species. Cyclic replacement of microcommunities within the over-all community may be taking place on a large or small scale. Replacement or recycling of nutrients may be lagging; too much may be tied up in woody vegetation, and the whole metabolism of the community may be slowing down. Thus the idea of the climax appears to be changing; the word takes on a different meaning. It is rapidly coming to mean those more or less stable and long-lived communities that develop late in succession in absence of disturbance. What comes after, how slowly or in what direction they will change, only time can tell.

Heterotrophic succession

Within each major community and dependent upon it for an energy source, are a number of microcommunities. Dead trees, animal carcasses and droppings, plant galls, tree holes, all furnish a substrate on which groups of plants and animals live, succeed each other, and eventually disappear, becoming in the final stages a part of the major community itself. In these instances, succession is characterized by early dominance of heterotrophic organisms, maximum energy available at the start, and a steady decline in energy as the succession progresses.

An acorn supports a tiny parade of life from the time it drops from the tree until it becomes a part of the humus (Winston, 1956). Succession often begins while the acorn still hangs on the tree. The acorn may be invaded by insects, which carry to the interior pathogenic fungi fatal to the embryo. Most often the insect that invades the acorn is the acorn weevil, *Curculio rectus*. The adult female burrows through the pericarp into the embryo and deposits its eggs. Upon hatching, the larvae tunnel through to the embryo and consume about half of it. If fungi—*Penicillium* and *Fusarium*—invade the acorn simultaneously with the weevil, or alone, they utilize the material. The embryo then turns brown and leathery and the weevil larvae become stunted and fail to develop. This represents the pioneer stage.

When the embryo is destroyed, partially or completely, by the pioneering organisms, other animals and fungi enter the acorn. Weevil larvae leave the acorn through an exit hole, which they cut through the outer shell. Through this hole, fungi feeders and scavengers enter. Most important is the moth *Valentinia glandenella,* which lays its eggs on or in the exit hole, mostly during the fall. Upon hatching, the larvae enter the acorn, spin a tough web over the opening, and proceed to feed on the remainder of the embryo and the feces of the previous occupant. At the same time several species of fungi enter and grow inside the acorn, only to be utilized by another occupant, the cheese mites, *Tryophagus* and *Rhyzozhyphus*. By the time the remaining embryo tissues are reduced to feces, the acorn is invaded by cellulose-consuming fungi. The fruiting bodies of these fungi, as well as the surface of the acorn, are eaten by mites and collembola and, if moist, by cheese mites too. At this time predaceous mites enter the acorn, particularly *Gamasellus,* which is extremely flattened and capable of following smaller mites and collembola into crevices within the acorn. Outside

141

on the acorn, cellulose and lignin-consuming fungi soften the outer shell and bind the acorn to twigs and leaves on the forest floor.

As the acorn shell becomes more fragile, holes other than the weevils' exits appear. One of the earliest appears at the base of the acorn where the hilum falls out. Through this, larger animals such as centipedes, millipedes, ants, and collembola enter, although they contribute nothing to the decay of the acorn. The amount of soil in the cavity increases and the greatly softened shell eventually collapses into a mound and gradually becomes incorporated into the humus of the soil.

Thus microcommunities illustrate the major concept of succession: that the change in the substrate is brought about by the organisms themselves. When organisms exploit an environment, their own life activities make the habitat unfavorable for their own survival, and instead create a favorable environment for different groups of organisms. Those responsible for the beginning of succession are all quite specialized for feeding in acorns, the later forms are less so, and the final group are generalized soil animals, such as the earthworms and millipedes.

Influences on succession

Over most of the settled parts of North America and other continents, extensive areas of original climax vegetation no longer exist. Succession either has been set back, modified, or arrested by man. Even new "climax" communities have been modified by the elimination of some plants through lumbering and overgrazing.

Fire

Fire, whether in climax vegetation or in a seral stage, sets succession back, influences the species composition, and shapes the character of a community. It long has played an important role in vegetational development, even in pre-settlement America. Fires, often set by Indians, held back the forest along the eastern edge of the prairie. More than 95 per cent of the virgin forests of Wisconsin were burned during the five centuries before the land was settled (Curtis, 1959). These fires not only enabled such species as yellow birch, hemlock, pines, and oaks to persist, but also, from an ecological viewpoint, were normal and necessary to perpetuate these forests (Maissurow, 1941; Curtis, 1959). The open ponderosa pine forests of southwestern United States evolved under the influence of natural fires. Forty years of fire exclusion from these forests have resulted in a thick growth of young pines, stagnation of stands, elimination of grass, and detrimental changes in the forest community (Cooper, 1960). Even-aged stands of Douglas fir, western white pine, and longleaf pine, red pine, and jack pine usually result from a fire-prepared seed bed. In Alaska, on the other hand, fires have converted white spruce stands into treeless herbaceous or shrub communities of fireweed and grass or dwarf birch and willow (Lutz, 1956), whose growth is so thick that forest trees cannot become established.

The effects of fire depend upon the intensity. Crown and severe surface fires may destroy all existing vegetation, while light and moderate surface fires may destroy only the undergrowth and damage, but not kill, thin-barked trees about their base. Not only does this cause fire scar in the butt log but it also serves as an avenue along which wood-rotting fungi can enter the tree. The destruction of the organic layer on the surface releases concentrations of nitrogen, potassium, phosphorous, and calcium. This produces lush herbaceous growth and rapid sprout and seedling development of the remaining trees and shrubs. But at the same time burning greatly alters the fauna of the forest soil, particularly their numerical abundance, and reduces the water-holding capacity of the soil.

The heat of fire destroys the seeds of many plants and eliminates them from the area. But other plants so depend upon fire for their existence that the lack of fires may exclude them from the forest. Jack pine and paper birch stands develop best where fire has prepared a suitable seed bed, with exposed mineral soil and a minimum of organic matter. The maximum seeding of jack pine occurs after fires, since dry heat of at least 80°F is required to open cones and release the seeds. Many cones remain closed on the tree and the seeds remain viable until they are opened by fire.

The plants that grow up after a fire originate from several sources. Some are carried in by the wind or by animals. The former are well represented by aspens, paper birch, pine, and some herbs; the latter by fleshy-fruited plants. Others, such as oaks, bracken fern, and some perennial grasses sprout from fire-resistant roots. Since the seeds of such trees as beech, birch, and hemlock are destroyed by heat, sprout trees—red oak, black oak, white oak, and scarlet oak—dominate the area, and other species are reduced to a minimum. In such a manner, fire can change the future composition of a forest (for a detailed discussion, see Ahlgren and Ahlgren, 1960).

Fire is a useful tool to control succession and to maintain economically more valuable seral stages. Prescribed burning—fire under control—is used as a management tool to eliminate hardwood understory beneath southern pines and thus perpetuate these intolerant trees, to prevent the encroachment of woody growth into grassland, to develop openings and browse for wildlife, and to maintain certain shrub communities, such as blueberries.

Lumbering

Removal of a forest, especially by clear-cutting, turns the land back to an earlier stage of succession. Unless followed by fire, the cutover area rapidly fills in with herbs and shrubs—blackberries, sumac, and dense thickets of sprout growth and seedlings of trees. The area passes quickly through the shrub stage to an even-aged pole forest (trees four to eight inches, diameter breast height). As the pole forest matures, the crown closes and shuts out the sunlight from the forest floor. This eliminates all but the most tolerant herbaceous and woody plants and reduces the stratification. Through time, trees in a better competitive position, those with larger crowns and more vigorous root systems, crowd out the subdominant trees and the area gradually passes into a mature and more highly stratified forest.

Man can modify the forest in many ways to meet his requirements. Early in the life of a new forest, trees of undesirable species and poor form, which in time would retard the growth of more valuable ones, can be removed. This improves (economically, at least) the composition of the stand and the quality

Figure 6-9 *Thinning in the forest to allow room for crown expansion and more rapid growth. (left) Before thinning; (right) after thinning.* (Photos courtesy K. L. Carvell.)

of the trees. Later, the maximum growth of crop trees can be encouraged by thinning. The increased space between the trees stimulates crown expansion and increases growth (Fig. 6-9 left and right).

Many of the most valuable and desirable timber trees exist in the lower seral stages instead of the climax. To maintain and reproduce this seral stage often is a problem. Stands of pine, balsam fir, and some spruces, aspen, and yellow poplar are maintained by clear-cutting the mature trees to expose the ground to sunlight. Only under this condition will intolerant seedlings survive. Leaving seed trees, clear-cutting in small blocks, and selection cutting—the removal of each tree or groups of trees with regard to its position in the stand and possibilities of future growth—all are used to hold a forest in the successional stage most desirable for timber production.

Mismanagement of the forest, such as indiscriminate clear-cutting and removal of all trees down to a certain diameter limit, also changes the forest composition. Highgrading, taking the best and leaving the poorest, not only eliminates certain tree species from the future forest but also tends to leave genetically inferior trees to supply seed for the future. Removal of the forest lowers, or perhaps raises (due to reduced transpiration) the water table, affecting some aquatic

144

communities, and causes irregular stream flow. Streams that dry up in the summer undergo drastic changes in community structure. Erosion of forest soil follows improper logging, adds life-choking silt to streams, and impairs water quality.

Grazing and browsing

Grazing by domestic and wild animals may arrest succession or even reverse it. Buffalo herds controlled the height of grass by grazing on the taller-grass species. This permitted the short grasses to assume dominance. Plant clipping by prairie dogs tends to decrease the proportion of annual grasses and forbs, to increase perennial forbs, and to influence the relative area of ground covered by each plant species (Koford, 1958). In prairies with both tall- and short-grass species, prairies dogs can develop and maintain a short-grass prairie. Overgrazing of grasslands by domestic stock results in denudation and erosion of the land. In rangelands of southwestern United States, overgrazing reduces the organic mat and thus the incidence of fire. Because of this, the reduced competition from grass, and dispersal of seeds through cattle droppings, mesquite and other unwanted shrubs rapidly invade the area.

The effects of overgrazing are well illustrated on the Wasatch Plateau in Utah. There the virgin subalpine meadows were so overgrazed in the 1880s and 1890s by cattle and sheep that the area was changed to a virtual desert. In spite of management efforts, accelerated soil erosion still continues (Ellison, 1954). The overgrazed meadows were taken over by annuals and early-withering perennials. In moderately grazed meadows, however, vegetation reacted differently to sheep and cattle grazing. Grazing by sheep tended to favor development of grasses and low shrubs, while grazing by cattle resulted in dominance by forbs, since grasses were suppressed.

If a relatively large number of cattle are allowed to graze in eastern woodlands year after year, they will in time destroy the forest. First, young trees and shrubs and lower limbs of taller trees are browsed, opening up the forest. The forest floor, unprotected by vegetation, is exposed to the wind; the soil dries out

Figure 6-10 A deer-browse line in the northern forest. Deer have removed all foliage as high as they could reach—a sure sign of overpopulation. (Photo courtesy of Michigan Conservation Department.)

and weeds invade the woodland. In time the understory completely disappears; some of the dominant trees die, both from natural causes and from the effects of reduced soil moisture and excessive exposure to sun and wind; and sufficient light reaches the forest floor to encourage grass. As the canopy is reduced to 50 per cent or less, opened in part by the dying tops in old trees, the sod cover becomes complete. Eventually most of the trees die, and the once-forested land is converted to an open field with a tight sod cover (Day and Den Uyl, 1932).

Overpopulations of wild grazing and browsing animals also influence community succession. In many parts of eastern North America, white-tailed deer, overstocked because of the failure to harvest does as well as bucks, and because of the lack of natural predators, have destroyed forest reproduction and developed a browse line, the upper limits on the trees at which a deer can reach food (Fig. 6-10). The effects of browsing vary widely between forests, depending upon the type and the region. In the Ottawa National Forest, for example, white spruce was little browsed by deer, while yellow birch, basswood, hemlock, white cedar, and aspen were eagerly sought and have been greatly reduced or eliminated (Graham, 1958). In mixed northern hardwood–hemlock stands, only sugar maple and red maple have been able to survive the effects of browsing and probably will dominate the future forest. Basswoods and hemlock were completely eliminated. Mule deer and elk in the Rocky Mountain National Park prevent the invasion of forest openings by trees and shrubs. Extensive studies indicate that only in areas protected from deer by fencing did aspen, willow, and other woody invaders grow (Fig. 6-11 above and below) (Gysel, 1960).

Cultivation

Cultivated plant communities are simple, highly artificial and consist mainly of introduced species well adapted to grow on disturbed sites. Such vegetation cannot survive or perpetuate itself without constant interference and assistance from man. Because of the very simple and homogeneous ecosystem involved, tillage brings with it new pests, such as the Japanese beetle, which spreads rapidly and is destructive to both cultivated and natural vegetation. Tillage also disturbs the structure of the soil by mixing the upper strata and by exposing it to erosion.

Accelerated erosion (in contrast to geological or natural erosion) is a result of cultivation and also poor management. Stripped of its protective vegetation and litter by plow, axe, and grazing, soil is removed by wind and water faster than it can be formed. As the upper layers of humus-charged, granular, high-absorptive topsoil are removed, humus-deficient, less stable, less absorptive, and highly erodable layers beneath are exposed. If the subsoil is clay, it absorbs water so slowly that heavy rains produce a highly abrasive and rapid runoff.

The intensity of water erosion is influenced by slope, the kind and condition of soil, land use, and rainfall. The least conspicuous type of water erosion is *sheet erosion,* a more or less even removal of soil over the field. Because it takes place slowly, the change in the color of soil from dark to light and the appearance of subsoil and bedrock often goes unnoticed for a long time. When runoff tends to concentrate in streamlets instead of moving evenly over a sloping field, the cutting force is increased and *rill erosion,* which produces small chan-

Figure 6-11 *Influence of elk and deer on vegetation. (above) When this exclosure was built, aspen saplings were numerous on the hillside. Elk, deer, and beaver have eliminated all those that are not within the exclosure. (below) Old scars on dying aspen resulted from elk feeding on the bark.* (Photos courtesy of L. W. Gysel and the *Journal of Forestry.*)

Figure 6-12 *Gully erosion. This gully began as a path used by cows. Another cow path cutting across the photograph looks like an open furrow.* (Photo courtesy Soil Conservation Service.)

nels down slope, results. On land areas where concentrated water cuts the same rill long enough or where runoff is concentrated in sufficient volume to cut deeply into the soil, highly destructive gulleys are formed (Fig. 6-12). *Gully erosion* often begins in furrows running up and down hill, in wheel ruts, livestock trails, and logging skid trails in the woods.

Bare soil, finely divided, loose and dry as it often is after tillage, is ripe for wind erosion. The forward velocity of the wind well above the soil surface is much higher than that near the surface, where it approaches zero. Just above the surface, wind movement is influenced by surface irregularities. These conditions produce eddies with an upward velocity two to three times the forward velocity near the surface. The eddies dislodge the most erodable grains of soil occupying the most exposed positions on the surface and move them along a short distance on the surface. Suddenly the grains shoot upward in a jumping movement, the height of which is influenced by size, density of the particle, and the surface. When they strike the ground again, they rebound and dislodge still other particles, forcing them to jump into the air. The impact of the particles on the surface initiates still another movement, surface creep. And very fine particles of dust, bounced by larger particles, rise high enough to be picked up by the wind and carried on as dust clouds. Often dust particles may be lifted high in the atmosphere and carried for hundreds of miles.

Erosion by wind or water impoverishes the land. It carries away organic layers, exposes the subsoil, depletes nutrients, changes soil structure, deposits soil elsewhere, increases runoff, and causes land ruin and abandonment. Land abandoned because of mismanagement is usually so degraded that natural vegetation has difficulty colonizing the area. Erosion worsens, gullies deepen, and conditions become progressively worse, unless drastic steps are taken to stop erosion and restore vegetation.

Often abandoned farm land is reforested with conifers, such as red pine or Norway spruce. When this is done, succession is speeded up and the area passes through a modified shrub stage of small conifers in five to eight years, into a tree stage within 20 to 25 years. In place of the usual deciduous community is a coniferous stand. A succession of animal life, associated with increasing height of tree, occurs in such stands. As height and cover density of the plantation increases, open-field species of wildlife are replaced by shrub and tree forms (Fig. 6-3).

Industrialization and urbanization

No land-use change is more complete and final than industrialization and urbanization, a climax type in human succession. Natural vegetation is destroyed by man and replaced by ecologically permanent bare areas of concrete, asphalt, and steel. But even here a diversified group of animals and some plants are able to exist. Norway rats, common rock pigeons, starlings, English sparrows, cockroaches, and flies are common to this environment, as well as some grasses, algae, and other plants able to gain a foothold in cracks in concrete and in vacant lots. Nighthawks have substituted the artificial canyons created by tall buildings for natural cliffs. Fumes from factories, coke ovens, and smelters destroy the vegetation of surrounding areas. Even after the cause has been eliminated, many years are required before the vegetation begins to return. Pollution of streams by sewage, industrial wastes, and siltation eliminates oxygen-demanding fish like trout; these are replaced by carp and bullheads, able to adapt to polluted conditions. Dam construction for power drowns terrestrial communities and converts part of the river community to a deep lake. Migrant fish, particularly the salmon, may be blocked from reaching their spawning grounds in the headwater streams.

Human settlement of an area from past to present has undergone a sort of succession. The first to live in or penetrate a region, the pioneers, are hunters and trappers, who, aside from harvesting animals, leave little mark on the land. They are followed by a subsistence farming or grazing culture, which can completely change a natural community. Some plants and animals may be destroyed, succession set back to an earlier and more economically productive stage, and new animals introduced. If the land is too poor or too abused to support human society economically, the land at this stage may revert back to

149

Figure 6-13 *Many areas once settled by man have been abandoned and the forest returned. Here an old graveyard has been reclaimed by white pine.* (Photo by author.)

natural vegetation. Traces of old settlements and abandoned land can be found throughout the country (Fig. 6-13). Ghost towns, old stone and rail fences, house and barn foundations, lilac bushes, wells and springs hidden back in the woods, all attest to former human occupancy of the land. Industrialization, urbanization, and suburbanization are the climaxes that follow the farming stage. The tremendous growth of suburbs onto fertile farmlands marks well this type of human succession.

The economic climax. Many of the vegetation types in the settled portion of the country exist not because of ecological succession but because of man's deliberate interference. Croplands, tame haylands and pastures, even golf courses, managed forests, and managed wildlife lands all occupy or are maintained on an area of land because of economic interests. Such communities can be regarded as economic climaxes since they represent the highest type economically allowed on the land (W. W. Chase, unpublished). Only when this land is abandoned does it eventually return to an ecological climax. The animals that fill the niches in the economic climaxes occupy these communities because they are adaptable to existing conditions. Even some of these are eliminated because they conflict to some degree with human interests.

Economic climaxes, however natural they may appear, are strictly artificial, often quite simple communities (see Elton, 1958). Most require some degree of maintenance: cultivation, fertilization, mowing, thinning, cutting, and spraying. Forests managed for timber production must fall into this category, for cutting practices are designed to maintain or to establish even-aged or uneven-aged stands and to change or maintain timber species of greatest economic interest. These economic climaxes change as man's economic interests change and with it the animal life. This concept should be kept in mind when studying or investigating the ecology of any area.

150

Radiation

Intense radiation such as that produced by unshielded nuclear reactors, by atomic and hydrogen bomb blasts, and by areas of fallout—up to 100 miles from the blast site—can have a pronounced effect on the plant community (see Chap. 4). Early successional stages, simple in structure, are more resistant to high levels of chronic gamma radiation than more complex systems, such as the forest. Early pioneers, the mosses and lichens, can withstand exposures of over 200,000 roentgens. Grasses, hemicryptophytes, and cryptophytes that have shoots and buds protected by the soil, and annuals, whose dormant seeds are radioresistant, can withstand months of exposures of radiation between 100 and 300 roentgens. Radiosensitive dominant species would be replaced by normally infrequent but radioresistant species. As seral communities become more complex, their radiosensitivity increases, and radioactivity that would hardly alter simpler ecosystems would cause major damage. Pine, the most sensitive of plants because of the low number of chromosomes (40), would be destroyed by chronic irradiations of between 20 and 60 roentgens, and the hardwoods would undergo transformation of leaves that reduces the thickness of the canopy. If radiation rises above 360 roentgens, the hardwood forest would be destroyed and the area would revert to a simple community of radioresistant grasses, annuals and perennials, and low shrubs (Woodwell, 1963).

Thus if a complex ecosystem is disturbed by high-intensity radiation, its basic structure is destroyed, the system is simplified and made unstable, and the number of species present is reduced. Long-continued disturbance favors vigorous organisms that reproduce rapidly and asexually. Radiation, even below sublethal levels, can cause mutations. Exposures necessary to cause such major changes are far above those now being received from natural sources and the present level of fallout, but they are well within the range possible over a large area from a nuclear explosion. Not only man, whose lethal exposure lies within a range of 500 to 1000 roentgens, would be affected but the natural ecosystem as well.

Past communities

The community changes and succession just discussed take place over a relatively short period of time and under similar climatic conditions. Communities also changed throughout geological periods of time, changes usually associated with shifts in climate. The emergence of mountains, sinking and rising of seas, and glaciation all influenced in part the climate and other environmental conditions of a given area. Many plant and animal species became extinct; one type of climax community was replaced by another.

The records of these past communities, their animals and plants, lie buried as fossils. From these, plant and animal associations of the past can be determined and in a broad way the climatic changes that brought about the gradual destruction of one stable community and the emergence of another. Such interpretation is based on the assumption that organisms of the past that had a structure similar to those living today also possessed similar ecological requirements. Thus one assumption is that if modern palms and broadleaf evergreens are tropical plants, then their ancient prototypes also lived in a tropical climate. The study of this past relationship of ancient flora and fauna to their environment is called *paleoecology*.

Of particular interest to the paleoecologist is the climatic and vegetational changes that followed the advance and retreat of glaciers. As the glaciers moved south in several advances, vegetation was destroyed and the relief or physiognomy changed radically. The climate about the edges of the glacier supposedly was

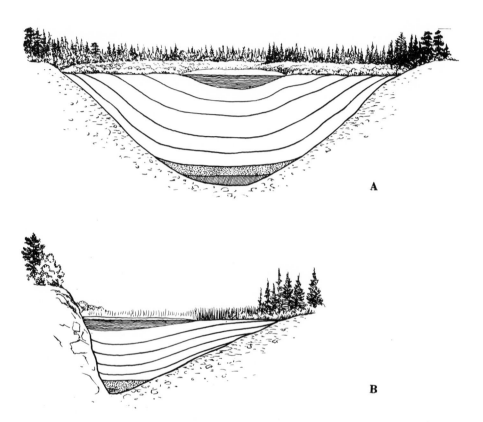

Figure 6-14 *A diagrammatic drawing of bog filling. (A) In a regular basin. Note that the deepest layers are in the center bottom, not along the sides. (B) In an irregular basin. Here the oldest layer occurs in the deepest pocket.* (Adapted after Potzger, 1956.)

rather cold and the growing conditions optimum only for tundralike vegetation. Recent evidence, however, suggests that the climate, particularly along the southern edges of the glacial advance, may not have been as cold as once thought and that some forest-tree species quickly invaded the glacial-drift country following deglaciation.

Changes in postglacial vegetation and climate are recorded in the bottoms of lakes and bogs. As the glaciers retreated, they left scooped-out holes and dammed-up rivers and streams, which filled with water to form lakes. Organic debris accumulated on the bottoms to form peat (Fig. 6-14 A and B). In the peat was

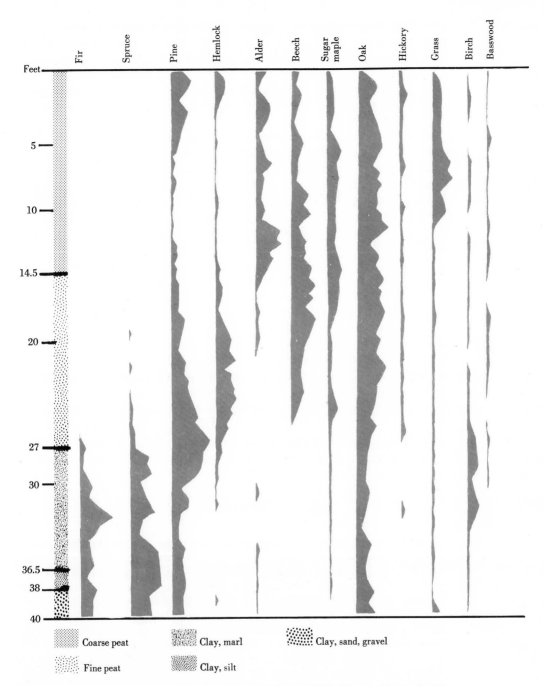

Figure 6-15 *Pollen diagram for Crystal Lake, Crawford County, Pennsylvania. The graphs indicate the percentage of various genera based on counts of 200 pollen grains for each spectrum level. Grass pollen counts are expressed as percentage of total tree pollen. Note five major forest successions: (1) initial spruce-fir forest with oak and pine; (2) pine forest with oak and birch; (3) hemlock with codominant oak and accessory hickory and beech; (4) oak-hickory forest; (5) pine; hemlock increasing, oak remaining, beech and hickory decreasing. (Adapted from Walker and Hartman, 1960.)*

153

embedded fossil pollen and spores and small invertebrates that blew in from adjacent vegetation, settled on the water, and sank. Microscopic examination of samples of organic bottom deposits obtained at regular intervals reveals fossil pollen. Identification of various genera is based on comparisons of fossil pollen to that of the same genera growing today. The relative abundance of pollen of several genera indicates the predominate vegetation of the specified depth of deposition (Fig. 6-15).

Generally five vegetational or climatic periods following glaciation are recognized. First spruce and fir were dominant, suggesting a cool, moist period. Following this was a period when pine was dominant, with an intermix of oak, suggesting a drier, warm climate. Then an invasion of hardwoods took place. In the first stage of this invasion, the climate apparently was humid and warm, for hemlocks, oaks, and beech were the dominant trees, but a later warm, dry period favored the oaks. This was followed by a return to pine and a reappearance of hemlock and spruce, which indicated a climatic shift to a cool, moist period. A sequence of postglacial forest vegetation from an area near the edge of the glaciers' furthest advance south is illustrated in Fig. 6-15.

Results of pollen investigation can only indicate trends in vegetation and climate through the past. At present it is impossible to determine the exact structure and composition of prevailing vegetation at any one time period. Inaccuracies are caused by variations in pollen production. Since some tree species produce more pollen than others, these would appear more abundant than they really were. Some pollen might have been carried a considerable distance by the wind and perhaps even mixed deeper by earthworms. Many pollen grains can be identified only to genera and not to species. Thus the oaks cannot be separated out to give a clue to the particular type of oak forest. And finally the possibility exists that some of the species had environmental requirements different from their modern-day counterparts.

SUMMARY

With the passing of time, natural communities change. Old fields of today return to forests tomorrow; weedy fields in the prairie country revert back to stable grassland. This gradual change from one community to another is called succession. It is characterized by a progressive change in species structure, an increase in biomass and organic-matter accumulation, and a gradual balance between community production and community respiration. This change is brought about by the organisms themselves. As they exploit the environment, their own life activities make the habitat unfavorable for their own survival. But in doing so, they create an environment for a different group of organisms. Eventually, however, an equilibrium, or steady state with the environment, is more or less achieved. This stage, usually called the climax, is self-maintaining and usually long-lived, as long as it is free from disturbance.

But relatively few communities are free from disturbance, and the greatest cause of disturbance is man himself. He has greatly modified natural communities the world over. Fire, more often man-caused than not, down through the centuries, sets back succession to an earlier stage and changes the composition and even the type of community. In cutting the forest for timber, man most often has tended either to remove the trees completely, or to take the best and leave the poorest in quality and the genetically inferior to reproduce the future forest. Overgrazing of forests and grassland by both domestic stock and mismanaged wild grazing animals has resulted in the denudation of grasslands and serious disturbance and even destruction of forests. To provide food for himself, man has cleared away natural vegetation and replaced it with simple, highly artificial communities of cultivated species, adapted to grow on disturbed sites. This has brought about an explosion of insect pests and accelerated erosion of unprotected soil. Nowhere is land change more complete than in industrial and urban areas, a climax type of human succession. Natural communities are completely destroyed and replaced by the concrete, asphalt, and steel of cities, highways, and dams. And the process is accompanied by air and water pollution from industrial and human wastes. Most communities exist only through man's continued, deliberate interference, usually motivated by economic interests. In these "economic climaxes," the animals and plants present either are desired by man or are adaptable to existing conditions.

In recent years man has added a new dimension to successional change: nuclear radiation from atomic testing and nuclear reactors. Such radiation can have a powerful effect both on community composition and directional change. Some plants and most animals are killed by radiation, while a few plants are radioresistant. Under intense radiation the basic community structure is destroyed and the ecosystem is simplified and unstable.

Perhaps the most outstanding characteristic of natural communities is their dynamic nature. They are constantly changing through time, rapidly in early stages of development, more slowly in the later stages. Even the seemingly most stable natural communities may change through time. That they have in the geological past is shown by fossil records in the earth. What changes will take place in the future, and how rapidly or how slowly they will come, only time can answer.

PART **III** *Aquatic and terrestrial habitats*

CHAPTER 7

Water as a medium for life

The most outstanding feature of fresh-water and marine communities is obviously water, for it is the medium in which the plants and animals of streams, ponds, lakes, and seas exist. In it, living organisms find both shelter and food and they utilize its dissolved minerals and gases. Water is the medium upon which the flow of energy and the cycling of nutrients in the aquatic ecosystem depends. Since the chemical and physical properties of water and its characteristics as a medium for life differ so sharply from the conditions found in the terrestrial environment, the substance deserves some attention.

The structure of water

Unlike the gaseous mixture of the atmosphere, water is a compound. Its formula is H_2O, which states simply that a molecule of the substance consists of two atoms of hydrogen and one of oxygen. But this is only a part of the

157

picture; the remainder rests with its structure. Each normal hydrogen atom consists of two subatomic particles, a positively charged $(+)$ proton and a negatively charged $(-)$ electron. The proton is 2000 times as massive as the electron and makes up the atom's central nucleus, about which the lighter electrons orbit. The nucleus of the oxygen atom, consisting of eight protons, is about 16 times as large as the hydrogen nucleus and its positive charge is about eight times as large. Orbiting about the oxygen nucleus are eight negatively charged electrons. Two are in orbit close to the nucleus, six in the outer shell. This allows room for two more. The hydrogen atom has room for one more. (The reason is that the number of electrons needed to fill the outer shell of electrons of increasingly larger diameters are 2, 8, 18, and 32.) As a result, the two atoms of hydrogen and one of oxygen readily combine. The two hydrogen atoms repel each other sufficiently so that they take positions in the molecule at an angle of 105 degrees apart. Since hydrogen is now sharing electrons with the oxygen, each hydrogen electron spends more time in positions between the oxygen and hydrogen nuclei, instead of spending equal time on all sides of the hydrogen nucleus. The charge distribution of the water molecules thus becomes asymmetrical, and the two positive charges of the water molecule are attracted to any other atoms with a negative electron. This attraction is satisfied by the negatively charged electrons of the hydrogen atoms, which form hydrogen bonds between water molecules.

Because of the arrangement of the hydrogen atoms and hydrogen bonds, liquid water consists of branching chains of oxygen tetrahedra. The thermal status of water in liquid state is such that hydrogen bonds are being broken as fast as they form. At low temperatures, the tetrahedral arrangement is almost perfect; when water freezes, the arrangement is a perfect lattice. Because of the separation of hydrogen atoms on the water molecule, the water molecules join at the vertexes of a tetrahedron, resulting in considerable open space between ice crystals in the lattice and thus decreasing its density. For this reason ice floats. As the temperature of frozen water is increased, this molecular arrangement becomes looser and more diffuse, resulting in random packing (because of the continuous breaking and reforming of hydrogen bonds) and contraction of molecules. The higher the temperature rises, the more diffuse the pattern becomes, until the whole structure (and the hydrogen bonds) breaks down and water melts. Upon melting, water contracts and its density increases up to a temperature of 3.98°C. Beyond this point, the loose arrangement of the molecules means a reduction in density again. The existence of this point of maximum density at approximately 4°C is of fundamental importance to aquatic life.

Sea water behaves somewhat differently. The density of sea water (salinity of 24.7 ‰ and higher), or rather its specific gravity relative to that of an equal volume of pure water (sp gr = 1) at atmospheric pressure, is correlated with salinity. At 0°C, the density of sea water with a salinity of 35 ‰ is 1.028. The lower its temperature, the greater becomes the density of sea water; the higher the temperature, the less the density. No definite freezing point exists for sea water. Ice crystals begin to form at a point on the temperature scale that varies with salinity. As pure water freezes out, the remaining unfrozen water becomes higher in salinity and lower in its freezing point until finally a solid block of ice crystals and salt is formed.

Physical properties

Specific heat

Water is capable of storing tremendous quantities of heat with a relatively small rise in temperature. It is exceeded in this only by ammonia, liquid hydrogen, and lithium. Thus water is described as having a high specific heat, the number of calories necessary to raise one gram of water one degree centigrade. The specific heat of water is given the value of 1.

Since such great quantities of heat must be absorbed before the temperature of natural waters such as the ponds, lakes, and the seas can be raised one degree centigrade, they warm up slowly in the spring and cool off just as slowly in the fall. This prevents wide seasonal fluctuations in the temperature of aquatic habitats and moderates the temperatures of local or worldwide environments.

Latent heat

Not only does water have a high specific heat, it also possesses the highest heat of fusion and heat of evaporation, collectively called latent heat, of all known substances that are liquid at ordinary temperatures. Large quantities of heat must be removed before water can change from a liquid to a solid, and conversely it must absorb considerable heat before ice can be converted to a liquid. It takes approximately 80 calories of heat to convert one gram of ice to a liquid state when both are at 0°C. This is equivalent to the amount of heat needed to raise the same quantity of water from 0°C to 80°C. A body of water at 0°C can heat up a large amount of cold air yet form only a small amount of ice.

Evaporation occurs at the interface between air and water at all ranges of temperature. Here again considerable amounts of heat are involved; 536 calories are needed to overcome the attraction between molecules and convert one gram of water at 100°C into vapor. This is as much heat as is needed to raise 536 grams of water 1°C. When evaporation occurs, the source of thermal energy may come from the sun, from the water itself, or from objects in or around it. Rendered latent at the place of evaporation, the heat involved is returned to actual heat at the point of condensation (see Chap. 4). Such phenomena play a major role in worldwide meteorological cycles.

Viscosity

The viscosity of water also is high because of the energy contained in the hydrogen bonds. Viscosity can be visualized best if one imagines or observes liquid flowing through a glass tube or clear plastic hose. The liquid moving through the tube behaves as if it consisted of a series of parallel concentric layers flowing one over another. The rate of flow is greatest at the center; but because of the amount of internal friction between layers, the flow decreases toward the sides of the tube. This same phenomenon can be observed along the side of any stream or river with uniform banks. The water along the streamside is nearly still, while the current in the center may be swift. This resistance between the layers is called viscosity.

159

This lateral or laminar viscosity is complicated by another type, eddy viscosity, in which water masses pass from one layer to another. This creates a turbulence both horizontally and vertically. Biologically important (see Chap. 8), eddy viscosity is many times greater than laminar viscosity.

Viscosity is the source of frictional resistance to objects moving through the water. Since this resistance is 100 times that of air, animals must expend considerable muscular energy to move through the water. A mucous coating on fish reduces surface resistance. Streamlining does likewise; in fact the body form of some aquatic organisms have evolved under the stresses of viscosity. The faster an aquatic organism moves through the water, the greater is the stress placed on the surface and the greater is the volume of water that must be displaced in a given time. Replacement of water in the space left behind by the moving animal adds additional drag on the body. An animal streamlined in reverse, with a short, rounded front and a rapidly tapering body, meets least resistance in the water (see Fig. 24-8). The acme of such streamlining is the sperm whale.

Surface tension

Within all substances, particles of the same matter are attracted to one another. Water is no exception. Molecules of water below the surface are symmetrically surrounded by other molecules. The forces of attraction are the same on one side of the molecule as on the other. But at the water's surface, the molecules exist under a different set of conditions. Below is a hemisphere of strongly attractive similar water molecules; above is the much smaller attractive force of the air. Since the molecules on the surface, then, are drawn into the liquid, the liquid surface tends to be as small as possible, taut like the rubber of an inflated balloon. This is surface tension, important in the lives of aquatic organisms.

The skin of water is able to support small objects and animals, such as the water striders and water spiders that run across the pond surface. To other organisms, surface tension is a barrier, whether they wish to penetrate into the water below or to escape into the air above. For some, the surface tension is too great to break; for other insects it is a trap to avoid while skimming the surface to feed or to lay eggs. If caught in the surface tension, the insect may flounder on the surface. The imagoes of mayflies and caddisflies find surface tension a handicap in their efforts to emerge from the water. Slowed down at the surface, these insects become easy prey for trout.

Surface tension is important in other ways to all life. It is the force that draws liquids through the pores of the soil and the conducting networks of plants. Aquatic insects and plants have evolved structural adaptations that prevent the penetration of water into the tracheal systems of the former and the stomata and internal air spaces of the latter.

SUMMARY

The unique characteristics of water shape life in aquatic communities. The fact that water is a liquid is outstanding, for liquids in nature are rare. (Mercury is the only other naturally occurring inorganic liquid.) Possessing its greatest density at 4°C, water becomes less dense as it warms and cools above and below this point, a feature of immense ecological importance. It possesses the ability to store a tremendous quantity of heat with only a small rise in temperature and to release heat slowly. This has considerable influence in the prevention of wide seasonal fluctuations in the temperatures of aquatic habitats. Water also possesses viscosity that is a source of frictional resistance to objects moving through it. Surface tension, caused by the unsymmetrical attraction of water molecules at and below the surface, creates a "skin" on the water, over which some organisms can move but through which others find it difficult to pass. All these attributes play an important role in the ecology of the aquatic world.

CHAPTER **8**

Lakes and ponds

Lakes are inland depressions containing standing water. They may vary in size from small ponds of less than an acre to large seas covering thousands of square miles. They may range in depth from a few feet to over 5000 feet deep. Ponds, however, are considered as small bodies of standing water so shallow that rooted plants can grow over most of the bottom. Most ponds and lakes have outlet streams; and both are more or less temporary features on the landscape, since filling, no matter how slow, is inevitable.

Lakes and ponds arise in many ways. Some North American lakes were formed by glacial erosion and deposition and a combination of the two. Glacial abrasion of slopes in high mountain valleys carved basins, which filled with water from rain and melting snow to produce tarns. Retreating valley glaciers left behind crescent-shaped ridges of rock debris, which dammed up water behind them. Numerous shallow kettle lakes and potholes were formed on the glacial drift sheets that cover much of northeasten North America and northwestern Europe. Lakes are also formed by the deposition of silt, driftwood, and other debris in the beds of slow-flowing streams. Loops of streams that meander over flat valleys and flood plains often become cut off, forming crescent-shaped oxbow lakes. Shifts in the earth's crust, either by the uplifting of mountains or by the breaking and displacement of rock strata, causing part of the valley to sink, develop depressions that fill with water. Craters of extinct volcanos, too, may fill with water; and landslides can block off streams and valleys to form new lakes and ponds. In a given area, however, all natural lakes and ponds have the same geological origin and the same general characteristics. But because of varying depths at the time of origin, they may represent several stages of succession.

Many lakes and ponds are formed by nongeological activity. Beavers dam up streams to make shallow but often extensive ponds. Man intentionally creates artificial lakes by damming rivers and streams for power, irrigation, and water storage, or by constructing small ponds and marshes for water, fishing, and wild-life. Quarries and strip mines fill with water to form other ponds.

Characteristics of lakes

The relatively still waters of lakes and ponds offer environmental conditions that contrast sharply with running water (see Chap. 10). Light penetrates only to a certain depth, depending upon turbidity. Temperatures vary seasonally and with depth. Since only a relatively small proportion of the water is in direct contact with the air and since decomposition is taking place on the bottom, the oxygen content of lake water is relatively low compared to that of running water. In some lakes, oxygen may become less with depth, but there are many exceptions. These gradations of oxygen, light, and temperature influence profoundly life in the lake, its distribution, and adaptations.

Temperature stratification

Each year the waters of many lakes and ponds undergo seasonal changes in temperature (Fig. 8-1). As the ice melts in early spring, the surface water, heated by the sun, warms up. When it reaches 4°C and becomes more dense, a slight temporary stratification develops, which sets up convection currents. Aided by the strong winds of spring, these currents mix the water throughout the basin until the water in the lake is uniformly 4°C. Now even the slightest winds can cause a complete circulation of the water between the surface and the bottom. This is the spring overturn, when the nutrients on the bottom, the oxygen on the top, and the plankton within are mixed throughout the lake.

With the coming of summer, the sun's intensity increases, and the temperature of the surface water rises. The higher the temperature of the surface water becomes, the greater is the difference in the density between the surface and deeper layers. Since the thermal density gradient opposes the energy of the wind, it becomes more difficult for the waters to mix. As a result, a mixing barrier or wall is established. The warm, freely circulating surface water, with a small but variable temperature gradient, is the *epilimnion* (Fig. 8-1 C). Below this is the wall, the *metalimnion,* a zone characterized by a very steep and rapid decline in temperature. Within the metalimnion is the *thermocline,* the plane at which the temperature drops most rapidly—1°C for each meter of depth. Below these two layers is the *hypolimnion,* a deep, cold layer, in which the temperature drop is gentle.

With the coming of autumn, the air temperature falls. The surface water

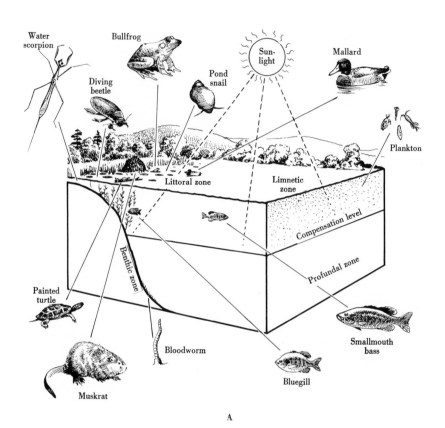

A

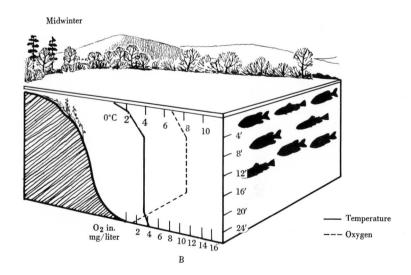

B

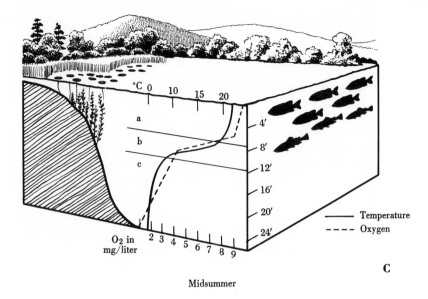

Midsummer

C

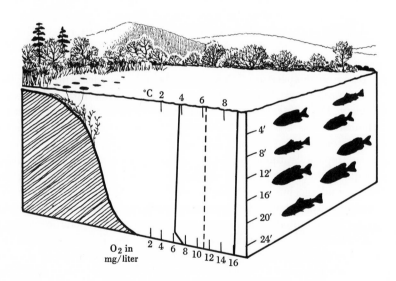

Spring and fall overturn

D

Figure 8-1 *These drawings summarize life in the lake as it is influenced by the seasons and seasonal stratification of oxygen and temperature. (A) A generalized picture of the lake in midsummer showing the major zones—the littoral, the limnetic, the profundal, and the benthic. The compensation level is the point at which the light is too low for photosynthesis. Surrounding the lake is a variety of organisms typical of the lake community. (B) The distribution of oxygen and* *temperature in a lake during midwinter and its effect on the distribution of fish life. The narrow fish are trout, representing the cold-water species; the bass silhouette, warm-water species. (C) In midsummer there is a pronounced stratification. A is epilimnion; B, the metalimnion; C, the hypolimnion. (D) During the spring and fall overturns, the oxygen and temperature curves are almost straight lines. The graphs are general, and represent no particular lake.*

loses heat to the atmosphere through evaporation, convection, and conduction. The temperature of the surface water drops and the thermocline sinks; the epilimnion increases until it includes the entire lake. The temperature once again is uniform from top to bottom, the lake waters circulate, and oxygen and nutrients are recharged throughout the lake. This is the fall overturn, which, through stirring actions caused by the slightest wind, may last until ice forms.

As the surface water cools below 4°C, it becomes lighter, remains on the surface, and, if the climate is cold enough, freezes; otherwise, it remains very close to 0°C. Now a slight inverse temperature stratification may develop, in which the water becomes warmer up to 4°C with depth. The water immediately beneath the ice may be warmed by solar radiation through the ice. Since this increases its density, this water subsequently flows to the bottom, where it mixes with water warmed by heat conducted from bottom mud. The result of this is a higher temperature at the bottom, although the over-all stability of the water is undisturbed. As the ice melts in spring, the surface water again becomes warm, currents pass unhindered, and the spring overturn takes place.

This is a general picture of seasonal changes in temperature stratification and must not be considered as a uniform condition in all deep bodies of water. In shallow lakes and ponds temporary stratification of short duration may occur; in others stratification may exist but no thermocline develops. In some very deep lakes the thermocline may simply descend during periods of overturn and not disappear at all. In such lakes the bottom water never becomes mixed with the top layers. But some form of thermal stratification occurs in all very deep lakes, including those of the tropics.

Based on temperature, lakes can be broadly classified into three basic groups (Hutchinson, 1957). Lakes that have two overturns during the year are called *dimictic*. Dimictic lakes are inversely stratified in winter and directly stratified in summer. These lakes are characteristic of temperate regions and of high mountains in subtropical regions. In warm oceanic climates and in the mountains of subtropical latitudes are lakes whose waters never cool sufficiently to allow complete circulation, except at the very coldest time of the year. Such lakes, which undergo but one overturn in a year, are called *warm monomictic*. The water is never below 4°C at any level; and in fact the temperature of the water in the hypolimnion is never lower than the mean temperature of the air at the time of the last circulation. These lakes too are directly stratified in summer. Lakes in polar and arctic regions may never rise above 4°C and circulation takes place only in summer. These are *cold monomictic* lakes. Freely circulating in summer, these lakes are inversely stratified in winter. There are a few other types. Lakes in the high mountains of equatorial regions, where there is little seasonal change in temperature, have waters that are continually circulating at a little above 4°C. These lakes, called *polymictic*, always lose just enough heat to prevent stable stratification. On the other hand there are some lakes in the humid tropics whose waters, always well above 4°C, circulate only at irregular intervals.

Oxygen stratification

Oxygen stratification during summer nearly parallels that of temperature (Fig. 8-1 C), although here again there are exceptions. In general the amount of oxygen is greatest near the surface, where there is an interchange between the water and atmosphere and some stirring by the wind. The quantity decreases with depth, a decrease caused in part by the respiration of decomposer organisms feeding on the organic matter dropping down from the layers above. In some lakes oxygen may vary little from top to bottom; every layer will be saturated relative to temperature and pressure. Water in a few lakes may be so clear that light penetrates below the depth of the thermocline and permits the development of phytoplankton. Here, because of photosynthesis, the oxygen content may be greater in deep water than on the surface.

During the spring and fall overturns when water recirculates through the lake, oxygen is replenished in the deep water and nutrients are returned to the top. In winter the reduction of oxygen in unfrozen water is slight, since bacterial decomposition is reduced and water at low temperatures holds a maximum amount of oxygen. Under ice, however, oxygen depletion may be serious and result in a heavy winter kill of fish.

Currents and seiches

Oxygen and thermal stratification, depth and position of the thermocline, circulation of nutrients, and distribution of organisms all are influenced by currents. The most conspicuous water movements observed are traveling surface waves, the result of wind pressures on the surface of lakes and ponds. Except for the effects they have on the shore line and shore organisms, surface waves are not too important biologically. More important are standing waves, or *seiches* (sāches), a term that comes from the French and means dry, exposed shoreline. These seiches are produced by an oscillation of a structure of water about a point or node.

There are two kinds of seiches, surface and internal. Both are produced by the wind blowing across the water's surface, by heavy rain showers, or perhaps even by changes in atmospheric pressure (see Bryson and Ragotzkie, 1960; Vallentyne, 1957).

When the wind blows across a lake or pond, it piles up water on the leeward end and creates a depression on the windward end. When the wind subsides, the current flows back; but since the momentum of the returning currents is not broken on the shore, a depression is created on the former leeward side, and the water flows back again. Thus an oscillation or rocking motion is established about a stationary node (Fig. 8-2). This continues until it is finally halted by the lake basin proper or by such meteorological forces as an opposite wind or rain. Although these surface seiches occur on all lakes, they can be observed visually only on larger lakes.

Internal seiches, not observable on the surface, occur during the summer in thermally stratified lakes. They are much more pronounced and exert a greater influence on life in the lake than surface seiches. Internal seiches are caused not only by the action of wind on the surface waters but also by density differences between warm and cold water. When the wind piles the water of the epilimnion up on the leeward side, the weight and circulation of the lighter water over the denser cold water tilts the thermocline and raises the hypolimnion on the windward side. When the wind stops, the raised hypolimnion, pushed down on and toward the leeward side, causes the epilimnion water to flow back toward the windward side. Thus an oscillation is established between the lighter layer of

167

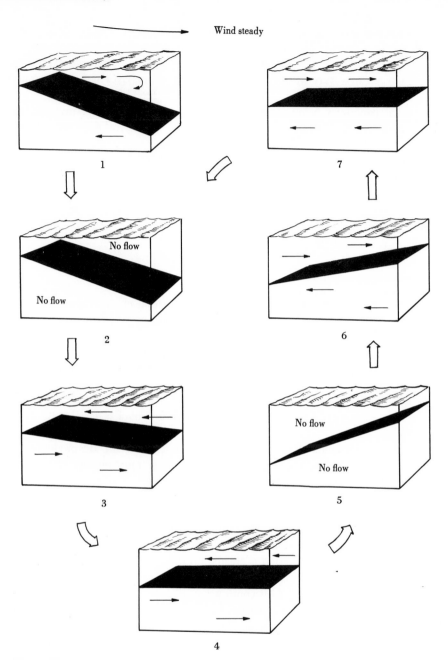

Figure 8-2 *A diagrammatic representation of a thermocline slope and subsequent seiches after the wind dies down.*

the epilimnion and the denser water of the hypolimnion (Fig. 8-2). In time, the oscillations are slowed by friction on the lake basin or by the wind from an opposite direction.

These oscillations move about a point in the center of the lake where resistance is highest. Here vertical displacement movement is the least, while the greatest displacement is on the windward and leeward ends. The position of internal

168

seiches can best be determined by charting the variations of the depth of a particular temperature over a period of hours. This movement makes difficult the determination of the true position of the thermocline, since its position at any one point is determined by the amplitude of the oscillation at that point.

Ecologically, internal seiches are important because they distribute heat and nutrients vertically in the lake and transport them into shallow water. The seiche sets up two rhythmic but opposite current systems above and below the thermocline, whose speed is the greatest when the thermocline is level (Fig. 8-2). A turbulence develops in the hypolimnion; without this turbulence the hypolimnion would become stagnant. In addition, plankton is moved up or down with the water mass. Even fish and other organisms are influenced by internal seiches.

The mixing of water and the transfer of nutrients also are carried on by *eddy currents*. These are small, turbulent currents, whose energy is dissipated at right angles to the major currents. Since these largely are horizontal and the turbulence is vertical, an interchange of adjacent water masses takes place. Here oxygen may be transferred downward and heat upward; nutrients and even plankton are intermixed. The degree of intermixing depends upon the intensity of the turbulence, which changes gradually from one depth to another.

Life in lakes and ponds

So far, lakes and ponds have been considered only as if they were natural laboratories in which chemical processes and demonstrations of physical laws could be observed. This was necessary in order to understand the biology of lakes and ponds, since the abundance, distribution, and diversity of lake and pond life are influenced by light, temperature, oxygen, and nutrients.

The energy source of the lake and pond ecosystem is sunlight. The depth to which light can penetrate is limited by the turbidity of the water and the absorption of light rays. On this basis, lakes and ponds can be divided into two basic layers—the *trophogenic zone*, roughly corresponding to the epilimnion, in which photosynthesis dominates; and the second, the lower *tropholytic zone*, where decomposition is most active. This zone is about the same as the hypolimnion. The boundary between the two zones is the *compensation depth*—the depth at which photosynthesis balances respiration and beyond which light penetration is so low that it is no longer effective. Generally the compensation depth occurs where light intensity is about 100 foot-candles, or approximately one per cent of full noon sunlight incident to the surface (see Edmondson, 1956).

The region of photosynthetic activity can be subdivided into two subzones. First is the *littoral*, or shallow-water zone, where light penetrates to the bottom. This area is occupied by rooted plants such as water lilies, rushes, and sedges. Beyond this is the *limnetic*, or open-water zone, which extends to the depth of effective light penetration. It is inhabited by plant and animal plankton and the *nekton*, free-swimming organisms such as fish, which are capable of moving about voluntarily. Common to both the tropholytic and trophogenic zones is the *benthic*, or bottom region. Although these areas are named and often described separately, all are closely dependent upon one another in nutrient cycles and energy flow (Fig. 8-3). The organisms that inhabit the benthic zone are known collectively as the *benthos*.

169

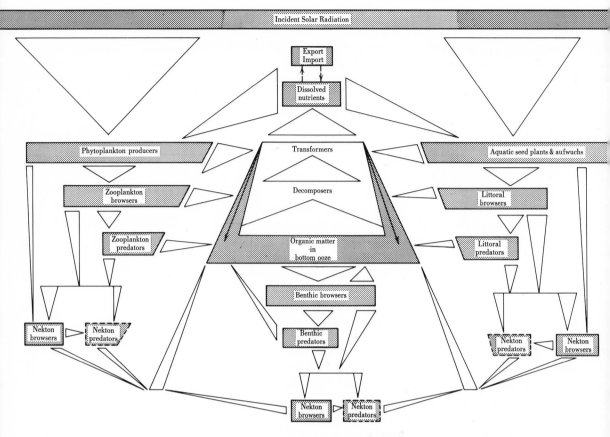

Figure 8-3 *A diagrammatic relationship between the littoral, limnetic, and benthic organisms and trophic structure in a lake. The heavy arrows of various sizes indicate the relative quantities of energy flow.* (This diagram was originally designed by Arnold Benson, West Virginia University.)

Limnetic life

The open water is a world of minute suspended organisms, the plankton. Dominant are the phytoplankton, among them the diatoms, desmids, and the filamentous green algae. Since these tiny plants alone carry on photosynthesis in open water, they are the base upon which the rest of limnetic life depends. Suspended with the phytoplankton are the animal, or zooplankton organisms, which graze upon the minute plants. These animals form an important link in the energy flow in the limnetic zone. Most characteristic are the rotifers, copepods, and cladocerans. Rotifers, the so-called wheelbearers, have at the front end of the body a circlet of moving cilia, which look like two rapidly rotating wheels. These cilia aid the organisms to pull algae and protozoa into the pharynx, where the food is crushed and ground. The crustaceans, cladocerans, and copepods filter phytoplankton, bacteria, and detritus out of the water by means of comblike setae on the thoracic appendages.

Movements and distribution of phytoplankton and most of the zooplankton are influenced largely by the physical forces already described. Unable to determine their own position in the water, these organisms must either float or sink. The ability to float depends upon the specific gravity of the organisms in relation to the specific gravity of the medium. If the specific gravity of an organism is the same as water, it will float; and if its specific gravity is greater, it will sink. The rate at which small bodies sink varies directly with their weight in excess of an equal volume of surrounding water, and their form, and inversely with viscosity. Provided viscosity and specific gravity remain unchanged, a sphere of 0.01 millimeter will sink 100 times more slowly than one of 0.1 millimeters. Also involved is the ratio of total surface area to the volume of the body. The greater the ratio, the greater the friction and thus the resistance to sinking (see Brooks and Hutchinson, 1950).

Many plankton organisms have adaptations for staying afloat or remaining suspended. Fresh-water diatoms and desmids have thin, siliceous shells, which reduce their weight. Some plankton organisms may live in a gelatinous envelope, which has about the same specific gravity as water. Others may have gas vacuoles or oil droplets in the body. Many plankton organisms have surfaces set with spines, ridges, horns, or setae or possess an elongated body, all of which increase the total surface area in relation to weight.

But eddy diffusion currents more than any floating device keep plankton from sinking. The currents maintain a mixing action that not only holds the organisms in suspension but also prevents a persistent stratification of plankton in the epilimnion.

Vertical distribution or stratification of plankton organisms is influenced by the physicochemical properties of water, especially temperature, oxygen, light, and current. Light, of course, sets the lower limit at which phytoplankton can exist. Since animal plankton feed on these minute plants, most of these too are concentrated in the trophogenic zone. Phytoplankton, by their own growth, limit light penetration and thus reduce the depth at which they can live. As the zone becomes more shallow, the phytoplankton can absorb more light and organic production is increased. But within these limits the depth at which the various species live is influenced by the optimum conditions for their development. Some phytoplankton live just beneath the water's surface; others are more abundant a few feet beneath, while those requiring colder temperatures live deeper still. Cold-water plankton, in fact, are restricted to those lakes in which phytoplankton growth is scarce in the upper region and in which the oxygen content of the deep water is not depleted by the decomposition of organic matter. Many of these cold-water species never move up through the metalimnion.

Since many of them are capable of independent movement, animal plankton exhibit stratification that often changes seasonally. In winter some plankton forms are spread evenly to considerable depths; in summer they concentrate in the layers most favorable to them and to their stage of development. At this season animal plankton undertake a vertical migration during some part of the twenty-four hour period. Depending upon the species and their stage of development, they spend the night or day in the deep water or on the bottom and move up to the surface during the alternate period to feed on phytoplankton (Fig. 8-4).

During the spring and fall overturns, the plankton are carried down, but at the same time nutrients released by decomposition in the tropholytic zone are

171

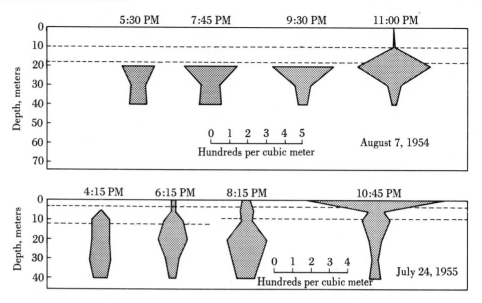

Figure 8-4 *The vertical distribution of the copepod* Limnocalanus macrurus *on two midsummer days. On August 7, 1954, the sunset was at 8:00 P.M., EST; on July 24, 1955, it was 8:15 P.M., EST. The maximum number reach the surface one and one-half to four hours before sunset. Note that this organism inhabits the deeper water. The broken lines represent the metalimnion.* (After Wells, 1960.)

carried upward into the impoverished upper layers. In spring, when the surface water warms and stratification again develops, phytoplankton have access to both nutrients and light. The spring bloom develops, followed, especially in shallow water, by a rapid depletion of nutrients and a reduction in plankton populations.

Free, to a large extent, from the action of weak currents and capable of moving about at will are nekton organisms, the fish, and some invertebrates. In the limnetic zone, fish make up the bulk of the nekton. Their distribution is influenced mostly by food supply, oxygen, and temperature (Fig. 8-1). During the summer, largemouth bass, pike, and muskellunge inhabit the warmer epilimnion waters, where food is abundant. In winter they retreat to deeper water. Lake trout, on the other hand, move to greater depths as summer advances. During the spring and fall overturn, when oxygen and temperature are fairly uniform throughout, both warm-water and cold-water forms occupy all levels.

Profundal zone

Below the depth of effective light, beneath the thermocline, lie the profundal waters. Diversity and abundance of life here are influenced by oxygen and temperature; and the organisms depend upon the rain of organic material from the layers above as their energy source. In highly productive waters, decomposer organisms so deplete the profundal waters of oxygen that little aerobic life can exist there. Since the profundal zone of a deep lake is relatively much larger, the productivity of the epilimnion is low in comparison to the volume of water, and decomposition does not deplete the oxygen. Here the profundal zone supports some life, particularly fish, some plankton, and such organisms as certain clado-cerans, which live in the bottom ooze. Other zooplankton may occupy this zone during some part of the day but migrate upward to the surface to feed. Only during the spring and autumn overturns, when organisms from the upper layers enter this zone, is life abundant in the profundal waters.

Easily decomposed substances floating down through the profundal zone are partly mineralized while sinking (Kleerekoper, 1953). The remaining organic debris, the dead bodies of plants and animals of the open water and decomposing plant matter from shallow water areas, settle on the bottom. This, together with quantities of material washed in by inflowing water, makes up the bottom sediments, the habitat of benthic organisms.

Benthic zone

The bottom ooze is a region of great biological activity, so great that oxygen curves for lakes and ponds show a sharp drop in the profundal water just above the bottom. Since organic muck lacks oxygen completely, the dominant organisms there are anaerobic bacteria. Under anaerobic conditions, decomposition cannot procede to inorganic end products. When the amounts of organic matter reaching the bottom are greater than can be utilized by the bottom fauna, odoriferous muck rich in hydrogen sulphide and methane results. Thus lakes and ponds with highly productive limnetic and littoral zones have an impoverished fauna on the profundal bottom. Life in the bottom ooze is most abundant in lakes with a deep hypolimnion in which oxygen is still available.

Some of the bottom species, such as the flatworm (Rhabdocoela), live on the surface of the ooze, but others burrow into the bottom mud to feed on decaying organic matter. Prominent among these are the rhizopods (Rhizopoda), amoeba-like protozoans encased in shells, the clam *Psidium*, and small crustaceans, including ostracods, isopods, copepods, and cladocerans. Other interesting bottom dwellers are the larvae of the phantom midges, which rise to surface at night and return to the bottom at dawn, and water bears (Tardigrada), which crawl through the ooze on stumpy legs with long, curved claws.

Many of these organisms live relatively deep in the ooze. They meet their limited oxygen demands by constructing tubes up through the ooze to the water. One of these, the bloodworm, or midge larva (*Tendipes*), sets up a current of water by movement within the tube. It utilizes the small quantity of oxygen through a hemoglobinlike pigment in its blood. The very abundant annelid worm, *Tubefex*, lives with its anterior end buried in the mud and its posterior end, which it undulates briskly, extended up in the water.

Most organisms of the profundal bottom are not unique to this zone. They represent for the most part a few species of the larger littoral bottom fauna that can tolerate severe stagnation. Even these, if subject to continuous stagnation, will be eliminated wholly or in part. Bottom fauna is restocked from egg stages carried over during periods of stress or by downward migration from the littoral bottom during seasonal turnover (Welch, 1952). But there are a few species found only on the profundal bottom. Among these are the amphipod *Pontoporeia affinis*, and the opossum shrimp *Mysis oculata*, var. *relicta*, which inhabit only

173

deep, cold-water lakes, where the oxygen may be less than 7 per cent of satura-tion.

As the water becomes more shallow, the benthos changes. The bottom materials —stones, rubble, gravel, marl, clay—are modified by the action of water, by plant growth, by drift materials, and by recent organic deposits. Increased oxygen, light, and food results in a richness of species and an abundance not found on the profundal bottom. Here on the bottom of the littoral zone live, in addition to the tube worms, the midges, and the water bears, numerous other plant and detritus feeders.

Closely associated with the benthic community are the *periphyton,* or *aufwuchs,* those organisms that are attached to or move upon a submerged sub-strate but do not penetrate it. Small aufwuchs communities are found on the leaves of submerged aquatics, on sticks, rocks, and other debris. The organisms found there depend upon the movement of the water, temperature, kind of substrate, and depth.

Periphyton found on living plants are fast growing, lightly attached, and con-sist primarily of algae and diatoms. Since the substrate is so short-lived, these rarely exist for more than one summer. Aufwuchs on stones, wood, and debris form a more crustlike growth of blue-green algae, diatoms, water mosses, and sponges. Burrowing into and living up in this crust is a host of associated animals —rotifers, hydras, copepods, insect larvae, and a wide variety of protozoans, such as *Stentor* and *Vorticella.* Unlike those on plants, the periphyton on more sub-stantial substrate are more persistent. Periphyton found in moving water, such as currents and waves on the lake shore, adhere tightly. In fact the various means of attachment of periphyton to the substrate are as varied as the methods phytoplankton use to remain afloat. Some aufwuchs organisms have gelatinous sheaths, tubes, or cups, and are attached to the substrate by gelatinous stalks or basal disks.

Littoral zone and ponds

Aquatic life is the richest and most abundant in the shallow water, where sun-light can reach the bottom. This is the littoral zone found about the edges of lakes and usually throughout the pond. The plants and animals found here vary with water depth, and a distinct zonation of life exists from deeper water to shore.

Duckweeds may cover the surface of the littoral water. The plants have thin, floating leaves with roots that hang down into the water. Their density increases as summer lengthens, until the mat becomes so thick in places that it prevents the sunlight from penetrating the water and destroys the submerged plants beneath.

The duckweed blanket (Fig. 8-5) supports a world of its own. Aquatic insects attach eggs on the roots and on the undersurfaces of the leaves. A caddisfly may build its portable shelter from whole plants, and filamentous and colonial algae cling to its roots. Desmids, diatoms, protozoans, rotifers, minute crustaceans, hydras, planarians, snails, and red water mites live on the under surface of the blanket. On the top live mosquitos and tiny collembolas.

Submerged plants such as the alga *Chara* and the pondweeds, found at water depths beyond that tolerated by emergent vegetation, serve as supports for small

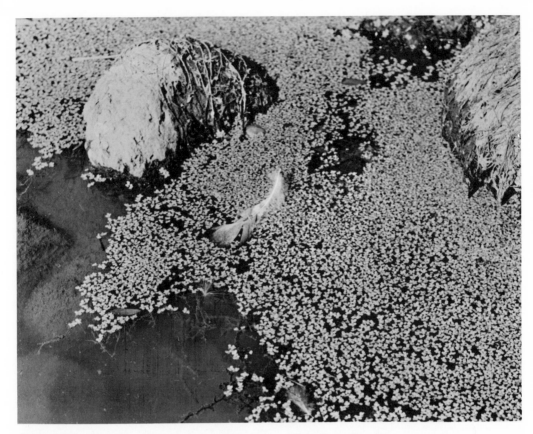

Figure 8-5 *A blanket of duckweed on quiet water.* (Photo by author.)

algae and cover for swarms of minute aquatic animals, worms, and snails. One of the most interesting of the submerged plants is the delicate, vinelike bladderwort, named for the bladderlike traps on the branches of each leaf. Each "bladder" has a slit-shaped opening, guarded by a valve and edged with teeth and bristling hairs. When protozoans, water fleas, and other minute organisms enter the opening of the slit, the valve opens and the animals are trapped in the bladder, where they are digested. Presence of bladderwort is a good sign that protozoans, rotifers, and small crustaceans are abundant.

Submerged plants are highly modified in structure. Living, as they do, completely immersed in water, they lack cuticle, which reduces transpiration in leaves exposed to the air. Lacking cuticle, submerged plants can absorb nutrients and gases directly from the water through thin and finely dissected, or ribbon-like, leaves. On many, the roots are small, poorly branched, and lack root hairs. The buoyance and protection of water eliminate the need for supporting tissues in the stems. Air chambers and passages are common in leaves and in the cortex of stems, where oxygen produced by photosynthesis is stored for use in respiration. For the most part, vegetative reproduction is highly developed.

As sedimentation and accumulation of organic matter increase toward the shore and the depth of water decreases, floating rooted aquatics, such as pond lilies and smartweeds, appear. Many of these floating plants have poorly developed root systems but highly developed aerating systems. Supporting tissue is greatly reduced and the spongy tissue in the stems and leaves is filled with large air spaces. The upper surfaces of floating leaves are heavily waxed to prevent clogging of the stomata by water. Underwater leaves of these same floating plants are like those of submerged plants, thin and small, while the floating leaves usually are large and different in form. The leaves and stems are leathery and tough and able to withstand the action of waves.

Floating plants offer food and support for numerous herbivorous animals that feed both on phytoplankton and the floating plants. The undersides and stems of plants support a highly interesting assemblage of organisms, among them protozoans, hydras, snails, and sponges. The periphyton include not only small algae but also such small animals as *Stentor, Actinophaerium,* and *Vorticella.*

In the shallow water beyond the zone of floating plants grow the emergents, plants whose roots and lower stems are immersed in water and whose upper stems and leaves stand above the water. Large areas of such plants make up the marsh, to be discussed later. Among these emergents are plants with narrow, tubular or linear leaves, such as the bulrushes, reeds, and cattails. With these are associated such broadleaf emergents as pickerelweed and arrowhead. The distribution and variety of plants vary with the water depth and fluctuation of the water level. Some plants, such as the cattail, do best in deeper water; reeds, sedges, and rushes, on the other hand, do better on shallow water and saturated soils. Some, such as the spike rushes, cannot complete their life cycle unless they are alternately covered by water and exposed to the air.

Life is abundant about the sheltering beds of emergent plants. Damselflies and dragonflies lay their eggs on submerged stems just below the water line. The water scorpion, nearly two inches long and resembling a walking stick, has a long air tube on the abdomen, Through this it draws air from the atmosphere while it hangs its head and raptorial forelegs two to three inches below the surface and waits to seize any prey that ventures near. Conspicuous diving insects are the backswimmers, the diving beetles, and the water boatmen. The first two are predacious. The abundant backswimmers have their backs keeled like boat bottoms and navigate upside down on the surface; beneath the surface they swim right side up. The diving beetles, usually black or brownish black in color, include some of the largest aquatic insects and some of the smallest, almost microscopic in size. Both the backswimmers and the diving beetles hang head downward in the water and dive swiftly after prey. Both feed on tadpoles, fish fry, and insects. The backswimmers, however, feed on the juices which they secure by piercing the prey with their piercing-sucking mouth parts. The water boatmen feed on algae, protozoa, and microscopic metazoa, which they gather by sweeping the fine material on the bottom into their mouths. They feed on algae filaments also, which they pierce with protrusible stylets to suck out the contents.

All three can remain under water for some time because they carry with them their own "scuba tanks" of air in the form of bubbles. The backswimmers carry a film of air on the abdomen; the diving beetles and water scavenger beetles carry a large bubble of air in the subelytral air space (beneath the wings), into which their spiracles open. The water boatmen, on the other hand, are wrapped in air and carry an additional supply trapped beneath the wings; because of this they must cling to plant stems and debris to remain submerged.

The air bubbles that these insects carry act as physical gills. The air in the bubble is composed of approximately 21 per cent oxygen and 78 per cent nitrogen, about the same as that of the atmosphere. When the insects are submerged, they withdraw oxygen from the bubble and give off carbon dioxide. But since carbon dioxide dissolves readily in water, it does not accumulate in the bubble. At the same time the nitrogen dissolves very slowly into the water. As the oxygen supply decreases, the tension or partial pressure of the nitrogen increases and maintains the surface of the bubble. As the oxygen tension inside the bubble decreases, it reaches a level at which it is less inside the bubble than outside. Unless the oxygen content of the water is sharply limited, oxygen will diffuse into the bubble almost as fast as it is used. Thus as long as sufficient nitrogen remains to provide an adequate surface for oxygen diffusion, the animal can remain submerged. When the oxygen is reduced to about one per cent of the total gas inside the bubble, the insect rises to the surface for a recharge of air.

Fish, such as pickerel and sunfish, find shelter, food, and protection among the emergent and floating plants; and the ubiquitous catfish, often tolerant of extreme conditions of turbidity, feeds close to the bottom. Fish of lakes and ponds lack the strong lateral muscles characteristic of fish living in swift water; and some, such as the sunfish, have compressed bodies, which permit them to move with ease through masses of aquatic plants.

Productivity classes of lakes

At this point one fact emerges—that production is greatest in lakes and ponds that are relatively shallow and that are rich in organic matter and nutrients. Because of the heavy accumulation of organic matter, oxygen depletion in the hypolimnion occurs during the summer. Such lakes are termed *eutrophic*. These contrast sharply with deep lakes, which often have steep sides. Littoral plants are scarce, and plankton growth is low in proportion to the total volume of water. The quantity of organic matter produced in relation to water volume is much less and the deep waters are continuously oxygenated (see the discussion earlier in this chapter). Since the amount of nutrients recycled is low per unit volume of water, deep lakes often are poor in phosphorus, nitrogen, and calcium. Such lakes are termed *oligotrophic*.

As oligotrophic lakes gradually fill in and become more shallow and as organic matter becomes more abundant, they may develop into eutrophic lakes. And eutrophic lakes, through time, may change, according to the law of succession, into marshes and temporary ponds.

A third type of lake to come under this classification is the *dystrophic*, which will be discussed in greater detail in the section on bogs. Dystrophic lakes are low in calcium carbonate, high in humus content, and very poor in nutrients.

Temporary ponds

Many are the shallow depressions and the remnants of old ponds that fill with water shortly after the first spring thaw. For a while they sparkle in the spring sunshine, but by early summer they are gone. Few give these ponds a second thought; some consider them a nuisance or a breeding place for mosquitos. Actually they merit close observation, for few places are more interesting. These transient pools of water are temporary ponds. They contain water only several months, usually in the spring, and are dry the rest of the year.

Because of extreme environmental conditions, the temporary pond is a difficult place for living organisms to inhabit. For a time the area is submerged; then follows a period of progressively drier conditions, until finally the bottom is dry and covered with woody or herbaceous growth. In winter the depression may hold some ice-covered water, collected from melted snow, but most of the area is frozen and snow covered. When the early spring thaw sets in, the depression fills with water and the cycle begins again.

During the few months that open water is present, the inhabitants of temporary ponds must complete their reproductive activity and meet in one way or another the problem of species survival during the dry period (see Chap. 4).

Animal life in the temporary pond is at low ebb during late winter and early spring. If the depression holds some water during the winter, the flatworm, *Phagocytes vernalis,* may be present, in company with the copepod *Cyclops.* Shortly after the snow melts, the fairy shrimp appears. It is the most typical inhabitant of the temporary pond. The fairy shrimp is a branchiopod, or gill-footed crustacean, so called because its leaflike thoracic feet are margined with gills. With these, it breathes and propels itself through the water. Fairy shrimp hatch during February and March from eggs laid the spring before. Alternate drying and freezing of eggs on the exposed pond bottom stimulates the processes of development and hatching (Weaver, 1943). Since such conditions do not usually occur in permanent ponds, fairy shrimp are confined to temporary pools or to ponds which undergo considerable drawdown of water during the summer.

The population of fairy shrimp reaches its height in April and disappears nearly as rapidly as it appeared. The sudden decline seems to be associated with an increase in predatory insects (Kenk, 1949). Even early in spring, while ice still clings to the edges of the pond and the water is very cold, individuals of predacious beetles appear. They lay their eggs in April and young larvae hatch to feed on fairy shrimp. Slow swimmers, the fairy shrimp soon fall prey to the beetles. As the fairy shrimp population declines, another temporary pond crustacean may appear, the clam shrimp, which has a bivalved carapace enclosing a compressed body.

As the water warms, activity increases. New pond residents appear, either by hatching from dormant eggs or cysts or by migrating to the pond. Frogs and salamanders arrive in March and April, court, mate, deposit their gelatinous eggs, and depart. Fingernail clams are common from February. These are small bivalves with rather plump shells and inconspicuous surface ridges. They emerge from the mud of the pond bottom in late autumn or early winter, grow to their maximum size the following spring, produce their young from brood pouches in each inner gill, and die. The young clams, in turn, burrow into the mud as summer approaches and emerge in early winter as the pond fills. Thus the life span of these clams is a little over one year.

By April the waters of temporary ponds are alive with small crustaceans, including the aquatic sow bug, water fleas, ostracods, and copepods. In addition to these minute crustaceans, vernal pools support abundant plankton organisms, perhaps encouraged by decaying vegetation on the pond bottom. Browsing on this plankton growth, algae, and organic debris are the scud and the crayfish. As the water level sinks, the crayfish resorts to burrows that reach ground water level, and here it stays until the spring thaw. In the pocket of water filling the burrow a great concentration of other small crustaceans find refuge.

The pond waters begin to drop in May, and by June the water is nearly gone. The crayfish has retreated to its burrow, insects have hatched from eggs, matured, and flown away. Eggs of shrimp, cysts of flatworms, and dormant mollusks lie buried in the bottom mud. But for many animals, the drying of the pond means death. Nymphs of insects not yet matured and some unhatched eggs are destroyed. Larvae of frogs and salamanders that fail to reach adult form before the pond dries perish.

Pond life has ended and in its place is mesophytic growth of willow and dogwood, cattail and sedge. Nine months later the pond will fill again and the cycle start anew.

SUMMARY

The temporary pond was perhaps the remnant of a lake or pond, a standing body of water that filled a depression in the earth. Before its "death," the lake was a nearly self-contained ecosystem. As with most lakes, it probably exhibited gradients in light, temperature, and dissolved gases. In summer its waters were stratified. It had a surface layer of warm, circulating water, the epilimnion, and a middle zone, the metalimnion, in which the temperature rapidly dropped. Below this was the hypolimnion, a bottom layer of denser water, approximately 4°C, often low in oxygen and high in carbon dioxide. When the surface water cooled in autumn, the difference in density between the layers decreased, and the waters circulated throughout the lake. A similar mixing of waters took place in spring when the lake warmed up. These seasonal overturns were important in recirculating the nutrients and in mixing the bottom waters with the top. Areas where light penetrated to the bottom of the lake, a zone known as the littoral, were occupied by rooted plants. Beyond this was open water, or the limnetic zone, inhabited by plant and animal plankton and fish. Below the depth of effective light penetration was the profundal region, where the diversity of life varied with the temperature and oxygen supply. The bottom, or benthic zone, was a place of intense biological activity, for here decomposition of organic matter was taking place. Anaerobic bacteria were dominant on the bottom beneath the profundal water, while the benthic zone of the littoral was rich in decomposer organisms and detritus feeders. Activities of plants and animals and sedimentation built up the lake bottom. Little by little, the zones of vegetation so characteristic of the littoral, the floating plants and emergents, pushed outward toward the middle. With time the lake grew smaller, to a pond, and then finally disappeared, replaced by a terrestrial community. Such is the ephemeral nature of lakes in the landscape.

SUGGESTED FIELD ACTIVITIES

When it comes to studying ecosystems, the fresh-water representatives provide some advantages over the terrestrial ones. The number of species of resident plants and animals is relatively small, which somewhat eases the problem of identification;

179

there are marked environmental changes within short distances; and the ecosystem is relatively closed.

In the study of any habitat, it is best to start small. Concentrate on a pond or at the most a small lake or a portion of it.

Since all aquatic habitats are influenced by the geology of the surrounding area, i.e., limestone or sandstone country, depth, chemical composition, etc., the observation of these features is a good place to begin.

Mapping is essential to the study of any natural habitat, and lakes and ponds are no exception. One does not need to spend a long time on this, but something fairly

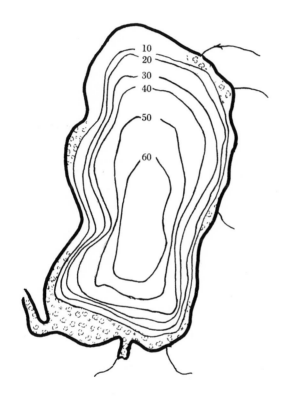

Figure 8-6 *A map of a lake showing depth profiles and a bed of aquatic vegetation.* (Redrawn from a map by New York State Conservation Department.)

accurate is necessary. The map needs to show the shape of the pond or lake, and the surrounding features, including the major zones of vegetation. In addition it should include the depth contours and the bottom vegetation (Fig. 8-6). Depth can be roughly determined by taking soundings with a weighted, marked line lowered from a boat. This can be done more accurately with a hydrograph or sonar, if available. Mapping will require a number of transects across the pond. The contours can be plotted and drawn on the map, or depths can be indicated by inserting the figures at appropriate places on the map. The bottom vegetation (weed beds) should be mapped and emergents as well as submerged vegetation indicated. The result should be a base map on which can be placed transparent overlays of transects, temperature and oxygen profiles, fish cover, spawning beds, waterfowl and other bird nests, etc.

Chemical and physical characteristics of the water should be determined by the methods outlined in Appendix B. From a boat, collect water samples from graduated depths and determine oxygen, hardness, acidity, etc., depth of light penetration, and the temperature profile.

Aquatic life

Biological studies of lakes and ponds can be approached from both a descriptive and an energetic point of view. For an over-all appreciation of the lake as an ecosystem, the energy approach is best; it is particularly well adapted for class work.

The following are some suggestions for undertaking a generalized study of the lake or pond as a habitat:

1. Make an over-all survey of life in the area. Collect the various forms, note their specific microhabitat, and identify as completely as possible.

2. Collect free-floating plants and zooplankton. Many of these can be held and grown for further observations in indoor aquaria. Observe how they are adapted for life in water.

3. Tow a plankton net at different depths (0.25 meter, 0.5 meter, 1.0 meter, etc.) and from the lake determine the density and species composition of the population at different depths. Vertical movements can be observed if samplings are done periodically through a 24-hour period.

4. Examine stones, leaves, and stems of floating and rooted plants for small animal life. Observe in respect to cover the occurrence and location of vertebrate populations, including evidence of transient and semipermanent residents.

5. Note the forms characteristic of these habitats:
Soil between roots and stems of emergent plants
Underside of floating leaves
Inside of floating leaves
Surface of stems and petioles of aquatic plants
Detritus at the base of aquatic plants
Submerged aquatics
Patches of mud covered with filamentous algae
Surface of pond animals.

6. By means of an Ekman dredge, sample the benthic fauna along a gradient from shallow to deep water. Determine the organic-matter content of the bottom muck.

7. A small pond, preferably a managed fish pond, is an excellent subject for the study of functional ecology. To do this, sample the phytoplankton and zooplankton as outlined in Appendixes C and D. For phytoplankton determine numbers, kind, biomass, and pigment density. Determine number, kind, and biomass of zooplankton. Sample the fish population. Numbers can be estimated by mark-recapture, using fin clipping as the marking method. Sample the bottom fauna. Use the light and dark bottle method to measure primary production. Summarize data by means of tables, pyramids of biomass, etc.

CHAPTER **9**

Bogs, swamps, and marshes

Bogs

Of all aquatic communities, none are more intriguing than bogs (Fig. 9-1). Although bogs are rather widely distributed over the humid regions of the earth they are best developed and most abundant in the cold northern forested regions in North America, Europe, and Asia. In physical and chemical characteristics and community composition, they differ sharply from lakes, ponds, and marshes.

Regardless of species composition or location, all bogs have several features in common. They usually develop where drainage is blocked, all have cushionlike vegetation, and all have an accumulation of peat. Most at some time have a marginal semifloating mat of vegetation, usually sphagnum moss and heaths.

Lakes, ponds, and abandoned stream meanders typically accumulate organic sediments on the bottom. If drainage is inadequate, the area is saturated with water the year around and little organic matter is carried away or mixed with mineral substrate. Through time, drainage is further congested by plant growth and the circulation of water in these lakes and ponds is reduced, creating anaerobic conditions. Since biological activity is slowed down by a combination of anaerobic conditions and cold temperatures, the organic debris is only partially decomposed to form peat. These peats release humic acids, which tinge the water brown. Bog-lake waters are low in electrolytes, especially calcium carbonate, and range from strongly acid to alkaline, a phenomenon imperfectly understood but apparently influenced by plant cover and peat. Water adjacent to bog vegetation may be acid or alkaline, but water with sphagnum moss, the dominant plant of bogs, is always acid. Sphagnum and peat can absorb bases from dissolved salts and thus free acids. Bog waters also are low in available nitrogen, potassium, and phosphorus, since these nutrient elements are tied up in the peat. These waters have a high CO_2 content and possess traces of hydrogen sulfide (H_2S), the result of activity by sulfur bacteria. Lakes and ponds exhibiting these characteristics are termed *dystrophic*.

Figure 9-1   A bog. This is a picture of the "muskeg furthest south," Cranberry Glades, Pocahontas County, West Virginia. Tamarack is absent, as is Laborador tea. But this is the southernmost point in the range of bog rosemary. Note the hummock effect of moss and lichens.

The decidedly acid condition of sphagnum bogs, accounts for their uniqueness. The harsh conditions limit the kind of plants able to survive there. Thus a bog community, consisting of plants incapable of growing in alkaline situations, develops.

Bog development begins much like succession in other lakes (Fig. 9-2). Open water is colonized by submerged and then floating plants, especially the yellow pond lily. The accumulation of organic matter raises the lake or pond floor. Many of these sediments, especially the finer materials, may oxidize, decompose, or remain suspended as colloids during their movement from the water's surface to the bottom. Often they will remain in solution until precipitated by bacterial, chemical, or photosynthetic activity to form a fine, soft deposit called a "false bottom."

Meanwhile reeds and sedges, cotton grass, buckbean, and marsh cinquefoil grow in the shallows. Sphagnum creeps into the area and fills the open spaces between the plants. When a consolidated mass of peat develops or when jutting rocks, logs, or other solid objects allow a foothold, a mat extends outward over the water (Fig. 9-2). Leading edges of plants, particularly buckbean, send out a buoyant network of rhizomes, which sprout new shoots above the water level. On this loose tangle, *Sphagnum* and *Hypinium* mosses grow, filling in the open

183

spaces and consolidating the mass. As the mat thickens, other plants, such as the cranberry, sweet gale, and bog rosemary appear (Fig. 9-3). Sphagnum mosses grow in rounded cushions about the bases of shrubs (Figs. 9-2 and 9-3) and annually add new growth on the accumulating remains of past moss generations. As the mat thickens and rises, other shrubs that are intolerant of very wet conditions invade it. Typical are leatherleaf and Laborador tea. Leatherleaf, found in practically all boreal bogs, is exclusively a bog species and is confined to that habitat. Usually it is the dominant shrub, but in some bogs Laborador tea occupies this position.

On the sides of sphagnum hummocks, in depressions between, and on the meadowlike floating mat of sedges and buckbean grow two outstanding bog inhabitants, the pitcher plant and sundew, both predacious plants. The flat leaves of the small sundew bear tentacles tipped with sticky globules, which ensnare insects. The pitcher plants have a rosette of bronzy, tubular leaves, which contain water. Insects that inadvertently wander into the leaves find themselves

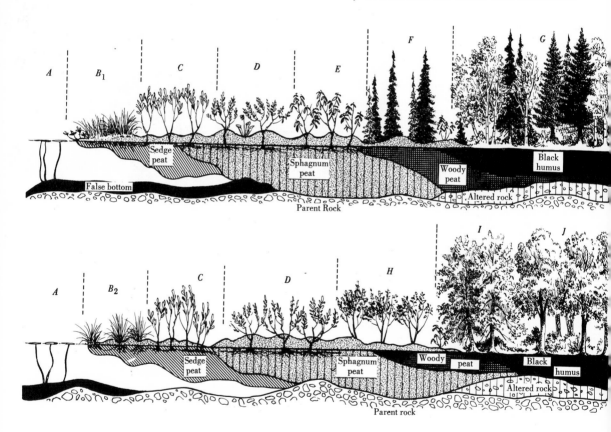

Figure 9-2 *Transects through two typical bogs showing the zones of vegetation, sphagnum mounds, and the nature of peat deposits and floating mat. A, Pond lily in open water; B1, buckbean and sedge zones; B2, sedge zones; C, sweet-gale zone; D, leatherleaf; E, Laborador tea; F, black spruce; G, birch, balsam, black spruce forest; H, mountain holly; I and J, silver and red maple. Tamarack is often associated with black spruce but is soon replaced by the spruce.* (Redrawn from Dansereau and Segadas-Vianna, 1952.)

Figure 9-3 *A close-up view of sphagnum moss and bog rosemary in a New York State bog.* (Photo by author.)

unable to crawl over the down-pointed hairs and fall into the water to drown. Here they apparently are digested by the plants, although the exact nature of this process and its function in the plant are not clearly understood. In spite of this digestive action and the low pH—approximately 4.5—of the fluid in the leaves, the mosquito, *Wyeomyua smithii,* passes through the egg, larval, and pupal stages within the cavity of the plant.

Along the edge of the bog where the peat mat is thick and reaches the bottom, the forest invades the shrub and sphagnum growth. Usually the first trees are scattered clumps and individuals of larch and black spruce, beneath which develop such plants as partridge berry and bunchberry. Eventually the forest thickens and advances as the mat closes toward the center of the lake. Because of its thin crown, tamarack allows a dense shrub growth to remain, but finally even this is replaced by black spruce, aborvitae, and balsam fir. In regions where deciduous forest is the climax, spruce is replaced by maples, birch, and balsam fir.

Peat accumulates and consolidates beneath the mat of sedges and heaths. The weight causes the mat to sink gradually to the bottom, where further decomposition is arrested. Occasionally the peat mat becomes infiltrated with alkaline water, which allows fermentation and decomposition of the peat. Pockets form beneath the surface; the peat mat sags and caves in. Patches of open water appear again. In the bog forest the evaporative power of the vegetation may become greater than the water-retaining capacity of the peaty material. Then succession tends toward a drier, more mesic condition. But lumbering, windthrow, or any action that destroys tree growth can reverse this process and convert the area back to early bog conditions. Thus succession in a bog may regress a number of times, delaying the time when stable vegetation will claim the area.

Life in the bog lake is restricted in the number of species, but the organisms present may be abundant. Phytoplankton are more abundant and richer in species than the zooplankton. Dominating the bog waters are varied and beautiful forms of desmids and a few blue-green algae. Among the zooplankton the testaceous rhizopods and the rotifers are the richest in species, and some forms are restricted to bog waters. Protozoans, too, are common, particularly *Sarcodina*.

More characteristic of bogs, perhaps, than the presence of a few species is the absence of many. Mollusks, except for certain Sphaeridae, are missing because of the lack of calcium. Among the aquatic insects are representatives of Odonata, Hemiptera, Trichoptera, Diptera, and Coleoptera. Fish are few in number or absent, but amphibians, especially the Ranidae, are universally present. Warblers are the most abundant birds of the bog forests, and the bog lemming is a common small mammal.

The moors

On drier ridges surrounding the dystrophic lake and bogs, and on flat, poorly drained areas, raised bogs or high moors develop (Dansereau and Segadas-Vianna, 1952). Sphagnum moss creeps into depressions up on the drier ridges. The spongy sphagnum with its tremendous water-holding capacity retains more and more precipitation in the ground. As a result mesophytic trees are replaced by trees and shrubs that live in a wet, acidic environment. The sphagnum accumulates, often to a height of several feet, and rises above the adjoining ground in extensive cushionlike mounds. As the mounds increase in size, they join, until the whole area becomes a raised bog surrounded by a swampy moat. Like the flat bog, the area eventually is occupied by concentric zones of vegetation interrupted by bog puddles and pools.

The marsh and swamp

Along the shallow margins of lakes and ponds and in low, poorly drained lands where water stands for several months of the year, wetland vegetation appears. Mostly this represents the last filling-in stages of lake and pond succession. Generally such areas are saturated or covered by water during the growing season. At times, particularly in early fall, the substrate may be exposed, a condition necessary for the germination of many wetland plants. The substrate is soft muck, rich in decaying organic matter mixed with mineral soil. As time passes, drainage gradually improves, for the vegetation continuously builds up the bottom with debris. The vegetation is discontinuous and distributed singly in small stands or clumps separated from one another (Fig. 9-4).

These wetlands are marshes and swamps. Biologically, they are among the richest communities and among the most interesting. Yet they are also the least appreciated and the first to be destroyed by filling and drainage.

Marshes are wetlands in which the dominant vegetation consists of reeds, sedges, grasses, and cattails; essentially they are wet prairies. *Swamps,* on the other hand, are wooded wetlands and in some cases represents a successional step from marsh to mesic forest. In other regions the swamp may develop without a preceding marsh stage.

Marsh

The floating plants of the premarsh stages were both protected and buoyed up by the water. But the emergent marsh plants, rising clear of the water, lack the

Figure 9-4 *A marshy border of a pond.* Foreground: *tussock sedge with invading alder;* middle foreground: *alder, willow, dogwood;* background: *elm and red maple. Note the old alder stems. The invading alder has been killed back in the past by high water levels.* (Photo by author.)

protection and buoyancy of the water. Instead the emergent plants are wandlike and flexible, able to bend before the stress of wind and water. Such plants require firm bases. Into the soft ooze, cattails, sedges, and associated plants send tough, fibrous rhizomes and roots. These develop a firm mat, which resists both waves and the pulling of the plant tops by wind and water. Thus marsh vegetation is restricted to plants that can tolerate submerged or waterlogged organic soil and which form firm mats or tussocks in the ooze.

Marshes vary in depth from deep water to shallow (Table 9-1). The maximum tolerable depth for emergent vegetation is about three feet. At this depth such plants as phragmites and wild rice grow. Shallow fresh-water marshes, those whose soil is waterlogged or submerged under as much as six inches of water, are dominated by cattails, sedges, and rushes. Wet meadows develop on soils raised enough to prevent standing water from remaining throughout the growing season but still waterlogged within a few inches of the surface.

Although grasses are the dominant marsh vegetation, other plants are there. In shallow, open water between the cattails and the reeds, algae is abundant, especially the green, coarse, threadlike *Spirogyra* and the net-forming *Hydrodicton*. Floating on the water's surface may be the silt-covered, jellylike alga, *Nostoc*. Other plants of the shallows include arrowheads and pickerel weed.

Plant life of the marshes supports a rich and abundant animal life. Snails, **187**

TABLE 9-1. A CLASSIFICATION OF WETLANDS

FRESH AREAS

INLAND FRESH AREAS	DESCRIPTION
1. Seasonally flooded basins of flats	Soil covered with water or waterlogged during variable periods but well drained during much of the growing season. In upland depressions and bottomlands. Bottomland hardwoods to herbaceous growth.
2. Fresh meadows	Without standing water during growing season; waterlogged to within a few inches of surface. Grasses, sedges, rushes, broadleaf plants.
3. Shallow fresh marshes	Soil waterlogged during growing season; often covered with 6 or more inches of water. Grasses, bulrushes, spike rushes, cattails, arrowhead, smartweed, pickerelweed. A major waterfowl-production area.
4. Deep fresh marshes	Soil covered with 6 inches to 3 feet of water. Cattails, reeds, bulrushes, spike rushes, wild rice. Principal duck-breeding area.
5. Open fresh water	Water less than 10 feet deep. Bordered by emergent vegetation: pondweed, naiads, wild celery, water lily. Brooding, feeding, nesting area for ducks.
6. Shrub swamps	Soil waterlogged; often covered with 1 foot or more of water. Alder, willow, buttonbush, dogwoods. Ducks nesting and feeding to limited extent.
7. Wooded swamps	Soil waterlogged; often covered with 1 foot of water. Along sluggish streams, flat uplands, shallow lake basins. North: tamarack, arborvitae, spruce, red maple, silver maple; South: water oak, overcup oak, tupelo, swamp black gum, cypress.
8. Bogs	Soil waterlogged; spongy covering of mosses. Heath shrubs, sphagnum, sedges.

COASTAL FRESH AREAS	
9. Shallow fresh marsh	Soil waterlogged during growing season; at high tides as much as 6 inches of water. On landward side, deep marshes along tidal rivers, sounds, deltas. Grasses and sedges. Important waterfowl areas.
10. Deep fresh marshes	At high tide covered with 6 inches to 3 feet of water. Along tidal rivers and bays. Cattails, wild rice, giant cutgrass.
11. Open fresh water	Shallow portions of open water along fresh tidal rivers and sounds. Vegetation scarce or absent. Important waterfowl areas.

TABLE 9-1 (*Continued*)

SALINE AREAS

INLAND SALINE AREAS	DESCRIPTION
12. Saline flats	Flooded after periods of heavy precipitation; water-logged within few inches of surface during the growing season. Vegetation: seablite, salt grass, saltbush. Fall waterfowl-feeding areas.
13. Saline marshes	Soil waterlogged during growing season; often covered with 2 to 3 feet of water; shallow lake basins. Vegetation: alkali hard-stemmed bulrush, wigeon grass, sago pondweed. Valuable waterfowl areas.
14. Open saline water	Permanent areas of shallow saline water. Depth variable. Sago pondweed, muskgrasses. Important waterfowl-feeding areas.

COASTAL SALINE AREAS	
15. Salt flats	Soil waterlogged during growing season. Sites occasionally to fairly regularly covered by high tide. Landward sides or islands within salt meadows and marshes. Salt grass, seablite, saltwort.
16. Salt meadows	Soil waterlogged during growing season. Rarely covered with tide water; landward side of salt marshes. Cord grass, salt grass, black rush. Waterfowl-feeding areas.
17. Irregularly flooded salt marshes	Covered by wind tides at irregular intervals during the growing season. Along shores of nearly enclosed bays, sounds, etc. Needlerush. Waterfowl-cover area.
18. Regularly flooded salt marshes	Covered at average high tide with 6 or more inches of water; along open ocean and along sounds. Salt-marsh cord grass along Atlantic. Pacific: Alkali bulrush, glassworts. Feeding area for ducks and geese.
19. Sounds and bays	Portions of salt-water sounds and bays shallow enough to be diked and filled. All water landward from average low tide line. Wintering areas for waterfowl.
20. Mangrove swamps	Soil covered at average high tide with 6 inches to 3 feet of water. Along coast of southern Florida. Red and black mangroves.

Adapted from S. P. Shaw and C. G. Fredine, 1956, *Wetlands of the United States*, U.S. Fish and Wildlife Serv. Circ. 39.

one of the most common marsh animals, feed on ooze and dead animal matter and in turn are consumed by birds and fish. Birds add the most color to marshlands. Here is found an avian richness hard to equal in other temperate communities. Characteristic of marshes are ducks; in fact the two are inseparable. The most typical mammalian member of the marsh community is the muskrat. This rodent uses cattails, sedges, and other plants to build its moundlike lodge, and it subsists on their roots and leaves.

Swamp

Swamps, like marshes, can be divided into two broad groups, deep water and shallow water; but here much of the similarity ends.

Deep-water swamps occur extensively on the flood plains of the larger southern river systems, especially in the Mississippi River drainage system and on the uplands of the coastal plain. Flood-plain swamps usually consist of southern cypress and tupelo gum, while upland swamps often are dominated by black gum and pond cypress; but all four species may grow in mixed stands. In more shallow water, sweet bay, slash pine, and pond pine are common associates. These deep-water swamp forests lack herbaceous plants but support abundant epiphytes, plants that grow perched on other plants. Outstanding among these epiphytes are bromalids, Spanish moss, and the more specialized tank epiphytes, whose leaves are shaped like gutters and collect water in the axils. These little tanks are occupied by a variety of small invertebrates, including mosquitoes. Orchids are abundant in swamps of the deep south. The best known is the cigar or cowhorn orchid, whose flowers—yellowish splotched with brown—are borne on long stalks.

Shallow-water swamps range from shrubby willows, alders, and buttonbush to oaks and maples. Where water is nearly permanent through the year, willow thrives, together with buttonbush, a shrub capable of growing in deep water. Alder likewise is tolerant of permanent shallow-water areas and is common throughout North America. Shallow-water swamp forests include such associates as elm, silver maple, red maple, white pine, and northern white cedar. Common southern swamp associates are overcup oak and water hickory. In the deep south, the understory of these swamps usually is a tangle of shrubs, vines, ferns, and palmetto.

Swamp vegetation, like that of the marsh, must meet the problem of anchorage in soft muck saturated with water. The root systems of trees are often massive, but they develop superficially and do not penetrate deeply. They spread widely and develop buttresses. These are exaggerated by deep-water swamp trees such as bald cypress and tupelo gum. The height and development of these swollen bases depend on the water depth at the start of the growing season. In addition, all deep-swamp dominant trees develop so-called pneumatophores from the superficial lateral root system that extends outward like cables. Most familiar are the knees of the swamp black gum, tupelo, and cypress; those of the latter may rise eight to ten feet above the low-water mark. Once it was thought that these knees acted in respiratory gas exchange, but their real function is unknown. They may serve to support the massive trees in the soft substrate.

An outstanding characteristic of shallow-water swamps is the rapid and uneven elevation of the land. The floor of the swamp is a series of depressions and rises created by fallen logs and upturned roots. On the rises grow ferns, vines, shrubs, and more mesic trees. Logs and tree bases are covered with mosses and liverworts, lichens and fungi. In spring and other periods of high water, the depressions are small pools; in dry weather they are little hollows, grown to mosses, liverworts, and marsh annuals. Thus across the swamp there is rapid and marked differentiation of microclimates, with varying moisture conditions and temperatures.

Variations in environmental conditions within the swamp provide a diversity of microhabitats for animals. The inhabitants range from aquatic and semiaquatic insects, turtles, snakes, alligators and crocodiles, ducks and herons to animals more closely associated with purely terrestrial situations, such as the deer, bear, and squirrel. Like the marsh, the swamp contains a richness of life too often little appreciated by man.

SUMMARY

The bog, marsh, and swamp represent late fill-in stages in lake succession, but swamps also develop on the flood plains of the larger river systems of southern North America. Each is distinctively different. Bogs, confined to northern regions, are characterized by blocked drainage conditions, an accumulation of peat, cushion-like vegetation, a marginal semifloating mat of plant growth, and acidic conditions, created largely by sphagnum moss. Only those plants tolerant of acidic conditions occupy the bog. Life is restricted in the number of plant and animal species, but the organisms present are often abundant. Marshes, on the other hand, are wetlands in which the grass life form is dominant, while swamps are wooded. Both may range from deep to shallow water, and both embrace a richness and diversity of life that is hard to equal in other temperate communities. Yet marshes and swamps too frequently are considered more as places to be drained or filled than as areas to be managed and preserved.

SUGGESTED FIELD ACTIVITIES

Bogs and marshes offer a wealth of opportunities for field observations. Some of the ideas suggested for lakes and ponds are also applicable to these communities.

Establish a measured transect line (or lines) from the edge of the bog or marsh to open water (or as close to it as possible), and along it locate a series of stations. At each station, probe with a peat sampler to determine the thickness of the peat. This can be plotted to show a vertical profile of the bog substrate. Attempt to determine the extent of water beneath the mat.

Note the changes in the vegetation along the transect. Indicate on a map the location of the shrub zone and measure its distance. Do the same for the sedge mat, and identify and list the species growing there. A few quadrats here might show the distribution and cover of several species of moss and lichens, if the patches are distinct.

Determine the depth and composition of the shrub communities and the forest. Handle these observations as suggested for shrub and forest habitats.

From this information draw up a picture of bog succession.

If time and resources permit, sample the peat to determine the past history of the bog. See Appendix C, Palynology.

Observe the animal life. Determine the characteristic animal species and the zones that they inhabit.

191

CHAPTER **10**

Flowing waters

Current or continuously moving water is the outstanding feature of streams and rivers. Current cuts the channel, molds the character of the stream, and influences the life and ways of organisms inhabiting flowing waters.

Streams may begin as outlets of ponds or lakes, or they may arise from springs and seepage areas. Added to this in varying quantities is surface runoff, especially after heavy or prolonged rains and rapid snow melt. Since precipitation, the source of all runoff and subsurface water, varies seasonally, the rate and volume of stream flow also fluctuates widely from flood conditions to a nearly dry stream bed.

As water drains away from its source, it flows in a direction dictated by the lay of the land and the underlying rock formations. Its course may be determined by the original slope and its irregularities; or the water, seeking the least-resistant route to lower land, may follow the joints and fissures in bedrock near the surface and shallow depressions in the ground. Whatever its direction, water is concentrated into rills that erode small furrows, which soon grow into gullies. Water, moving downstream, especially where the gradient is steep, carries with it a load of debris that cuts the channel wider and deeper and which, sooner or later, is deposited within or along the stream. At the same time, erosion continues at the head of the gully, cutting backward into the slope and increasing its drainage area. Just below its source, the stream may be small, straight, and often swift, with waterfalls and rapids. Further downstream, where the gradient is less and the velocity decreases, meanders become common. These are formed when the current, deflected by some obstacle on the floor of the channel, by projecting rocks and debris, or by the entrance of swifter currents, strikes the opposite bank. As the water moves downstream, it is thrown back to the other side again. These abrasive forces create a curve in the stream, on the inside of which the velocity is slowed and the water drops its load. Such cutting and deposition often causes valley streams to change course and to cut off the meanders to form oxbow lakes. When the water reaches level land, its velocity is greatly reduced, and the load it carries is deposited as silt, sand, or mud.

At flood time the material carried by the stream is dropped on the level lands, over which the water spreads to form flood-plain deposits. These flood plains on which man has settled so extensively are a part of the stream or river channel used at the time of high water, a fact that few people recognize. The current at flood time is swiftest in the normal channel of the stream and slowest on the flood plain. Along the margin of the channel and the flood plain, where the rapid water meets the slow, the current is checked and all but the fine sediments are dropped on the edges of the channel. Thus the deposits on the flood plain are higher on the immediate border and slope off gradually towards the valley side.

When a stream or river flows into a lake or sea, the velocity of the water is suddenly checked and the load of sediment is deposited in a fan-shaped area about the mouth of the river to form a delta. Here the course of the stream is broken into a number of channels, which are blocked or opened with subsequent deposits. As a result the delta is characterized by small lakes and swampy or marshy islands. Material not deposited at the mouth is carried further out to sea, where it settles on the bottom. Eventually the sediments build up above the water to form a new land surface.

Characteristics of the stream

The character of a stream is molded by the velocity of the current. This velocity varies from stream to stream and within the stream itself; and it depends upon the size, shape, and steepness of the stream channel, the roughness of the bottom, the depth, and the rainfall.

The velocity of flow influences the degree of silt deposition and the nature of the bottom (Fig. 10-6). The current in the riffles is too fast to allow siltation, but coarser silt particles will drop out in the smooth or quiet sections of the stream. High water increases the velocity; it moves bottom stones, scours the stream bed, and cuts new banks and channels. In very steep stream beds, the current may remove all but very large rocks and leave a boulder-strewn stream.

Flowing water also transports nutrients to and carries waste products away from many aquatic organisms, and may even sweep them away. Balancing this depletion of bottom fauna, the current continuously reintroduces bottom fauna from areas upstream. Similarly, as nutrients are washed downstream, more are carried in from above. Because of this, the productivity of primary producers in streams is 6 to 30 times that of those in standing water (Nelson, and Scott, 1962). The transport and removal action of flowing water benefits such continuous processes as photosynthesis.

The temperature of the stream is not constant. In general, small shallow streams tend to follow but lag behind air temperatures, warming and cooling with the seasons but never falling below freezing in winter. Streams with large areas exposed to direct sunlight are warmer than those shaded by trees, shrubs, and high steep banks (Fig. 10-1). This is ecologically important, since temperature affects the composition of the stream community.

The constant swirling and churning of stream water over riffles and falls result in greater contact with the atmosphere. Thus the oxygen content of the

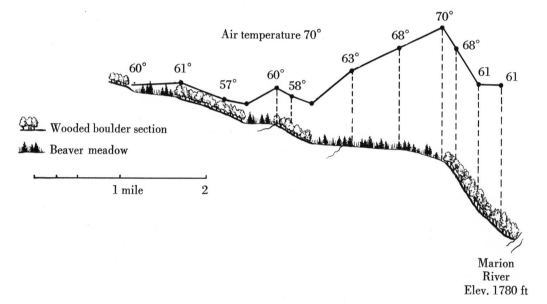

Figure 10-1 *Profile of Bear Brook (Adirondack Mountains) and a graph of its water temperatures, showing the warming effect of open beaver meadows and the cooling effects of wooded boulder stream. (From* Biological Survey of the Raquette Watershed, *New York State Conservation Department, 1934.)*

water is high at all levels and often is near saturation point for the existing temperature. Only in deep holes or in polluted waters does dissolved oxygen show any significant decline.

Free carbon dioxide in rapid water is in equilibrium with that of the atmosphere, while the amount of bound carbon dioxide is influenced by the nature of the surrounding terrain and the decomposition taking place in pools of still water. Most of the carbon dioxide in flowing water occurs as carbonate and bicarbonate salts. Streams fed by ground water from limestone springs receive the greatest amount of carbonates in solution. Because of a coating of algae and ooze on the bottom, little calcium carbonate is added by the action of carbonic acid on a limestone stream bed (Neel, 1951).

The degree of acidity and alkalinity, or pH, of the water reflects the CO_2

content as well as the presence of organic acids and pollution. The higher the pH of stream water, the richer the natural waters generally are in carbonates, bicarbonates, and associated salts. Such streams support more abundant aquatic life and larger trout populations than streams with acid waters, which generally are low in nutrients.

Most streams receive a part of their basic energy supply from land, as well as from connected ponds and backwaters. Many of the first-level consumer organisms in the stream are detritus feeders, much of whose food comes from the terrestrial vegetation along the banks. The primary consumers in a Piedmont stream in Georgia obtained 66 per cent of their energy from leaf material and other organic debris in the water (Nelson and Scott, 1962). Marginal stream vegetation also supplies a major portion of food for secondary consumers, especially in late spring and summer. Brook trout in northern West Virginia feed largely on aquatic organisms from March through May, when these invertebrates are most abundant. In June the fish showed a more pronounced shift to invertebrates. From July to September emergent and terrestrial organisms comprised 60 to 80 per cent of the total food the fish consumed (Redd and Benson, 1962). Intensive agriculture within the watershed may increase the supply of nutrients carried to the stream by runoff and drainage (Allen, 1960). This stimulates a dense growth of attached algae in the stream bed, which changes the stream environment, increases the food supply, and modifies the composition of the bottom fauna.

Fast streams

Fast or swiftly flowing streams are, roughly, all those whose velocity of flow is 50 cm per sec or higher (Nielsen, 1950). At this velocity the current will remove all particles less than 5 mm in diameter and will leave behind a stony bottom. The fast stream is often a series of two essentially different but inter-related habitats, the turbulent riffle and the quiet pool (Figs. 10-2 and 10-3). The waters of the pool are influenced by processes occurring in the rapids above, and the waters of the rapids are influenced by events in the pool.

The riffles are the sites of primary production in the stream (see Nelson and Scott, 1962). Here the aufwuchs assume dominance and occupy a position of the same importance as the phytoplankton of lakes and ponds. The aufwuchs consist chiefly of diatoms, blue-green and green algae, and water moss. Extensive stands of algae grow over rocks and rubble on the stream bed and form a slippery covering familiar and often dangerous to fishermen and others who wade the stream. Growth during favorable periods may be so rapid that the stream bottom is covered in 10 days or less (Blum, 1960). Many small algal species are epiphytes and grow on the tops of or in among other algae.

The outstanding feature of much of this algal growth is its ephemeral nature. Scouring action of water and the debris it carries tears away larger growth, epiphytes and all, and sends the algae downstream. As a result there is a constant contribution from upstream to the downstream sequence.

Above and below the riffles are the pools. Here the environment differs in chemistry, intensity of current, and depth. Just as the riffles are the sites of organic production, so the pools are sites of decomposition. They are the catch

Figure 10-2 *The two different but related habitats in a stream, the riffles (foreground) and the pool. (Photo by author.)*

basins of organic materials, for here the velocity of the current is reduced enough to allow a part of the load to settle out. Pools are the major sites for free CO_2 production during the summer and fall, which is necessary for the maintenance of a constant supply of bicarbonate in solution (Neel, 1951). Without pools, photosynthesis in the riffles would deplete the bicarbonates and result in smaller and smaller quantities of available carbon dioxide downstream.

Over-all production in a stream is influenced in part by the nature of the bottom. Pools with sandy bottoms are the least productive, since they offer little substrate for either aufwuchs or animals. Bedrock, although a solid sub-

Figure 10-3. *The segment of the stream where the transect in Fig. 10-6 was taken. (Photo by courtesy of Arnold Benson.)*

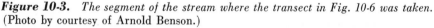

strate, is so exposed to currents that only the most tenacious organisms can maintain themselves (Fig. 10-4). Gravel and rubble bottoms support the most abundant life, since they have the greatest surface area for the aufwuchs, provide many crannies and protected places for insect larvae, and are the most stable (Table 10-1) (Figs. 10-4 and 10-5). Food production decreases as the particles become larger or smaller than rubble. Insect larvae, on the other hand, differ in abundance on the several substrates. Mayfly nymphs are most abundant on rubble, caddisfly larvae on bedrock, and Diptera larvae on bedrock and gravel (Pennak and Van Gerpen, 1947).

Figure 10-4 *A fast mountain stream in a deep woods. The bottom is largely bedrock.* (Photo by author.)

The width of the stream also influences over-all production. Bottom production in streams 20 feet wide decreases by one-half from the sides to the center, and in streams 100 feet wide it decreases one-third (Pate, 1933). Streams 6 feet or less in width are four times as rich in bottom organisms as those 19 to 24 feet wide. This is one reason why headwater streams make such excellent trout nurseries.

Life in a fast stream

Although the pools and the riffles are more or less distinct, no clear-cut differences exist in the animals that inhabit them. Some animals of the riffles are carried by the current to the pools; others move back and forth between the two at will, as do the trout. For these, the riffles furnish food and the pools shelter. A good trout stream should be about 50 per cent in pools and 50 per cent in riffles.

TABLE 10-1. Bottom Types, Showing Average Amounts of Available Fish Food per Square Foot in Each

NUMBER OF DETERMINATIONS	TYPE OF BOTTOM	AVERAGE WEIGHT PER GRAM PER SQUARE FOOT		
		1933	1932	1931
32	Silt and mud	3.63	3.07	2.90
100	Rubble	2.96	2.47	0.67
38	Large rubble	2.27	1.55	0.5
31	Small rubble	4.11	3.53	0.85
53	Coarse gravel	1.35	1.51	1.02
30	Fine gravel	1.05	0.93	0.84
6	Sand	0.55	0.10	

From Pate, 1933.

But the majority of stream inhabitants live in riffles, on the underside of rubble and gravel, where they are sheltered from the current. Characteristic of the riffle insects are the nymphs of mayflies, caddisflies, true flies, stoneflies, and alderflies or dobsons. In the pools the dominant insects are the burrowing mayfly nymphs, dragonflies and damselflies, and water striders.

A major reason for the richer aquatic life in the riffles is the current. Stream animals depend upon flowing water to aid their respiration and to bring them food. If riffle fauna are transplanted to still water, many suffocate in a few hours. Although quiet water may contain more than a sufficient amount of oxygen to meet their needs, the organisms become surrounded by a closely adhering film of liquid that forms a sort of cloak and is impoverished of substances, including oxygen. In fast water, such a cloak cannot form and the absorbing and respiratory surfaces are in continuous contact with oxygenated water (Ruttner, 1953).

A streamlined form, which offers lessened resistance to water current, is typical of many animals of fast streams, such as the black-nosed dace and the brook trout (Fig. 10-5). Among the insect larvae, the "howdy" mayfly nymph is unique for its streamlined body, its strongly plumed cerci, and its ability to dart among stones in swift water. Also able to move from stone to stone are the mayflies of the genus *Baetis,* which are fishlike in form.

Other insect larvae possess extremely flattened bodies and broad, flat limbs, with which they cling to the undersurface of stones where the current is very weak. Typical among these are the mayflies of the genera *Stenonema, Rhithrogena,* and *Iron.* Their eyes are dorsally located and their gills are platelike, a characteristic of mayflies that do not have to agitate the water around them to secure circulation. Similarly flattened are the stonefly nymphs, with two cerci and the tufts of filamentous gills on the bases of the legs below the thorax. Another example of body flattening even more extreme is the larvae of the water penny beetle. Viewed from the top the water penny appears as an encrustation on the stone. But underneath the widened, protective, sucker-forming covering of the back is the body of the beetle larva. The flattening of the body enables the animals to inhabit the thin crevices and the undersides of stones away from the strong current (Nielsen, 1950).

Other forms attach themselves temporarily in one way or another to the substrate. The black-fly larvae, *Simulium,* occur in such numbers on the down-current sides of stones that they have gained the name "black moss." They attach themselves to rocks by means of a circlet of rows of outwardly directed hooks on a swollen posterior. Attached to the center of the circlet are muscles that contract to pull the hooks inward (Nielsen, 1950). When the muscles are relaxed, the hooks move outward, releasing the hold. This allows the larvae to move about slightly on a silken web, secreted by the salivary glands and placed on the rock by the larva. Head end downstream, the larvae hang swaying in the water. They strain out the food brought by the current by means of feeding fans on the head.

The larvae of certain species of caddisflies construct cases of sand or small pebbles (Fig. 10-6), which protect them from the wash of the current. Some

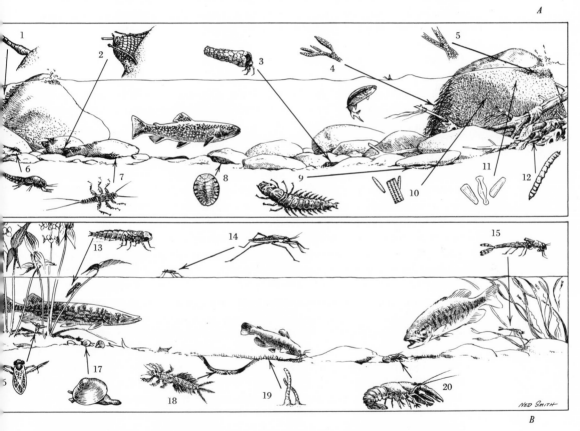

Figure 10-5 *Life in a fast stream compared to that in a slow stream. (1) Black-fly larva; (2) net-spinning caddisfly; (3) stone case of caddisfly; (4) water moss (Fontinalis); (5) alga Ulothrix; (6) mayfly nymph (Isonychia); (7) stonefly nymph (Perla); (8) water penny; (9) hellgrammite; (10) diatoms (Diatoma); (11) diatoms (Gomphonema); (12) cranefly larva; (13) dragonfly nymph; (14) water strider; (15) damselfly nymph; (16) water boatman; (17) fingernail clam (Sphaerium); (18) burrowing mayfly nymph (Hexagenia); (19) bloodworm; (20) crayfish. The fish in the fast stream, above, are (left) brook trout, (right) redbelly dace. The fish in the slow stream, below, are (left to right) northern pike, bullhead, and smallmouth bass.*

199

species have portable houses, the weight of which increases with the velocity of the current. The thickened walls act as ballast to hold the case on the bottom. Other species have cases firmly cemented to the sides and bottoms of stones. The net-spinning caddisflies firmly cement to stones funnel-shaped nets, the open ends of which face upstream. The larval inhabitants feed on the minute plants and animals swept into the meshes of the nets. Free-living caddisfly larvae, *Rhyacophila*, roam over the stones. Equipped with hooks on the anal prolegs and strong anal claws, these caddisflies grasp irregularities on the stone. They creep along, lengthening and shortening their bodies and clinging alternately with their anal prolegs and their short, stout thoracic legs. These caddisflies, however, form stone cases for pupation (Ross, 1944).

Algae and water moss also are attached permanently to the substrate (Fig. 10-5). Water moss and heavily branched filamentous algae are held to rocks by strong holdfasts and are aligned with the current. In addition, the algae are covered with a slippery, gelatinous coating. Other algae grow in spheric, wart-like or cushionlike colonies with smooth, gelatinous surfaces. Some species are reduced to simplified platelike forms, which grow in closely appressed sheets that follow the contours of the rocks. In limestone water some algae, such as *Phormidium* and *Audouinella*, secrete calcium carbonate to cover the entire growth in a crust. These may be overgrown at certain seasons by such algae as *Cladophora*. Alga growth in streams often exhibits zonation on rocks; the growth is influenced by both depth and current (Fig. 10-5) (Blum, 1960).

Sticky undersurfaces aid snails and planarians to remain stationary in the current. Snails can cling tightly to rubble in flowing water, and often such bottoms in hard-water streams support large populations.

The few ciliates living in the stream differ little from those of still water and exhibit no adaptation for current. This is possible because of the rapid decrease in the current near the bottom. In the submicroscopic distances from the bottom, current is almost zero. Here in this slowly moving water the ciliates live.

In spite of these adaptations, many bottom organisms tend to drift down-stream to form a sort of traveling benthos. This is a normal process in streams, even in the absence of high water and abnormal currents (Muller, 1954). This drift consists mainly of organisms that are free-ranging, such as the mayfly larva, *Baetis*, and the scud, *Gammarus*. Apparently it prevents an overpopulation of offspring in upstream areas as they grow larger and require more food. This drift is so characteristic of streams that the mean rate of drift can serve as an index of the production rate of a stream (Waters, 1961). The drift method, in addition to involving a smaller sampling error and less effort than other methods of determining production, also has the advantage of not destroying the producing population.

Slow streams and rivers

As the current slows a noticeable change takes place in streams (Fig. 10-7). Silt and decaying organic matter accumulate on the bottom. Faunal organisms are able to move about to obtain their food, and a plankton population of a sort develops. The composition and configuration of the stream community approaches that of standing water.

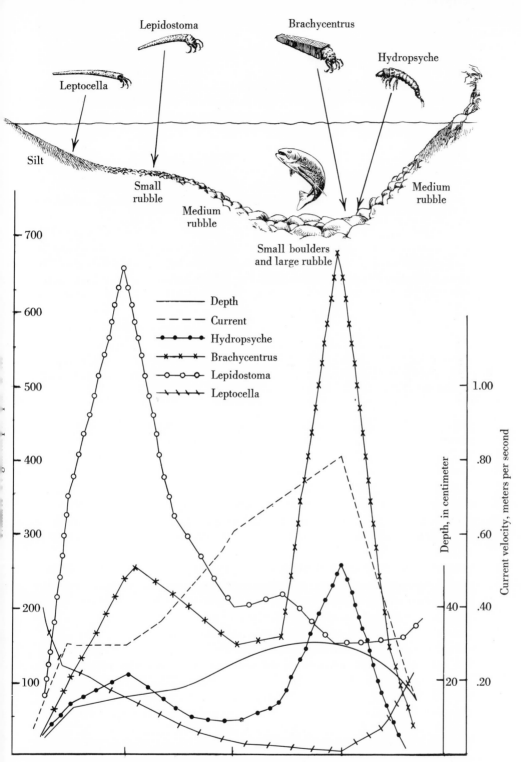

Figure 10-6 *Distribution of four species of caddisfly in relation to water depth and current across a 12-meter transect of a high mountain stream in Colorado. Note that two species,* Hydropsyche *and* Brachycentrus, *are in deep, fast water, while the remaining two are in shallow, less swift water where silt is deposited on the bottom.* (Data and graphs from Arnold Benson, West Virginia University.)

Figure 10-7 *A slow stream reflects the sky of a summer afternoon.* (Photo by author.)

With increasing temperatures, decreasing current, and accumulating bottom silt, organisms of the fast water are replaced gradually by organisms adapted to these conditions. The brook trout and the sculpin give way to smallmouth bass and rock bass, the dace to shiners and darters. With current at a minimum, many resident fish lack the strong lateral muscles typical of the trout and have compressed bodies that permit them to move with ease through masses of aquatic plants. Mollusks, particularly *Sphaerium* and *Pisidium,* and pulmonate snails, crustaceans, and burrowing mayflies replace the rubble-dwelling insect larvae (Fig. 10-5). Only in occasional stretches of fast water in the center of the stream are remnants of headwater-stream organisms found.

As the volume of water increases, as the current becomes even slower and the silt deposits heavier, detritus feeders increase. Tube-dwelling annelids and midges are common (Fig. 10-5), as are the bottom-feeding catfish, suckers, and the introduced carp. Backswimmers, water boatmen, and diving beetles inhabit the sluggish stretches and backwaters of rivers; and where water conditions are suitable, muskies, pike, and turtles are common. Rooted aquatics appear. Emergent vegetation grows along the river banks, and duckweeds float on the surface. Indeed the whole aspect approaches that of lakes and ponds, even to zonation along the river margin (Fig. 6-4).

The higher water temperature, weak current, and abundant decaying matter promote the growth of protozoan and other plankton populations. Scarce in fast water, plankton increase in numbers and species in slow water. Rivers have no typical plankton of their own. Those found there originated mainly from backwaters and lakes. In general, plankton populations in rivers are not nearly as dense as those in lakes. Time is too short for much multiplication of plankton, since relatively little time is needed for a given quantity of water to flow from its source to the sea. Also occasional river rapids, often some distance in length, kill many plankton organisms by violent impact against suspended particles and the bottom. Aquatic vegetation filters out this minute life as the current sweeps it along. Plankton populations at the beginning of the Shenango River, which arises out of Pymatuning Reservoir in northwestern Pennsylvania, are the same as those found in the reservoir itself. But 11 miles downstream, the plankton populations decreased by 73 per cent (Hartman and Himes, 1961). Interestingly, the proportion of silica-cased diatoms increased downstream.

Pollution

Few streams exist that in some way have not been affected by man through pollution from silt, sewage, and industrial wastes. The magnitude of ecological changes produced depends upon the kind of pollutant and the quantity in both time and space.

Industrial pollution, most serious in larger streams and rivers, is very complex. Water withdrawn from streams and used for cooling in certain manufacturing processes and then returned again raises the stream temperature and lowers dissolved oxygen. Disposed water, used for flushing and chemical treatment, imparts bad tastes and odors and even toxic substances to stream water. Discharges from chemical plants and sulphurous wastes from pulp and paper mills are highly poisonous to aquatic life. Sterile stream bottoms and brown water are mute testimony of this. Many chemical wastes, perhaps harmless alone, react with other chemicals to produce highly toxic conditions. Two parts per million of copper or eight parts of zinc alone will not harm fish, but as little as one-tenth part of the two combined will eliminate fish in a stream. Many spectacular and tragic kills of fish and other aquatic organisms result from a sudden influx of such chemical pollutants. More recently, detergents have become an added problem. Acid water from both deep and surface coal mines have destroyed stream life in coal regions and so reduced bacterial activity that biological purification of sewage and other organic wastes in water is impossible.

With the coming of the atomic age, radioactive wastes from uranium mills and atomic-energy plants present a serious problem. Streams cannot purify themselves naturally of radioactive wastes, as they can of organic wastes. Radioactive materials, however, are increasingly diluted as they are carried downstream; some are deposited on the bottom; others are taken up by aquatic organisms, both plant and animal. On the other hand, even minute amounts in the stream or lake may become concentrated many thousands of times greater in living tissue and be passed along through the food chain. Perch living in a lake that received dissolved radioactive matter from an inlet stream contaminated by seeps from a nearby liquid-atomic-waste disposal area had a radiostrontium-90 concentration in the bones 3000 times greater than that in the lake water (Ophel, 1959, 1963).

Raw sewage dumped into streams sharply changes biological conditions, and even sewage disposal plant effluent, rich in nutrients, can upset ecological stability. Streams can purify themselves by natural processes, the breakdown of organic matter by bacterial activity. The time required depends upon the degree of pollution and the character of the stream. A fast-flowing stream constantly saturated with oxygen will purify itself much faster than a slow stream. As sewage enters a stream, it is dispersed and the solids settle to the bottom, where they are attacked by aerobic bacteria. This depletes the oxygen, but this loss is offset by the absorption of more oxygen from the air into the stream. The carbon-dioxide and hydrogen-sulfide content of the water in the discharge area are high. Normal stream life, particularly vertebrates and mollusks, is absent, and the dominant organisms consist of a number of protozoans, mosquito larvae, and tubifex worms. Below this zone of active decomposition, flowing waters dilute the pollutants. Although conditions are improved, the stream still is far from normal. Green algae are present but reduced in numbers; bacteria still are abundant and oxygen is low. Downstream the pollutants are diluted further, dissolved oxygen is higher, and organisms tolerant of such conditions, such as carp, catfish, chiromonid larvae, and protozoans, inhabit the area. Eventually the water becomes clean and fresh again and normal populations of fish and invertebrates reappear.

In far too many streams, however, conditions become worse downstream. No sooner has the stream somewhat recovered from its polluted condition than another town dumps in its sewage. As a result, the stream carries a greater load than it can recover from, aerobic conditions no longer exist, and putrifaction occurs. Aerobic bacteria are replaced by anaerobic, and normal stream life is completely destroyed. Putrifying bacteria alone remain and the stream becomes a foul-smelling open sewer.

Although water pollution affects aquatic organisms, the organisms themselves also produce changes in the stream. In badly polluted water, populations of tubifex worms, *Asellus,* and *Chironomus* larvae are so high that they too reduce the oxygen supply (Westlake, 1959). *Chironomus* larvae alone can lower the oxygen content by over 1.0 parts per million per mile of river. Dense plant populations, stimulated by nutrient content of the water, cause additional, wide diurnal and seasonal changes in the oxygen content of rivers.

The pronounced effect of sewage pollution on aquatic organisms has been exploited as a means of detecting and measuring pollution in natural waters. One method (Patrick, 1949) is based on the effect of pollution on community structure—on all groups of plants and animals in the stream but especially on the sessile and attached forms. This technique relies on both the tolerance and competitive ability of the organisms, and on the assumption that a healthy stream has a number of species of all ecological groups. Species intolerant of low oxygen disappear and are replaced by more tolerant organisms, more or less in proportion to the reduction of the intolerant species.

Since this method requires an enormous amount of survey work and identification, a modified method, involving only four groups of benthic organisms, the oligochaetes, snails, bivalve mollusks, and chironomids, has been devised (Gaufin, 1957). The exact number of each group is counted and recorded without further breakdown into species and the data analyzed statistically. From this, a reference control chart for the area is constructed. If the results of

Figure 10-8 *Silt carried to the stream, by erosion and destruction of streambanks, is deposited in the stream where the current slows.* (Photo by author.)

future surveys indicate an abnormal change in population densities from the control, then pollution or change in pollution can be suspected.

Siltation, caused by erosion of farmlands, roadsides, construction, and other forms of soil disturbance, is the most insidious form of pollution, for it is widespread, often goes unnoticed, and the damage it does is often permanent. Silt can change a cold, clear trout stream to a warm, murky one, inhabited by fish tolerant of turbid waters and muddy bottom.

Silt destroys stream habitats (Fig. 10-8), changes the environment, and kills aquatic organisms. Clay soils suspended in water block out light and prevent the growth of aquatic plants. Silt settles on the stream bottom, covering sites for insect larvae and smothering mussels and other bottom organisms. Silt also blankets sewage and other organic material and retains it in place. Here it is decomposed, depleting the oxygen supply (Ellis, 1936). Aquatic insects characteristic of rubble disappear and burrowing forms appear (Eustin and Hiller, 1954). Caddisflies and mayflies are replaced by bloodworms. Evidence indicates that high turbidity kills fish by clogging the opercular cavities and gill filaments with silt. Since water cannot reach the gill filaments, blood aeration is impeded, and sooner or later the fish die from CO_2 retention, anoxemia, or both. Similarly the mantle and gills of mollusks are either clogged or injured by soil particles (Cordone and Kelly, 1961). Silty water flowing through the gravel nests or redds of trout and salmon causes heavy mortality of eggs. Silt clogs the spaces between the gravel, reducing the water flow through the redd, and settles on the eggs. With insufficient water washing them, the eggs die from the lack of oxygen. Thousands of miles of trout and salmon water have been destroyed by siltation, which more than any other cause limits the natural reproduction of trout and salmon.

205

Springs

Many streams are born as springs back in the woods or in pasture fields. A spring is a concentrated flow of ground water issuing from openings in the ground. Springs may range from tiny seep holes, through which the water oozes to form wet spots in the ground, to large fissures in rocks or openings in the ground that are cleaned out and enlarged by percolating water. If the rate of flow is great enough, pools of water nearly devoid of suspended matter form around the point of discharge. Runoff water erodes a channel away, which is the beginning of a stream, while precipitated mineral matter is deposited in the vicinity of the pool.

From an ecological viewpoint, the spring pool is important as a natural constant aquatic environment. Compared to lakes and rivers, its temperature is relatively constant, as is its chemical composition and water velocity. The organisms do not modify the pool environment, for almost as rapidly as the water is altered by photosynthesis and aquatic organisms, it is replaced by fresh water from the ground.

Springs, from a production standpoint, can be classified as autotrophic or heterotrophic. Large springs, those of first magnitude, such as the famous Silver Springs of Florida, are usually autotrophic and support a standing crop of such producer organisms as algae and submerged aquatic plants. Plankton are usually absent. This base supports a consumer pyramid of aquatic insects, snails, fish, and turtles (see Odum, 1957*a*, 1957*b*). Pasture springs are heterotrophic. For the community as a whole, a large portion of the assimilated energy is supplied by imports of organic debris. Primary production is small, while herbivore production is large since detritus feeders comprise the bulk of the spring fauna (Teal, 1957).

SUMMARY

From its source to its mouth, the stream exhibits changes in its character. Up in the hills, the headwater streams are small, shallow, usually swift, and cold. Production is high, but the nutrients are carried downstream by the current. To exist in the current, the organisms of fast-flowing waters may be streamlined in shape or flattened to conceal themselves in the crevices of and underneath rocks; or they may attach themselves in one fashion or another to the substrate. Downstream, the volume of flow, augmented by tributaries, increases, the channel becomes wider and deeper, and the waters are not nearly so swift. In lowlands, the flow is slow, and the bottom is soft with silt and mud. Aquatic plants and animals characteristic of ponds and lakes replace life of the swift headwaters. But there is no clear-cut boundary between the swift and slow water communities. Like the vegetation continuum, one gradually blends into the other, reflecting a longitudinal gradient in temperature, velocity of current, and often pH. Certain conditions, such as changes in current velocity, may reappear along the gradient, and with this a return of some fast-water populations. But life in the streams of most settled parts of the country has been affected by pollution from industrial wastes, sewage, and siltation. Organisms of natural waters are replaced by those tolerant of turbid waters, low in oxygen.

SUGGESTED FIELD ACTIVITIES

Stream mapping

As in the study of other habitats, a map is almost a necessity. A section of stream, if not too wide, can be laid out in a grid and the surface plan of the bottom mapped on paper. This should show such major features as: current flow, large stones, current deflection around the stones, depth contours (far easier to determine here than in lakes and ponds), distribution and nature of vegetation, and bottom substrate. By using transparent overlays, one can plot in the distribution of aquatic organisms in relation to current, depth, bottom substrate, etc. Line transects run across the stream will be helpful in determining the distribution of aquatic organisms.

Stream activities

Below are some suggested studies that can be done on the stream habitat, but before undertaking any of them, the physical and chemical characteristics of the habitat, including current, must be measured (see Appendix B).

1. Make a general survey of the stream, collecting different organisms, noting their position in the stream and the microhabitat they occupy—under stones, in rapid water, in debris along shore, etc.

2. Establish square-meter quadrats along a transect across the stream, list the species, and count their numbers. Relate the occurrence and density of population to distance from shore, current, substrate, etc.

3. Undertake a study of a particular group of organisms in the stream, such as mayflies or caddisflies. Determine the species present and relate their distribution to distance from shore, current, bottom type, etc. Note the different niches each occupies in the stream.

4. Study the food habits of some of the larger species and construct a simple food web. To do this, observe the animals under natural conditions and analyze the gut contents of collected individuals (be sure to distinguish between material that passes through undigested and that which is digested).

5. Study the location and behavior of organisms. The feeding and breeding habits, physiology, and behavior largely determine why a species lives where it does.

a. Breeding and feeding habits.

b. Location under different environmental conditions.

c. Mode of respiration and type of gills.

d. Reactions to various stimuli of temperature, light.

e. Reaction to lack of oxygen and to dissolved substances (must be done in the laboratory).

6. Study the case building by caddisflies, especially insofar as the cases are influenced by current.

7. Since stream organisms tend to drift downstream, the rate and amount of drift in relation to population density, production, and environment can make an interesting study. Drift can be sampled by placing nets (with at least 39 meshes per linear inch) one foot wide and three feet long at stations located on the downstream end of a riffle. Select spots where the depth and current are reasonably uniform.

a. What organisms make up the drift? What are their characteristics?

207

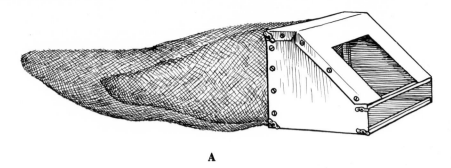

A

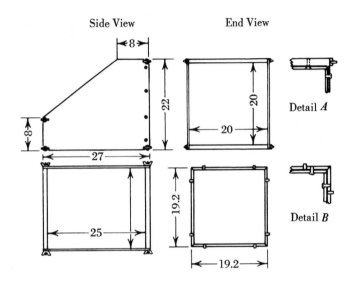

Side View   End View

Figure 10-9 (A) *A modified Surber bottom sampler.* (Redrawn from Withers and Benson, 1962.) (B) *Construction details for the Surber bottom sampler.*

Detail *A*

Detail *B*

B

b. Compute the drift rate on the basis of volume of organisms (milliliters) per hour per standard foot of width. A standard foot of width is equivalent to one foot of width if the stream width at the sampling site is exactly equal to the average width. In practice, the volume per hour should be multiplied by a ratio of width about 100 feet above sampling site to width at collection site.

c. Compare the drift rate with the bottom standing crop. Do this for several streams. There should be a close relationship between the two. The drift rate is a useful index to the production of stream-bottom fauna and eliminates the necessity of destroying a part of the producing population.

Sampling stream-bottom organisms

Samples of stream-bottom organisms can be taken with a modified Surber bottom-fauna sampler (Fig. 10–9). This consists of a brass frame with stainless-steel side pieces and a current baffle. To this is attached on a removable brass frame a fine net of 74 meshes per linear inch and a coarse net with 19 meshes per linear inch. The latter is fitted in the sampler in front of the fine net to produce a cone or cone effect. Flanges on the insert prevent its being forced into the fine net in the rear.

This modified sampler picks up many small organisms that might otherwise be lost. In fact collection of virtually all macroorganisms is assured. In addition one obtains two subsamples with respect to size, and the small organisms are associated with fine detritus only. (Withers and Benson, 1962)

This sampler encloses a specified area of stream (500 cm^2), which is the sample unit. Organisms, detritus, and trash are scrubbed free from the substrate, and the current washes it into the net. Transfer the contents to a container and take back to the lab for examination and sorting.

Artificial stream habitat

Just as it is often desirable to observe pond and lake inhabitants in an indoor aquarium, so it is with stream organisms. But the problem of maintaining a stream population under artificial conditions is more difficult. However, a set up that works fairly well consists of a length of gutter, preferably wood, set on an angle with water from an outlet running in at the top and draining into a sink at the bottom. Water depth can be controlled by inserting a series of wooden partitions, each notched in the top, through which water pours like little waterfalls from one compartment to the next. The bed of the "stream" should be lined with small stones and gravel.

Conditions in a slow stream or pool can be simulated by arranging a series of shallow pans, one above the other. Each is filled with an overflow pipe covered with a fine wire filter. If the overflow pipes are arranged about nine inches above the next pan, the oxygen concentration will approach saturation.

Production

The stream can also be approached from a functional viewpoint. By means of techniques suggested in Appendix C, determine primary production in riffles. Pools might be handled as ponds. Try modifying some of the techniques suggested for ponds.

CHAPTER **11**

Estuaries,
tidal marshes,
and swamps

Waters of all streams and rivers eventually drain into the sea; and the place where this fresh water joins the salt is called an *estuary*. More precisely, estuaries are bodies of water bordered by and partly cut from the ocean by a land mass that did not originate from the sea. Estuaries differ in size, shape, and volume of water flow, all influenced by the geology of the region in which they occur. As the river reaches the encroaching sea, the stream-carried sediments are dropped in the quiet water. These accumulate to form deltas in the upper reaches of the mouth and shorten the estuary. When silt and mud accumulations become high enough to be exposed at low tide, tidal flats (Fig. 11-1) develop, which divide and braid the original channel of the estuary. At the same time, ocean currents and tides erode away at the coast line and deposit material on the seaward side of the estuary, also shortening the mouth. If more material is deposited than is carried away, then barrier beaches, islands, and brackish lagoons appear.

Current and salinity, both very complex and variable, shape life in the estuary, where the environment is neither fresh water nor salt. Estuarine currents result from the interaction of a one-direction stream flow, which varies with the season and rainfall, with oscillating ocean tides, and with the wind (Ketchum,

210

Figure 11-1 *A muddy tidal flat covered with blue mussels.* (Photo by author.)

1951; Burt and Queen, 1957). Because of the complex nature of the currents, generalizations about estuaries are difficult to make.

Salinity varies vertically and horizontally, often within one tidal cycle. Vertical salinity may be the same from top to bottom or it may be completely stratified with a layer of fresh water on top and a layer of dense, saline water on the bottom. Salinity is homogeneous when currents, particularly eddy currents, are strong enough to mix the water from top to bottom. The salinity in some estuaries may be homogeneous at low tide; but at flood tide a surface wedge of sea water moves upstream more rapidly than the bottom water. Salinity is

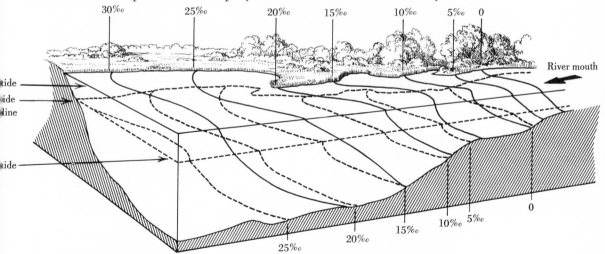

Figure 11-2 *A generalized diagram of an estuary showing the vertical and horizontal stratification of salinity from the river mouth to the estuary at both high and low tide. At high tide the incoming sea water increases the salinity toward the river mouth; at low tide the salinity is reduced. Note also how salinity increases with depth, since the lighter fresh water flows over the denser salt.*

211

then unstable and density is inverted. The sea water on the surface tends to sink, as lighter fresh water rises, and mixing takes place from the surface to the bottom. This phenomenon is known as tidal overmixing. Strong winds, too, tend to mix salt water with the fresh (Barlow, 1956) in some estuaries; but when the winds are still, the river water flows seaward on a shallow surface over an upstream movement of sea water and only gradually mixes with the salt. Horizontally, the least saline waters are at the river entrance, and the most saline at the mouth of the estuary (Fig 11-2). The configuration of the horizontal zonation is determined mainly by the deflection caused by the incoming and outgoing currents. In all estuaries of the northern hemisphere, outward-flowing fresh water and inward-flowing seawater are deflected to the right because of the earth's rotation. As a result, salinity is higher on the left side (Fig 11-2).

Since the quantity of fresh water pouring into the estuary varies through the year, salinity also varies. Salinity is the highest during the summer and during periods of drought, when less fresh water flows into the estuary. It is the lowest during the winter and spring, when rivers and streams are discharging their peak loads. At times this change in salinity can happen rather rapidly. For example, early in 1957 a heavy rainfall broke the most severe drought in the history of Texas. The resultant heavy river discharge reduced the salinities in Mesquite Bay on the central Texas coast by over 30 parts per thousand in a two-month period. At the height of the drought, salinities ranged from 35.5 to 50 parts per thousand but after the drought was broken, the salinities ranged from 2.3 to 2.9 parts per thousand (Hoese, 1960). Such rapid changes have a profound impact on the life of the estuary (see below).

The salinity of the open sea is fairly constant—33 to 35 parts per thousand, with an average of 35 parts per thousand. The metallic ions that account for this salinity are predominately sodium and chloride. The average salinity of fresh water, on the other hand, is about 0.065 parts per thousand, and of hard fresh water, 0.30 parts per thousand. Since the concentration of metallic ions carried by streams will vary from drainage to drainage, the salinity and chemistry of estuaries differ. The proportion of dissolved salts in the estuarine waters remains about the same as that of sea water, but the concentration varies in a gradient from fresh water to sea (Fig. 11-2).

Exceptions to these conditions exist in regions where evaporation from the estuary may exceed the inflow of fresh water from river discharge and rainfall (a negative estuary). This causes the salinity to increase in the upper end of the estuary, and horizontal stratification is reversed.

Temperatures in estuaries fluctuate considerably diurnally and seasonally. Waters are heated by solar radiation and inflowing and tidal currents. High tide on the mud flats may heat or cool the water, depending on the season. The upper layer of estuarine water may be cooler in winter and warmer in summer than the bottom, a condition which, as in a lake, will result in a spring and autumn overturn.

Mixing waters of different salinities and temperatures acts as a nutrient trap. Inflowing river waters more often than not impoverish rather than fertilize the estuary, except for phosphorus. Instead, nutrients and oxygen are carried into the estuary by the tides. If vertical mixing takes place, these nutrients are not soon swept back out to sea but circulate up and down between organisms, water, and bottom sediments.

Life in the estuary

Organisms inhabiting the estuary are faced with two problems—maintenance of position and adjustment to changing salinity. The bulk of estuarine organisms are benthic and are securely attached to the bottom, buried in the mud, or occupy crevices and crannies about sessile organisms. Motile inhabitants chiefly are crustaceans and fish, largely young of species that spawn offshore in high-salinity water. Planktonic organisms are wholly at the mercy of the currents. Since the seaward movement of stream flow and ebb tide transport plankton out to sea, the rate of circulation or flushing time determines the nature of the plankton population. If the circulation is too vigorous, then the plankton population may be relatively small. For example, local populations of the copepod *Acartina* are in most instances unable to maintain themselves in Great Pond on Cape Cod, and depend upon continuous recruitment from deeper layers (Barlow, 1955). Even then their ability to maintain themselves varies landward to the sea. Landward, *Acartina* depends upon additions from deeper layers. In the central part of the estuary, reproduction alone is able to balance the loss of those transported out to sea. But seaward, the mortality is so great that a small population is able to exist only by the addition of new stock from the landward part. Thus for any planktonic organism to become endemic in an estuary, reproduction and recruitment must balance the losses from the physical processes that disperse the population.

Salinity dictates the distribution of life in the estuary. Essentially the organisms of the estuary are marine, able to withstand full sea water. Except for andromonous fishes, no fresh-water organisms live there. Some estuarine inhabitants cannot withstand lowered salinities, and these species decline along a salinity gradient. Sessile and slightly motile organisms have an optimum salinity range within which they grow best. When salinities vary on either side of this range, either up or down, populations decline. Two animals, the clam worm and the scud, illustrate this situation. Two species of clam worm, *Nereis occidentalis* and *Neanthes succinea*, inhabit the estuaries of the southern coastal plains of North America. *Nereis* is more numerous at high salinities, and *Neanthes* is most abundant at low salinities. In European estuaries the scud *Gammarus* is an important member of the bottom fauna. Two species, *Gammarus locusta* and *G. marina*, are typical marine species and cannot penetrate very far into the estuary. Instead they are replaced by a typical estuarine species, *G. zaddachi*. This species, however, is broken down into three subspecies, separated by salinity tolerances. *G. zaddachi* lives at the seaward end, *G. z. salinesi* occupies the middle, and *G. z. zaddachi*, which can penetrate up into fresh water for a short time at least, lives on the landward end (Spooner, 1947; Segerstråle, 1947).

Size influences the range of motile species within the estuarine waters (Gunter, 1961). Smaller and younger fish inhabit waters of lower salinity and move down to more saline water as they grow larger. Thus the estuary serves as a sort of marine nursery, a place where young fish as well as other organisms, such as the blue crab, are protected from predation and competing species unable to enter low-salinity water. The young of such herbivorous and detritus-feeding fish as menhaden, striped mullet, hog choker, and croaker sometimes occur in hordes. Toward fresh water, the marine species drop out and are not replaced by fresh-water forms. In fact the mean number of species progressively decreases from the mouth of the estuary to upstream stations (Wells, 1961).

The role of the estuary as a nursery and the behavior of young fish in this habitat is well illustrated by the ecology of young winter flounder in the Mystic River estuary in eastern Connecticut (Pearcy, 1962). Adult winter flounder move inshore into shallow, semi-isolated inlets and the upper estuary to spawn. The eggs are demersal, that is, they sink to the bottom and are adhesive —they remain where they settle. As a result, the young are concentrated in the area where the eggs were laid, and the spawning grounds become the nursery. Nonbouyant, the larvae remain near the bottom, where, because a counter current is well developed, drift to the sea is minimal. Daily loss amounted to only three per cent per day, just one-third of the loss that would be expected if the larvae were uniformly distributed from the surface to the bottom. As the larvae mature, they move down the estuary and arrive in deep water by fall and early winter. Little needs to be added to stress the importance of the estuary to our commercial fisheries. Continuing destruction of this habitat by dredging and pollution can only hasten the disappearance of a number of our commercially important fish, such as the winter flounder, as well as other offshore and estuarine life.

Since salinities in estuaries vary considerably, organisms must be able to cope with changes in osmotic pressures. Some excrete excess water as fast as it enters the body, by means of kidneys, flame cells, and contractile vacuoles. Others increase internal hydrostatic pressure, especially by strong contractions of the body wall. Salt retention (discussed in Chap. 4) is still another method. A fourth solution common among estuarine animals such as snails, clams, shrimp, and crabs is an impermeable covering. Clams close up during periods of low salinity and function on stored glycogen available for anaerobic utilization; once this energy source is gone, the clam must open and suffer the consequences if the salinity is not back in the tolerable range.

Salinity changes often affect larval forms more severely than adults. Larval veligers of the oyster drill *Thais* succumb to low salinity more easily than the adults. A sudden influx of fresh water, especially after hurricanes or heavy rainfall, sharply lowers the salinity and causes a high mortality of oysters and their associates. When the drought-breaking heavy rainfall sharply reduced the salinities of Mesquite Bay in Texas (see above), the high-salt-tolerant marine sessile and infaunal mollusks were completely wiped out. The high-salinity community of the oyster *Ostrea equestris* and the mussel *Brachidontes exustus* was replaced by the the oyster *Crassostrea virginica* and the mussel *Brachidontes recurvus*. The rapid lowering of the salinity did not kill fish or other motile forms, which apparently moved out of the area (Hoese, 1960).

The oyster bed and the oyster reef are the outstanding communities of the estuary. Here the oyster is the dominant organism about which life revolves. Oysters may be attached on every hard object in the intertidal zone or they may form reefs, areas where clusters of living oysters grow cemented to the almost-buried shells of past generations. Oyster reefs usually lie at right angles to tidal currents, which bring planktonic food, carry away wastes, and sweep the oysters clean of sediment and debris.

214

Closely associated with oysters are encrusting organisms such as sponges, barnacles, and bryozoans, which attach themselves to oyster shells and are dependent on the oyster or algae for food. The oyster crab strains food from the oyster's gills (Christensen and McDermoth, 1958), and a pyramidellid snail lives an ectoparasitic life by feeding on body fluids and tissue debris from the oyster's mouth (Hopkins, 1958). Beneath and between the oysters live polychaete worms, decapods, pelecypods, and a host of other organisms. In fact, 303 different species have been collected from the oyster bed (Wells, 1961).

Tidal marshes

On the alluvial plains about the estuary and in the shelter of the spits and offshore bars and islands exists a unique community, the tidal marsh (Fig. 11-5). Although to the eye tidal marshes appear as waving acres of grass, they are instead a complex of distinctive and clearly demarked plant associations. The reasons for this complex are again the tides and salinity. The tides perhaps play the most significant role in plant segregation, for two times a day the salt-marsh plants on the outermost tidal flats are submerged in salty water and then exposed to the full insolation of the sun. Their roots extend into poorly drained, poorly aerated soil, in which the soil solution contains varying concentrations of salt. Only plant species with a wide range of salt tolerance can survive such conditions (Fig. 11-3). Thus from the edge of the sea to the highlands, zones of vegetation, each recognizable by its own distinctive color, develop.

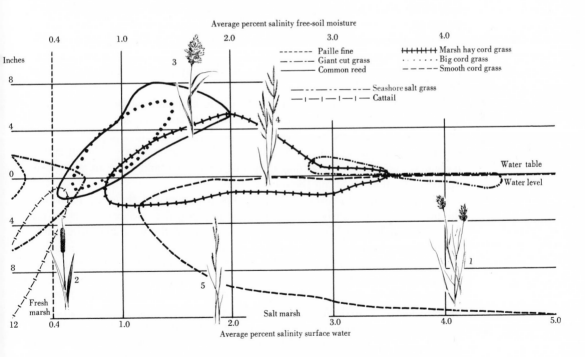

Figure 11-3 *Approximate ranges of species dominance among fresh and salt marsh plants in relation to water and salinity.* (Adapted from *Water*, U.S. Department of Agriculture Yearbook of Agriculture, 1955, p. 450.)

Tidal salt marshes begin in most cases as mud or sand flats, first colonized by algae and, if the water is deep enough, by eelgrass. As organic debris and sediments accumulate, eelgrass is replaced by the first salt-marsh colonists—the sea poa, *Puccinellia,* on the European coast, and salt-water cord grass, *Spartina alterniflora* var. *glabra,* on the coast of eastern North America. Stiff, leafy, up to 10 feet tall, and submerged in salt water at every high tide, salt-water cord grass forms a marginal strip between the open mud flat to the front and the higher grassland behind (Fig. 11-4). Next is a band of greenish, short, marsh-hay cord grass, *Spartina patens,* also covered by the tides. This grass grows so heavy and forms such a tight mat that few other plants can grow in this zone. Beyond the *Spartina* and on a rising ground level is a zone of rushes, the black grass, *Juncus,* so called because of its very dark green color, which becomes almost black in fall. Rarely are the rushes covered by ordinary high tides, but often they are submerged by neap tides of spring and fall. Near the high-tide mark, between the cord grass and the rushes, may be a strip of poorly drained saline area, where saltwort with fleshy, succulent, jointed stems, and the salt grass grow. Beyond the black grass a narrow belt of tussock-forming grasses may mark a transition between the marsh below and the upland vegetation above.

Two conspicuous physiographic features of the salt marshes are the meandering creeks and the salt pans. The creeks are the drainage channels that carry the tidal waters back out to sea. The formation of these creeks is a complex process. In some cases, the channels are formed by water deflected by minor irregularities on the surface. In estuarine marshes, the river itself forms the main channel. Once formed, the channels are deepened by scouring and heightened by a steady accumulation of organic matter and silt. At the same time, the heads of the creeks erode backward and small branch creeks develop. Where lateral erosion and undercutting take place, the banks may cave in, blocking or overgrowing the smaller channels. The distribution and pattern of the creek system play an important role in the drainage of the surface water and the drainage and movement of the water in the subsoil.

Across the tidal marshes are many circular to elliptical patches of vegetation, different from the dominant plants about them and concentrically arranged about small depressions in the earth. These depressions are salt pans. At high tide they are flooded; at low tide the depressions remain filled with salt water. If shallow enough, the water may evaporate completely and leave an accumulating concentration of salt on the mud.

Pans come about in several ways. The great majority of them are formed as the marsh develops. Early plant colonization is irregular and bare spots on the flat become surrounded by vegetation. As the level of the vegetated marsh rises, the bare spots lose their water outlet. If such a pan eventually becomes attached to a creek, normal drainage is restored and the pan eventually becomes vegetated. Other pans, especially in sandy marshes, are derived from creeks. Marsh vegetation may grow across the creek bottom and dam a portion of it; or lateral erosion may block the channel. With drainage no longer effective, water remains behind after the flood tide, inhibiting the growth of plants. Often a series of such pans may form on the upper reaches of a single creek. Still another type is the rotten-spot pan, caused by the death of small patches of vegetation from one cause or another. Perhaps it may be due to small depressions, which result in the eventual waterlogging of the soil, or it may be due to patches of trash that remain behind after snowmelt in the spring. Retardation of vegetative growth under these patches induces further accumulation in the same spot the following winter. Eventually the vegetation is completely killed and a bare area results (see Miller and Egler, 1950; Chapman, 1960).

Pans support a distinctive vegetation, which varies with the depth of the water and salt concentration. Pools with a firm bottom and sufficient depth to retain tidal water support dense growths of wigeon grass, *Ruppia maritima*, with long, threadlike leaves and small, black, triangular seeds relished by waterfowl (Fig. 11-4). The pools are usually surrounded by those forbs such as sea lavender that add so much color to the sea coast. Shallow depressions in which water evaporates are covered with a heavy algal crust and crystallized salt. At best, they support only saltwort, pale green in summer and scarlet in fall. Some such pans are occasionally invaded by forbs and a yellow, stunted growth of salt-water cord grass, considered by some botanists to be a variety of the species occupying the first major zone of estuarine vegetation (see Chapman, 1960).

Ecologically, the estuary, its sounds, creeks, marshes, and mud and sand flats are all one production unit. The marshes produce an excess of organic material. In fact less than five per cent of the net production of a *Spartina* marsh is consumed by insects and other herbivores; and two-thirds of that consumed by the major herbivore, the salt-marsh grasshopper, passes through the gut undigested and available to other organisms (Smalley, 1960). Excess organic matter in the marsh is transported into estuarine waters, where it is available to a whole host of decomposers and other detritus feeders, such as the horse mussel, important in the phosphorus cycle. While filtering water to obtain its food, the mussel excretes large quantities of organic particles as pseudofeces, which sink to the bottom (Kuenzler, 1961).

As soon as organic debris is buried more than a few millimeters, either through the movements of animals or by further deposition on top, an anaerobic environment is created. Here bacteria and nematodes live on organic matter, utilizing it by parallel oxidizing and reducing reactions (Teal and Kanwisher, 1961). This results in the accumulation of such end products as methane, hydrogen sulfide, and ferrous compounds. Increasing degrees of reduction suppress biological activity. In fact if the bacteria of the mud are supplied with oxygen, their rate of energy degradation increases 25 times. Thus the tidal marsh is a horizontally stratified system in which free oxygen is abundant in the surface and absent in the mud. Between these two extremes is a zone of diffusion and mixing of oxygen.

The exposed banks of tidal creeks that braid through the salt marshes support a dense population of mud algae, the diatoms and dinoflagellates, photosynthetically active all year. Photosynthesis in summer is highest during high tides; in winter it is highest during low tides, when the sun warms the sediments (Pomeroy, 1959). Some of the algae are washed out at ebb tide and become a temporary part of the estuarine plankton, available to such filter feeders as the oysters. Thus the salt marsh functions both as a source of food and of fertilizer for the estuary.

Unfortunately salt marshes and their colorful inhabitants (see McAtee, 1939) are disappearing before human activity. (For an unspoiled salt marsh see Fig. 11-5.) Regarded by man as wasteland, the marshes have been ditched, drained, filled for real estate and industrial development, or used as garbage dumps. A few have been utilized for marsh hay. Mowing year after year reduces the vitality

217

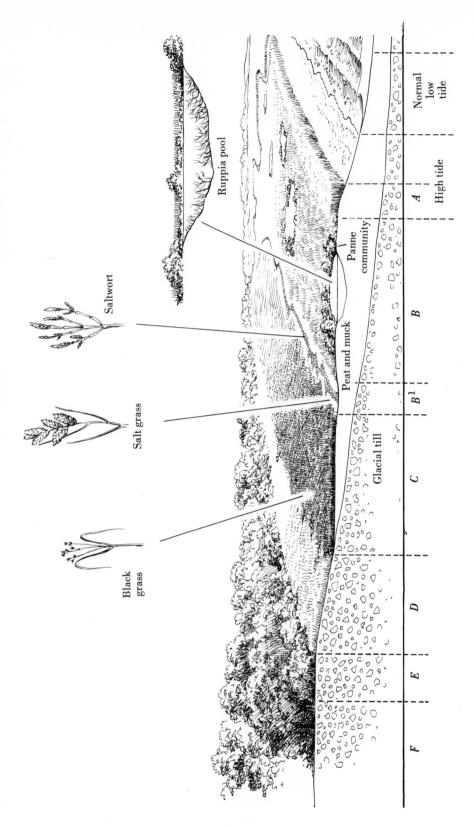

Figure 11-4 *A generalized view of a tidal marsh on the northeastern Atlantic Coast of the United States. Note the braiding of the tidal streams and the zonation of marsh vegetation, reflecting the gradients of water depth and salinity. (A) Zone of salt-water cord grass; (B) marsh-hay cord grass; (B'), saltwort and salt grass; (C) black grass, Juncus; (D) grassland—switch grass, fresh-water cord grass; (E) shrub zone; (F) forest. For details, see text. (Drawing based in part on data from Miller and Egler, 1950; Chapman, 1962; and author's photographs and sketches.*

Saltwort

Salt grass

Black grass

Ruppia pool

Panne community

Peat and muck

Glacial till

A High tide

B

B¹

C

D

E

F

Normal low tide

Figure 11-5 *A view of an unspoiled tidal marsh on the northeastern coast of the United States.* (Photo by author.)

of dominant species and destroys the normal accumulation of mulch. The soil is exposed, the upper slopes erode, and the area is invaded by forbs. Ditching destroys the normal drainage pattern and may produce the conditions it was designed to destroy (Miller and Egler, 1950). The turf line or pile of excavated material along the sides of the ditch often retards drainage and aids in the development of natural levees created by silt deposition during high tides. These levees so alter the surface drainage that elongate panes or pools form between the ditches, a situation the ditches originally were designed to correct.

Mangrove swamps

Mangrove swamps replace tidal marshes in tropical regions, and in North America they reach their best development along the southwest coast of Florida and southward. As with the salt marsh, the vegetation is influenced by salinity and the tides. The pioneering red mangrove colonizes the submerged soft-bottomed shoals protected from the full beat of the surf. It has a peculiar system of branching prop roots that extend downward like stilts from the trunks and lower branches. The seeds germinate on the tree to form club-shaped hypocotyls 30 cm long. They hang by two cotyledons until they drop into the water or the mud below. If the mud is deep enough, the seedling may take root. If not, the seedling rises to the surface and for a while floats horizontally, often drifting with the wind and tidal currents far from its point of origin. Eventually the root end becomes waterlogged and the seedling floats in a vertical position until the tip of the root touches bottom in shallow water. If the bottom is soft, the roots form rapidly, the young plant is anchored, and a new mangrove blossoms above water. As the plant grows, new prop roots sprout from the limbs and grow down to the water. The tangle of roots block tidal currents, which drop their load of organic debris among the mangroves. This, together with falling leaves and the droppings of birds, gradually builds up the soil to high-tide level (Davis, 1940).

At the upper limits of high tide, the black or honey mangrove replaces the red. This mangrove does best in a sandy or less organic soil and tolerates a shorter period of flooding. It has pencil-like pneumatophores rising through the substrate

219

from shallow, horizontal roots. The flowers produce abundant nectar used by bees, and the leaves exude excess salts on the leaf surface, where it is washed away by the rain. Behind the black mangrove and on firm ground at the edge of the tide line may be a zone of white mangrove. The white mangrove also possesses pneumatophores, but they are fewer in number and smaller. Above the normal high tides grows a relative of the white mangrove, the button mangrove, with loose bark and twisted and often prostrate trunk.

Associated with the mangroves are a number of vines and shrubs. The ivy, *Cissis,* climbs through the mangrove crowns and sends long, cordlike, aerial roots down to the ground. A spreading, succulent-leafed shrub, the saltwort, grows on the wet, salty mud.

Birds are the most colorful and conspicuous inhabitants of the mangroves. In the water about the feet of mangrove roots and in the shallow mangrove pools live an assortment of small fish. Fiddler crabs crawl through the tangle of mud and roots and small coon oysters grow attached to the roots.

SUMMARY

Estuaries, where the fresh water meets the sea, and their associated tidal marshes and swamps are a unit in which the nature and distribution of life are determined by salinity. In the estuary itself, salinity declines from the mouth back up the river. This decrease in salinity is accompanied by a decline in estuarine fauna, since the fauna consists chiefly of marine species. The estuary serves as a nursery for marine organisms, for here the young can develop protected from predators and competing species, unable to withstand the lower salinity. Tidal marshes add to the productivity of the estuary. Composed of salt-tolerant grasses and flooded by daily tides, most of the primary production goes unharvested by herbivores. The excess organic matter is carried out to the estuary by the tides, where it is utilized by decomposers and detritus feeders. If vertical mixing between the fresh water and the salt occurs in the estuary, then the nutrients are circulated up and down between the organisms and bottom sediments. The importance of the tidal marsh as a nutrient source to the estuary and the role of the estuary as a nursery for such marine species as the flounder and oyster should be reason enough for their protection. Yet the pollution of the estuaries and the filling in of tidal marshes, unless the trend is stopped, may have a deleterious effect on the productivity of the shallow seas.

SUGGESTED FIELD ACTIVITIES

Many of the suggestions given for introductory work in stream and marsh habitats are applicable to tidal marshes and estuaries. Investigations of the estuary are much more difficult than those for small rivers and streams. Often a relatively large boat and more elaborate equipment is needed. A method of determining the rate of flow of an estuary is given in Appendix B. Sampling the bottom and fish fauna will require dredging and seines. The tidal marsh at low tides can be studied in much the same manner as the fresh-water marsh.

CHAPTER 12

The seashore

Where the edge of the land meets the edge of the sea there exists the fascinating and complex world of the seashore. Rocky, sandy, muddy, protected, exposed to the pounding of incoming swells, all shores have one feature in common; they are alternatingly exposed and submerged by the tides. Roughly, the region of the seashore is bounded on one side by the height of the extreme high tides and on the other by the height of extreme low tides. Within these confines, conditions change from hour to hour with the ebb and flow of the tides. At flood tide the seashore is a water world; at ebb tide it belongs to the terrestrial environment, with its extremes in temperature, moisture, and solar radiation. In spite of all this, the seashore inhabitants are essentially marine, adapted to withstand some degree of exposure to the air for varying periods of time.

The tides

Since life on the shore is influenced by ebb and flow of the tides, the tides deserve some attention, although the theories and technical aspects must be found in other books.

One of the fundamental laws of physics is Newton's law of universal gravitation. The law states that every particle of matter in the universe attracts every other particle with a force that varies directly as the product of their masses and inversely as the square of the distance between them. This is the reason why apples fall to the earth; it is also, in part, why the planets revolve about the sun. The earth attracts the apple, the apple in turn attracts the earth; but since the mass of the earth is so much greater, the apple falls to the ground. Likewise, the sun and its planets exert an attraction on each other; but the sun, being the largest, exerts the most powerful force. There is also an attraction between the earth and the moon. Since the moon is much closer to the earth than the sun, it exerts a force twice as great as that of the sun. The gravitational pull of the sun and the moon each cause two bulges in the waters of the oceans. The two caused by the moon occur at the same time on opposite sides of the earth on an imaginary line extending from the moon through the center of the earth. The tidal bulge on the moon side is due to gravitational attraction; the bulge on the opposite side occurs because the gravitational force there is less than at the center of the earth. As the earth rotates eastward on its axis, the tides advance westward. Thus any given place on the earth will in the course of one daily rotation pass through two of the lunar tidal bulges, or high tides, and two of the lows or low tides, at right angles to the high. Since the moon revolves in a 29½-day orbit around the earth, the average period between successive high tides is approximately 12 hours, 25 minutes.

The sun also causes two tides on opposite sides of the earth; and these tides have a relation to the sun such as the lunar tides have to the moon. Because they are less than one-half as high, solar tides are partially masked by lunar tides except for two times during the month, when the moon is full and when it is new. At these times, the earth, the moon, and the sun are nearly in line and the gravitational pulls of the sun and the moon are additive. This causes the high tides of those periods to be exceptionally large, with maximum rise and fall. These are the fortnightly spring tides, a name derived from the Saxon *sprungen,* which refers to the brimming fullness and active movement of the water. When the moon is at either quarter, the pull of the moon is at right angles to the pull of the sun and the two forces interfere with each other. At this time the differences between high and low tide are exceptionally low. These are the neap tides, from an old Scandinavian word meaning "barely enough."

Tides are not entirely regular nor are they the same all over the earth. They vary from day to day in the same place, following the waxing and the waning of the moon. They may act differently in several localities within the same general area. In the Atlantic, semidaily tides are the rule. In the Gulf of Mexico, the alternate highs and lows more or less efface each other, and flood and ebb follow one another at about twenty-four hour intervals to produce one daily tide. Mixed tides are common in the Pacific and Indian oceans. These are combinations of the other two, with different combinations at different places. Local inconsistencies of tides are due to many variables. The elliptical orbit of the earth about the sun and of the moon about the earth influence the gravitational pull, as does the declination of the moon—the angle of the moon in relation to the axis of the earth. Latitude, barometric pressure, offshore and onshore winds, depth of water, contour of shore, and natural periods of oscillation, or internal waves (see Seiches, Chap. 9), modify tidal movements.

Figure 12-1 *A large rock jutting out into the sea shows the broad zones of life exposed at low tide. Note the heavy growth of bladder wrack or rockweed on the lower side, the white zone of barnacles near the top.*

The rocky shore

As the sea recedes at ebb tide, rocks glistening and dripping with water begin to appear. Life hidden by tidal water emerges into the open air, layer by layer. The uppermost layers of life are exposed to the air, wide temperature fluctuations, intense solar radiation, and desiccation for a considerable period of time, while the lowest fringes on the intertidal shore may be exposed only briefly before the flood tide submerges them again. These varying conditions result in one of the most striking features of the rocky shore, the zonation of life (Fig. 12-1). Although this zonation may be strikingly different from place to place as a result of local variations in aspect, nature of the substrate, wave action, light intensity, shore profile, exposure to prevailing winds, climatic differences, and the like, it possesses everywhere the same general features. All rocky shores have three basic zones, characterized by the dominant organisms occupying them (Fig. 12-2).

Where the land ends and seashore begins is difficult to fix. The approach to a rocky shore from the landward side is marked by a gradual transition from lichens and other land plants, the maritime zone, to marine life, dependent in part at least on the tidal waters. The first major change from land shows up on the supralittoral fringe (Fig 12-3), where the salt water comes only every fortnight on the spring tides. It is marked by the black zone, a patchlike or beltlike encrustation of Verrucaria-type lichens and Myxophyceaa algae such as *Calothrix* and *Entrophsalis*. Capable of existing under conditions so difficult that few other plants could exist, these blue-green algae, enclosed in slimy, gelatinous sheaths, and their associated lichens represent an essentially nonmarine community, on which graze basically marine animals, the periwinkles (Doty, in Hedgpeth, 1957). Common to this black zone is the rough periwinkle that grazes on the wet algae covering the rocks. On European shores lives a similarly adapted species, the rock periwinkle, the most highly resistant to desiccation of all the shore animals.

Below the black zone lies the littoral, a region covered and uncovered daily by the tides. It is universally characterized by the barnacles, although often they are hidden under a dense growth of fucoid seaweeds or kelp (a brown alga, Phaeophyceae) and in the more northern reaches of the North American and European coasts by the red algae (Rhodophyceae). The littoral tends to be divided into subzones. In the upper reaches the barnacles are most abundant. The oyster, blue mussel, and the limpets appear in the middle and lower portions of the littoral, as does the common periwinkle, the second of the three periwinkles common to the rocky shore.

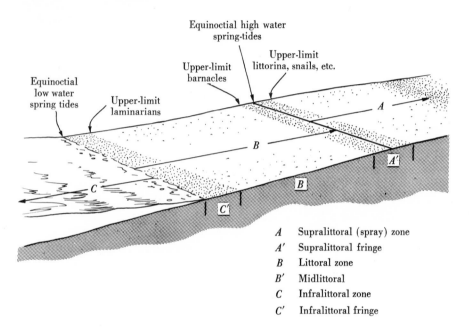

A	Supralittoral (spray) zone
A'	Supralittoral fringe
B	Littoral zone
B'	Midlittoral
C	Infralittoral zone
C'	Infralittoral fringe

Figure 12-2 *A diagram of the basic zones on a rocky shore. Use this as a guide when studying the subsequent drawings of zonation on rocky shores.* (Adapted from Stephenson, 1949.)

Of all the animals of the littoral, the common periwinkle, which may range from the high water of neap tides to the low water of spring tides, is the most adaptable. It may live on bare rock, among barnacles, among seaweeds, and on soft mud; it is at home equally on the shores exposed to open sea and in sheltered bays. The periwinkle clings to crevices and seaweeds by the foot. At low tide on hot days the animal draws into the shell, across the mouth of which is a thin film of mucous. The mucous spreads over the surface of the rock, hardens, and glues the margin of the shell to the stone. The foot is then pulled in, the operculum is closed, and the animal is protected from desiccation.

Barnacles (Figs. 12-2 and 12-3) are the most distinctive organisms of the littoral. At low tide their chiseled limestone whiteness forms a distinctive belt

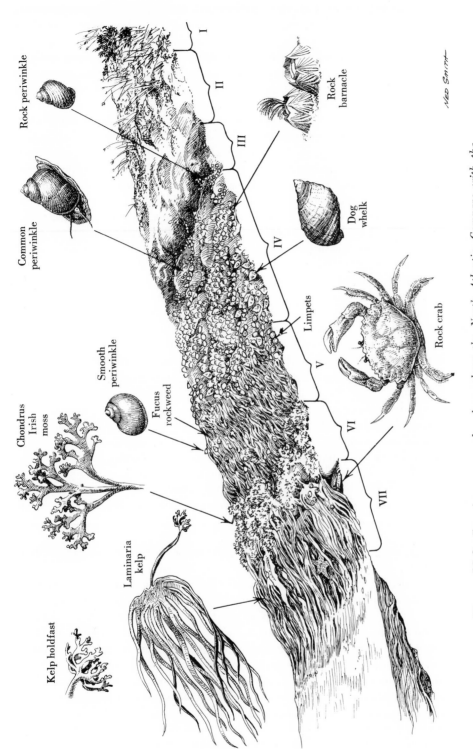

Figure 12-3 *Zonation on a rocky shore along the North Atlantic. Compare with the generalized diagram, Fig. 12-2. (I) Land: lichens, herbs, grasses, etc.; (II) bare rock; (III) zone of black algae and rock periwinkles; (IV) barnacle zone: barnacles, dog whelks, common periwinkles, mussels; (V) the fucoid zone: rockweed and smooth periwinkles; (VI) Chondrus zone: Irish moss; (VII) laminarian zone: kelp (Zonation drawing based on the data from Stephenson, 1954, and author's photographs and observations; all sketches drawn from life or specimens.)*

Rock periwinkle

Common periwinkle

Smooth periwinkle

Chondrus Irish moss

Kelp holdfast

Fucus rockweed

Laminaria kelp

Rock barnacle

Dog whelk

Limpets

Rock crab

NED SMITH

across the rocky shore. Two kinds are involved, *Chthamalus,* which occupies the upper limits of the littoral, and the larger *Balanus,* which lives lower downshore (see Chap. 21). Barnacles are sedentary crustaceans, glued to stones and dependent upon tides to bring them their sustenance. They are cone-shaped, with six fitted plates for their sides and with a door of four plates covering the top. At low tide, the door plates are closed, which protects the barnacles from drying. As the first tidal waters flow over them, the doors open; and the barnacles thrust out six pairs of branched, slender, wandlike appendages to sweep in the diatoms and other microscopic life in the water.

Found among the barnacles is a rock-clinging mollusk able to move freely about, the limpet. The limpets, in common with the barnacles, are cone-shaped, but they grow much larger. And like their associate they, too, lead a planktonic existence before they settle on the shore. When the tide is in, they move about from their home "base" to browse on the algae covering the rock. This they efficiently remove by their scraping organ, the radula; in fact they may ingest particles of rock and leave striations on the stone. Their grazing area, which extends about three feet from "home," is kept nearly barren of algae. If the limpets are removed, the surface of the stone is soon colonized by *Entromorpha, Porphyra,* and *Fucus* algae. When it has finished grazing, the limpet by some means returns to its "home," where it clings during ebb tide. It pulls its shell down tightly against the rock, to which it has fitted itself either by grinding the rock surface to fit the shell or by fitting the shell margins to the stone. The limpet secures its attachment by its strong, flat, rounded foot. The harder the seas pound against the rocks and the limpets, the more tightly the animals hold fast.

A highly colored predatory snail about the size of the common periwinkle, the dog whelk, moves about on the intertidal shore to prey on mussels (to be discussed later), barnacles, and to a limited extent, the browsing snails. The whelk attacks barnacles by forcing the valves apart and then inserting its probiscus into the exposed tissues. To feed on the adult blue mussel, the dog whelk drills through the shell; but they can successfully obtain young mussels by prying open the bivalve shells. Diet greatly influences the color of whelks. Those feeding primarily on mussels have brown, black, and mauve-pink shells, while those feeding on barnacles have white shells.

Occupying the lower half of the littoral zone of colder climates and in places overlying the barnacles are an ancient group of plants, the brown algae, more commonly known as rockweeds, or wrack (*Fucus*). Rockweeds attain their finest growth on protected shores, where they may grow seven feet long; on wave-whipped shores they are considerably shorter. The rockweeds that live furthest up on the tidelands are channeled rockweeds, or wrack, a species found on the European but not the American shore. It is replaced here by another, the spiral rockweed, a low-growing, orange-brown alga, whose short, heavy fronds end in turgid, roundish swellings. The spiral rockweeds on the northeastern coast form only a very narrow band, if present at all, for it is replaced by the more abundant bladder rockweed and, in sheltered waters only, the knotted rockweed. The bladder rockweed can withstand the heavy surf best, since it is shorter, has a strengthening midrib, and possesses great tensile strength. Both the bladder and knotted rockweeds have gas-filled bladders, which tend to buoy them up at high tide. Rockweeds have no roots—they draw their nutrients from the sea water

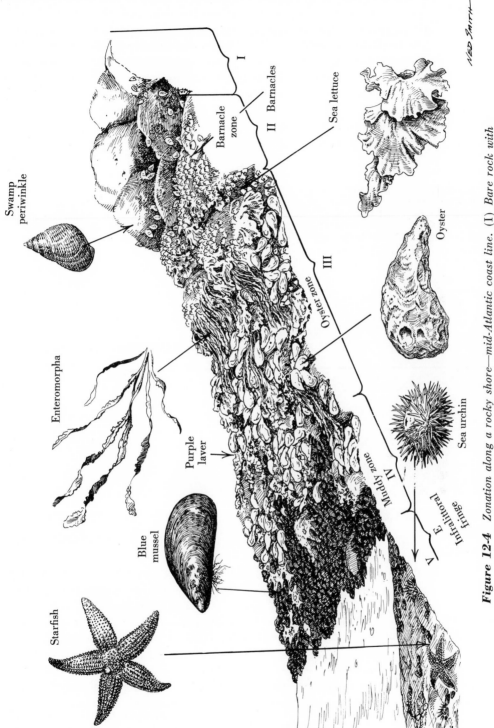

Figure 12-4 Zonation along a rocky shore—mid-Atlantic coast line. (I) Bare rock with some black algae and swamp periwinkle; (II) barnacle zone; (III) oyster zone: oysters, Entromorpha, sea lettuce, and purple laver; (IV) muddy zone: mussel beds; (V) infralittoral fringe: starfish, etc. Note absence of kelps. (Zonation drawing based on Stephenson, 1952; sketches done from life or specimens.)

Swamp periwinkle

Barnacle zone

II Barnacles

Sea lettuce

Oyster

Enteromorpha

Oyster zone

III

Purple laver

Sea urchin

Muddy zone

IV

Infralittoral fringe

V

Blue mussel

Starfish

NED SMITH

surrounding them—but they cling to the rocks by means of disk-shaped holdfasts.

At low tide the rockweeds lie draped over the rocks. Limpets and smooth periwinkles browse on the fronds, while underneath lie starfish and young green crabs. In the sediments live scarlet ribbon worms, minute bristle worms and the predaceous nereids, or clam worms. Minute copepods and mites are abundant. On the fronds of rockweeds are attached encrusting animals, such as the flowerlike, pink-colored hydroid *Clava*. Also attached to the fronds of rockweed are the coiled tubes of the small polychaete worm, *Spirorbis*. The snail-like tube is a calcareous secretion of the worm itself, which lives permanently inside and feeds by thrusting out its head and filtering food animals with filamentous tentacles.

Figure 12-5 *A close-up view of a blue mussel bed (see also Fig. 11-1).* (Photo by author.)

The lower reaches of the littoral zone may be occupied by blue mussels (Fig. 12-4), instead of rockweeds. This is particularly true on shores where the hard surfaces have been covered in part by sand and mud. No other shore animal grows in such abundance; the blue-black shells packed closely together may blanket the area (Fig 12-5). Although mussels, in common with other bivalves, possess a flattened foot, it is not suited for gripping. So this mollusk attaches itself to the substrate by a byssus, the threads of which are formed initially as a thick fluid by a gland in the foot. This fluid issues from the mussel along a groove that extends along the posterior of the foot, spreads out in a rounded disk at the surface of attachment, and hardens into tough threads. If the threads are broken, the mussel forms new ones and reattaches itself. By such means the mussels are able to move about and raise themselves above the rising level of the mud.

Mussels feed on plankton, which they strain from the water by a pair of broad, two-plated gills that extend along the length of the body. The water enters the gill cavity through an opening at the posterior end and leaves by an outgoing opening just above.

Near the lower reaches of the littoral zone, mussels may grow in association with a red alga, *Gigartina,* a low-growing, carpetlike plant. The algae and the mussels together often form a tight mat over the rocks. Here, too, grows another seaweed, Irish moss, which grows in carpets some six inches deep. Its color is variable, ranging from purple to yellow and green; its fronds are branched and tough (Fig. 12-3), and when covered by water the plant has an iridescent sheen. Here, well protected in the dense growth from the waves, live infant starfish, sea urchins, brittle stars, and the bryozoan sea mats or sea lace, *Membranipora.* These bryozoans are almost microscopic, tentacled, colonial animals, which form thin films in which each chamber is visible, giving the colony the appearance of lace.

The lowest part of the littoral zone, uncovered only at the spring tides and not even then if the wave action is strong, is the sublittoral fringe. This zone, exposed for relatively short periods of time, consists of forests of the large brown alga, *Laminaria,* one of the kelps (Fig. 12-3), with a rich undergrowth of smaller plants and animals among the holdfasts. Limpets, horse mussels, and other bivalves are abundant here, together with encrusting organisms, copepods, isopods, amphipods, sea squirts, crabs, segmented bristleworms, and starfish. Starfish wait out the low tide beneath the seaweed, beneath rocks, and in pools. At high tide they range out over the mussel beds to feed on the bivalves. Moving onto the mussel, the starfish humps its body and grips the valves of the shells with its tube feet. By continuously pulling on the valves and gradually inserting its thin stomach into the mussel, the shell finally opens. The starfish then digests the bivalve externally with its protruding stomach. A related echinoderm, the globular, spiny sea urchin also is common in the sublittoral fringe.

Beyond the sublittoral fringe is the sublittoral zone, the open sea. This zone is principally neretic and benthic and contains a wide variety of fauna, depending upon the substrate, the presence of protruding rocks, gradients in turbulence, oxygen tensions, light, and temperature. This offshore zone is extremely interesting to explore by skin diving. Appropriately, this area is becoming known to marine biologists as the scuba zone.

Variations in zonation

The zonation just described is essentially that of the North Atlantic Coast north of Cape Cod. This coast is duplicated in part by the rocky coasts of the British Isles, for 85 per cent of the plants and 65 per cent of the animals are shared in common (Stephenson, 1949). Although adhering to the same general pattern, the details of zonation vary on other rocky shores wherever they exist. This variation in eastern North America is due to temperature influenced by latitude and to that great river of the sea, the Gulf Stream.

Southern Atlantic Coast

From the Florida Straits to Cape Hatteras, the Gulf Stream follows the edge of the continental shelf. On the east coast of Florida, the shelf is narrow; where the waters flow close to shore, especially in extreme southern Florida and the Keys, tropical fauna flourish. North of Cape Kennedy, the Gulf Stream swings out from the coast, but at Cape Hatteras in the Carolinas the shelf narrows and the Gulf Stream comes closer to shore. This area marks an indefinite temperature barrier whose effects are more pronounced in winter than in summer. During the summer, the fauna of these warm temperate waters range north to Cape Cod. A huge sandspit jutting out into sea, Cape Cod deflects the Gulf Stream eastward away from North America and cups the cold Laborador currents in its northern shores (a fact well recognized by anyone who has plunged into the waters along both shores of the Cape in summer). Since distribution of life in the seas is strongly influenced by temperature, Cape Cod marks the northernmost distribution of many warm, temperate-water species and the south-ern-most distribution of arctic species. Within recent years even this has been changing, for with a general warming trend occurring in the arctic waters, southern species such as the green crab and the mantis shrimp are extending their range northward. Cape Cod also marks a radical change in the substrate of the shores from sand to rock. Thus from Cape Cod northward the intertidal regions are characterized by a heavy growth of seaweeds, vast numbers of periwinkles, and millions of barnacles and mussels.

South of the Cape, rocky shores are scarce, but where a rock substrate does exist, as in jetties and breakwaters, rocky-shore fauna appear, although the composition of the community differs somewhat from that of the northern coast. In the warm, temperate waters from Cape Kennedy to Cape Hatteras, some species appear and disappear on a north-south gradient (Stephenson and Stephenson, 1952). The shore populations include tropical forms distributed as far north as North Carolina; the cold-water species extend somewhat south of Hatteras. Mixed with these two are the more cosmopolitan species that occupy longer or shorter stretches of the Atlantic Coast from Cape Cod to Cape Kennedy. Within this wide range of coastline, seasonal variations exist, with a strengthening of the southern element in summer, the northern element in winter. But in spite of the physical and biological variations, the intertidal zone exhibits the same common features. The supralittoral fringe possesses the typical black zone of encrusting algae and lichens, including such species as *Entrophysalis deusta* and *Calothrix pulvenata*, but the periwinkles are extremely scarce, a sharp contrast to the northern rocky coast (Fig. 12-5). Faunal inhabitants include the rapid isopod, or sea roach, ghost crabs, and fiddler crabs. The littoral is characterized by a barnacle zone, occupied in the upper limits by *Chthamalus* and on the seaward side by the larger *Balanus*. Below, but overlapping the barnacles, is a belt of oysters, mussels, and a red seaweed, the ribbonlike purple laver (Fig. 12-5). Here too grow the green seaweeds, *Ulva* and *Entromorpha*, and the brown bladder rockweed. Beyond this is a zone of mud claimed by the mussels, mixed algae, the orange sponge, limpets, predaceous whelks, the anemones, and sea urchins.

The rocky, clinkerlike coraline shores of the Florida Keys is a tropical world, yet even here the major intertidal zones are discernible (Stephenson, 1950). The supralittoral fringe is especially well developed and is subdivided into subzones, a white, a gray, and a black. The white zone is the meeting place of land and sea and is occupied by such maritime species as the purple-clawed hermit crab, rapid crabs, and the sea roach. The gray zone occupies rocks wetted only part of the time, often only during the high waters of spring tides. This is the first zone of macroscopic marine algae, characterized by the mosslike *Bostrychia.* The periwinkle *Littoria ziczac,* the beaded periwinkle *Tectarius,* and other small, boldly colored snails graze on the algal film. The black zone claims areas completely submerged by the high waters of spring tides and is coated with an encrusting growth of the blue-green algae *Entrophysalis* and *Brachtrichia,* utilized by the periwinkles. Below the black zone is the littoral, characteristically yellowish in color. Only in the upper littoral do the barnacles live, and they vary in numbers from complete absence to crowded colonies. They include the small barnacle *Chthamalus stellatus* and the large barnacle *Tetraclita squamosa,* which occupies the lower barnacle zone. Associated with the barnacles are the neritid snails, the ribbed mussel, chitons, and the everpresent predatory whelks. Large algae, so characteristic of the littoral of the northern shores, are absent; the seaweeds here are short, mossy, turflike, or encrusting. The lower part of the littoral is inhabited by two dominant colonial organisms, sheets of small, bubblelike green alga, *Valonia,* and masses of sedentary tube-dwelling gastropods, *Spiroglypus.* Below the yellow zone lies the lower reef, the most distinctive feature of which is the extensive growth of the yellow, carpetlike alga, *Laurencia.* Beyond this are the reef flats, a world of corals rich in many marine plants and animals. This, however, is not a part of the intertidal region.

Pacific coast

The intertidal regions of the Atlantic Coast of North America fall into tropical, warm temperate, and cold temperate regions. On the intertidal Pacific Coast, these regions are obscured by complex arrangements of currents and water masses. As a result, the intertidal flora and fauna possess many common features from Alaska to the outer coast of California. Typical zonation, suggestive of the cold temperate Atlantic Coast, exists. There is a black, supralittoral fringe occupied by the periwinkle, *Littorina scutularia.* The littoral is inhabited by barnacles, the upper zone by *Chthamalus,* the lower by *Balanus.* The lower littoral supports both mussels and kelp. The growth of kelp often is prolific, but the conspicuous east coast species, the bladder, serrated, and spiral rockweeds, are missing. The Pacific Coast rockweeds lack bladders and serrations, and all are hermaphroditic. They vary widely in size and general appearance, in the shape of the receptacles, and in habitat, yet taxonomically they still appear to represent one species, *Fucus distichus,* also found along the Atlantic Coast (Stephenson, 1961). The sublittoral possesses two subzones, a strip of bare rocks and below this a zone of mossy, beardlike algae and a colorful array of large starfish.

Perhaps the most striking feature of the Pacific Coast intertidal region is the contrast between north-facing and south-facing shore (Stephenson, 1961). The supralittoral fringe on the north-facing shore is narrower than on the south and is located much higher on the shore. There is also a correspondingly higher shift in the barnacle zone, which is much deeper on the north-facing shores. The barnacle zone on the south-facing shores involves two genera, an upper zone of *Chthamalus* and a lower *Balanus* zone. *Chthamalus* is missing entirely on north-facing shores. The main zone of kelp is up to four feet higher on the north-facing coast, and its sublittoral has a somewhat different faunal composition than the south-facing shores. Particularly characteristic of the north is the tube worm,

Figure 12-6 *Tidal pools. (left) A rock pool nestled in a "canyon" on a rocky shore. (right) A tiny rock pool on the ledge of a huge rock. Note the bladder wrack, the barnacles, and the transparency of the water.*

Serpula vermicularis, a weak fringe of kelp, and a rich group of echinoderms and anemones, all of which seemingly replace the band of short, carpetlike algae of the south-facing shore.

Tide pools

When the tide flows out, it leaves behind in rock crevices, in rocky basins, and in depressions, pools of water that dot the rocky shores (Fig. 12-6). These are tide pools, "microcosms of the sea," as Yonge (1949) describes them. They represent distinct habitats, which differ considerably from the exposed rock and the open sea, and even differ among themselves. At low tide all the pools are subject to wide and sudden fluctuations in temperature and salinity, but these changes are most marked in shallow pools. Under the summer sun the temperature may rise above the maximum many organisms can tolerate. As the water evaporates, especially in the smaller and more shallow pools, salinity increases and salt crystals may appear around the edges. When rain or land drainage brings fresh water to the pool, salinity may decrease. In deep pools such fresh water tends to form a layer on the top, developing a strong salinity stratification in which the bottom layer and its inhabitants are little affected. Obviously pools near low tide are influenced least by the rise and fall of the tides; those which lie near and above the high-tide line are exposed the longest and undergo the widest fluctuations. Some may be recharged with sea water only by the splash from breaking waves or occasional high spring tides. Regardless of their position on the shore, most pools suddenly return to sea conditions on the rising tide and experience drastic and instantaneous changes in temperature, salinity, and pH. Life in the tidal pools must be able to withstand wide and rapid fluctuations in their environment.

Tidal pools are fascinating places, one as interesting as the other, for often they differ in the organisms they contain. Small pools high up on the shore and subject to rapid evaporation may hold little more than the reflection of the sky or perhaps the little copepod *Tigriopus,* which can survive the high temperatures and salinities. Pools of the upper shore may have thin, pink encrustations of a calcareous alga, *Lithothamnion,* or support a bright-green growth of a tubelike alga, *Entromorpha.* Or they may be lined with a crustose growth of a brown alga, *Ralfsia,* which holds a wide variety of microscopic life. Periwinkles may live in the pools, as well as barnacles and mussels on whose shell may grow threadlike colonies of hydroids. The common seashore insect, *Anurida,* runs on the surface film. Like some of its fresh-water counterparts, this insect holds a film of air about its body when it enters the water. This air bubble enables the insect to remain submerged during high tide, ready to roam over the rocks at low tide in search of dead animal matter, on which it feeds. Pools on the lower shore may contain more diverse and more colorful forms—green crumb-of-bread sponges, which obtain their green color from symbiotic algae scattered through the tissues, yellow sponges, mussels, starfish, and anemones. One small tidal pool investigated contained 5185 individuals representing 45 macroscopic species (Bobvjerg and Glynn, 1960).

All this life in the pools adds still another dimension to the environment-oxygen balance. If algal growth is considerable, oxygen content of the water varies through the day. Oxygen will be high during the daylight hours but will be low at night, a situation that rarely occurs at sea. The rise of carbon dioxide at night means a lowering of pH. Only organisms well adapted to these extreme short-term fluctuations in the environment can colonize the pools.

Loose rocks and boulders

The rocky shore represents one extreme of the intertidal habitat; the sandy beach, soon to be discussed, represents the other. Lying between these two are those shores covered with loose stones and small boulders mixed in a matrix of mud and sand. Like the undersides of stream-bottom stones, the rocks and boulders of the seashore also support an abundance of life (Fig. 12-7). Stones embedded in sand and gravel on the lower zones are subject to abrasion great enough to prevent the growth of algae and barnacles. But unless buried in the mud, the undersides of these stones support populations of those organisms requiring protection from sunlight, desiccation, and violent water movements. These animals live in almost perpetually calm seawater, which remains behind long after the tide has gone out. Because of low illumination, algae are scarce. The fauna utilize the food suspended in the water about them and organic debris dropped about the stones, or they leave the area by night to feed. The nature of the faunal community depends upon the stability of the rocks. If the rocks are easily overturned by the waves, the populations beneath will die from exposure. If rock movement is greatest in the winter, then the summer population will consist largely of summer annuals. Because small stones of pebble size are so unstable, beaches covered with them are usually barren of life.

The undersurfaces of rocks may support a few periwinkles (Fig. 12-7), a host

Figure 12-7 *The underside of a small boulder exposed at low tide. Note the barnacles, the periwinkles, the dog whelk. Scud were abundant in the water beneath the stone.* (Photo by author.)

of small crustaceans such as the shore skipper *Orchestia* and the amphipod *Gammarus*. Other amphipods live in tubular nests made from the fragments of weeds. The small, coiled *Spirorbis*, so common on seaweeds, also attaches itself to the undersides of stones, as do the serpulid worms with limy tubes and the broad, flattened scale worms. Rock-boring worms, such as species of *Potamilla* and *Polydora*, may also live here. Crabs seek shelter beneath the rocks, together with starfish, sea urchins, and worms of many kinds. Where organic debris has accumulated, the omnivorous bristle worms, *Nereis*, and related genera abound. These worms live in irregular burrows beneath the stones and feed on plant and animal debris. Associated with them and feeding upon them are the ribbon worms, or nemertines. Where organic matter has accumulated to such a point that it creates a rich and odoriferous muck, the substrate beneath the stones may be covered with thin, twisting masses of redthreads. Examining the undersurfaces of stones on the intertidal beach can be rewarding; only be sure to return the stones to their original positions if the small communities they support are to be preserved.

Sandy shores

The sandy shore at low tide appears barren of life, a sharp contrast to the life-studded rocky shores. But the beach is not as dead as it seems, for beneath the wet and glistening sand, life exists, waiting for the next high tide.

The sandy shore in some ways is a harsh environment; indeed the very matrix of this seaside environment is a product of the harsh and relentless weathering of rock, both inland and along the shore. Through eons of time, the ultimate products of rock weathering are carried away by rivers and waves to be deposited as sand along the edge of the sea. The size of the sand particles

234

deposited influences the nature of the sandy beach, water retention during low tide, and the ability of animals to burrow through it. Beaches with relatively steep slopes usually are made up of larger sand grains and are subject to more wave action. Beaches exposed to high waves are generally flattened, for much of the material is transported away from the beach to deeper water, and left behind is fine sand (Fig. 12-8). Sand grains of all sizes, especially the finer particles in which capillary action is greatest, are more or less cushioned by a film of water about them, reducing further wearing away. The retention of water by the sand at low tide is one of the outstanding environmental features of the sandy shore.

Existence of life on the surface of the sand is almost impossible. It provides no surface for attachments of seaweeds and their associated fauna; and the crabs, worms, and snails so characteristic of rock crevices find no protection here. Life then is forced to exist beneath the sand (Fig. 12-9).

Life of the sandy beach does not experience the same violent fluctuations in temperature as that of the rocky shores. Although the surface temperature of the sand at midday may be 10 or more degrees centigrade higher than the returning sea water, the temperature a few inches below remains almost constant throughout the year. Nor is there a violent fluctuation in salinity, even when fresh water runs over the surface of the sand. Below ten inches, salinity is little affected. Organic matter accumulates within the sand, especially in sheltered areas. This detritus offers food for some inhabitants of the sandy beach, but where it accumulates in large amounts, it prevents the free circulation of water. A region of stagnation and oxygen deficiency results, characterized by anaerobic bacteria and by the formation of ferrous sulfides. The iron sulfides cause a zone of blackening, the depth of which varies with the exposure of the beach.

Most animals of the sandy beach either occupy permanent or semipermanent tubes within the sand, or they can burrow rapidly into the sand when they need to do so. Except for a few beach hoppers and a few plant-feeding insects,

Figure 12-8 *A long stretch of sandy beach pounded by the surf. Although the beach appears barren, life is abundant just beneath the sand.* (Photo by author.)

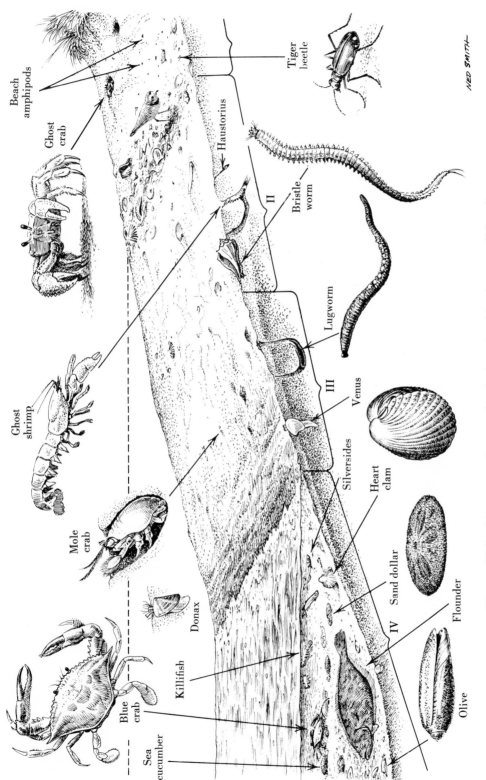

Beach
amphipods

Ghost
crab

Tiger
beetle

NED SMITH

Ghost
shrimp

Haustorius

II

Bristle
worm

Lugworm

III

Venus

Mole
crab

Silversides

Heart
clam

Donax

Sand dollar

Blue
crab

Killifish

IV

Flounder

Sea
cucumber

Olive

Figure 12-9 *Life on a sandy ocean beach along the Atlantic coast. Although strong zonation is absent, organisms still change on a gradient from land to sea. (I) Supratidal zone: ghost crabs and sand fleas; (II) flat beach zone: ghost shrimp, bristle worms, clams; (III) intratidal zone: clams, lugworms, mole crabs; (IV) subtidal zone. The dotted line indicates high tide.*

the true sand dwellers feed on particulate and suspended organic matter carried to the beach by the tides or supplied by the decomposition of other animal and plant debris on the beach. For this reason, sandy shores containing the greater amounts of organic matter support more life. The multicellular invertebrates of the beach obtain oxygen either by gaseous exchange with the water through the outer covering or by breathing through gills and elaborate respiratory siphons.

Zonation of animal life exists on the beach but is hidden and must be discovered by digging. Based on the animal organisms, the sandy shores can be divided roughly into supralittoral, littoral, and sublittoral zones, but a universal pattern similar to that for the rocky shores is lacking (Dahl, 1953).

Pale, sand-colored ghost crabs (Fig. 12-9) and beach hoppers, scavengers of the drift line, occupy the upper beach, the supralittoral. Like the periwinkle of the upper rocky shores, these animals are more terrestrial than marine. Ghost crabs live most of their lives above the tide line, where they spend the daylight hours in their burrows—simple shafts ending in enlarged dens—and where they hunt by night. They return daily to the wave line to dampen their gill chambers, and during the reproductive season, they must return, however briefly, to the sea that once mothered them.

The beach flea, or sand hopper, too, is a marine form that has nearly forsaken the sea. It seldom if ever enters the water, and if submerged for very long it may drown; yet it requires the dampness and salinity of the shore. The sand hopper lives in burrows above the tide line by day; by night it emerges to feed. If the tide is out, it wanders across the intertidal beach to feed on bits of seaweed. At dawn or high tide the beach hoppers return to the high beach, dig their tunnels anew, close the "door" with sand, and wait out the daylight or high tide, until night or low tide return.

The intertidal beach, the littoral, is the zone where true marine life really appears. Although it lacks the variety found in the intertidal rocky shores, the populations of individual species often are enormous. The energy base for sandy-beach fauna is organic matter, much of it made available by bacterial decomposition, which goes on at the greatest rate at low tide. The bacteria are concentrated about the organic matter in the sand, where they escape the diluting effects of water. The products of decomposition are dissolved and washed into the sea by each high tide, which in turn brings in more organic matter for decomposition. Thus the sand beach is an important site of biogeochemical cycling, supplying the offshore waters with phosphates, nitrogen, and other compounds.

Some animals of the sandy beach obtain their food by actively burrowing through the sand and ingesting the substrate to obtain the organic matter it contains. The commonest of all these sandworms is the lugworm (Fig. 12-9), responsible for the conspicuous coiled and cone-shaped casts on the beach. Near each cast, which marks one opening of a U-shaped burrow in which the lugworm lies, is the other opening, a funnel-shaped depression, down which the substrate material flows to the worm.

Another subterranean sand burrower is the trumpet worm, which lives in a movable, cone-shaped tube fashioned from sand grains. This tube may project slightly above the level of the sand while the worm works head down in the sand. The trumpet worm has comblike tentacles on its head, which it uses to

237

loosen the sand and sort among the grains for particles of organic matter. It draws water for respiration through the narrow end of the tube.

Two other animals that sort through the sands for food are the sand-burrowing amphipod *Haustorius* and the ghost shrimp (Fig. 12-9), but the methods they use are different. *Haustorius* swims upside down in the tidal waters like fairy shrimp but rights itself to burrow in the sand. Here it feeds on minute organic particles clinging to the sand grains and floating between them. The ghost shrimp found on the low-tide end of the littoral zone is a burrower. It excavates a vertical burrow several feet deep in the sand, where it stays at low tide. At high tide, the shrimp moves up to the mouth of the burrow and sifts through the sand grains for organic detritus, bacteria, and diatoms.

Other sandy beach animals obtain their food by sorting their filtering particles of organic matter from the tidal waters. Two of these are "surf-fishers" who advance and retreat up and down the beach with the flow and ebb of the tide. One is the mole crab, which lies partially buried within the sand and allows the surf to roll over it. Then, as the surf subsides and the waves recede, it peers through the sand and extends its antennae into the current. It then draws the antennae through the feeding appendages to remove the captured food. As the tide advances, whole populations of mole crabs will leave the sand, ride the surf up the beach, and then quickly burrow into the sand as the waves fall back. The other is a bivalve, *Donax,* the coquina clam, found on the Atlantic, Gulf, and Pacific coasts. At flood tide, the coquina emerges from the sand and is carried shoreward. As the waves lose force, the coquina, digging into the substrate with its stout foot, buries into the sand. Once settled, it extends its divided siphon to the surface to pick up detritus and to discharge wastes as pseudofeces. As the tide recedes, the clam moves seaward with the outgoing current and spends the low tide in the sublittoral. This movement with the tides is characteristic of coquina of the Atlantic and Gulf coasts. The Pacific coast species appears to be more sedentary (Hedgpeth, 1957).

The sublittoral zone and the sublittoral fringe is inhabited by still other bivalves and clams. One of the most characteristic is the heart clam, or common cockle, which may occur in tremendous numbers. It is globular in shape, with conspicuous radial ridges on the shell and a large powerful foot. Like the coquina, this clam strains out microscopic phytoplankton. It moves freely across the surface but can burrow rapidly into sand with the aid of its powerful foot. The most rapid burrower of all is the razor clam, so named because of its elongated, razor-shaped shell. It possesses an enormous and powerful foot, which it pushes out anteriorly. Its foot virtually pulls the rest of the animal into the sand, where it retreats deeply at low tide.

Associated with these essentially herbivorous animals are the predators, ever present whether the tide is in or out. Near and below the low-tide line live predatory gastropods, which, like the dog whelks of the rocky shore, prey on the bivalves, which they hunt beneath the sand. These predatory gastropods either have a strong muscular foot, a streamline-shaped shell, or both, which enables them to dig with ease through the sand. The moon snail, in particular, possesses a strong muscular foot, which enables it to hunt mollusks as far as a foot beneath the surface. In the same area lurk the predatory portunid crabs, such as the blue crab (Fig. 12-9) and the green, which feed on mole crabs, clams, and other organisms. They, like the snails, move back and forth with the tides.

The incoming tides bring with them other predators, such as the killifish and silversides. As the tides recede, gulls and shore birds scurry across the sand to snatch up or probe the sand for food.

Within the beach sand live vast numbers of microscopic copepods, ostracods, nematodes, and gastrotrichs, all making up the interstitial life (Pennack and Zinn, 1943; Pennack, 1951). The interstitial fauna are in general elongated forms with the setae, spines, or tubercles greatly reduced. The great majority do not have pelagic larval stages. These animals feed largely on microscopic algae, bacteria, and detritus. Interstitial life, best developed on more sheltered beaches made up of larger sand particles, shows seasonal variations, reaching its maximum development in the summer months.

An array of other animals can be found just above the low-tide line and in the sublittoral. Among them are the starfish and the related sand dollar (Fig. 12-9). The latter animals, disk-shaped and wafer thin, have supporting pillars inside the shell and a five-pointed-star design faintly marked on the disk. In the sand lives the heart urchin, which inhabits a chamber six or more inches deep. It remains in contact with the surface by a mucus-lined channel. A detritus feeder, it collects organic debris from the sand about the mouth of the channel with modified tube feet, which the urchin extends up through the tunnel.

Although much of the interest on the sandy shores may be directed to beach animals themselves, the drift line should not be ignored. Here one may find strays from the open sea washed up on shore. Common in this tidal debris may be the thin, papery shell of the paper nautilus, actually its elaborate egg case, the horned egg cases of skates, beadlike egg chains of the whelks, and a variety of bivalve shells. Jellyfish may be washed ashore in numbers, and on southern shores they may include the dangerous Portuguese man-of-war. Even pieces of driftwood washed ashore should be examined, for these may harbor such organisms as the gooseneck barnacle and the burrowing shipworms, of which there are many species. More often than not, the shipworms themselves will be gone, but the long, cylindrical tunnels penetrating all parts of the wood remain.

SUMMARY

The drift line marks the furthest advance of tides on the sandy shore; on the rocky shore, the tide line is marked by the zone of black algal growth on the stone. The most striking feature of the rocky shore, its zonation of life, is the result of alternate exposure and submergence by the tides. The black zone marks the supralittoral, the upper part of which is flooded only every two weeks by the spring tides. Submerged daily by the tides is the littoral, characterized by barnacles, periwinkles, mussels, and fucoid seaweeds. Uncovered only at the spring tides is the sublittoral, dominated by large, brown, laminarian seaweeds, Irish moss, and starfish. Left behind by outgoing tides are the tidal pools, "microcosms of the sea." These are distinct habitats, subject over a 24-hour period to wide fluctuations in temperature and salinity, and inhabited by a varying number of marine organisms, depending upon the amount of submergence and exposure. Sandy shores, in contrast to the rocky ones, appear barren of life at low tide; but beneath the sand, conditions for life are more amenable than on the rocky shore. Inhabitants of the sandy beach occupy

239

permanent or semipermanent tubes in the sand and feed on organic matter carried to the shore by the tides. Zonation of life is hidden beneath the sand, where the variety of life is less than on the rocky shore. But whether hidden beneath the sand or exposed on the rocks, all forms of life at the edge of the sea exhibit a remarkable adaptation to the ebb and flow of the tides.

SUGGESTED FIELD ACTIVITIES

The first encounter with life on the seashore is apt to be bewildering, for one can find here representatives of nearly every group in the animal kingdom; and much the same can be said for plants. In addition there is a wide variation in the environment over a very short distance; and the ebb and flow of the tides add to it a degree of instability. All this has had a profound influence on the adaptations of animals and plants. So the first step in any study of the seashore is to become acquainted with its inhabitants and the niches they occupy. Collect some of the organisms for further study and make accurate notes on their microhabitat, habits, etc.

Since many of the seashore inhabitants are soft-bodied and contractile, here is a hint on handling them. First anesthetize such organisms in one of several ways: (1) Place the organisms in an isotonic magnesium-chloride solution (73 MgCl, 6 H_2O per liter of tap water); (2) add some Epsom salts ($MgSO_4$) directly to sea water in a container; (3) slowly drip alcohol into a pan containing the animals; (4) add a few shreds of tobacco to a small amount of fluid containing the animals. Then fix and preserve in a 5 to 10 per cent solution of formalin.

Seashore zonation

The first step is to prepare a map drawn on the horizontal to show the general features and another on the vertical to show the slope, or beach profile. This can be done with an Abney level and stadia rods. If these are unavailable, then the profile can be plotted by the use of two wooden rods as follows:

1.   Cut two wooden rods five feet long and one inch by one inch in cross section. Cut in large notches at one-foot intervals and smaller notches at one-tenth-foot intervals. Nail a small wooden plate about four inches square on the bottom to keep the sticks from sinking into the sand. These rods are held vertically one rod length apart in a line extended across the beach.

2.   The observer holding the landward rod aligns his eye with the top of the seaward rod and the horizon, then reads and records the distance down from the top of his own rod to the point that is interesected by his own line of sight. Based on the assumption that the line of sight is level, this distance is the measure of the distance in elevation of the beach at two points five feet apart.

3.   To continue the profile, move one of the rods to a point five feet on the opposite side of the other rod, and take a second reading. Continue to the water's edge.

4.   Note the differences in elevation as + or − according to whether the leading rod is lower or higher than the sighting one. Differences in elevation are summed up and plotted against the horizontal distance to construct the whole profile. Sea level can be determined from bench marks established by geodetic surveys, from topographical maps, or it can be estimated from the depth of the water at the seaward end of the profile as compared with a table of predicted tides.

On the vertical profile indicate the positions of high and low tides. This can be determined from tide charts and observations. Record the depth of flooding, the time flooded, the time exposed, the temperature of water at high tide, the temperature of the beach surface at low tide.

Locate one or more transects on the shore and indicate their position on the horizontal map. Along this transect locate a number of one-meter-square quadrats.

Working from the advancing tide shoreward (to make maximum use of available time), record the plants found in the square-meter quadrats and determine their coverage. Make a count of the animals, including the sessile ones. Be sure to examine the substrate beneath the kelp, etc. At the same time, take temperature and light readings on top of and beneath the seaweeds, in the shadow of rocks, etc.

Be sure to record where each species disappears completely and another begins. Record this on both the vertical and horizontal maps.

Using the quadrat data, set up a table of the distribution of plants by coverage and of animals by number per square meter, arranged from high tide to low. This will give you a quantified picture of the distribution of life along the shore.

Record other animal life at low tide: the appearance of gulls, terns, sandpipers, plovers—their numbers and feeding behavior. These animals move in to feed when the beach is exposed. And be sure to examine carefully the debris along the drift line.

Don't forget the shore at night. There are a large number of nocturnal forms one never sees by day.

If boats are available, draw a plankton net through the water over the shore at high tide. Observe the schools of fish. Some of these might be collected with a seine if the water is quiet enough.

Finally map out the distribution of organisms and plot the zones as they are in the figures in Chap. 12.

Time might well be spent in investigating some of the microhabitats on the rocky seashore. Two particularly rewarding ones are under the rocks and tidal pools.

Under rock fauna

Select in the upper littoral zone a few rocks as large as can be overturned that are resting on or are partially embedded in sand or gravel. First note the physical site of the rock in relation to the substrate on which it rests, the tide level, and the degree of protection from wave action. Overturn the rock and make immediate notes on the active population that scurries rapidly to cover. Record the total faunal forms present and note the positions they occupy on the rock. Some are surface dwellers, others are cranny dwellers, others are true rock borers. These can be located by breaking apart samples of small rocks. When finished, *replace the rock in normal position*. To fail to do so will destroy the area for further study.

Tidal pools

Because they are a little world unto themselves, tightly restricted, subject to wide environmental extremes, and composed of a few species, rock pools are especially interesting.

The first step is to map the pool. This can be done quite easily by constructing a grid of light string over the top and then using the grid as a guide to map the vegetation and barnacle growth on the bottom, as well as on the vertical walls. If the pool is large, a few short transects may be laid out across the pool; but if the pool is small (several square meters), then work with the whole unit.

Determine the number of cubic feet of water the pool contains. Record the temperature of the water, especially midway between tides and at replenishment time. Determine the salinity at these two periods and the oxygen content of the water.

The animal population in the tidal pools consists of residents, partial residents, and temporary inhabitants, those who are carried in by the tide or who move in and out on their own accord. Remove and weigh the standing population (crop) and return to the pool. Count the number of sessile animals, the mussels and barnacles, over a period of several weeks, and note the change.

The daily movement of temporary and partial residents can be investigated by marking these animals, the crabs and snails, with dabs of paint. Use a different code for each day. Record the results in a table form:

DATE	NUMBER OF SNAILS, CRABS, ETC., MARKED	NUMBER UNMARKED	TOTAL POPULATION

From this determine the population turnover.

From observations in the field and dissections in the lab determine the food habits of the rock-pool inhabitants and construct a food web for the tiny community. Remember gulls may visit the pools and carry away crabs.

Some estimates of production would round out the study. This can be done by the light and dark bottle method or by the chlorophyll method. Some production studies by the chlorophyll method might well be carried out for each of the major zones, the seaweeds, and algae growing on the rock surfaces.

CHAPTER **13**

The soil

Soil is the crossroad of terrestrial communities. The number of organisms that live and move in only a square foot of soil stretches the imagination. In addition to the full-time residents, nearly 95 per cent of all insects spend a part of their life cycle below ground. The soil is the site of decomposition of organic matter and of the return of mineral elements to the nutrient cycle. Roots occupy a considerable portion of the soil, to which they tie the vegetation and from which they pump water and minerals in solution needed by the plants for photosynthesis and other biochemical processes. Vegetation in turn influences soil development, its chemical and physical properties and organic-matter content. Thus the soil acts as a sort of pathway between the organic and mineral worlds.

Soil formation

Soils begin with the weathering of rock and rock materials. Exposed to the combined action of wind, water, and temperature, rock surfaces peel and flake away. Water seeps into crevices, freezes, expands, and cracks the rock into smaller pieces. Accompanying this disintegration and continuing long after it is the decomposition of the rock material itself. Water and carbon dioxide combine to form carbonic acid, which reacts with calcium and magnesium in the rock to form carbonates. These either accumulate deeper in the soil material or are carried away, depending on the amount of water passing through. Primary minerals, especially those containing aluminum and silicon, such as feldspar, are converted to secondary minerals, such as clay. Iron compounds are oxidized to the red ferric state or reduced to the gray-colored ferrous state. Fine particles, especially clays, are shifted or rearranged within the mass by percolating water and on the surface by runoff, wind, or ice. Eventually the rock is broken down into loose material, which may remain in place, but more often than not much of it is lifted, sorted, and carried away. Material transported from one area to another by wind is known as loess, that transported by water as alluvium, lacustrine—or lake—and marine deposits, and by glacial ice as till. In a few places soil materials come from accumulated organic matter such as peat. Materials formed in place are called residual.

The mantle of unconsolidated material is called the regolith. It may consist of slightly weathered material with fresh primary minerals or it may be intensely weathered and consist of highly resistant minerals such as quartz. Because of variations in slope, climate, and native vegetation, many different soils can develop in the same regolith. The thickness of the regolith, the kind of rock from which it was formed, and the degree of weathering affect the fertility and water relations of the soil.

Eventually plants root in this weathered material. More often than not intense weathering goes on under some plant cover, particularly in glacial till and water-deposited materials, since they already are favorable sites for some plant growth. Thus soil development often begins under some influence of plants. They root, draw nutrients from mineral matter, reproduce, and die. Their roots penetrate and further break down the regolith. The plants pump up nutrients from its depths and add them to the surface, and in doing so recapture minerals carried deep into the material by soil forming processes. By photosynthesis, plants capture the sun's energy and add a portion of it, as organic carbon—approximately 18 billion metric tons, 1.7×10^{17} kilocalories—to the soil each year. This energy source, the plant debris, enables bacteria, fungi, earthworms, and other soil organisms to colonize the area.

The breakdown of organic debris into humus is accomplished by decomposition and finally mineralization. Higher organisms in the soil—millipedes, centipedes, earthworms, mites, springtails, grasshoppers, and others—consume fresh material and leave partially decomposed products in their excreta. This is further decomposed by microorganisms, the bacteria and fungi, into various compounds of carbohydrates, proteins, lignins, fats, waxes, resins, and ash. These compounds then are broken down into simpler products such as carbon dioxide, water, minerals, and salts. This latter process is called *mineralization*.

The soil humus so produced is not stable. It represents a stage in the decomposition of soil organic matter. New humus is being formed as old humus is being destroyed by mineralization. The equilibrium set up between the formation of new humus and the destruction of the old determines the amount of humus in the soil.

Activities of soil organisms, the acids produced by them and the continual addition of organic matter to mineral matter, produce profound changes in the weathered material. Rain falling upon and filtering through the accumulating organic matter picks up acids and minerals in solution, reaches mineral soil, and sets up a chain of complex chemical reactions. This continues further in the regolith. Calcium, potassium, sodium, and other mineral elements, soluble salts, and carbonates, are carried in solution by percolating water deeper into the soil or are washed away into streams, rivers, and eventually the sea. The greater the rainfall the more water moves down through the soil and the less moves upward. Thus, high precipitation results in heavy leaching and chemical weathering, particularly in regions of high temperatures. These chemical reactions tend to be localized within the regolith. Organic carbon, for instance, is oxidized near the surface, while free carbonates precipitate deeper in the rock material. Fine particles, especially clays, also move downward. These localized chemical and physical processes in the parent material result in the development of layers in the soil, called *horizons,* which impart to the soil a distinctive profile. Within a horizon, a particular property of the soil reaches its maximum intensity and away from this level decreases gradually in both directions. Thus each horizon may vary in thickness, color, texture, structure, consistency, porosity, acidity, and composition.

In general soils have four major horizons: an organic, or O, horizon and three mineral horizons, the A, characterized by major organic-matter accumulation and by the loss of clay, iron, and aluminum; the B, characterized by an illuvial concentration of all or any of the silicates, clay, iron, aluminum and humus, alone or in combination and by the development of granular, blocky, or prismatic structure; the C, material underlying the two horizons, either alike or unlike the material from which the soil is presumed to have developed. Below all this may lie the R horizon, the consolidated bedrock. Because the soil profile is essentially a continuum, often there is no clear-cut distinction between one horizon and another. Horizon subdivisions (Fig. 13-1) are indicated by arabic numbers, e.g., O1, O2, A1, A2, etc.; lowercase letters are used to indicate significant qualitative departures from the central concept of each horizon; e.g., $A2_g$ or B_t.

The O horizon, once designated as L or A_{oo}, and F, H or A_o, is the surface layer, formed or forming above the mineral layer and composed of fresh or partially decomposed organic material. This, as well as the upper part of the A horizon, is the region of the soil where life is most abundant. It is subject to the greatest changes in soil temperatures and moisture conditions and contains the most organic carbon.

The A horizon, the first of the mineral layers, is characterized by an organic-matter accumulation developing or developed near or at the surface, and by the loss of clay, iron, and aluminum. It consists largely of resistant minerals, such as quartz and others of sand or silt size.

The B horizon lies directly beneath the A. Generally it has a concentration of iron and aluminum compounds, clay, and humus. These have been leached from the A horizon or exist as a residual formed by means other than leaching. The B horizon may or may not have a stronger, darker, or redder color because of iron coatings than do the horizons above and below. Usually the B horizon is firmer and may have granular, blocky, or prismatic structure. This horizon may be absent in some soils.

The A and B horizon of soils together are referred to as the solum. Different types of surface horizons (epipedons) and subsurface horizons within the solum are diagnostic for particular soil environments and are of major significance in the classification of soils.

The C horizon consists of material (once incorrectly called parent material) either the same as or different from the material from which the solum is presumed to have been formed. This C material is little affected by the soil-forming processes, although the material may be modified by weathering outside the zone of biological activity. The C horizon also includes the contrasting layers of unconsolidated materials once included in the former D horizon.

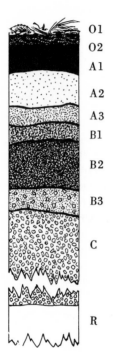

O1
O2
A1
A2
A3
B1
B2
B3
C
R

Figure 13-1 A generalized profile of the soil. Rarely does any one soil possess all of the horizons shown. O1: Loose leaves and organic debris. O2: Organic debris partly decomposed or matted. A1: A dark-colored horizon with a high content of organic matter mixed with mineral matter. The A horizon is the zone of maximum biological activity. A2: A light-colored horizon of maximum leaching. Prominent in podzolic soils; faintly developed or absent in chernozemic soils. A3: Transitional to B, but more like A than B. Sometimes absent. B1: Transitional to B but more like B than A. Sometimes absent. B2: A deeper-colored horizon of maximum accumulation of clay minerals or of iron and organic matter; maximum development of blocky or prismatic structure or both. B3: Transitional to C. C: The weathered material, either like or unlike the material from which the soil presumably formed. A gley layer may occur, as well as layers of calcium carbonate, especially in grasslands. R: Consolidated bedrock.

The organic horizon or forest floor

Of all the horizons of the soil, none is more important or ecologically more interesting than the forest floor or the organic horizon. A close relationship exists between litter and humus, and the environmental conditions in the forest community—the internal microclimate of the soil, the moisture regime, its chemical composition, and its biological activity. The forest floor plays a dominant role in the life and distribution of many forest plants and animals, in maintenance of soil fertility, and in many of the soil-forming processes. The nature and quality of the forest organic layer depend in part on the kind and quality of forest litter. And the fate of that litter and the development of the humus layer is conditioned by the activity of microflora and soil animals. In fact many active humus forms undergo initial breakdown in the bodies of animal organisms. To complete the circle the composition and density of the soil fauna is influenced by the litter. Thus as Bernier (1961) put it, the forest humus is both "a consequence and a cause" of local ecological conditions.

The importance of the organic layer was stressed early in the history of ecology. Darwin in his famous work of 1881, "The Formation of Vegetable Mould through the Action of Worms, with Observations on Their Habits," pointed out the influence of these animals on the soil. About the same time, in 1879 and 1884, the Danish forester P. E. Müller described the existence of two types of humus formation in the forest soil, which he called mull and mor. Not only did he observe differences in vegetation, soil structure, and chemical composition, but he discovered differences in their fauna also. Müller considered mull and mor as biological, rather than purely physiochemical, systems and regarded the fauna present as aiding their formation. Others have regarded mull and mor from the physical and chemical point of view, with little regard for the biological mechanisms involved. Actually both are the result of interaction of all three.

Mor, characteristic of dry or moist acid habitats, especially heathland and coniferous forest, has a well-defined unincorporated and matted or compacted organic deposit resting on mineral soil. It results from an accumulation of litter that is slowly mineralized and remains unmixed with mineral soil. Slow though mineralization may be, it is the manner in which this process proceeds that distinguishes mor from other humus types. The main decomposing agents are fungi, both free living and mycorrhizal, which tend to depress soil animal activity and to produce acids; nitrifying bacteria may be absent. Vascular cells of leaves disappear first, leaving behind a residue of mesophyll tissue. Proteins within the leaf litter are stabilized by protein-precipitating material, making them, in some cases, resistant to decomposition. Because of limited volume, pore space, acidity, type of litter involved, and the nature of its breakdown, mor is inhabited by a small biomass of the smaller soil animals. These organisms have little mechanical influence on the soil but live instead in an environment of organic material cut off from the mineral soil beneath.

Mull, however, develops by a different process. Characteristic of mixed and deciduous woods, on fresh or moist soils with a reasonable supply of calcium, mull possesses only a thin scattering of litter on the surface, and the mineral soil is high in organic content. All organic materials are converted into true humic substances, and because of animal activity, these are inseparably bound to the mineral fraction, which absorbs them like a dye. Because of less acidity and a more equitable base status, bacteria tend to replace fungi as the chief decomposers, and nitrification is rapid. Soil animals are more diverse and possess a greater biomass, a reflection of more equitable distribution of living space, of oxygen, of food and moisture, and of a smaller fungal component. This faunal diversity is one of mull's greatest assets, because the humification process flows through a wide variety of organisms with differing metabolism. Not only do these soil animals fragment vegetable debris and associate it with mineral particles, thus enhancing microbial and fungal activity, but they also incorporate the humified material with mineral soil. This constant interchange of material takes place from the surface to the soil and back again. Plants extract nutrients from the soil and deposit them on the surface. Then the soil plants and animals reverse the process.

Between the two extremes, the mull and mor, is moder, the insect mull of Müller. In this humus type, plant residues are transformed into the droppings of small arthropods, particularly Collembola and mites. Residues not consumed by the fauna are reduced to small fragments, little humified and still

247

showing cell structure. The droppings, plant fragments, and mineral particles all form a loose, netlike structure held together by chains of small droppings. In acid moder, the shape of the droppings are destroyed by the washing action of rain water; and under more extreme conditions, humus leached from the droppings acts as a binding substance to form a dense, matted litter approaching a mor. At the other end of the spectrum, the border line between moder and mull, the droppings of large arthropods, which are capable of taking in considerable quantities of mineral matter with food, are common. However, moder differs from mull in higher organic-matter content, restricted nitrification, and a more or less mechanical mixture of organic components with the mineral, the two being held together by humic substances, but yet separable. In other words, the organic crumbs are deficient in mineral matter in contrast to mull, in which the mineral and organic parts are inseparably bound together.

Litter source plays a decisive role in its decomposition and in the direction that this takes, whether to mull, mor, or moder. Litter from plants growing on nutrient-rich soil under favorable temperature and moisture conditions encourages the development of an active microfauna and bacteria able to mineralize the material rapidly. Beech and sugar maple, which grow on soils of a wide range of fertility, will produce mull on rich soils and moder on poor soils (Bernier, 1961). Some plant litters, such as pine and spruce needles, are high in lignins, which resist decomposition and inhibit the decomposition of cellulose (Lutz and Chandler, 1946). Tannin, common in oak litter, may prevent the rapid breakdown of protein and often gives rise to raw humus. Litter types influence the abundance and composition of soil fauna, which play an active role in humus formation, and the lack of which results in reduced humification. Different plants, different parts of plants, and even particular plant tissues are attacked selectively by various soil animals. Soil animals mix and bind organic matter with mineral and influence aggregate formation in the soil. The interplay of these two, vegetation and fauna, may result in the reversibility of mull and mor. As vegetation changes either by succession or by the establishment of other plant species, the soil fauna changes and with it the type of litter breakdown. Chemical treatments with fertilizers or pesticides, which may increase nutrient status or perhaps kill off certain soil organisms, likewise may result in a change in the type of forest litter decomposition.

Profile differentiation

Profile differentiation and the nature of the soil, the content and distribution of organic matter, its color, and its chemical and physical characteristics are influenced over large areas by the combined action of vegetation and its prime determinant, the climate (Fig. 13-2). Thus the soil beneath native grassland differs from that beneath forest trees.

Grassland vegetation developed in the sub-humid-to-arid and temperate-to-tropical climates of the world: the plains and prairies of North America, the pampas of South America, the steppes of Russia, and the veldt of Africa. Dense grass-root systems may extend several feet below the surface. Each year nearly all the vegetable material above ground and a part of the root system are turned back to the soil as organic residue. Although this material decomposes rapidly the following spring, it is not completely gone before the next cycle of

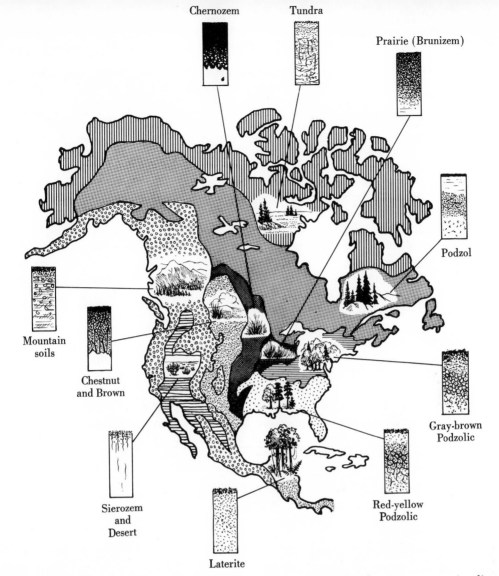

Chernozem

Tundra

Prairie (Brunizem)

Podzol

Mountain soils

Chestnut and Brown

Gray-brown Podzolic

Sierozem and Desert

Red-yellow Podzolic

Laterite

Figure 13-2 *The great soil groups. This map of North America shows the general distribution of the important zonal, or great soil, groups of the continent and points out the general relation of soils to vegetation and climate. The majority of soils illustrated here (the exception is the tundra) are those that develop on well-drained sites. In the humid regions bases do not accumulate in the soils because of the leaching processes associated with high rainfall. Podzol soils, characterized by a very thin organic layer on top of a gray, leached soil lying over a dark-brown horizon, generally develop in a cool, moist climate under coniferous forest. Under deciduous forest in a cool, temperate, moist climate develop the Gray-brown Podzolic soils. These differ from podzols in that the leaching is not so excessive and beneath the organic layer is a horizon of greyish-brown leached soil. The Red and Yellow soils occur in a warm-temperate, moist climate of southeastern North America. Developed through podzolization with some laterization, yellow soils are characterized by grayish-yellow leached horizon over a yellow one; the red by a yellowish-brown leached soil over a deep-red horizon. In the tall-grass country with a temperate, moist climate is Prairie or Brunizem soil, the result of calcification. It is very dark brown in color, grading through lighter brown with depth. West of this lies the Chernozems, black soils high in organic matter, some three to four feet deep, which grade into lime accumulations. They developed under tall- and mixed-grass prairie. Closely related are the Chestnut and Brown soils, dark brown and grading into lime accumulations at one to four feet. These soils developed under mixed- and short-grass prairie. In desert regions are Sierozen (or Gray) and Desert soils. They are pale grayish in color, low in organic matter, and closely underlaid with calcareous material. Lateritic soils, typical of tropical rain forest where decomposition and leaching are rapid, have a thin organic layer over a reddish leached soil. In high mountains are a variety of soils, here vaguely classified as mountain soils. Many of them are stony and lack any well-developed horizons. Tundra soils (see Chap. 19) are variable, but the common one is a gley, subject to considerable disturbance from frost action and underlaid with a permanently frozen substrate.*

death and decay begins. The humus then becomes mixed with mineral soil by the action of soil inhabitants, developing a soil high in organic matter. The humus content is greatest at the surface and declines gradually with depth. Since the amount of rainfall in grassland regions generally is insufficient to remove calcium and magnesium carbonates, these accumulate at the average depth that the percolating waters reach. The high calcium content of the surface soil is maintained by grass, which absorbs large quantities from lower horizons and redeposits them on the surface. Likewise there is little loss of clay from the surface layer. This process of soil development is called *calcification*.

Soils developed by calcification have a distinct *A* horizon of great thickness and an indistinct *B* horizon, characterized by an accumulation of calcium carbonate. The *A* horizon is high in organic matter and nitrogen, except in tropical and subtropical regions. There the soils are high in clay and subject to much shrinkage and swelling. This creates serious problems in handling these tropical soils for agricultural production.

Forests are the dominant vegetation in the humid regions. Here the cycle of organic-matter accumulation differs from that of the grassland. Only part of the organic matter, leaves, twigs, and some trunks, is turned over annually. Leaves, which are the largest source of organic matter, and vegetation of the ground layer remain on the surface. Dead roots add little to soil organic matter since they die over an irregular period of time and are not concentrated near the surface. Because only the leaves are returned regularly to the soil and much of the mineral matter and energy is tied up in trunk and branches, most of the currently available nutrients turned back to the soil come from annual leaf fall. The amount of nutrient return varies with the species composition of the forest, since trees differ in the nutrient content of their leaves. For example basswood, quaking aspen, hickories, American elm, and flowering dogwood contain more calcium in their leaves and return more calcium to the soil than sugar maple, red maple, yellow birch, and red oak (Lutz and Chandler, 1946). And the latter return more than beech, red pine, white pine, and hemlock.

Rainfall in forested regions is sufficient to leach away many basic elements, especially calcium, magnesium, potassium, iron, and aluminum. Since trees take up fewer bases than grasses do, they generally return an insufficient amount back to the surface soil to prevent it from becoming acid, although the degree of acidity will vary, depending upon the forest composition and its site. Some forests in the southern Appalachians, particularly those containing yellow poplar and basswood and growing on north and northeast slopes, have rather high, often neutral pH in surface horizons, even though they grow on soils weathered from acid sandstone (unpublished data from van Eck and Smith). Increased acidity may cause the dispersion and downward movement of organic and clay colloids. A soil developed by this process is called podzolic and the process *podzolization*. The name comes from the Russian, meaning "ash beneath," and refers to the leached horizon of strongly podzolized soils. The latter are characterized by a white-colored A_2 horizon and a brilliant, yellow-brown *B* horizon, the result of accumulations of iron and aluminum compounds and humus. Iron accumulations in some podzol soils may act as a cement, creating a hardpan layer in the *B* horizon. This layer, called ortstein, impedes the free circulation of air and water.

In the humid subtropical and tropical forested regions of the world, where rainfall is heavy and temperatures high, the soil-forming process is different. Because temperatures are uniformly high, the weathering process in these regions is almost entirely chemical, brought about by water and its dissolved substances. The residues from this weathering—bases, silica, alumina, hydrated aluminum silicates, and iron oxides—are freed. Since precipitation usually exceeds evaporation, the water movement is almost continuously downward. With only a small quantity of electrolytes present in the soil water because of continual leaching, silica and aluminum silicates are carried downward, while sesquioxides of aluminum and iron remain behind. The reason for this is that these sesquioxides are relatively insoluble in pure rain water, while the silicates tend to be precipitated as a gel in solutions containing humic substances and electrolytes. Humic substances act as protective colloids about iron and aluminum oxides and prevent their precipitation by electrolytes. The end product of such a process is a soil of iron and aluminum oxides and quartz, invariably acidic, deficient in bases, low in plant nutrients, and intensely weathered to great depths. Because of the large amount of iron oxides left, these soils possess a variety of reddish colors and they generally lack distinct horizons, except for a darkened surface layer. Below, the profile is unchanged for many feet. The clay has a stable structure, is very pervious to water, and is easily penetrated by plant roots. This soil-forming process is termed *laterization* or *latosolization*.

Arid and semi-arid regions have relatively sparse vegetation. Because of the lack of plant growth, which is limited by low rainfall, there is very little organic matter and nitrogen in the soil. Light precipitation results in slightly weathered and slightly leached soils high in plant nutrients. Their horizons usually are faint and thin. In these regions occur areas where soils contain excessive amounts of soluble salts, either from parent material or from the evaporation of water draining in from adjoining land. The infrequent rain water penetrates the soil, but soon afterward evaporation at the surface draws the salt-laden water upward. The water evaporates, leaving saline and alkaline salts at or near the surface, to form a crust, or *caliche*.

Calcification, podzolization, and laterization, all are processes that take place on well-drained soil. Under poorer drainage conditions a different soil-development process is at work. The slope of the land determines to a considerable extent the amount of rainfall that will enter and pass through the soil, the concentration of erosion materials, the amount of soil moisture, and the height at which the water will stand in the soil (Fig. 13-3). The amount of water that passes through or remains in the soil determines the degree of oxidation and breakdown of soil minerals. In areas where water stays near or at the surface most of the time, iron, because of an inadequate supply of oxygen, is reduced to ferrous compounds, which give a dull gray or bluish color to the horizons. This process is called *gleization* and results in a horizon more or less sticky, compact, and structureless. Gley soils often are high in organic matter, because more is produced than can be broken down by humification, greatly reduced because of the absence of soil microorganisms. On gentle to moderate slopes, where drainage conditions are improved, gleization is reduced. As a result, the subsoil will show varying degrees of mottling of grays and browns. On hilltops, ridges, and steep slopes, where the water table is deep, the subsoil is reddish to yellowish brown from the oxidized iron compounds (Fig. 13-3).

In all, five drainage classes are recognized (Fig. 13-3). Well-drained soils are those in which plant roots can grow to a depth of 36 inches without restriction due to excess water. On moderately well-drained soils, plant roots can grow to a depth of 18 to 20 inches without restriction. In somewhat poorly drained soils, plant roots cannot grow beyond a depth of 12 or 14 inches. Poorly drained soils are wet most of the time. Usually they are characterized by the growth of alders, willows, and sedges. On very poorly drained soils, water stands on or near the surface most of the year.

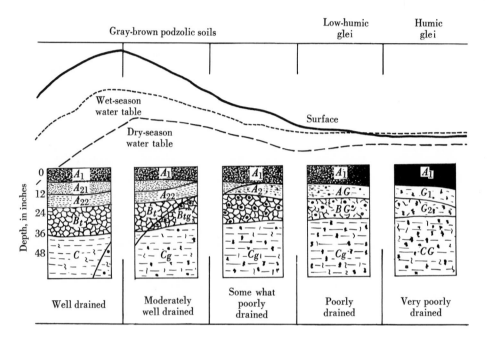

Figure 13-3 *Effect of drainage on the development of gray-brown podzolic soils. Wetness increases from left to right. The diagram above represents the topographic position the profiles might occupy. Note that the strongest soil development takes place on well-drained sites where weathering is maximum. The least amount of weathering takes place on very poorly drained soils where the wet-season water table lies above the surface of the soil. G or g indicates mottling; t indicates translocated silicate clays. (In part after Knox, 1952.)*

Soils and time

The weathering of rock material; the accumulation, decomposition, and mineralization of organic material; the loss of minerals from the upper surface, and gains in minerals and clay in lower horizons and horizon differentiation all require considerable time. Well-developed soils in equilibrium with weathering and erosion may require 2000 to 20,000 years for their formation. But soil differentiation from parent material may take place in as short a time as 30 years. Certain acid soils in humid regions develop in 100 years, since the leaching process is speeded by acidic materials. Parent materials heavy in texture require much longer to develop into "climax" soils, because of impeded downward flow of water. Soils develop more slowly in dry regions than in humid ones. Soils on steep slopes often remain young regardless of geological age because rapid erosion removes the soil nearly as fast as it is formed. Flood-plain soils age little through time because of the continuous accumulation of new materials. Young soils are not as deeply weathered as and are more fertile than old soils, since they have not been exposed to the leaching process as long. The latter tend to be infertile because of long-time leaching of nutrients without replacement from fresh material.

Soil morphology

In the field, differences between soils and between horizons within a soil are primarily reflected by variations in texture, arrangement, structure, and color. The *texture* of a soil is determined by the proportion of different size soil particles. It is partly inherited from parent material and partly a result of soil-forming processes. The particles are classified on the basis of size into gravel, sand, silt, and clay. Gravel consists of particles larger than 2.0 millimeters. Sand ranges from 0.05 to 2.0 millimeters, is easily seen, and feels gritty. Silt consists of particles from 0.002 to 0.05 millimeters in diameter which scarcely can be seen by the naked eye, feels and looks like flour. Clay particles, too fine to be seen even under the ordinary microscope, are colloidal in nature. Clay controls the most important properties of soils, including plasticity and exchange of cations and anions between soil particles and soil solution.

Most soils are a mixture of these various particles. Based on the proportions of the various particles contained in them, soils can be grouped into four texture classes. Coarse-textured soils are loose, consist mainly of sand and gravel, and hold particles together when moist. They hold only small amounts of water and supply some plant nutrients. Medium-textured soils are mixtures of sand, silt, and clay high enough in fine particles to hold water and plant nutrients. Moderately fine-textured soils are fairly high in clay. Moderately sticky and plastic when wet, they may form a crust on the surface if organic matter is too low. Fine-textured soils contain more than 40 per cent clay, are very sticky and very plastic when wet, hold considerable water and plant nutrients, but may have restricted internal drainage. Soil texture may vary through the profile. Surface horizons tend to be more coarsely textured than the B horizons, since the clay particles may have been lost from the surface and deposited deeper in the soil.

Soil particles are held together in clusters or shapes of various sizes, called *aggregates* or *peds*. The arrangement of these aggregates is called *soil structure*. Like texture, there are many types of soil structure. Soil aggregates may be classified as granular, crumblike, platelike, blocky, subangular blocky, prismatic, and columnar (Fig. 13-4). Structureless soil can be either single grained or massive. Soil aggregates tend to become larger with increasing depth. Structure is influenced by texture, the plants growing on the soil, and other soil organisms.

Color has little direct influence on the property of a soil, but considered with other properties, it can tell a good deal about the soil. In fact it is one of the most useful and important characters for the identification of soil. In temperate regions dark-colored soils generally are higher in organic matter than light-colored ones. Well-drained soil may range anywhere from very pale brown to dark brown and black, depending upon the organic-matter content. But it does not always follow that dark-colored soils are high in organic matter. In warm temperate and tropical regions, the dark clays may have less than three per cent organic matter. Red and yellow soils are the result of iron oxides, the bright colors indicating good drainage and good aeration. Other red soils obtain their color from parent material and not from soil-forming processes. Well-drained yellowish sands are white sands containing a small amount of organic matter and such coloring material as iron oxide. Red and yellow colors increase from the cool regions to the equator. Quartz, kaolin, carbonates of lime and magnesium, gypsum, and various compounds of ferrous iron give whitish and

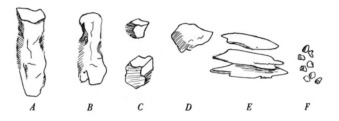

A B C D E F

Figure 13-4 *Some types of soil structure.* (A) *Prismatic;* (B) *columnar;* (C) *angular blocky;* (D) *subangular blocky;* (E) *platelike;* (F) *granular.* (Adapted from *Soil Survey Manual,* U.S. Department of Agriculture Handbook No. 18.)

grayish colors to the soil. The grayest are permanently saturated soils in which the iron is in the ferrous form. Imperfectly and poorly drained soils are mottled with various shades of yellow-brown and gray. The colors of soils are determined with the use of standardized color charts.

Soil classification

Each combination of climate, vegetation, soil material, slope, and time results in a unique soil, the smallest repetitive unit of which is called a *pedon*. Soils even within a small area may vary considerably. Changes in slope, drainage, and soil material account for local differences between soil individuals. These soil individuals are roughly equivalent to the lowest category in the soil classification system—the *soil series*. The present soil taxonomic system consists of orders

(Table 13-1), suborders, great groups (Fig. 13-2), families, and series. In the new classification system, names of lower classification units always end with the formative syllable of their respective order preceded by other syllables connotative of various soil properties. At the highest taxonomic level, emphasis is placed on the presence or absence of certain diagnostic soil horizons that result from the interaction of soil forming factors, primarily climate and vegetation. Soil series are named after the locality in which they were first described. For example, the Ovid series in New York was named after the town of Ovid; the Miami after the Miami River in western Ohio. Like the species among plants and animals, soil series are defined in terms of the largest number of differentiating characteristics and they occur in fairly limited areas. Higher categories of taxonomy combine series into larger groupings distinguished by even fewer differentiating properties. At the highest level of classification, one recognizes between only the classes which roughly correspond with broad climatic zones (Fig. 13-2).

TABLE 13-1.   New Soil Orders[1] and Approximate Equivalents in Old Classification[2]

ORDER	FORMATIVE SYLLABLE	DERIVATION AND MEANING	APPROXIMATE EQUIVALENTS
1. Entisol	ent	(coined from recent)	Azonal soils, and some Low Humic Gley soils
2. Vertisol	ert	(L. *verto,* for inverted)	Grumusols
3. Inceptisol	ept	(L. *inceptum,* for young)	Ando, Sol Brun Acids, some Brown Forest, Low Humic Gley, and Humic Gley soils
4. Aridisol	id	(L. *aridus,* for arid)	Desert, Reddish Desert, Sierozem, Solonchak; some Brown and Reddish-Brown soils, and associated Solonetz
5. Mollisol	oll	(L. *mollis,* for soft)	Chestnut, Chernozem, Brunizem (Prairie) Rendzinas, some Brown, Brown Forest, and associated Solonetz and Humic Gley soils
6. Spodosol	od	(Gk. *spodos,* for ashy)	Podzols, Brown Podzolic soils, and Ground-water Podzols
7. Alfisol	alf	(coined from Al-Fe)	Gray-brown Podzolic, Gray Wooded soils, Noncalcic Brown soils, degraded Chernozem, and associated Planosols and Half-Bog soils
8. Ultisol	ult	(L. *ultimus,* for last)	Red-Yellow Podzolic soils, Reddish-Brown Lateritic soils of the U.S., and associated Planosols and Half-Bog soils
9. Oxisol	ox	(Fr. *oxide,* for oxidized)	Lateritic soils, Latosols
10. Histosol	ist	(Gk. *histos,* for organic)	Bog soils

[1] Soil Survey Staff, Soil Classification, A Comprehensive System, Soil Conservation Service, Washington, D.C., 1960.
[2] M. Baldwin, C. E. Kellogg, and J. Thorp, Soil Classification, in Soils and Men, 1938 U.S.D.A. Yearbook of Agriculture, pp. 979–1001, Washington, D.C., 1938.

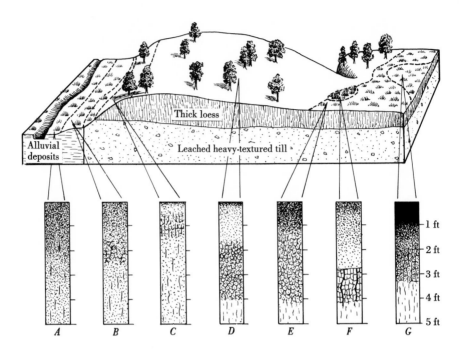

Figure 13-5 *Effect of topography and native vegetation on the soil. This diagram shows the normal sequence of eight representative soil types from the Mississippi to the uplands in Illinois. The drawing also illustrates how bodies of soil types fit together in the landscape. Boundaries between adjacent bodies are gradations or continuums, rather than sharp lines.*

The lower part of the diagram pictures the profiles of seven of the soils, showing the color and thickness of the surface horizon and the structure of the subsoil. Note how the natural vegetation that once covered the land (trees for forest, grass clumps for grass) influenced surface color. The diagram also shows how topographic position and distance from the bluff influence subsoil development.

Profile A is a bottomland soil (Sawmill) formed from recent sediments and has not been subjected to much weathering. Profile B (Worthen) on the foot slope also developed from recent alluvial material and shows little structure. Profile C (Hooper) on the slope break
developed from a thick loess on top of leached till, while the soil on the bottom of the slope developed directly from the till. Profile D is an upland soil (Seaton) formerly covered with timber. It possesses a light surface color and lacks structure, the result of a rapid deposition of loess during early soil formation, holding soil weathering to a minimum. Profile E represents an upland soil (Joy) developed under grass. Note the dark surface and lack of structure, again the result of rapid deposition of loess. Profile F (Edgington) is a depressional wet spot. Extra water flowing from adjacent fields increased the rate of weathering, resulting in a light-colored grayish surface and subsurface and a blocky structure to the subsoil. This indicates a strongly developed soil. The depth of subsoil suggests that considerable sediment has been washed in from the surrounding area. Profile G (Sable) represents a depressional upland prairie soil. Note deep, dark surface and coarse, blocky structure. Abundant grass growth produced the dark color. (After Veale and Wascher, 1956.)

Every soil series has neighboring soil series with unlike properties, into which it grades abruptly or gradually. If these several soils found side by side have developed from the same soil material but differ mainly in natural drainage and slope, they are said to form a *catena* (see Fig. 13-3). When soils are mapped, unlike soils for reasons of scale or practical use may be grouped together into *associations*. When occurring in inseparable patterns, soils are mapped as *complexes* (Fig. 13-5). In detailed mapping, a soil series can be subdivided into *types*, *phases*, and *variants*.

SUMMARY

Whatever their classification, whatever the major or minor differences between them, all soils are the base for terrestrial ecosystems. Soil is the site of decomposition of organic matter and of the return of mineral elements to the nutrient cycle. It is the home of animal life, the anchoring medium for plants, and their source of water and nutrients. Soil begins with the weathering of rocks and minerals, which involves the leaching out and the carrying away of mineral matter. Its development is guided by slope, climate, original material, and native vegetation. Plants rooted in the weathering material further break down the substrata, pump up nutrients from its depths, and add all-important organic material. This material, through decomposition and mineralization, is converted into humus, an unstable product that is continuously being formed and destroyed by mineralization. As a result of the weathering process, accumulation and breakdown of organic matter, and the leaching of mineral matter, horizons or layers are formed in the soil. Of these there are four: the O, or organic, layer; the A horizon, characterized by an accumulation of organic matter and a loss of clay and mineral matter; the B horizon, in which mineral matter accumulates, and C, the underlying material. These horizons may be further divided into subhorizons. Of all the horizons, none is more important than the humus layer, which plays a dominant role in the life and distribution of plants and animals, in the maintenance of soil fertility, and in much of the soil-forming process. Humus usually is grouped into three types: mor, characteristic of acid habitats, whose chief decomposing agents are fungi; mull, characteristic of deciduous and mixed woodlands, whose chief decomposing agents are bacteria; and finally moder, which is highly modified by the action of soil animals.

Profile development is influenced over large areas by the vegetation and climate. In grassland regions, calcification is the chief soil-forming process, in which calcium accumulates at the average depth reached by percolating water. In forest regions, podzolization, involving the leaching of calcium, magnesium, iron, and aluminum from the upper horizon and the retention of silica, takes place. In tropical regions, laterization, in which silica is leached and iron and aluminum oxides are retained in the upper horizon, is the major soil-forming process. Gleization takes place in poorly drained soils. Organic matter decomposes slowly and iron is reduced to the ferrous state.

Differences between soils and between horizons within soils are reflected by variations in texture, structure, and color. Each combination of climate, vegetation, soil material, slope, and time results in a unique soil, of which the smallest repetitive unit is the pedon. Soil individuals equivalent to the lowest category in the soil classification system are the soil series. These may be further categorized into families, great groups, suborders, and orders.

Thus there is much more to soils than most people suspect. But of all the many

Figure 13-6 *A soil profile showing some of the difficulties encountered. Here roots and the B horizon extend below a layer of rock.* (Photo by author.)

aspects of soil, perhaps the most important is that it is the crossroad between the organic and mineral worlds and a substrate for teeming life.

SUGGESTED FIELD ACTIVITIES

Study of soil

To understand something about life in and on top of the soil, one must investigate the soil environment first. A good place to begin is to learn something about the geology and soils of the area. Read about the geology of the region in a good reference book for the area. Then examine as many deep roadside and open mine cuts as possible to observe the various kinds of materials. Follow this up with a study of the most recent soil survey for the particular area. These soil surveys, the most recent of which are plotted on air photographs, are published by the Soil Conservation Service, United States Department of Agriculture, and are available from the Superintendent of Documents, Washington 25, D.C. Either the local Soil Conservation Service Office or the County Agent can tell you if such soil surveys are available for your area.

Soil profile

Since the distribution of soil inhabitants and the vegetation is influenced by the nature of the soil, some attention must be given to the soil profile (Fig. 13-6). To become familiar with a soil profile, make a vertical cut through a well-drained soil. A good place to do this is along a roadside cut, but be careful to select an area where no debris or fill has been added to the surface soil. Observe the depth of the various horizons, their texture, color, and pH. Measure the pH of the three major horizons with a soil-pH test kit. What is the difference and what does it indicate? Make a sketch of the soil profile, indicating the horizons, their depth, color, and pH. If possible, make a similar cut in a wooded section and note the difference between disturbed and undisturbed soil. Then sample the profile of the soil in an area where water stands most of the year. How does this compare in color and organic-matter content with well-drained soils? Note the difference between the vegetation growing on the well-drained soil and that growing on the wet areas. Select an area where the slope of the land is variable and possesses a number of drainage conditions. Dig into the subsoil of each drainage class and compare the color of the subsoil on the top of the ridge with that lower on the slope and at the bottom of the slope. Notice the differences in the type or condition of the vegetation growing on these various drainage situations. Dig a pit to expose *A* and *B* horizons under a deciduous and a coniferous woodland, or under an old, established grassland and a woods. Compare the distribution of organic matter. Learn from your local Soil Conservation Service Office the major soil groups found in your area and their location. Examine the profiles of these various soil groups.

Soil organic matter

A general idea of the physical effects of organic matter in the soil can be demonstrated as follows:

Collect lumps of soil from a natural-sod fencerow, forest, eroded land, or heavily farmed land.

Take three wide-mouthed glass jars and fill with water to within one inch of the top. Insert the lumps of soil into small wire racks made from hardware cloth, and lower them gently into the jars. Observe closely and note what happens. What was the appearance of the soil samples before being inserted into the water? Which soil fell apart and dropped to the bottom of the jar and why? What effect does organic matter have on soil structure? What influence would organic matter in the soil have on water falling on the soil surface?

Soil and water relations

The water-holding capacities of various soils can be observed by undertaking some simple experiments, indoors or out in the field.

1. Take 10 jars and 10 cans that will fit on top, cloth toweling, a quantity each of clay, sand, and humus, and soil from a cultivated field lacking organic matter, from a well-managed grassland, and from a woodland.

Dry the soil samples. With a thin nail, punch five holes in the bottoms of the tin cans. Use the same nail, so that all the holes will be the same size. Cut a circle of the towel to fit the bottom of the can, to hold in the soil. Fill each can one-third full, using one of the following soils in each: clay; sand and humus; clay and sand; clay and humus; half sand and half humus; and one-third each of sand, clay, and humus. Label each can as it is filled, pack the soil tightly, and set on top of the jar. Pour a measured quantity of water on the soil of the first can, then the second, etc. Record for each sample (1) the minutes before all water enters the soil; (2) the minutes before water begins to drip; (3) the minutes before water stops dripping; (4) the quantity of water that came through.

In the remaining three cans place a sample of hard, cloddy soil from the cultivated field, soil from the grassland, and soil from the woods. Follow the same procedure as above and record data as above. Note through which of the experimental and natural soils the water passed most rapidly. Which soils held the most water and why? Through which did most of the water pass? What would happen to plants growing on each soil during a wet season; a dry season?

2. Take six large tin cans and cut the bottom out of the can below the rim.

259

Keep the rim on the other end for strength. Mark the can two inches from the end without the rim.

Locate a spot in each of the following sites, as close together as possible: (1) ungrazed, unburned woodland with ground litter one-half to one inch deep; (2) grazed woodland; (3) a fencerow or park where the grass has not been disturbed for some time; (4) a heavily grazed pasture; (5) a managed hayland; (6) eroded land where the subsoil has been exposed.

In each of the above locations drive a can, rimless end down, into the ground. Place a wide board on the can and tap with a hammer until the can is sunk to the two-inch mark. Do not disturb the plant material or the soil in the can. Add one quart of water to each and record (1) the time the water was poured into the can; (2) the time the water completely entered the soil (if the water penetrates too slowly, you may have to settle for the penetration of half a can of water, etc.). From this determine the time required for the quart of water to drain into the soil. Which soil would have the greatest runoff? How did the vegetation affect water infiltration?

The above is strictly demonstrational rather than experimental, but it does emphasize visibly some important points about soil-water relationships. The same can also be said for the suggestions concerning soil temperatures.

Soil temperature

The soil itself influences soil temperature and its variations. Since soil temperatures, like those of aquatic environments, exhibit a vertical gradient that influences the vertical distribution of soil organisms, soil-temperature characteristics under different conditions are worth some study. Before measuring comparative soil temperatures, however, be sure all conditions are uniform except for the influence being measured. For example, if you wished to determine the effect of sun and shade on soil temperatures, the site selected should have the same soil, same general moisture conditions, slope, etc.

The same basic procedure should be followed for all the suggested comparative studies listed below. First take the air temperature. Then take the soil temperature (see Appendix B) at the surface, 3-inch, and 6-inch depths in the morning, noon, and late afternoon on several different days. Obtain the temperatures for soils:

1. In an open area and in the shade
2. In areas of dry, wet, and damp conditions
3. Of various textures
4. On north and south slopes
5. Under different plant cover. In this instance select areas that are nearly alike in slope, moisture, and soil texture.

CHAPTER 14

Life in the soil

Beneath the surface of the ground exists another world, with its whole chain of life, its predators and prey, its herbivores and carnivores, and its fluctuating populations. Because of their abundance, feeding habits, and ways of life, these small organisms cannot help but have an important influence on the other world a few inches above them. Yet the soil is, for all practical purposes, a community separate from that above the ground (Fig. 14-1). Its energy source is the dead bodies and feces from the community above.

The soil as an environment

The soil is a radically different environment for life than the one above the surface, yet the essential requirements do not differ. Like animals that live outside the soil, soil fauna require living space, oxygen, food, and water.

To the soil fauna, the soil in general possesses several outstanding characteristics as a medium for life. It is relatively stable, both chemically and structurally. Any variability in the soil climate is greatly reduced compared to above-surface conditions. The atmosphere remains saturated or nearly so, until

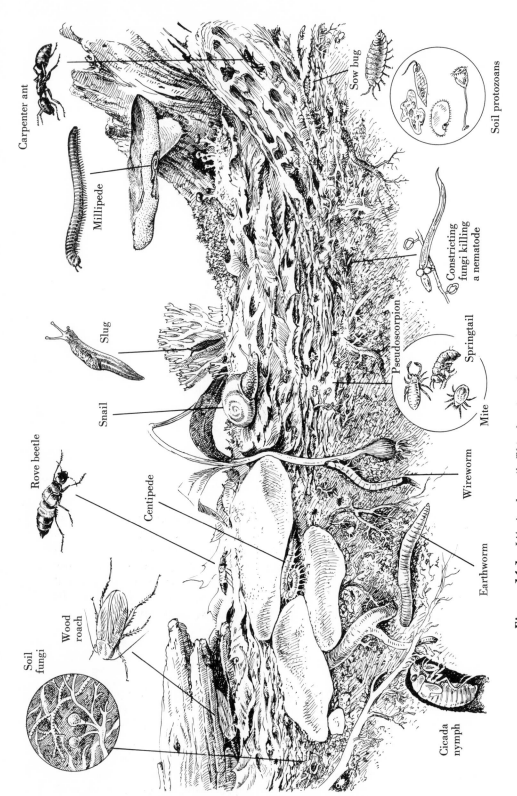

Figure 14-1 Life in the soil. This drawing shows only a tiny fraction of the organisms that inhabit the soil and litter. Note the fruiting bodies of the fungi, which in turn furnish food for animals.

Carpenter ant

Millipede

Sow bug

Soil protozoans

Constricting fungi killing a nematode

Slug

Snail

Pseudoscorpion

Springtail

Mite

Wireworm

Rove beetle

Centipede

Earthworm

Soil fungi

Wood roach

Cicada nymph

soil moisture drops below a critical point. The soil affords a refuge from high and low extremes in temperature, wind, evaporation, light, and dryness. This permits soil fauna to make relatively easy adjustments to unfavorable conditions.

On the other hand, soil has low penetrability. Movement is greatly hampered. Except to such channeling species as earthworms, soil pore space is very important, for this determines the nature of the living space, the humidity, the gaseous condition of the environment. The variability of these conditions creates a diversity of habitats, which is reflected by the diversity of species found in the soil (Birch and Clark, 1953). The number of different species, representing practically every invertebrate phylum, found in the soil is enormous. There are 250 species of Protozoa alone in English soils (Sandon, 1927). The number of species of soil animals exclusive of Protozoa found in a variety of habitats in Germany varied from 68 to 203 (Frenzell, 1936). In the soil of a beech woods in Austria live at least 110 species of beetles, 229 species of mites, 46 species of snails and slugs (Franz, 1950). E. C. Williams (1941) counted 294 species of soil animals, exclusive of Protozoa, in the Panama Rain Forest.

Only a part of the soil litter is available to most soil animals as living space. Spaces between the surface litter, cavities walled off by soil aggregates, pore spaces between individual soil particles, root channels and fissures, all are potential habitats. Most of the soil fauna are limited to pores and cavities larger than themselves. The distribution of these forms in different soils is often determined in part by the structure of the soil (Weis-Fogh, 1948), for there is a relationship between the average size of soil spaces and the fauna inhabiting them (Kuhnelt, 1950). In loose soils with crumb structure, large species of mites (Orbatei) are found, in contrast to smaller forms inhabiting compact soils. Larger soil species are confined to upper layers, where the soil interstices are the largest (Haarløv, 1960).

Water in the spaces is essential, since the majority of soil fauna is active only in this. Soil water is usually present as a thin film covering the surface of soil particles. This film contains, among other things, bacteria, unicellular algae, protozoa, rotifers, and nematodes. Most of these are restricted in their movements by the thickness and shape of the water film in which they live. Nematodes are less restricted, for they can distort the water film by muscular movements and thus bridge the intervening air spaces. If the water film dries up, these species encyst or enter a dormant state. Millipedes and centipedes on the other hand are highly susceptible to desiccation and avoid it by burrowing deeper into the soil (Kevan, 1962).

Excess water and the lack of aeration are detrimental to any soil animals. Excessive moisture, which typically occurs after heavy rains, often is disastrous to some soil inhabitants. Air spaces become flooded with deoxygenated water, producing a zone of oxygen shortage for soil inhabitants. If earthworms cannot evade this by digging deeper, they are forced to the surface, where they die from excessive ultraviolet radiation. The snowflea (a Collembola) comes to the surface in the spring to avoid excess soil water from melting snow (Kuhnelt, 1950). Many small species and immature stages of larger species of centipedes and millipedes may be completely immobilized by a film of water and unable to overcome the surface tension imprisoning them. Adults of many species of these organisms possess a waterproof cuticle that enables them to survive some temporary flooding.

Soil acidity long has been regarded as having an important effect on soil fauna. But since pH is readily measured, it has been overplayed in an attempt to correlate soil characteristics with the fauna. C. H. Bornebusch (1930) regarded a pH of 4.5 as inimical to earthworms, yet some earthworms, such as *Lumbricus rubellus,* are quite tolerant of relatively acid conditions. While every species of earthworm has its optimum pH and while some species, such as the *Dendrobaenus,* are characteristic of acid conditions, most of them seem to be able to settle in most soils, provided they contain sufficient moisture (Petrov, 1946). In northern hardwood forests, earthworms are most abundant both in species and in numbers when the pH is between 5.5 and 4.1 (Stegeman, 1960). Mites and springtails (Collembola) can exist in very acid conditions (Murphy, 1953).

The faunal community

The interrelations of the organisms living in the soil are very complex; but within the upper layers of the soil, energy flows through a series of trophic levels similar to those of surface communities.

The primary sources of energy in the soil community are the dead plant and animal matter and feces from the ground layer above. These are broken down by the microbial life—bacteria, fungi, protozoans. The latter two in particular digest food extracellularly and absorb the dissolved sugars. These organisms are the ones well supplied with the enzymes necessary for the breakdown of cellulose into usable food. Upon this base rests a phytophagous consumer layer, which obtains its nourishment from assimilable substances of living plants, as do the parasitic nematodes and root-feeding insects; from fresh litter as do the earthworms; and from the exploitation of the soil microflora. Some members of this latter group, such as some protozoa and free-living nematodes, feed selectively on the microflora. Others, including most earthworms, pot worms, millipedes, and small soil arthropods, ingest large quantities of organic matter and utilize only a small fraction of it, chiefly the bacteria and fungi, as well as any protozoa and small invertebrates contained within the material. On the next trophic level are the predators—the turbellaria, which feed on nematodes and pot worms, the predatory nematodes and mites, insects, and spiders. In such a manner does the community in the soil operate on an energy source supplied by the unharvested organic material of the world above.

Prominent among the larger soil fauna are the Oligochaetes, which include two common families, the Lumbricidae (earthworms) and the Enchytraeidae (white or pot worms). The latter are small, whitish worms, which abound in the upper three inches of the soil if humidity is fairly constant. They are able to live under a greater variety of conditions than earthworms, but their numbers undergo violent fluctuations. Populations are at a maximum in winter and at a minimum in summer. They are not extensive burrowers and appear to divide the earth and humus more finely than earthworms. Little is known about their feeding biology beyond that they ingest organic debris, from which they may digest bacteria, protozoa, and other microorganisms (Nielsen, 1961).

264   Earthworms may have considerable influence on the physical structure of the soil, an influence that depends in part on the species inhabiting the soil, the relative proportions of the species, and their numbers. Some species, such as *Lumbricus terrestris* and *Allolobophora longa,* work deep, even down to the C horizon, and develop well-defined burrow systems three to six feet deep. Others, such as *Eisenia rosea* and *A. Chlorotica,* are shallow working and are more or less confined to the top six inches. These earthworms of shallow depths have no well-developed burrow systems and produce few casts. Only under unfavorable conditions, like drought, do these earthworms burrow deep into the soil.

Earthworm activity in the soil consists mainly of burrowing, of ingestion and partial breakdown of organic matter, and of subsequent egestion in the form of surface or subsurface casts. Ingested soil is taken during burrow construction, mixed with intestinal secretions, and passed out either as aggregated castings on or near the surface or as a semiliquid in intersoil spaces along the burrow. Earthworms pull organic matter into their burrows and ingest some of this, which is then partially or completely digested in the gut. Casts of soil passed through the alimentary canal contain a larger proportion of soil particles less than 0.002 inches in diameter than uningested soil and a higher total nitrogen, organic carbon, exchangeable calcium and magnesium, available phosphorus, and pH.

Surface casting and burrowing slowly overturn the soil. Subsurface soil is brought to the top and organic matter is pulled down into and incorporated with the subsoil to form soil aggregates. These aggregates result in a more open structure in heavy soil and bind particles of light soil together.

The amount of soil worked over by earthworms is tremendous. Evans (1948) reports that the weight of worm casts produced per year on English fields varied from one to five tons. This variance is due primarily to the different ratios of only two of the several earthworms present, *Allolobophora noctura* and *A. longa.* He estimated that from 4 to 36 tons of soil passes through the alimentary tract of the total earthworm population living on an acre in a year.

Earthworms show a decided preference for certain leaves. The night crawler, *Lumbricus terrestris,* feeds on broadleaf litter rather than pine and soft-textured foliage. In one experimental study (Johnston, 1936) these earthworms accepted immediately large-toothed aspen, white ash, and basswood, took with less relish and did not entirely consume sugar maple and red maple, and did not eat red oak at all. In a European study (Lindquist, 1942) earthworms preferred the dead leaves of elm, ash, and birch, ate sparingly of oak and beech, and did not touch pine or spruce needles.

Millipedes probably are the next most important group of litter feeders. They and their somewhat similar associates, the centipedes, are essentially animals of the woodland floor. Millipedes found in nonwooded areas usually are considered relics of forest fauna, but centipedes are able to adapt to deforested land. Millipedes occupy essentially three woodland habitats, the floor and aerial parts of vegetation, the litter and upper soil layer, and the areas underneath bark and stones and in rotten logs and stumps.

Adult millipedes, the so-called thousand legs, seemingly bear two pairs of walking legs per segment; actually the abdominal segments are fused into pairs to produce this characteristic. The three most common forms are the oval, pill millipedes, the Glomerids; the flat-backed Polydesmids, with flattened lateral expansions; and the large Iuloids. The former two are not adapted to burrowing and they must find refuge against both floods and drought in surface retreats. Iuloids, however, burrow extensively in the soil. Millipedes ingest leaves, particularly those in which some fungal decomposition has taken place, for lacking the enzymes necessary for the breakdown of cellulose, they live on the fungi contained within the litter. Different species of millipedes ingest varying quantities of litter, depending upon the tree species (Van der Drift, 1951). *Iulus* consumes more red-oak litter, *Cylindroiulus* more pine.

The chief contribution of millipedes to soil development and to the soil ecosystem is the mechanical breakdown of litter, making it more vulnerable to microbial attack, especially by the saprophytic fungi.

Litter feeders of importance are the snails and slugs, which among the soil invertebrates possess the widest range of enzymes to hydrolyze cellulose and other plant polysaccharides, possibly even lignin (Nielsen, 1962). In Australian rain forests, amphipods are a conspicuous part of the fauna and play a major part in the disintegration of the leaf litter (Birch and Clark, 1953).

Not to be ignored are the termites (Isoptera), white, wingless, social insects closely related to the roaches that appeared toward the end of the Carboniferous period and reached their full structural and social development by the end of the Triassic period. Termites, together with some Dipteran and beetle larvae, are the only larger soil inhabitants that are able to break down the cellulose of wood. This they accomplish with the aid of a mutualistic protozoan living in the termite's gut. The termite has a mouth structure adapted to ingest wood; the protozoan produces the enzymes that effectively digest cellulose into the simple sugars that the termite can use. Together, the two organisms function perfectly. Without the protozoan, the termite could not exist; without the termite the protozoan could not gain access to wood.

In spite of their role in the disintegration of wood, termites do not play a major role in the temperate soils, but in the tropics they dominate the soil fauna. In these regions they are responsible for the rapid removal of wood and other cellulose-containing materials, twigs, leaves, dry grass, structural timbers, etc., from the surface.

The tropical termites are so efficient that it is difficult to maintain humus in the soil or to develop mulch covering over the soil, all of which presents an agricultural problem in humus-deficient areas. In addition to removal of organic matter, the termites are important soil churners. They move considerable quantities of soil, perhaps as much as 5000 tons per acre, in constructing their huge and complex mounds. In semidesert country the openings and galleries of subterranean termites allow the infrequent rains to penetrate deep into the subsoil rather than to run off the surface (Kevan, 1962).

Of all the soil animals, the most abundant and widely distributed are the mites (Acaria) and the springtails (Collembola). Both occur in nearly every situation where vegetation grows, from the tropical rain forest to the tundra. Flattened dorsoventrally, they are able to wiggle, squeeze, and even digest their way through tiny caverns in the soil. Here they browse on fungi or search for prey in the dark interstices and pores of the organic mass.

The most numerous of the two, both in species and in numbers, are the mites, tiny, eight-legged arthropods from 0.1 to 2.0 mm in size. They may or may not have eyes, depending on whether they live near or below the surface. If they lack eyes, then the subterranean mites have elaborate sensory setae. The most common mites in the soil and litter are the Orbatei. In the pine-woods litter of Tennessee, for instance, they make up 73 per cent of all the litter mites (Crossley and Bohnsack, 1960). These mites live largely on fungal hyphae that attack dead vegetation as well as the sugars digested by this microflora, which these arthropods follow in evergreen needles. Fallen spruce and fir needles are first attacked by fungi, which break down the contents and structure. As soon as the needles are softened, the mites lay their eggs in them (Jacot, 1939). Upon hatching, the mite larvae ingest the palisade cells about them and advance into the areas they have cleared ahead. Behind them they leave piles of oval feces, utilized by midge larvae and bacteria, and cleared areas ready for further invasion by fungi.

The Collembola, the most generally distributed of all insects, are of very ancient lineage. Their remains have been found in the lower Devonian deposits in Scotland, long before the earliest winged insects appeared. Typically the springtails may be brightly colored, or completely white, and possess a remarkable springing organ at their posterior end, which enables them to leap comparatively great distances. From this they have earned their popular name, "springtails." The springtails are small, from 0.3 to 1 mm. Surface dwellers have eyes, and those that live deeper in the soil are eyeless. They are more sensitive than mites to moisture deficiencies but can better withstand short periods of flooding.

Collembola consist of two groups, the round springtails, or *Symphypleona,* and the long springtails, or *Arthropleona.* Neither have specialized feeding habits. They consume decomposing plant materials, largely for the fungal hyphae they contain.

Recent studies of food habits of soil arthropods and the enzymes they possess (Engelmann, 1961; Nielsen, 1962) are changing long-held ideas concerning the role of soil arthropods and other so-called litter-feeding invertebrates. Because they lack the enzymes necessary for the breakdown of cellulose, these organisms apparently must utilize the fungi, the bacteria, and the protozoa in the litter they ingest. Mechanical breakdown of litter may be one of their roles in the soil community, but more important they act as a control on the soil microflora populations. By feeding directly on the fungi and thus reducing the biomass, the soil invertebrates undoubtedly affect the chemical activity of the soil microflora. The extent of this, as well as effects of animal predation on fungi, remain as yet unknown.

The small arthropods are the principle prey of spiders, beetles, especially the Staphylinidae, the pseudoscorpions, the mites, and centipedes. The latter, dorso-ventrally flattened myrapods with one pair of walking legs to each segment except the last, are one of the major invertebrate predators. Centipedes kill and capture their prey by means of two poison fangs, modified legs of the first trunk segment. The two most common groups are the nonburrowing, swift-running lithobiomorphs and the geophilomorphs, which burrow, earthwormlike, into the soil. Predaceous Mesostigmata mites prey on herbivorous mites, nematodes, enchytraeid worms, small insect larvae, and other small soil animals.

Most of the microorganisms of the soil, the protozoa and rotifers, myxobacteria and nematodes, feed on bacteria and algae. Nematodes are ubiquitous, found wherever their need for a film of water in which to move is met. Soil and fresh-water nematodes form one ecological group, with many species in common. But in the soil they exist at much higher densities than in fresh water, up to 20 million per square meter. They are most abundant in the upper two inches in the vicinity of roots, where they feed on plant juices, soil algae, and bacteria. A few are predaceous.

Also found in the organic layer of woodland and meadow soils, especially those with a cover of moss, are other representatives of fresh-water inhabitants, the rotifers. They feed largely on detritus and algae. Tartigrades or "water bears," too, are moss dwellers, for here they find the alternating wet and dry conditions they require for their existence.

These bacterial and algae feeders, in turn, are consumed by various predacious fungi. Among these, there are three groups: the Zoopagales, an order of Phycomycetes that preys chiefly on protozoans, although a few species prey on nematodes; the endozoic Hyphomycetes and the ensnaring Hyphomycetes, both of which capture and digest nematodes, crustaceans, rotifers, and, to an extent, protozoans (Maio, 1958; Doddington, in Kevan, 1955). The Zoopagales possess sticky mycelia, which capture the prey like flypaper. After the animal has been captured, the fungus injects into the animal's body cavity daughter filaments, which digest its contents, leaving in the end only the shriveled integument filled with hyphae.

The endozoic Hyphomycetes release spores, which stick to the integument of nematodes. Germ tubes penetrate the tube of the animal and develop into internal mycelium. The host becomes progressively more sluggish until it dies, after which the absorption of the body contents of the animal is completed. Spore-producing hyphae grow out through the skin of the dead nematode.

The most remarkable group of fungi, extremely common in the soil, are the nematode-trapping Hyphomycetes, which possess morphological adaptations that enable them to capture their prey. One of the commonest forms of traps is a network of highly adhesive loops, which catch and hold nematodes on contact. After a struggle, the animal dies and a narrow branch of hyphae penetrates and fills the body of the animal and absorbs its contents until only the skin is left. Others possess sticky, knoblike processes, to which the nematodes adhere. But the most unusual of all is the rabbit-snare trap, of which there are two types, nonconstricting and constricting. Both possess rings of filaments attached by short branches to the main filament. Each ring trap consists of three curved cells; and its inside diameter is just large enough to permit a nematode attempting to pass through to become wedged and unable to withdraw. In the constricting type ring, the friction of the nematode's body stimulates the ring cells to inflate to about three times their former volume and to grip the nematode in a strangle hold. The response is rapid; complete distention of the cells is accomplished within one-tenth of a second.

Others groups of animals, although feeding largely on the surface and contributing little to litter breakdown, are important as soil mixers. Outstanding among these are the ants and the burrowing mammals, prairie dogs, moles, and woodchucks. Ants are especially important as soil animals, for they are widely distributed, pioneer new sites, and bring up large quantities of soil from below ground. Mounds of the harvester ant dot large areas of the North American plains. The ants on one area moved an estimated 3400 tons of soil per acre in constructing their mounds (Thorpe, 1949). Prairie dogs raise earth from lower levels and deposit it at the surface, where it is broken down by weathering and incorporated with organic material. They carry surface soil down to plug passage-ways, and on clay soils they increase the proportion of fine soil particles on the surface. On one area prairie dogs and badgers were credited with converting a silt-loam soil to a loam (Thorpe, 1949). The amount of soil moved by prairie dogs is large. In northern Colorado, the average volume of earth in dog mounds is three cubic feet; with a burrow density of 25 per acre, the soil in the mounds would weigh over three tons (Koford, 1958). In central Oklahoma, the total volume of 12 burrows with 25 entrances and 599 feet of tunnels was 95 cubic feet, or roughly four tons of earth moved for each 25 entrance holes (Wilcomb, 1954). Moles, too, move considerable quantities of earth, although the amount has not been calculated. Their varied influences include improving the natural drainage and aeration of soil and increasing organic matter by burying surface vegetation and litter under their hills.

Abundance and distribution

If diversity of a species is one characteristic of soil faunas, then their enormous numbers is another.

Quantitative studies of soil-faunal populations were made possible by the development of the funnel extraction method by the Italian entomologist Antonio Berlese, in 1905. This was later improved by others (see Kevan, 1955, 1962). Early faunal counts were made in beech mor and mull by Bornebusch in Denmark and Ulrich (1933) in Germany, but because the samples were too large and the extraction methods poor, they underestimated their populations (Van der Drift, 1951). Larger populations were discovered as methods were improved. Bornebusch's maximum number obtained for a beech mull was 79 million per acre, while Forrslund in 1947 came up with 4410 million per acre. In fact Forrslund by directly examining small samples from Swedish forest sites obtained a population equivalent of 2,300,000 arthropods per square meter.

Because of the variability of sample depths and sizes and of differing efficiencies of extractions, accurate comparisons cannot be made; but they do give some indication of the numbers involved. Overgaard (1949) in a study of 31 localities in Denmark found that nematodes varied from 708 million to 81 million per acre. Evan (1948) estimated the earthworm population in a 300-year-old pasture at Rothamsted at 167,000 per acre, and Bornebusch obtained a population figure of 1,450,000 earthworms per acre in a beech mull forest. Mites and Collembola are the dominant soil arthropods and constitute 85 per cent of the total number of animals in the soil (Salt et al., 1948). Mites accounted for 83 per cent of all the soil fauna in a pine woods in Tennessee, where the number of soil animals was estimated at 102,000 per square meter. Protozoans occur in tremendous numbers. Flagellates appear to be the most common, ranging from 100,000 to 1,000,000 per gram of soil; amoebas from 50,000 to 500,000; and ciliates up to 1000 per gram of soil (Waksman, 1952). A majority of these also inhabit fresh waters.

The numerical population of soil animals in mor is much larger than in mull, mainly because mites and springtails dominate the former. In Denmark the number of soil animals increased from oaks to beech and spruce (Bornebusch, 1930; Stevanovic, 1956), but on a biomass basis, mull supported the largest population. Bornebusch found that 50 to 80 per cent of the fauna in mull humus of the broadleaf forest were earthworms. He found, however, a tremendous variation in biomass in 10 Danish forest localities. Spruce raw humus had but 0.90 grams per square meter, while a rich mull had a biomass of 200 grams per square meter, or 1,590 pounds per acre. This is equivalent to the weight of livestock carried by a first-class Danish pasture. Evans and Guild (1948) obtained a considerably smaller biomass of 163 grams per square meter on a 300-year-old English pasture.

Soil fauna shows a marked zonation, with the densest populations concentrated in the upper surface layers. Grasslands do not show the same strong demarkation between surface and deep horizons, for the humus is more uniformly distributed. Eaton and Chandler (1942) found that the greatest number of arthropods always occurred in samples composed of litter in the process of fragmentation. Large numbers continued to be present in the upper humus layer, but a gradual reduction took place in the deeper parts. In natural heathland representing a mor humus, 96 per cent of the population was concentrated in the upper two and one-quarter inches and the remaining four per cent was scattered through the profile. In grasslands, 67 per cent of the mites and springtails inhabited the 0 to 6 inch zone and 33 per cent in the 6 to 12 inch zone (Murphy, 1953). Oribatei mite populations are greatest in the O layer, since most of them feed on fungi in the litter. Larger species of these mites have their optimum in the O1 layer, since they feed on molds and algae growing in the youngest litter material. There appears, however, to be a correlation between the size of animals and the structure of the soil. Larger species are confined to the upper layers, while the smaller, flatter species are most numerous in the deep soil layers. Vertical distribution of microarthropods is determined largely by water content, food, size of the soil spaces, and light in the litter layer (Kevan, 1962).

Soil faunas show marked and often violent fluctuations in numbers. These fluctuations are both seasonal and diurnal and are reflections of changes in temperature and moisture. The greatest fluctuations occur at the surface and decrease with depth. The daily vertical migration of the springtails appears to be conditioned chiefly by the degree of solar radiation and the degree of dew accumulation at night (Jacot, 1940). The downward migration of these and other microarthropods, however, is impeded, if not inhibited, by the mineral layer of the soil (Haarløv, 1960). Some soil invertebrates move deeper into the soil during the fall and winter and return to the surface the following spring (Dowdy, 1944). This migration often coincides with temperature overturns. During periods of drought, some species, such as earthworms, withdraw from the upper layers; or like the nematodes, they may enter an anabiotic state to become active again when conditions are favorable; others, such as the springtails, may die out. Still other species, as the Oribatei mites, seem to be adapted to extreme environmental conditions.

Relationship of soil populations to cover types

Distribution of the animals on the surface is influenced by vegetation types, and certain animals are characteristic of each. Much the same situation appears to exist beneath the surface of the soil. The species composition and age of the vegetation stand, the base status of the soil, and drainage, among others, affect soil faunal composition and number. Mixed stands are richer both in species and in numbers than pine and spruce stands (Pschorn-Walcher, 1952). Accumulated coniferous needles may provide suitable environmental conditions, while deciduous litter provides a sufficiently palatable food source to maintain the litter-feeding population of soil mites at a high level (Murphy, 1952). This mixture effect also seems to extend to mixed coniferous stands. White pine–hemlock stands supported a more varied soil fauna than pure white pine or red pine stands (Bellinger, 1954). Nearly 60 species of Collembola were found in mixed stands, compared to 30 to 40 species in the other areas. Litter fauna under hemlock seems to be poorer than under white pine (Hope, 1943). The fact that white pine litter has a calcium content of one to two per cent undoubtedly influences this increase, just as in the case of mixed stands of deciduous and coniferous forms. "The calcium content of the litter source," writes P. W. Murphy (1953) "may have an important influence on the faunal and floral population, and on the composition of the latter will depend the nature of the humus formation." This is pointed out in a study of Read and Walker (1950), who found that red cedar in a Connecticut pine plantation, through its influence on the calcium content and pH of the surface soil beneath, brought about and maintained favorable conditions for earthworm activity.

The development of some groups of animals is influenced by soil change, whereas other groups develop in parallel with plant succession (Gretschy, 1952). Soil conditions become more favorable for the increase of soil fauna with reforestation. Reforestation produces a tendency toward a richer fauna of larger size with a greater proportion of Oribatei mites. Wooded sites support a larger number of soil fauna than treeless sites (Jahn, 1950). Connecticut white pine and red pine stands supported larger populations than unplanted old fields. Distribution of earthworms across old fields in New York seems to be influenced by the type of woody cover coming in (Smith, 1956). Earthworm populations on plots with woody vegetation were significantly larger than those on plots with a sod cover only. Sod plots had the lowest organic matter in the soil.

SUMMARY

Organisms present in the soil, like all other animal populations, reflect their environment. Their abundance and faunal composition depend upon the nature of the soil, its nutrient status and the vegetation present, the kind of litter it produces, and the ability of the plants to return calcium and other nutrients to the soil. The soil animals, in turn, play their role in influencing the future development of the upper soil layers. The direct decomposition of the plant litter is accomplished by the microflora, the bacteria, and fungi. The soil invertebrate fauna makes the organic matter more readily available to the microflora by the mechanical breakdown of the litter, by exposing new areas for fungal invasion, by spreading fungal spores through their feces, and by increasing surface area exposed to attack by bacteria and fungi. But the soil fauna also consumes great quantities of fungi and depress bacterial and fungal populations. The predaceous species in turn influence the population levels of the litter-feeding and decomposer organisms. Such is the chain of life in the world beneath the surface of the ground.

271

SUGGESTED FIELD ACTIVITIES

Study of the soil inhabitants

At an elementary level the study of the soil community is sadly neglected. Yet often it is most conveniently located and offers considerable opportunities to observe ecological principles. There are of course difficulties. For one thing, soils are highly variable and environmental conditions may differ within a few yards. But even this situation is filled with opportunities for comparative work. Then the soil contains a superabundance of small and unfamiliar organisms, which present problems in identification. But even this is not insurmountable. For general work, identification down to the genus or even order is all that is necessary. A number of new keys are available to guide the beginner. Of these, the best by far is the one that appears in the book *Soil Zoology*.

Any study of the soil inhabitants should be accompanied by observation on the soil environment as outlined in Chap. 13. Especially important is moisture data. Moisture dictates the distribution and life of soil organisms. Population aggregation and movements reflect moisture conditions and fluctuations.

Large litter fauna

The larger litter fauna—the millipedes, centipedes, woodlice, etc.— is a logical beginning for the study of the soil community. They are easily observed, are not overwhelmingly numerous, and are more easily identified. The first step in the study of these and other litter fauna is to prepare a map of a limited study area, on which pertinent features, such as change in litter composition, stones, stumps, debris, changes in moisture conditions over a range of weather conditions, etc., are plotted. On this map you can indicate diurnal and nocturnal distribution of the litter fauna. Horizontal and vertical movements within the area and interchange between localized aggregations can be detected by observing the positions of marked individuals over a period of time. Millipedes, sow bugs, and other larger arthropods can be marked with cellulose paints (those containing ethyl acetate and obtainable at hobby shops) for individual identification. Marked individuals offer a fine opportunity to estimate population density by means of the mark-recapture method—as yet little used in soil faunal studies—as well as estimates of population turnover.

Later, variation can be introduced by creating artificial habitats—boards, pieces of crockery, or heaps of wet peat placed under flower pots. From this one can gain a clearer idea of faunal distribution, habitat preferences of different species, and the speed with which various species spread into new and unoccupied habitats.

Earthworms

Like the large litter fauna, the earthworms are relatively easy to study, and serve well as representatives of the burrowing fauna of the soil. The number of species is not large, and with some effort the larger species at least can be identified with a good key.

A study of earthworms again begins with a good map of the study area, indicating vegetation, including presence of woody growth, wet areas, small knolls, etc. Sample plots one yard or one meter square are located at random; if the area under study is very small, such as 8 or 10 square yards, then the whole area could be marked out in yard-square grids and each quadrat sampled. Samples of the soil from each quadrat are taken to determine pH, calcium content, and organic matter. The

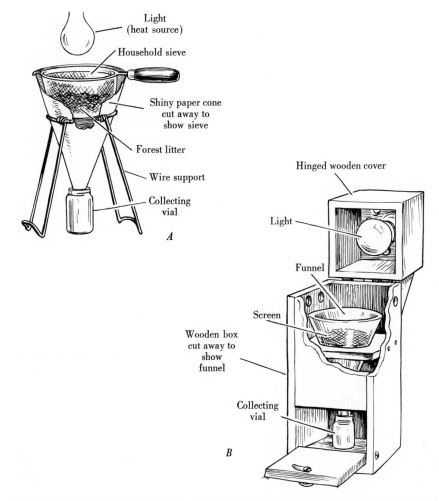

Figure 14-2 *Although the Berlese and other types of funnels can be purchased commercially, they can be constructed easily in the workshop. A is a relatively simple one, sufficient for introductory work. B is more elaborate and more efficient.*

earthworm population in each quadrat is sampled. This presents some difficulties, for no really successful method for doing this has yet been devised. From my own experience, I would recommend a combination of potassium-permanganate solution and a shovel. Soak the quadrat with the permanganate solution. Rarely will this penetrate beyond three feet, more often considerably less, but the solution will drive the earthworms within the wetted zone to the surface, where they can be collected, killed, and fixed in alcohol. (Keep the specimens straight for identification.) After the earthworms' movement to the surface stops, proceed with the shovel and dig out the quadrat as deep as necessary to remove deep-burrowing species. The soil must be hand sorted for maximum recovery. The number and species composition of earthworm population for each quadrat should then be plotted on the map and correlated with pH, calcium, organic matter, vegetation, and moisture. From this information you may be able to draw some conclusions on earthworm distribution as influenced by the soil environment.

273

Small soil arthropods

The most difficult component of soil fauna to study are the soil arthropods. They are the most numerous, the most difficult to identify, and possibly the most difficult to sample accurately. Nematodes, white or pot worms, and protozoans are the worst, but these are not considered here, for they require specialized techniques for their extraction that will not be discussed. Those interested are referred to the book *Progress in Soil Zoology* (Murphy, 1962).

Soil arthropods can be extracted from the soil by means of a Tullgren funnel, an improved version of the Berlese funnel, the construction of which is simple (Fig. 14-2). Essentially it consists of a heat source and a smooth funnel, preferably glass, and a shelf of hardware cloth on which to place the sample. The heat from the lamp and then desiccation drives the arthropods downward, until they fall into the collecting bottle beneath the funnel.

The procedure is rather simple. Place the sample of litter or soil on the hardware cloth shelf, so fitted in the funnel that air space is present between the wire and the wall of the funnel. To begin extraction, open the lid of the funnel 90° and turn on the 100-watt bulb. After about 16 hours, depending on sample size and moisture content, change to a 15-watt bulb and shut the lid. There will be two periods of arthropod exodus, the first wave due to heat, the second due to desiccation. The collecting bottle beneath the funnel may contain alcohol, formalin, or water. Water may be preferable, since it increases the humidity gradient toward which the animals move. The animals are then sorted and identified under the microscope.

These funnels are adequate for introductory soil biology. For more efficient extraction, necessary for serious studies in soil zoology, a better extractor is required. A new extractor for woodland litter has been described by Kempson, Lloyd, and Ghelardi (1963) in the journal *Pedobiologia*. The funnels are replaced by wide-mouthed bowls filled with an aqueous solution of picric acid. The acid not only preserves the specimens but also produces by evaporation a high humidity in the air just under the sample. The humid air is cooled by conduction from a cold-water bath in which the bowls are immersed.

CHAPTER 15

The grasslands

When the explorers looked out across the prairies for the first time, they witnessed a scene they had never before experienced. Nowhere in all western Europe had they seen anything similar. Lacking any other name to call them, the explorers named these grasslands "prairie," from the French, meaning "grassland." This was the North American prairie and plains, the climax grassland that occupied the midcontinent. It was one of the several great grassland regions in the world, including the steppes of Russian, the pustza of Hungary, the South African veld, and the South American pampas. In fact at one time grasslands covered about 42 per cent of the land surface of the world; but today much of it is under cultivation. All have in common a climate characterized by high rates of evaporation and periodically severe droughts, a rolling-to-flat terrain, and animal life that is dominated by grazing and burrowing species.

Grasslands in the eastern forested regions of North America are successional stages on the road back to forest. When the settlers cleared the land for farms, they introduced grasses brought over from Europe, bluegrass, for one, orchard grass, timothy, and redtop. These and others dominate the haylands and pastures and even seral grasslands of much of North America.

275

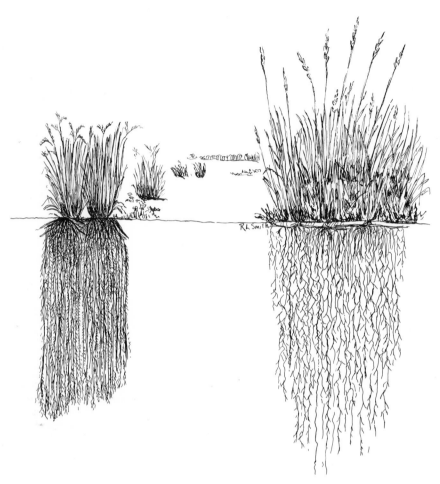

Figure 15-1 *Growth form of a sod grass (left), crested wheatgrass, and a bunch grass (right), little bluestem. Also shown is a cross section of root penetration and distribution in the soil (maximum depth: 7 feet).* (Root diagrams are general but based on numerous photographs by J. F. Weaver.)

The grasses that make up the haylands, pastures, and prairies are either sod formers or bunch grasses. As the names imply, the former develop a solid mat of grass over the ground (Fig. 15-1), while the latter grow in bunches (Fig. 15-1), the space between which is occupied by other plants, usually herbs. Orchardgrass, broomsedge, crested wheatgrass, and little bluestem are typical bunch grasses, which form clumps by the erect growth of all shoots and spread at the base by tillers. Sod-forming grasses, which include such species as Kentucky bluegrass and western wheatgrass, reproduce and spread by underground stems. Some grasses may be either sod or bunch, depending upon the local environment. Big bluestem will develop a sod on a rich, moist soil and form bunches on a dry soil.

Associated with the grasses are a variety of legumes and forbs. Cultivated **276** haylands and pastures usually are planted to a mixture of grasses and such legumes as alfalfa and red clover. With these may grow unwanted plants, such as mustard, dandelion and daisy. Seral grasslands often consist of a mixture of native grasses, such as timothy and bluegrass, and an assortment of herbaceous plants, including cinquefoil, wild strawberry, daisy, dewberry, and goldenrod. On the prairie, legumes and forbs, particularly the composites, are important components of the climax grassland (Weaver, 1954). From spring to fall, the color and aspects of the grassland change from pasqueflower and buttercups to goldenrod.

Stratification

Grasslands possess essentially three strata, the roots, the ground layer, and the herbaceous layer (Fig. 15-2). The root layer is more pronounced in grasslands than in any other major community. Half or more of the plant is hidden beneath the soil; in winter this represents almost the total grass plant, a sharp contrast to the leafless trees of the forest. The bulk of the roots occupy rather uniformly the upper one-half foot or so of the soil profile and decrease in abundance with depth. The depth to which the roots of grasses extend is considerable. Little bluestem reaches four to five and one-half feet (1.3 to 1.7 meters) and forms a dense mat in the soil to two and one-half feet (0.8 meters) (Weaver 1954). Roots of blue grama and buffalograss penetrate vertically to three feet (1 meter). In addition, many grasses possess underground stems, or rhizomes, that serve both to propagate the plants and to store food. On the end of the rhizome, which has both nodes and scalelike leaves, is a terminal bud, which develops into aerial stems or new rhizomes. Rhizomes of most species grow at shallow depths, not over four or five inches deep. The exotic quackgrass is notorious among farmers for its tough rhizomes. Forbs such as goldenrod, asters, and snakeroot possess large, woody rhizomes and fibrous roots that add to the root mat in the soil. Some, such as snakeroot, have extensive taproots

Figure 15-2 *A cross section of a hayfield showing several strata in grasslands. Note the tall grass (timothy) and the denser "understory" of legumes (clover and alfalfa) and grass blades.* (Photo by author.)

16 feet (5 meters) long, and rushlike lygodesmia, common in many prairies, extends down 21 feet (6 + meters) in mellow soil. Among hayland plants, alfalfa possesses a taproot that grows to a considerable depth.

All the roots of grassland plants are not confined to the same general area of the soil but develop in three or more zones. Some plants are shallow rooted and seldom extend much below two feet. Others go well below the shallow-rooted species but seldom more than five feet. Deep-rooted plants extend even further into the soil and absorb relatively little moisture from the surface soils.

The ground layer is characterized by low light intensity during the growing season and by reduced windflow. Light intensity decreases as the grass grows taller and furnishes shade. Temperatures decrease as solar insolation is intercepted by a blanket of vegetation and windflow is at a minimum (see Fig. 4-12). Even though the grass tops may move like waves of water, the air on the ground is calm. Conditions on grazed lands are different. Since the grass cover is closely cropped, the ground layer receives much higher solar radiation and is subject to higher temperatures and to greater wind velocity near the surface.

Grasslands, unmowed, unburned, and ungrazed, accumulate a layer of mulch on the ground surface. The oldest layer consists of decayed and fragmented remains of fresh mulch. Fresh mulch consists of residual herbage, leafy and largely undecayed. Three or four years must pass before natural grassland herbage will decompose completely (Hopkins, 1954). Not until mulch comes in contact with mineral soil does the decomposition process, influenced by compaction and depth, proceed with any rapidity. As the mat increases in depth, more water is retained, creating very favorable conditions for microbial activity (McCalla, 1943).

The amount of accumulated mulch often is enormous. On a relict of a climax prairie, organic matter and other humic materials amounted to 9600 pounds per acre, 6300 pounds of it fresh mulch and 592 pounds fresh herbage (Dhysterhaus and Schmutz, 1947). Another prairie supported 5000 pounds of fresh mulch per acre and 9000 pounds of humus (Dix, 1960).

Grazing reduces mulch, as do fire and mowing. Light grazing tends to increase the weight of humic mulch at the expense of fresh (Dix, 1960); moderate grazing results in increased compaction, which favors an increase in microbial activity and a subsequent reduction in both fresh and humic mulch. Burning reduces both, but the mulch structure returns two to three years after a fire on lightly grazed and ungrazed lands (Tester and Marshall, 1961; Hadley and Kieckhefer, 1963). Mowing greatly reduces fresh mulch and in a matter of time humic mulch also. An unmowed prairie accumulated 4.5 tons of humic mulch per acre, while a similar prairie, mowed, had less than one ton (Dhysterhaus and Schmutz, 1947).

The influence of mulch on grasslands still is a point of controversy. Mulch aids in the infiltration of water and prevents erosion. In range management, the question is how much natural mulch is needed for the sustained yield of grass. Where mulch can accumulate, the grassland maintains itself; but in areas of little or no accumulation, retrogression sets in and the grassland deteriorates to weeds or mesquite. Some range ecologists, however, maintain that a heavy mulch results in decreased forage production, smaller root biomass, lower caloric value of the living shoots (Hadley and Kieckhefer, 1963), and affects the character and composition of grasslands by reducing understory plants (Weaver and Rowland, 1952).

The herb layer may vary from season to season and from year to year, depending upon the moisture supply. Essentially the layer consists of three or more strata, more or less variable in height, according to the grassland type (Coupland, 1950). Low-growing and ground-hugging plants, such as wild strawberry, cinquefoil, violets, dandelions and mosses, make up the first stratum. All of these become hidden, as the season progresses, beneath the middle and upper layers. The middle layer consists of shorter grasses and such herbs as wild mustard, coneflower, and daisy fleabane. The upper layer consists of tall grasses and forbs, conspicuous mostly in the fall.

Grassland types

Eastern grasslands

Grasslands in the eastern forest region are either tame or seral. In highly developed agricultural areas, tame grasslands are the major representatives of this vegetation type and their development and maintenance enabled a number of grassland species—grasshopper sparrows, dickcissels, bobolinks, meadowlarks, prairie deer mice, and cottontail rabbits—to expand their range.

Tame grasslands usually are more rank and dense than seral ones and must be managed to be maintained. Management consists of fertilization, mowing, plowing, and reseeding when needed, or at regular intervals if hay and pasture are a part of the crop rotation. Haying removes cover and exposes the ground surface to high solar radiation in late spring and early summer. Seral grasslands usually contain a mixture of native and tame grasses, especially on more fertile soils. Since much of the land is abandoned because of its natural or man-made infertility, these grasslands are dominated either by poverty grass, cinquefoil, and dewberry, or by broomsedge.

Tall-grass prairie

The tall-grass prairie occupies, or rather occupied, a narrow belt running north and south next to the deciduous forest. In fact, it was well developed within a region that could support forests. Oak-hickory forests did extend into the grassland along streams and rivers, on well-drained soils, sandy areas, and hills. Prairie fires often set by Indians in the fall stimulated a vigorous growth of grass and eliminated the encroaching forest. When the settlers eliminated fire, oaks invaded and overtook the grassland (Curtis, 1959).

Big bluestem was the dominant grass of moist soils and occupied the valleys of rivers and streams and the lower slopes of the hills. The foliage stood two to three feet tall and the flower stalks three to twelve feet, so high that cattle were hidden in the grass. A sod former, big bluestem occupied perhaps only 17 per cent of the soil surface, yet the foliage was so thick and spread so widely that few plants were able to grow in the understory. Associated with bluestem

Figure 15-3 *Buffalo, which once roamed the plains in countless numbers, epitomize the North American grasslands.* (Photo courtesy South Dakota Game and Fish Department.)

were a number of forbs, goldenrods, compass plants, snakeroot, and bedstraw. Although grasses dominated the biomass, they were not numerically superior. Studies on remnant prairies in Wisconsin (Curtis, 1959) show that legumes comprised 7.4 per cent of all species, grasses 10.2, composites 26.1. The high percentage of nitrogen-fixing legumes accounts in part for the annual production of 7000 to 9000 pounds of dry matter per acre (8500 kilos/hectare).

Drier uplands in the tall-grass country were dominated by the bunch-forming needlegrass, side-oats grama, and prairie dropseed. Like the lowland, the drier prairie contained many species other than grass. In Wisconsin, composites accounted for 27.5 per cent of all species, butterfly weed and legumes 4.6 per cent each, and grasses 13.7 (Curtis, 1959). The suggestion has been made that perhaps the xeric prairie might be more appropriately called "daisyland."

Like the forest, the tall-grass prairie, as well as other types, is a continuously changing series of species ranging from those best adapted to wet, poorly aerated soils, such as slough grass, through those plants represented by big bluestem that flourish on mesic soils of high fertility, to those such as blue grama and a whole host of colorful forbs that dominate the xeric sites. Interestingly, no important genera of grasses or forbs have species that are at their optimum in all sections of the continuum nor have all their species with an optimum at any one particular point on the gradient (Curtis, 1959).

Mixed prairie

West of the tall grass is the mixed-grass prairie (Fig. 15-3), in which mid-grasses occupy the lowland and short grasses the higher elevations. The mixed prairie, typical of the northern Great Plains, embraces largely the needlegrass–grama grass community, with needlegrass-wheatgrass dominating gently rolling soils of medium texture (Coupland, 1950). Because the mixed prairie is characterized by great annual extremes in precipitation, its aspect varies widely from year to year. In moist years midgrasses are prevalent, while in dry years short grasses and forbs are dominant. The grasses here are largely bunch and cool-season species, which begin their growth in early April, flower in June, and mature in late July and August.

Short-grass plains

South and west of the mixed prairie and grading into the desert is the short grass plain, a country too dry for most midgrasses. The short-grass plains reflect a climate where the rainfall is light and infrequent (10 to 17 inches in the west, 20 inches in the east), the humidity low, the winds high, and the evaporation rapid. Shallow rooted, the short grasses utilize moisture in the upper soil layers, beneath which is a permanent dry zone into which the roots do not penetrate. Sod-forming blue grama and buffalograss dominate the short-grass plains, accompanied by such midgrasses as western wheatgrass, side-oats grama, and little bluestem. On wet bottomlands, switchgrass, Canada wild rye, and western wheatgrass replace grama and buffalograss. Because of the dense sod, fewer forbs grow on the plains, but prominent among them is purple lupine.

Just as the tall-grass prairie was destroyed by the plow, so has much of the short-grass plains area been ruined by overgrazing and by plowing for wheat, which, because of low available moisture, the land could not support. Drought, lack of a tight sod cover, and winds turned much of the southern short-grass plains into the Dust Bowl, the recovery from which has taken years.

Desert grasslands

From southeastern Texas to southern Arizona and south into Mexico lies the desert grassland, similar in many respects to the short-grass plains except that triple-awn grass replaces buffalograss (Humphrey, 1958). Composed largely of bunch grasses, the desert grasslands are widely interspersed with other vegetation types, such as oak savanna and mesquite. The climate is hot and dry. Rain falls only during two seasons, summer (July and August) and winter (December to February) in amounts which vary from 12 to 16 inches in the western parts to 20 inches in the east; but evaporation is rapid, up to 80 inches per year. Vegetation puts on most of its annual growth in August. Annual grasses germinate and grow only during the summer rainy season, while annual forbs grow mostly in the cool winter and spring months.

Like the tall-grass prairies on the eastern rim of the grasslands, the desert grasslands on the west exist because of fires, which periodically swept across them and eliminated the mesquite, the cacti, and low trees. Without fire the desert grasslands, long before their discovery by white man, would have been a land of low trees with an understory of grasses and small shrubs.

Separated from the midcontinent grasslands by the Rocky Mountains is the California prairie, composed largely of needlegrass and bluegrass. A region of winter rains, much of the California prairie is either under cultivation or is overgrazed.

Grassland and grazing

Since the prairie and plains once held the greatest concentration of herbivores in the world, it was only natural that, once settled, the same lands should support a grazing economy. Scattered widely across the plains were herds of buffalo and pronghorned antelope, animals that rarely stayed on one area long enough to overgraze the range. Their numbers were checked by wolves, coyotes, and Indians, who depended on the buffalo for their way of life. But in a short eighty years after the white man settled the plains, the buffalo was gone, and replaced first by the longhorns and later by modern beef cattle. Fences were built and the ranges were overstocked. Grazing too early in the spring to allow the plants to grow sufficient food reserves for winter soon upset the natural balance of the range. The grasslands degenerated.

Unable to withstand heavy grazing, such highly palatable plants as big and little bluestem, prairie and tall dropseed, and nitrogen-fixing legumes and forbs disappear, often within two to three years. Freed from competition, bluegrass and side-oats grama, daisy fleabane and ironweed increase. If the prairie continues to deteriorate, the area is invaded by such plants as weedy wheatgrass, brome grass, little barley, and annual dropseeds (Voigt and Weaver, 1951, Curtis, 1959). Degeneration is not confined above ground; it goes on underground as well. The dry weight of roots of palatable grasses such as bluestem decreases up to 75 per cent as the grassland deteriorates from high-grade to low-grade pasture (Weaver, 1954). Grazing on desert grasslands increases the spread of mesquite because of the lessened competition from grass and because of seed dissemination by domestic stock (Humphrey, 1958). Protection from fire adds to this.

There are other consequences. Because no litter is added to the ground, mulch deteriorates and disappears. Water, once retained and fed into the soil, runs off the surface, taking the topsoil with it. Lacking moisture and nutrients, the original plants cannot maintain themselves, and the vegetative cover continues to decrease until only an erosion pavement remains (for a full discussion see Ellison, 1960). To maintain grasslands in good condition, at least one-third of the year's growth must be left to supply the annual addition to the mulch (Dyksterhuis and Schmutz, 1947).

Grasslands and drought

Dry weather for years at a time has always been a part of the plain's climate. Some grassland plants, such as blue grama, buffalograss, and even bluegrass survive short periods of drought by becoming dormant; others, such as big bluestem, survive by deep rooting. A number of grasses have a short growing season during the cool part of the year. Some prairie grasses respond quickly to moisture at the end of a dry spell. Buffalograss, although more sensitive to drought than blue grama, revives more quickly when the rains return. When drought is prolonged, however, the vegetational composition of the grassland changes. During the seven years of drought during the 1930s, little bluestem was reduced up to 75 per cent over much of its range, as were shallow-rooted forbs such as stiff sunflower and prairie coneflower (Coupland, 1958, 1959). Bare areas caused by their death were filled by the highly drought-resistant western wheatgrass, so successful a competitor for a scant supply of water that it caused the death of more mesic species. In places, the depleted grasslands, particularly those covered by dust, were invaded by such weedy plants as many-flowered aster and daisy fleabane (Robertson, 1939). Big bluestem persisted and needlegrass, side-oats grama, and bluegrass spread eastward into the prairie. In the short-grass prairies blue grama and buffalograss decreased from a basal area of 89 per cent to 22 per cent (Weaver and Albertson, 1956). Essentially the mesic tall-grass prairie became a mixed-grass prairie; the mixed changed to a short-grass plains and the latter became a dust bowl. When moisture returned to normal, the original communities were restored, except in the Dust Bowl, where so much of the original soil was lost through wind erosion in the droughts of the 1930s that the area has not yet fully recovered.

Grassland animal life

Seral or climax, grasslands support similar forms of life, although only in the prairies and plains do the distinctive grassland animals, such as buffalo, prairie chickens, and prairie dogs, live. Within the several strata of vegetation, the roots, ground layer, and herb cover, much of the animal life exists (Fichter, 1954). Invertebrates, particularly insects, which occur in an incredible number and variety of species, occupy all strata at some time during the year. Throughout the twelve months, there is a definite seasonal distribution. During winter, insect life is confined largely to the soil, litter, and grass crowns, where these organisms overwinter as pupae or eggs. Soil occupants in spring are chiefly earthworms and ants, the latter being the most prevalent. In some eastern meadows they make up to 26 per cent numerically of the insect populations (Wolcott, 1937). The ground and litter layer harbors the scavenger carabid beetles and predaceous spiders, the majority of which are hunters rather than web-builders, since supports for strong webs are limited. Life in the herbaceous layer varies as the strata become more pronounced from summer to fall. Here invertebrate life is most diverse and abundant. Homoptera, Coleoptera, Orthroptera, Diptera, Hymenoptera, Hemiptera, all are represented. The cicadellid leaf-hoppers rise in swarms as one walks through the grass. Frothy secretions surrounding young spittlebugs cling to plant stems during the summer months. Grasshoppers and field crickets, insect singers of the fields, are most abundant in late summer and early fall. Insect life reaches two highs during the year, a major peak in summer and a less well-defined one in the fall.

Mammals are the most conspicious vertebrates of the grasslands and the majority of these are herbivorous. On the grasslands evolved a large and rich ungulate fauna. The bison (Fig. 15-3) and antelope of North America were equaled in numbers only by the richer and more diverse ungulate fauna of the East African plains. Today herds of cattle have replaced the buffalo, and rodents and rabbits now have the distinction of being the most abundant native vertebrate herbivores, many of which are fossorial or burrowing.

Grassland animals all share some outstanding traits. Hopping or leaping is a common method of locomotion among grasshoppers, jack rabbits, and jumping mice. Long, strong hind legs enable these animals to rise above the level of the grass tops, where visibility is unimpeded. Speed, too, is well developed. Some of the world's fastest mammals, such as the pronghorned antelope, live in the grasslands. Because of the dense, thick grass and the lack of trees for singing perches, some grassland birds, especially the bobolink, meadowlarks, and horned larks have conspicuous flight songs, which advertise territory and attract a mate.

Across the prairies and plains a very close relationship exists between plants and animals. The two most typical and conspicuous plains animals are the prairie dog and the harvester ant, whose burrows and mounds dot the landscape. Both have several traits in common; they denude areas about the mound or burrow, they turn over and mix considerable quantities of soil, and they influence the nature of the grassland community. Occasionally prairie dogs will invade a clearing about an ant hill; and just as often the ants will establish hills on top of prairie-dog mounds (Koford, 1958).

Relationship of the prairie dogs to vegetation is very complex, yet typical of a range rodent's influence on plant life. Roundly condemned by many ranchers for the destruction of plant cover and reduction of grazing capacity, the prairie dog is regarded by others as instrumental in creating and maintaining the grassland. The virtues of the animal appear to change from one region of the plains to another. Since tall grass inhibits the activity of prairie dogs— they cannot see over it or move through it with ease—the range of the rodent once ended at the edge of the tall and midgrass prairie. When the tall grasses were destroyed by overgrazing and replaced by short grasses and forbs, the prairie dogs moved in, a symptom of range deterioration (Osborn and Allen, 1949). Over much of the plains, however, the prairie dog appears to be instrumental in the development and maintenance of a short-grass community, especially when they have some assistance from grazing animals—the buffalo of the past and the cattle of today.

By clipping shrubs, prairie dogs prevent the encroachment of woody vegetation into grasslands. They eliminate such annuals as annual brome and Russian thistle by feeding on them early in the growing season. This allows the perennial grasses and forbs to increase. Forbs, especially bigbract verbena, are common in dogtowns, and the mounds themselves are very favorable sites for annual forbs such as amaranths and scarlet globemallow. The ultimate effect of the prairie dogs is to produce a heterogeneous vegetation consisting of an abundance of short grasses, particularly buffalograss, a large variety of perennial and annual forbs, and a scarcity of shrubs. In mixed prairies, these animals alone can develop and maintain a short-grass community; but the prairie dogs can invade tall grass only after the vegetation has been reduced by overgrazing (Osborn and Allen, 1949).

The prairie dog has been poisoned wholesale over much of its range because of implied competition with cattle for forage. The real influence of these rodents on the reduction of forage has never been adequately determined (Koford, 1960), although some estimate that they may consume up to one-third of the forage produced (Fitch and Bentley, 1949).

Prairie dogs, pocket gophers, and other burrowing rodents affect other life in the plains. Plain cottontails appear to be most abundant where the burrowing rodents are plentiful, since the rabbits use the burrows for cover and nesting sites. Camelback crickets, beetles, and mites live in the relatively constant temperature and humidity of the rodent burrows. Deer mice feed on the seeds of annual forbs that grow on the mounds and seek the supply stored by harvester ants. Coyotes, bobcats, badgers, hawks, owls, and snakes live on rodents and rabbits. Elimination of rodents checks the growth of forbs, the preferred food of pronghorned antelope; and the open ground, once inhabited by deer mice, supports a thick growth of grass and a heavy mulch that are attractive to meadow mice. Deep litter appears to be an important feature of bobolink and savanna sparrow habitat (Tester and Marshall, 1961). Grasshopper populations seemingly inhibited by deep litter are highest in areas of light-to-moderate litter depth. The interrelationship between animals and litter depth needs much more investigation.

The grassland grouse, like the prairie dog and buffalo, once were abundant on the plains. In the tall-grass country on the edge of the eastern forest lived the sharp-tailed grouse. Its habitat is a combination of grassland and brushland, maintained chiefly by burning (Fig. 15-4). Once this land is protected from fire, the forest returns and the sharptails go (Hamerstrom et al., 1957). This is the high price being paid for overextended fire control and the reforestation of abandoned land. Prairie chickens, a subspecies of the eastern heath hen, occupy the grassland proper, although the ranges of the two grouse overlap (Fig. 15-5) and the prairie chicken utilizes some light shrub cover. At one time their low, rolling boom haunted the grasslands in spring, but overgrazing, plowing, and poor grassland management are destroying increasing amounts of prairie-chicken habitat. The species is in danger of following the heath hen into oblivion.

Scattered through the northern prairies and plains are small bodies of water —potholes, marshes, and sloughs, surrounded by cattails, bulrushes, and sedges. These potholes are highly attractive to ducks, coots, rails, gulls, and other water birds. In fact this area produces or produced the bulk of ducks in North America. Today a majority of these potholes have been and are being destroyed by drainage, reducing the waterfowl populations. This, like the plight of the prairie grouse, illustrates an ecological truism that without a place to live no species can exist.

Animal life in the seral and tame grasslands of eastern North America depends

Figure 15-4 *To maintain open grassland, fire is a useful and necessary tool. Here is a controlled burn area, where fire was used to destroy incoming woody growth. Note the unburned area in the foreground and the fireline, a plowed furrow.* (Photo courtesy Michigan Conservation Department.)

upon management by man for the maintenance of its habitat. But mowing, man's major management tool, also results in the destruction of habitat at a critical time of year. Nests of rabbits, mice, and birds are exposed at the height of the nesting season. Losses often are heavy from both mechanical injury and predation, although most species will remain on the area to complete or reattempt nesting activity. Increased popularity of grassland farming with emphasis on grass ensilage and hay further reduces the value of such lands for many species of bird and mammals. Grass for ensilage is cut early, at the very start of the breeding season, eliminating nesting cover and forcing most of the population elsewhere. This is one of the causes for the decline in numbers of such farm game species as bobwhite quail and cottontail rabbits.

Pasturelands, more often than not, are so badly overgrazed that they support little in the way of vertebrate life. The two most common inhabitants are the killdeer and horned lark. Rotation pastures, those broken down into small units that are grazed on a rotational basis, may support more grassland life, but this still needs to be determined.

Seral grassland, because of its infertility and plant cover of poverty grass and broomsedge, does not usually support as wide a variety of life as hay fields. Poverty grass–dewberry fields are inhabited by grasshopper sparrows, vesper sparrows, horned larks, and meadow mice, but deep-grass species, the meadowlark, bobolink, and Henslow sparrow, are few, if not entirely absent. Broomsedge fields contain grasshopper sparrows, meadowlarks, meadow mice, and cotton rats. Both seral types offer poor browse for herbaceous species

Figure 15-5 *An interspersion of brushy areas and grassland furnishes a habitat for both the sharp-tailed grouse and the prairie chicken. If the shrub growth increases, the prairie chicken will disappear. (Photo courtesy Michigan Conservation Department.)*

such as cottontail rabbits and deer, although deer do feed on young broomsedge sprouts in early spring. Otherwise these dominant grasses are unpalatable to cattle and to native herbivores alike.

SUMMARY

Grasslands, once covering extensive areas of the globe, including the midcontinent of North America, have shrunk to a fraction of their original size because of man's requirements for crop and grazing lands. With them also declined or disappeared many of the large grazing herbivores, replaced in part by cattle and sheep. Clearing of the forest, the planting of hayfields, and the development of seral grasslands on disturbed sites extended the range of some grassland animals into once-forested country. Seral or climax, grasslands consist of sod formers, bunch grasses, or both, the latter of which often provide excellent nesting sites for birds and small mammals. When grasslands are undisturbed by grazing, mowing, or burning, they accumulate a layer of mulch, which retains moisture, influences the character and composition of plant life, and provides shelter for some animals. Insects occur in great numbers and in a wide variety of species; and mammals are the conspicuous vertebrates of the grasslands. The prairie dog of the plains, now much reduced in its range, is typical of the burrowing animals common to grasslands. Because of its feeding and tunneling activities, the prairie dog prevents the encroachment of shrubs and annuals and allows the perennial grasses and forbs to increase. Among the birds, the prairie chicken epitomizes the grassland, but its rolling boom is almost silent, as overgrazing and plowing have destroyed its habitat. Even in the seral and managed grasslands of the forested regions, habitat for animals is declining as agricultural practices change and as more and more abandoned land reverts back to forest.

SUGGESTED FIELD ACTIVITIES

1. Quantitatively describe the grassland and old-field plant community, as suggested in Appendix C.
2. Observe the various strata within the grassland. What plants dominate the upper stratum? The lower?
3. Study the effects of grazing on the grassland, tame or native. Exclosures are useful here. Compare weights of plants outside and inside the exclosure. What is the per-cent utilization? What plants increase under grazing? What plants decrease?
4. Compare the animal life in grazed and ungrazed areas. Use sweep-net quadrats for insects; trap lines for small mammals. Observe larger animal life. Counts can be made of prairie-dog burrows and groundhog holes.
5. Dig a soil trench and observe the soil profile, the distribution of organic matter, and the distribution of plant roots.
6. Study the rise and decline of insect populations. Note the appearance of certain forms, the decline of others. Sample the soil invertebrate fauna.
7. The grassland (and old-field) ecosystem is well adapted for the study of community structure and function. The plant material can be sampled by the harvest method, the insects by sweep-net quadrats, the soil arthropods by extraction, earthworms by potassium-permanganate method. Set out trap lines for small mammals, and determine the density and composition of the breeding bird population. Study

287

the soil profile. Analyze and test the soil. Determine the biomass for each trophic level and construct a pyramid of biomass.

The heterotrophic metabolism in the litter can be estimated by placing a sample of litter in a plastic box containing a dish of sodium hydroxide. A control box contains the sodium hydroxide but no litter. As the carbon dioxide is produced by respiration of the animals, it will be absorbed as a carbonate by the sodium hydroxide. The amount of sodium hydroxide remaining after a period of time is determined by precipitating the carbonate as barium carbonate and then titrating, as is done in oxygen determination. Estimate carbon dioxide by substracting the sodium hydroxide remaining in the soil box from that in the control, where no carbon dioxide was being added.

CHAPTER **16**

Shrublands and the desert

Shrublands of forested eastern North America and the timbered mountains of the West are, like the grasslands of the midcontinent, seral, a stage in the land's progress back to forest. In the arid southwest and in the dry foothills of the mountains bordering the great American desert, shrubs are climax vegetation.

Seral shrub communities

Seral shrub communities have received scant attention. As a result, their ecology has never been properly studied.

On drier uplands, shrubs rarely exert complete dominance over herbs and grass. Instead the plants are scattered or clumped in grassy fields, the open areas between filled with the seedlings of forest trees, which in the sapling stage of growth occupy the same ecological position as tall shrubs. Typical are the hazelnut, forming thickets in places, sumacs, chokecherry, and shrub dogwoods. But on wet ground the plant community often is dominated by tall shrubs and contains an understory intermediate between that of a meadow

Figure 16-1 *A seral shrub community in winter on flat, poorly drained site. It is dominated by alder and red-twigged dogwood. The spruce were planted, but survival is low and growth poor because of a combination of shrub competition and poor soil drainage.* (Photo by author.)

and a forest (Curtis, 1959). In northern regions the common tall shrub community found along streams and around lakes is the alder thicket, composed of alder, or alder and a mixture of other species such as willow and red-osier dogwood. Alder thickets are relatively stable and remain for some time before being replaced by the forest (Fig. 16-1). Out of the alder country, the shrub carr community (carr is an English name for wet-ground shrub communities) occupies the low places. Dogwoods are some of the most important species in the carr. Growing with them are a number of willows, which as a group usually dominate the community.

The shrub community contains an interesting collection of animal life, many occupants being species that are common to the edge of the forest. Alder flycatchers, red-winged blackbirds, and swamp sparrows are typical of alder thickets. And where shrubs meet grass fields or forest, there one finds quail, ruffed grouse, and cottontail rabbits.

Shrub thickets are valued as food and cover for game, and many shrubs, such as hawthorn, blackberry, sweetbriar, and dogwoods, rank high as game food. However the over-all value of different types of shrub cover, its composition, quality, and the minimum amounts needed, have never been assessed. There is some evidence (Egler, 1953; Niering and Egler, 1955) that even where the forest is the normal end of succession, shrubs can form a stable community that will persist for many years. If incoming tree growth is removed either by selective spraying or by cutting, the shrubs eventually form a closed community resistant to further invasion by trees. This could have wide application to power line rights-of-way.

Chaparral

In the semiarid country of western North America, as well as in regions bordering the Mediterranean, in southern Australia, and middle Chile, is a community of xeric broadleaf, evergreen shrubs and dwarf trees not over 2.5 meters (8 feet) tall. In North America this community is called chaparral and in the Mediterranean region, maqui. It is characteristic of regions where winters are mild and rainy and the summers are long, hot, and dry. For the most part an understory is lacking and the ground litter, highly inflammable, ranges from light to heavy. Heavy seeders, many plant species of the chapar-

290

ral require the heat and the scarring action of fire to induce germination. For centuries periodic fires have roared through the chaparral, clearing away the old growth, making way for the new, and recycling nutrients through the ecosystem again. When man came to the chaparral, he changed the fire situation. Either he attempted to overcontrol fire in this type of vegetation, in which complete exclusion is impractical, thus seeding real disasters, or he allowed the chaparral to overburn. In the absence of fire, chaparral grows tall and dense and yearly adds more leaves and twigs to those already on the ground. During the dry season the shrubs, even though alive, will nearly explode when ignited. Once set on fire by lightning or man, an inferno follows. Sooner or later this is bound to happen in the chaparral.

Once fire swept, the land returns either to lush green sprouts coming up from buried root crowns or to grass, if a seed source is nearby. The grass and the vigorous young sprouts are excellent food for deer (Taber and Dasmann, 1958), sheep, and cattle. But as the sprout growth matures, the chaparral becomes even more dense, the canopy closes, the litter accumulates, and the stage is set for another fire.

In lowlands near the grasslands, burned-over chaparral can revert to grass, which can be maintained by periodic controlled burns. At high elevations, where the pine forest begins, hot fires in the chaparral and pine result in the destruction of the forest and the encroachment of chaparral into higher country.

The vegetation of the chaparral varies with geographical location, with altitude, and with the direction of slope. North slopes in California chaparral are cloaked with live oak, deer brush, California laurel, and manzanita. The south slopes are covered with chamise and buck brush (Taber and Dasmann, 1958). In heavy chaparral the south-facing slopes have little herbaceous growth and scant litter. North slopes have an accumulation of leaves and a scattering of understory ferns. As altitude increases, north-slope species creep around to the east and west and even to southern exposures. In Arizona the north-facing slopes at low elevations are covered by chaparral, the south-facing slopes with grassland and desert shrub (Swank, 1959). At higher elevations the north-slope vegetation changes to pine, the south slope to chaparral. Arizona chaparral includes shrub oak, mahogany, manzanita, and desert ceanothus. The chaparral is mule deer country, as well as the haunt of wood rats, bobcats, brush rabbits, and mountain and California quail.

Desert

Climax shrub communities are confined mostly to arid regions, the deserts, and they include a varied assortment of life well adapted to exist in a climate nearly void of rain.

Deserts occur in two distinct belts about the earth, one confined roughly about the Tropic of Cancer, the other about the Tropic of Capricorn. Deserts are defined by geographers as land where evaporation exceeds rainfall. No specific rainfall can be used as a criterion, but deserts may range from extremely arid ones to those with sufficient moisture to support a variety of life.

Deserts are the result of several forces. One that leads to the formation of deserts and the broad climatic regions of the world is the movement of air

291

masses over the earth. As the earth spins, it produces gigantic air swirls. Hot air over the equator rises to form an equatorial zone of low pressure. The rising air flows away to both sides and descends earthward in two subtropical zones as high-pressure areas. North and south of these are two more zones of ascending air and low pressure and then the polar regions of descending air and low pressure. As air rises, it cools and drops its moistures; but as air descends, it warms up and picks up moisture, drying out the land. The high-pressure areas also alter the course of rain. The high-pressure cell off the coast of California and Mexico deflects rainstorms moving south from Alaska to the east and prevents moisture from reaching the southwest. In winter, high-pressure areas move southward, allowing winter rains to reach southern California and parts of the North American desert.

The turning of the earth produces the ocean currents. As cold polar waters move from the Arctic and the Antarctic toward the equator, and in places contact the edges of continents, they are augmented by upwelling from frigid ocean depths. Winds blowing over the cold waters become cold also; they carry very little moisture, only fog and mist, and produce little rain. Thus the west coast of California and Baja California, the Namib desert on coastal southwest Africa, and the coastal edge of the Atacama in Chile may be shrouded in mist, yet remain extremely dry.

Mountain ranges also play a role in desert formation by causing a rain shadow on their lee side. The High Sierras and the Cascade Mountains intercept rain from the Pacific and help maintain the arid conditions of the North American desert. And the low eastern highlands of Australia effectively block the southeast trade winds from the interior of that continent. Other deserts, such as the Gobi and the interior of the Sahara, are so remote from the source of oceanic moisture that all the water has been wrung from the winds by the time they reach those regions.

Man, too, has had a hand in the creation of new deserts through poor land management, especially around the periphery of existing desert areas. Virgin lands, even in dry climates, are able to support some vegetation. The roots of trees, shrubs, and grasses tap the deeper water supply and bind the soil, but once these are eliminated, through fire, grazing, and cultivation, the destructive forces of erosion are loosened. Fires are set to clear semiarid land for cultivation or to encourage the growth of grasses and eliminate the trees. Then, overcultivated and overgrazed, the land is exposed to wind and water erosion. Exhausted from cultivation, the lowlands are abandoned to grazing, first by cattle, then later by sheep and goats. Cultivation moves up to the high lands, and here the same cycle is repeated. Eventually the destruction is total. The vegetation and top soil are gone; bedrock is exposed; the land has reached the point of no return. In this way, the deserts are marching south through Africa into the African plains, and similarly they are encroaching on the semiarid grasslands of North America. The same land-use pattern is thought to have played a part in the downfall of the Mayan civilization and the decline of Greece and Rome. The once-rich lands of the southern Mediterranean that supported a great civilization are now barren, rock-filled, and impoverished. (For further discussion see Lowdermilk, 1953; Dale and Carter, 1955; Thomas, 1956; Stamp, 1961.)

In recent years man has attempted, with great success, to bring some deserts back into production. But in doing so he is tapping reservoirs of water deep beneath the desert floor. Such "mining" of water is filled with danger, for once this water, like mineral wealth, is gone, it is irreplaceable. Thus the short-term agriculture and human occupancy of the desert may end with an even more sterile environment.

In spite of differences in physical appearances, all deserts have in common low rainfall, high evaporation (seven to fifty times as much as precipitation), and a wide daily range in temperature, from hot by day to cool by night. Low humidity allows up to 90 per cent of solar insolation to penetrate the atmosphere and heat the ground. At night the desert yields the accumulated heat of the day back to the atmosphere. Rain, when it falls, is often heavy and, unable to soak into the dry earth, rushes off in torrents to basins below.

The topography of the desert, unobscured by vegetation, is stark and, paradoxically, partially shaped by water. Unprotected, the soil erodes easily during violent storms and is further cut away by the wind. Alluvial fans stretch away from eroded, angular peaks of more resistant rocks. They join to form deep expanses of debris, the *bajadas*. Eventually the slopes level off to low basins, or *playas,* which receive waters that rush down from the hills and water-cut canyons, or *arroyos*. These basins hold temporary lakes after the rains, but water soon evaporates and leaves behind a dry bed of glistening salt.

The aridity of the desert may seem inimical to life, yet in the deserts life does exist, surprisingly abundant, varied, and well adapted to withstand or circumvent the scarcity of water.

The ways by which plants and animals of arid regions meet the water problem have been discussed earlier (Chap. 4). Essentially plants either are drought evaders or drought resistors. The evaders persist as seeds, ready to sprout and grow when moisture and temperature are favorable, to flower, produce seeds, and die. Drought resistors have evolved means of storing water, locating underground water, or reducing needs by shedding leaves and by reducing leaf size to cut down on transpiration. This results in plants peculiar in habit and structure.

In sharp contrast to the forest, the struggle in the desert is not one of plant against plant for light and space, but one of all plants for moisture. Since little layering exists in the desert plant community, light is not a problem. Because moisture is limited, plants are mostly low; and because of competition for moisture, the plants are widely spaced.

Desert shrubs fall into two broad groups, woody-stemmed and soft, brittle-stemmed. Woody-stemmed shrubs, embracing such species as creosote bush, acacias, and cassias, are moderately branched and form buds at the termination of their seasonal growth. The soft, brittle-stemmed shrubs—sagebrush, shadscale, and burro bush—possess indeterminate growth and do not form resting buds. These are not confined to the American desert proper but grow in the semiarid grasslands on its periphery.

In the matrix of shrubs grows a wide assortment of other plants, the yuccas, cacti, small trees, and ephemerals. In the southwestern American desert large succulents rise above the shrub level and change the aspect of the desert all out of proportion to their numbers (Fig. 16-2). Like forest trees and prairie grasses, most desert species grow their best in certain topographical situations. The giant saguaro, the most massive of all cacti, grows on the bajadas of the Sonoran desert with other smaller, brilliant-flowered cacti. Other plants—ironwood, smoke

Figure 16-2 Saguaro domi-nates the aspect of this desert. Note the water-shaped topography. (Photo courtesy Arizona Game and Fish Department.)

tree, palo verde—grow best along the banks of intermittent streams, not so much because of their moisture requirements but because their hard-coated seeds must be scraped and bruised by the grinding action of sand and gravel during flash floods before they can germinate.

The ephemeral, or annual-flowering, plants supply seasonal brilliance to the desert. Since they grow only when moisture is adequate, these plants do not possess the leathery leaves, water-storage organs, or other adaptations to resist desiccation. They survive from one favorable period to another as seeds. They flourish best on sandy soils, for here the moisture easily penetrates the soil and the ground warms rapidly, favoring germination of seeds.

Although the annuals of the southwestern American desert are in so many ways similar to the annuals of more humid climates, they differ in one highly specialized way, the time of germination. This must correspond with periods of adequate rainfall if the population is to persist. There are two periods of flowering in the American desert, after the winter rains come in from the Pacific northwest and after the summer rains move up from the southeast out of the Gulf of Mexico. Some species flower only after the winter rains, others after the summer, while a few flower during both seasons.

Why these plants respond so unerringly to moisture has been the subject of considerable research (Went, 1955). Out of this has come the discoveries that none of the seeds would germinate unless the surface soil received an equivalent of one-half to one inch of rain and that the seeds have on their coats a water-soluble growth inhibitor, which is washed away by a sufficient amount of percolating water. Thus the seeds are prevented from germinating after a trivial shower. The temperatures likewise are critical. Each species of desert annual has a definite and rather narrow limit of tolerance and will not grow in any quantity except when the moisture and temperatures are within these limits. For this reason the winter and summer annuals can be divided according to the temperatures at which they germinate and at which they survive. For winter annuals to germinate the first rains have to be well over 10 millimeters and preferably over 20, and the night temperatures have to be above freezing.

The desert is not the same everywhere. Differences in moisture, temperature, soil drainage, alkalinity, and salinity result either in the variation of dominants or in different groups of associated plants. Basically, the North American desert can be divided into two parts, the northern cool desert—the Great Basin—and the hot desert of the southwest—the Mohave, the Sonoran, and the Chihuahuan. The two, however, grade one into the other.

Sagebrush is the dominant plant of the cool desert, together with saltbush, shadscale, hop sage, winterfat, and greasewood. The plant communities of the Great Basin are simple, consist of essentially the same life forms, and form nearly the same stands of monotonous gray and gray-green for miles.

Hot deserts are dominated mostly by creosote bush accompanied by bur sage or burro bush. Together they often form a monotonous uniform growth broken only in areas of favorable moisture and soil by tall growths of acacia, saguaro, palo verde, and mesquite (Fig. 16-3). Of the hot deserts the Mohave, transitional between the Great Basin and the Sonoran, is the poorest in species, has the simplest vegetational composition, and contains some species in common with the Great Basin. Mostly it is a rolling plain covered with creosote bush and sagebrush, its monotony broken by volcanic mountains and the curious Joshua trees, a spine-studded yucca found nowhere else.

Figure 16-3 Saguaro–mesquite–bur sage community. (Photo courtesy Arizona Fish and Game Department.)

Figure 16-4 *Palo verde–saguaro community. Rainfall here is about 14 to 16 inches. In the distance, the east-facing slopes are covered with chaparral.* (Photo courtesy Arizona Game and Fish Department.)

South of the Mohave is the Sonoran desert, which contains a richly diversified vegetation of shrubs, trees, and succulent cacti (Shreve, 1951). Here the vegetation is the most dense of the American desert, the life forms—from small drought-deciduous trees to evergreen semishrubs and succulents—are most numerous, the number of species is the greatest, and the height most diverse. Although the physiognomy and structure of the vegetation throughout this desert is very similar, the dominants and subdominants differ. And although the life forms and structure are nearly the same, the floral composition is different. On higher slopes where more moisture is available grow the deep red-flowered ocotillo and the green-barked palo verde (Fig. 16-4). The drier plains are occupied by low-growing flowers, jatrophos, brittle bush, acacia, and organ-pipe cactus, while in the low washes smoke trees grow.

Within the Sonoran desert grows the richest variety of ephemerals, for here exists a variety of conditions not found elsewhere in the desert country. Many of these and other small plants grow in close association with or beneath the shade of old trees and shrubs, where conditions produced by an accumulation of wind-blown soil, organic debris of leaves, and broken plant stems about the bases of the large plants are more favorable for their germination and growth (Muller, 1953).

The Chihuahuan desert, which extends into Mexico, presents a different aspect. Intermediate between the Great Basin and the Sonoran, this desert is characterized by long-barreled cacti, yuccas, candelilla, and guayule. On the valley floors grow large patches of colo del zorro, a foxtail-like grass; and on the wind-ripple gypsum dunes a vigorous, aromatic, sumac squawbush, once used by Indians for baskets.

Animal life

Under a harsh and shimmering sun, the deserts may appear void of animal life, yet animals do thrive there. Like plants, desert animals are either drought resistors or drought evaders. Drought evaders, like the ephemeral plants, make a sudden and dramatic appearance. For eight or nine months, perhaps even several years, eggs of insects and other invertebrates and insect pupae lie dormant. When the rains arrive and plants flourish, the deserts swarm with insects—crickets, grasshoppers, ants, bees and wasps, butterflies, moths, and beetles. Young bees emerge from underground cells at the very time the particular flowers on which they feed are in flower. Tiny shrimp appear in temporary ponds and lakes only after sufficiently heavy rains have fallen to form them, perhaps only several times in a century. Amphibians, like the spadefoot toad, also make a brief appearance during the periods of winter and summer rains. Spadefoots estivate in underground cells lined with a gelatinous substance for eight or nine months of the year, appear when rainfall saturates the soil, move to the nearest puddle, mate, and lay eggs, from which young tadpoles hatch in a day or two. These tadpoles rapidly mature and metamorphose into functioning adults capable of digging their own retreat in which to estivate until the next rainy period. Birds nest during the rainy season when food is most abundant for the young. If extreme drought develops during the breeding season, some birds do not reproduce. Among some desert birds, the endocrine control of reproduction seems to depend upon rainfall rather than upon day length (Keast, 1959). A few birds, such as the swift, poorwill, and Allen and Anna's hummingbirds, become torpid when food is scarce (Bartholomew, Howell, and Cade, 1957). Small rodents, such as the kangaroo or pocket mice, estivate during periods of most severe drought. Not only does this prolong the period during which the animal can live on energy reserves, but it also achieves a considerable saving of water, since the reduced ventilation of the lungs lowers the pulmonary evaporation of water. In addition, the lower body temperature reduces the amount of water needed to saturate the expired air (Schmidt-Nielsen, 1964).

But the desert also contains many animals that are active the year round, all of which have evolved ways of circumventing aridity and heat by physiological adaptations or by feeding and activity habits. By restricting their activity to the cooler parts of the day, early morning, late evening and night, these animals escape the heat of the desert. It is no coincidence that most desert animals are

297

nocturnal. The most conspicuous daytime animals of the desert are lizards, and even they move from the sun to the shade of shrubs, rocks, or underground rodent burrows. Snakes, much less abundant than lizards, are active by night. Rodents are chiefly burrowing and spend the hot day underground, where the temperatures may be 70 degrees Fahrenheit lower than on the sun-baked surface. During extremely dry periods the kangaroo rat seals its burrow by day, which keeps its chamber moist.

This rodent, kangaroolike, with long tail and powerful hind legs—which has its ecological counterparts in the jerboas and gerbils of Africa and the Middle East, and the marsupial kangaroo mice and pitchi-pitchi of Australia—lives all year without drinking water. It feeds on dry seeds and dry plant material even when succulent green plants are available. The kangaroo rat obtains its water from its own metabolic processes and from hygroscopic water present in its food. To conserve water, the animal remains in its burrow during the day. It possesses no sweat glands, and because the temperature of its expired air is low, it has a lower evaporation rate from its lungs relative to O_2 uptake than is found in larger mammals. Its urine is highly concentrated (24 per cent urea and salt two times the concentration of sea water) and its feces have a low water content (Schmidt-Nielsen, 1952, 1964).

A similar method of water conservation is found among the desert lizards. They possess the ability to precipitate uric acid from urine that, as it leaves the kidney, has the same percentage of urea as the lizard's blood. The urine held in the cloaca is changed to an uric acid precipitate. Since the fluid left has a lower concentration of urea than the blood, the water is reabsorbed osmotically (Schmidt-Nielsen, 1964). Highly concentrated urine, relatively dry feces—the water being reabsorbed back into the body—and the utilization of metabolic water are common water-conservation measures among desert animals.

The large ears of such desert mammals as the kit fox and the jack rabbit may serve to reduce the need of water evaporation to regulate body heat. The ears may function as efficient radiators to the cooler desert sky, which on clear days may have a radiation temperature of 25 degrees centigrade below that of the the animal (Schmidt-Nielsen, 1964). By seeking shade where the ground temperatures are low and solar radiation is screened out, by sitting in depressions, where radiation from hot ground surface is obstructed, the jack rabbit through the two large ears (400 cm²) could radiate 5 kcal per day. This is equal to one-third of the metabolic heat produced in a 3-kg rabbit. Such a radiation loss alone may be sufficient to take care of the necessary heat loss without much loss of water.

Most desert insects are abundant only during the rainy period, when their emergence is timed with the flowering of desert plants. But some are active throughout the year, the most notable of these being the harvester ant, which lives on seeds gathered from the desert floor and stored in underground graneries. During periods of drought these ants in the California desert gather mainly the seeds of two kinds of plants, wooly plantain and comb bur. When the winter rains come and the annual plants flower and seed, the ants gather the seeds of these other plants and ignore for the time being the seeds of plantain and the comb bur. But when the dry season returns, the ants again exploit their staple food source. This utilization of a constant food supply enables the insect to remain active through the desert year.

SUMMARY

In spite of the harsh environment, life in the desert is abundant and varied. The plants and animals have evolved ways to circumvent aridity and high temperatures. Desert animals avoid the heat by becoming nocturnal in habit, by seeking shady places, or by spending the day in underground burrows. Drinking water they obtain from succulent plants, from the blood and body fluids of their prey, or from the metabolic oxidation of carbohydrates and fats. Further water conservation involves reabsorption of water from urine and feces. Plants evade aridity by living through the dry period as seeds, which sprout when sufficient rainfall arrives, by storing water in the plant body, or by shedding leaves and possessing small leaves that reduce transpiration. Shrubs dominate desert plant life; and changes in shrub composition over the various deserts give each its own distinctive character. In North America there are two major types of deserts, the cool desert of the Great Basin, dominated by sagebrush, and the hot desert of the southwest, dominated by creosote bush and cacti. Deserts occupy about one-seventh of the land surface of the earth and are largely confined to a worldwide belt between the Tropic of Cancer and the Tropic of Capicorn. Deserts are largely the result of the climatic patterns of the earth, as well as the locations of mountain ranges and the remoteness of land areas from sources of oceanic moisture. For centuries man has lived on the periphery of the desert, and few peoples have made it their home. Today modern man is looking to the desert as potential agricultural land and a place to live. Settlement of the desert is being achieved by tapping deep but unreplenishable water reserves beneath the desert floor. Successful though such attempts may be now, the danger exists that man's occupancy of the desert may so "mine" the area of water and nutrients that even more arid conditions will result. Before deserts are exploited, man should first understand their ecology, about which we know so little.

SUGGESTED FIELD ACTIVITIES

There are two general types of deserts in North America, the cold and the hot. Somewhat different approaches will be needed in introductory studies of each.

Cold desert

1. Sample the vegetation by the line-intercept or plotless method.
2. Determine the life forms of plants.
3. Investigate the relationship of plant distribution to the salt content of the soil.
4. Excavate a few sample areas and note the distribution of plant roots.
5. Observe animal signs. Sample the animal population. Determine the composition and density of the breeding bird population on a 40-acre area.

Hot desert

1. For large shrubs and cacti, obtain data on density. Because of the rather regular spacing, use the random-pairs method.
2. Study the low-growing vegetation by the line-intercept method.
3. Excavate and note the distribution of roots in a sample area.
4. Map the vegetation in relation to slope, moisture, drainage basins, etc. From this, draw conclusions about the distribution of desert plants.
5. Note the animal life on the study area, as suggested under the cold desert.

299

6. Both deserts offer an opportunity for the determination of net production. Little work of this nature has been done in the desert ecosystem.

Shrub communities

1. Sample the community by the line transect method or the variable plot method. If the former method is used, base the cover on a projection of the crown to the ground.

2. Sample the understory vegetation. Are the plants characteristic or are they remnants of past communities?

3. Compare the shrub cover and composition for different slope exposures and altitudes. This is significant in high mountain country and in chaparral.

4. Observe animal signs, especially deer browse. Choose three or four species commonly browsed by deer, and then locate several transects across the area and establish 100 observation points. At each point note whether the closest plant of each of the key species is browsed or unbrowsed. When finished, compute the average percentage that each key species has been browsed. Seventy-five to ninety per cent indicates heavy browsing; over ninety per cent indicates overbrowsing.

5. Study the insect life, small mammals, and birds. Determine the density and composition of the breeding bird population on a 15- to 20-acre area.

6. Estimate the net production of the shrub community (see Appendix C).

CHAPTER 17

The forest

When the first settlers came ashore at Jamestown and Plymouth Rock, they faced the eastern edges of one of the greatest expanses of forest in the world. This was the eastern deciduous forest, which extended from the Atlantic coast inland to the prairie and from southern Canada south to the Gulf of Mexico. It contained, quite unknown to the settlers, hundreds of new species of trees. In fact in the coves of the southern Appalachians grew more varieties of trees than in all of Europe. The woods were thick and deep, so dense that, as someone said, a squirrel could travel from the Atlantic to the Mississippi without touching the ground. This was an exaggeration, for there were innumerable openings, the result of fires, Indian or lightning set, and of Indian settlements and their cultivated patches of corn and squash and orchards. Yet the statement does convey something of the vastness of the eastern forest.

The eastern forest consists of a number of forest community types, which intergrade into one another. The northern segment of the deciduous forest complex is the hemlock–white pine–northern hardwoods forest, which occupies southern Canada, and extends southward through northern United States and along the high Appalachians into North Carolina and Tennessee. Beech,

301

sugar maple, basswood, yellow birch, black cherry, red oak, and white pine are the chief components. White pine was once the outstanding tree of the forest. But since most of it was cut before the turn of the century, it now grows only as a successional tree on abandoned land and as scattered trees through the forest. On relatively flat, glaciated country with its deep, rich soil grow two somewhat similar forests, the beech–sugar maple forest, restricted largely to southern Indiana and central Minnesota and east to western New York; and the sugar maple–basswood forest, found from Wisconsin and Minnesota south to northern Missouri. South of this is the extensive central hardwood forest. The central hardwood can be divided into three major types. The first is the cove, or mixed mesophytic, forest, which consists of an extremely large number of species, dominated by yellow poplar. This forest, which reaches its best development on the northern slopes and deep coves of the southern Appalachians, is one of the most magnificent in the world. Much of its original grandeur has been destroyed by high-grading and fire, but even in second- and third-growth stands, its richness is apparent. On more xeric sites, the southern slopes and drier mountains, grows the oak-chestnut forest. The chestnut, killed by blight, has been replaced by additional oaks. The western edge of the central hardwoods in the Ozarks and the forests along the prairie river systems are dominated by oak and hickory.

The southern pine forests of the coastal plains of the South Atlantic and Gulf States are considered part of the temperate, deciduous forest, since they represent a seral rather than a final stage. Unless maintained by fire and cutting, these forests are succeeded by such hardwoods as oak, hickory, and magnolia. Magnolia and live oak dominate the climax forest of the southern Gulf States and much of Florida.

North of the eastern deciduous forest is the continent-wide belt of coniferous forest, which extends from New England, northern New York, and southern Canada north to the tundra, westward to the Pacific, and southward through the Rockies and Sierras into Mexico. The northern coniferous forest starts out as pine and hemlock mixed with hardwoods, a gradient or ecotone of the northern hardwood forest. Eastern hemlock, jack pine, red pine, white pine, and white cedar are characteristic. Originally the pine forests were most highly developed about the Great Lakes, but they were destroyed by exploitative logging in the 1880s and 1900s. The coniferous forest extends southward from New England through the high Appalachians. Here at high elevations the spruce and fir, the major forest type of the north woods, end. In the southern Appalachians, red spruce and Frasier fir dominate; but north, in the Adirondacks and White Mountains on into Canada and across the continent to Alaska, white spruce, black spruce, and balsam fir form the matrix of the forest. Occupying, for the most part, glaciated land, the northern coniferous forest is a region of cold lakes, bogs, rivers, and alder thickets. This same boreal forest encircles the northern part of the globe.

South of Alaska, the coniferous forest differs from the northern boreal forest, both floristically and ecologically. The reasons for the change are climatic and topographic. Moisture-laden winds move inland from the Pacific, meet the barrier of the Coast Range, and rise abruptly. Suddenly cooled by this upward thrust into the atmosphere, the moisture in the air is released as rain and snow in amounts up to 635 cm (250 inches). During the summer when the winds shift to the northwest, the air is cooled over chilly northern seas. Though the rainfall is low, the cool air brings in heavy fog, which collects on the forest foliage and drips to the ground to add perhaps 127 cm (50 inches) more of moisture. This land of superabundant moisture, high humidity, and warm temperatures supports the "temperate rain forest," a community of lavish vegetation dominated by western hemlock, western red cedar, Sitka spruce, and Douglas fir. Further south, where the precipitation still is high, grows the redwood forest, occupying a strip of land about 730 km (450 miles) long.

The air masses that dropped their moisture on the western slopes of the Coast range descend down the eastern slopes, heat up, and absorb moisture, creating the conditions that produce the Great Basin deserts already discussed. The same air rises up the western slopes of the Rockies, cools, and drops moisture again, although far less than it did on the Coast Range. Here in the Rockies develop several coniferous forest associations, influenced to a great extent by elevation. At high elevation, where the winters are long and snow is heavy, grows the subalpine forest, characterized by Engelmann spruce, alpine fir, and white-barked and bristle-cone pines. Lower elevations support Douglas fir and ponderosa pine. The aridity-tolerant ponderosa pine more often than not has an understory of grass and shrubs.

Forests similar to those of the Rocky Mountains grow in the Sierras and Cascades. Alpine forests there consist largely of mountain hemlock, red fir, lodgepole pine. At lower elevations grow the huge sugar pine, incense cedar, and the largest tree of all, the giant sequoia, which grows only in scattered groves on the west slopes of the California Sierras.

A deciduous seral stage, common to much of the western coniferous forest and the northern coniferous forest as well, is the aspen parkland, supporting trembling aspen, the most widespread tree of North America. The aspen is an important segment of the coniferous forest, for it is utilized by deer, grouse, bear, snowshoe hare, and beaver.

Contrasting sharply with the temperate forest vegetation of North America is the tropical rain forest of Central and South America. The rain forest or some variation of it—the monsoon forest, the evergreen savanna forest, the montane rain forest—forms a worldwide belt about the equator. The largest continuous rain forest is found in the Amazon Basin of South America. West and Central Africa and the Indo-Malayan region are other major areas of tropical rain forest. Although the rain forest is remote and incompletely studied (see Richard, 1952; Cain and Castro, 1959), its contrasts and similarities to other American forests deserve some comment.

The rain forest, so-called because of its constant high humidity, grows in a land where seasonal changes are minimal. The mean annual temperature is about 26° C (79° F), the mean minimium rarely goes below 25° C (77° F) and heavy rainfall occurs through much of the year. Under such perpetual mid-summer conditions, plant activity continues uninterrupted, resulting in very luxurious growth. Tree species number in the thousands, none of which are usually dominant and the majority of which are represented by a very few individuals. Communities with single dominants usually are limited to certain soils and to areas of particular combinations of soils and topography. The tree trunks are straight, smooth, and slender, often buttressed, and reach 25 to 30 meters (82 to 98 ft) before expanding into large, leathery, simple leaves. Climb-

303

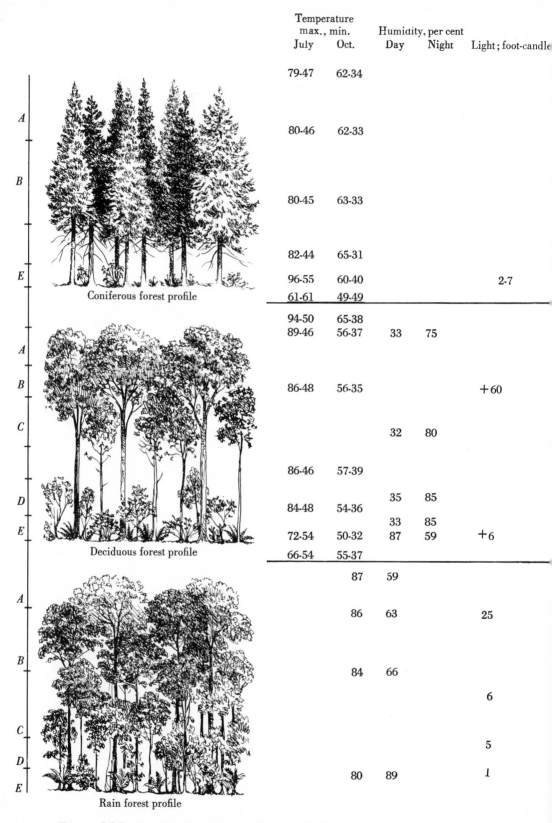

Figure 17-1 *Stratification of a coniferous, deciduous, and tropical rain forest. For details see text.* (SOURCES: Coniferous forest: Atkins, 1957; Fowells, 1948; Vezina, 1961. Deciduous forest: Christy, 1952; McCormick, 1959. Rain forest: Davis and Richards, 1933.)

ing plants, the lianas, long, thick, and woody, hang from trees like cables, and epiphytes grow on the trunks and limbs. The undergrowth of the dark interior is sparse and consists of shrubs, herbs, and ferns. Litter decays so rapidly that the clay soil, more often than not, is bare. The tangled vegetation, popularly known as the jungle, is a second-growth forest that develops where the primary forest has been despoiled.

Stratification of the forest

Because of the variety of life forms of forest vegetation, forests are often highly stratified (Fig. 17-1). The mixed tropical rain forests consist of five layers above the soil. The uppermost, or A, stratum, consists of trees 35 to 42 meters (116 to 138 feet), whose deep crowns rise above the rest of the forest to form a discontinuous canopy. Below this is the B stratum, also discontinuous, of lower trees 20 meters (66 feet) high. Strata A and B are not clearly separated from one another and together form an almost complete canopy. The lowest tree stratum, C, is continuous and is often the deepest layer and, unlike A and B, very well defined. The D layer, usually poorly developed in the dense shade, consists of shrubs, young trees, tall herbs, and ferns. The E, or ground layer is made up of tree seedlings and low herbaceous plants.

Highly developed, uneven, aged, deciduous forests usually consist of four strata (Fig. 17-2). The A, or upper canopy, consists of dominant or codominant trees and corresponds to the A and B layers of the tropical rain forest. Beneath this and corresponding to the C layer of the rain forest is the lower tree canopy. Below is the D, or shrub layer. The ground (E) or field layer consists of herbs, ferns, and mosses. Its composition varies with the seasons, from spring with the trilliums and hepaticas to the fall with its asters and goldenrods.

Figure 17-2   *Well-developed stratification of a deciduous forest as seen from a manmade clearing.* (Photo by author.)

Figure 17-3 *The interior of a dense, even-aged, deciduous forest often has a poorly developed stratum beneath the canopy.* (Photo by author.)

Even-aged stands, the results of fire, clear-cut logging, and other disturbances often have poorly developed strata beneath the canopy because of the dense shade. The low tree and shrub strata are thin and the ground layer often is poorly developed, except in small, open areas (Fig. 17-3). Stratification in coniferous forests is somewhat similar to that in even-aged deciduous stands, for here too the lower strata are poorly developed and the ground layer consists largely of ferns, mosses, and very few herbs (Fig. 17-4). However, old-stand pitch

Figure 17-4 *The interior of a virgin stand of red spruce on the Monongahela National Forest, Pocahontas County, West Virginia.*

pine may have three strata, an upper canopy, a shrub layer of blueberries, and a thin herbaceous layer. Jack pine may have four strata: an upper canopy of jack pine, a lower tree canopy of incoming hardwoods, a low shrub and tall herb layer, and a low herb layer of grasses and sedges.

Environmental stratification

A forest is like a blanket over the land, the top of which receives the full impact of the wind, rain, and sun. The various strata, determined in part by light and moisture, modify the environment from the forest canopy to the forest floor. Stratification of light and temperature is as pronounced here as in some aquatic communities.

Figure 17-5 The understory of a pine forest is poorly developed because of the lack of light. Note the accumulation of litter. (Photo by author.)

Light. Bathed in full sunlight, the uppermost layer of the canopy is the brightest part of the forest. From here on down through the forest strata, the light intensity is progressively reduced to only a fraction of full sunlight (Fig. 17-1). In an oak forest, only about six per cent of the total midday sunlight reaches the forest floor, and the brightness of the light is about 0.4 per cent of that of the upper canopy. Pines generally form a dense upper canopy that excludes so much sunlight that the lower strata cannot develop (Fig. 17-5). Pitch pine, Virginia pine, and jack pine have rather open crowns, which allow more light to reach the forest floor than oak, hickory, beech, or maple (Fig. 17-6). Conditions are different with spruce and fir. The upper crown, a zone of

307

Figure 17-6 Thin-crowned pine, such as jack pine, allow more light to reach the forest floor. This in turn encourages the development of a herbaceous and shrub stratum. (Photo by author.)

widely spaced narrow spires, is open and well lighted, while the lower crown is most dense and intercepts most of the light (Fig. 17-7).

There are seasonal differences of light intensity within the forest. The greatest extremes exist in the deciduous forest. The forest floor receives its maximum illumination during March and April, before the leaves appear; and a second, lower peak occurs in the fall. The darkest period is in midsummer. Light in the coniferous forest is reduced approximately the same throughout the year, since the trees retain their foliage. Here illumination is the greatest in midsummer, when the sun's rays are most direct and the lowest in winter when the intensity of incident sunlight is the lowest.

Figure 17-7 Spire-shaped, the spruce has a fairly open upper canopy; the crown is densest in the lower one-half to one-third. (Photo by author.)

Humidity and moisture. The forest interior is a humid place, a fact soon discovered by those who spend midsummer working in the woods. The humidity is high because of plant transpiration and poor air circulation. Variation of humidity inside the forest is influenced in part by the degree to which the lower strata are developed. Within these layers, leaves are adding moisture to the immediate surrounding air, increasing the humidity just above each. Thus layers of increasing and decreasing humidity may exist from the forest floor to the canopy. During the day, when the air warms and its water-holding capacity increases, relative humidity is the lowest. At night, when temperatures and moisture-holding capacities are low, relative humidity in the forest rises. The lowest humidity in the whole forest is a few feet above the canopy, where air circulation is the best. Highest humidity is found near the forest floor, the result of evaporation of moisture from the ground and the settling of cold air from the strata above.

Rainfall over the forest is intercepted by the canopy and the understory. Some is held back by the leaves and evaporated back into the atmosphere; the remainder reaches the forest soil. The amount of rainfall intercepted depends upon the type and age of the forest. In general, conifers intercept more rainfall than hardwoods, although they show considerable variation (Table 17-1). In summer, a relatively greater portion of rainfall is intercepted during a light shower than during a heavy rain. During the latter the leaves are beaten downward and release the rain intercepted earlier in the storm, permitting up to 90 per cent of the rain water to penetrate the canopy (Wood, 1937). During a light rain the leaves do not bend but hold the water, which subsequently runs down the leaf stem, twigs, and trunk as stemflow. This water enters the soil in a relatively narrow band around the base of the tree, where it follows the larger root systems into the soil.

TABLE 17-1. RAINFALL INTERFERENCE BY FOREST TREES OF DIFFERENT SPECIES

SPECIES	TOTAL RAINFALL, INCHES	PER CENT INTER- CEPTION	PER CENT THROUGH- FALL	PER CENT STEM- FLOW	REFERENCE
Red Pine	13.4	18.7	80.1	1.2	Voigt, 1960
Hemlock	13.4	33.1	60.9	5.9	Voigt, 1960
Beech	13.4	24.7	65.7	9.6	Voigt, 1960
Ponderosa pine	47.0	12.0	84.0	4.0	Rowe and Hendrix, 1951

The amount of water involved in stemflow is much lower on coniferous stands than in hardwoods (Voigt, 1960). Water reaching the base of red pine is equivalent to one-fifth of the amount that falls in the open; but around the beech with its smooth bark, two and one-half times as much water enters the soil as it does in the open during the same storm. This is ecologically significant, for small mesic environments colonized by moisture-demanding plants are created around the bases of trees. The ecological effects of the tree-base microclimates are well worth some investigation.

The amount of rain that penetrates the forest varies across the canopy. Rainfall close to the trunk is lighter than elsewhere, and the amount increases as the distance from the center of the crown increases (Stout and McMahon, 1961), a fact generally unrecognized in some ecological studies. The amount penetrating the canopy also may vary with the direction of the storm.

Temperature. The highest temperatures in the deciduous forest at least are in the upper canopy, since this stratum intercepts solar radiation. Temperatures tend to decrease through the lower strata. The most rapid decline occurs from the leaf litter down through the soil.

The temperature profile of coniferous forests tends to be somewhat the reverse of those of deciduous forests, particularly in those containing sprucelike trees. Here the coolest layer is in the upper canopy, perhaps because of greater air circulation, and the temperature increases down through the several strata to the forest floor.

The temperature profile changes through the twenty-four-hour period. At night, temperatures are more or less uniform from the canopy to the floor. This is due to the fact that radiation takes place most rapidly in the canopy; as the air cools it sinks and becomes slightly heated by the warmer air beneath the canopy. During the day, the air heats up, and by midafternoon temperature stratification becomes most pronounced. On rainy days the temperatures are more or less equalized, since water absorbs heat from warmer surfaces and transfers it to the cooler surfaces.

Temperature stratification varies seasonally (Christy, 1952). In fall when the leaves drop and the canopy thins, temperatures fluctuate more widely at the various levels. Maximum temperatures decrease from the canopy downward but rise again at the litter surface. The soil, no longer shaded by an overhead canopy, absorbs and radiates more heat than in summer. Below the insulating pavement of litter, temperatures decrease again through the soil. Thus there may be two temperature maximums in the profile, one in the canopy, the other on the surface of the litter. Winter temperatures decrease from the canopy down to the small tree layer, where in some forests they rise and then drop at the litter surface. From here the temperature increases rapidly down through the soil. During spring, conditions are highly variable. Maximum temperatures are found on the leaf-litter surface, which at this season of the year intercepts solar radiation, and temperatures decrease upward toward the canopy.

Wind. Anyone who has entered a woods on a windy day is well aware of how effectively the forest reduces wind velocity. The influence of forest cover on wind velocity varies with the height and density of the stand and the size and density of the crown. Over-all wind velocities inside the forest may be reduced by 90 per cent, and velocity near the ground usually ranges from one to two per cent of wind velocity outside (Fig. 4-14, above). Velocities in the open and cutover stands and in wintertime deciduous forests are greater than in dense stands and in coniferous forests, the latter of which are most effective in reducing the flow of wind.

The forest edge deflects the wind upward and over the trees, where the roughness of the canopy surface reduces the velocity (Fig. 4-13). The velocity of wind in the forest is not a constant percentage of the speed of the wind above the canopy. During the midday, for example, when the temperature decreases with height, this percentage decreases as the wind velocity above the crown increases (Fig. 4-14, below).

Forest animal life

Deciduous and coniferous forests

Although the deciduous and coniferous forests involve, with some exceptions, different species of animal life, the ecological niches and the adaptations of animals are similar. In general the diversity of animal life is associated with the stratification of and growth forms of plants. Some animals are associated with or spend the major part of their life in a single stratum; others may range over two or more. Arthropods, in particular, confine their activities to one stratum (Dowdy, 1951). Sixty-seven per cent of all the arthropod species in Missouri oak-hickory forests inhabited one stratum only and seventy-eight per cent of a red cedar forest were so restricted. None of the arthropod species were common to all strata and only two per cent ranged through as many as four strata.

The greatest concentration and diversity of life are found on and just below the ground layer, where humidity and temperature are fairly constant. (This already has been discussed in the chapter on the soil community.) Many animals, the soil invertebrates in particular, remain in the subterranean strata. Others, the mice, shrews, ground squirrels, foxes, burrow into the soil for shelter or food but spend considerable time above ground. The larger mammals live on the ground layer and feed on herbs, shrubs, and low trees. Birds move rather freely between several strata, but even here there is some restriction. Ruffed grouse, spruce grouse, hooded warblers, and ovenbirds occupy essentially the ground layer but may move up into the tree to feed, to roost, or to advertise territory. Some invertebrates, such as the millipedes and spiders, move up into the upper strata at night when humidity is favorable, a vertical migration that is somewhat similar to that of the plankton organisms in lakes and seas (Dowdy, 1944).

Other species occupy the upper strata—the shrub, low tree, and canopy (Fig. 17-8). Red-eyed vireos inhabit the lower tree stratum of the eastern deciduous forest, the wood peewee the lower canopy. Blackburnian warblers and scarlet tanagers dwell in the upper canopy, where they are very difficult to observe. Flying squirrels and the tree mouse are mammalian inhabitants of the canopy, while the woodpeckers, nuthatches, and creepers live in the open space of tree trunks between the shrubs and the canopy. Most of the intensive work on stratification of bird life in the temperate deciduous forest has been done in European woodlands, where one biologist (Turcek, 1951) found that 15 per cent of the bird species in an oak-hornbeam forest nested on the ground, 25 per cent in the herb and shrub strata, and 29 per cent in the canopy. Thirty-three per cent of the total population occupied the forest canopy, where more niches apparently were available; but its biomass was less than the ground and shrub populations. The ground layer, however, was the feeding area for 52 per cent of the species; herb and shrubs, 9 per cent; tree trunk, 10 per cent; tree foliage, 23 per cent; and the open spaces, 6 per cent. In deciduous forests, the diversity of bird species seems to be related to the height and density of foliage and resulting stratification, rather than to plant species composition (MacArthur and MacArthur, 1961).

As habitats, deciduous and coniferous forests differ chiefly in foliage arrangement and retention. The stiff, needle-like leaves of conifers, arranged spirally

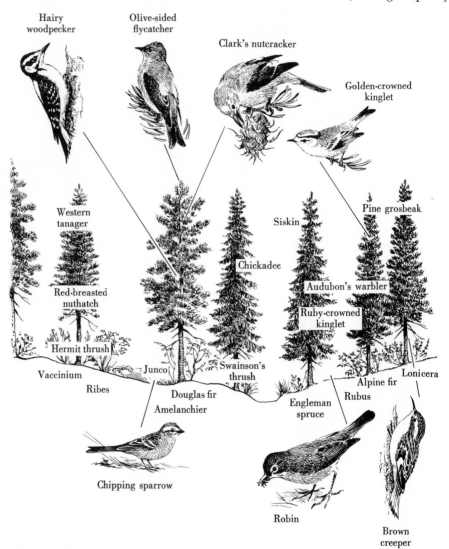

Figure 17-8 *Foraging niches of some birds in a spruce-fir forest in Wyoming.* (After Salt, 1957.)

around the branches, restrict the movements of some birds. And the poor decomposition of accumulated litter in coniferous forests is not favorable to small-animal life, especially the soil invertebrates (see Chap. 14). Coniferous forests provide better winter cover for wildlife. The presence of such shelter often is decisive in the survival of white-tailed deer in winter deer yards.

Differences also exist within deciduous and coniferous forests, even within a given region. In Wisconsin, xeric forests and south-facing slopes are inhabited by such birds as the scarlet tanager, blue jay and red-eye towhee. Mesic forests are occupied by wood thrushes, redstarts, and least flycatchers (Bond, 1957). The dry, shaded forest floor is the haunt of the ovenbird, while well-shaded ground is preferred by the Canada warbler (Kendeigh, 1945). Moisture regimes also strongly influence the distribution of litter fauna. In extensive reforestation areas in New York State, where pine and spruce have been planted over thousands of acres, a definite species preference for certain conifer growth forms existed among birds (Smith, 1956). The pine forests attracted the lowest number of species—eight—and were preferred by the black-throated green warbler. Spruce plantings held 22 species, of which the magnolia and Nashville warblers were the most common. The greater diversity of species in spruce undoubtedly reflected the greater abundance of niches offered by the spirelike crowns and the branches retained close to the ground. The low branches also provided excellent winter cover for grouse, snowshoe hares, and cottontail rabbits. But because of the difficulty they had in moving through the dense growth of spruce in winter, white-tailed deer sought the pine.

Some animals commonly associated with the deciduous forest—the white-tailed deer, the black bear, and the mountain lion, for example—actually range over both the deciduous and coniferous forests. Their north-south distribution appears to be limited more by climate, especially temperature, than by vegetation. The red squirrel, commonly associated with coniferous and mixed hardwood-coniferous forests, is quite common in deciduous woodlands, including oak, in the northern part of its range. But in the southern Appalachians this squirrel is restricted to the northern hardwood–coniferous forests of the high elevations and does not inhabit the oak forests at lower elevations, where the climate is warmer. On the other hand, warblers characteristic of northern coniferous forests, the magnolia and the black-throated green, are common in purely deciduous northern hardwood and oak forests of the Appalachian Mountains in West Virginia; and a northern mammal associate, the red-backed mouse, lives on the forest floor (unpublished data). Possibly these animals were associated with the hemlock, and after the hemlock was cut, they adjusted to the purely hardwood situation.

Tropical rain forest

Contrasting sharply with life in the temperate deciduous and coniferous forests is life in the tropical rain forests. Animal species are more diverse, since there is a greater variety of niches. Stratification of life is most pronounced here, where six distinct feeding strata are recognized (Harrison, 1962). (1) An insectivorous and carnivorous feeding group, consisting largely of bats and birds, works the upper air above the canopy. (2) Within the A–C canopy, a wide variety of birds, fruit bats, and mammals feed on leaves, fruit, and nectar. A few are insectivorous and mixed feeders. (3) Below the canopy, in the middle zone of tree trunks, is a world of flying animals, birds, and insectivorous bats. (4) Here too are the scansorial mammals, which range up and down the trunk, entering both the canopy and the ground zones to feed on the fruit of epiphytes growing on the tree trunk, on insects, and other animals. (5) Large ground animals make up the fifth feeding group. This includes large mammals and, rarely, birds, living on the ground and lacking climbing ability, that are able to reach up into the canopy or cover a large area of the forest. They include the plant feeders that either browse on the leaves, eat fallen fruit or root tubers, and their attendant carnivores. (6) The final feeding stratum includes the small ground animals, birds, and small mammals capable of some climbing, which search the ground litter and lower parts of tree trunks for food. This includes insectivorous, herbivorous, carnivorous, and mixed feeders.

The tropical rain forest has been compared to a lake. The canopy, area of primary production, represents the phytoplankton, exploited directly by insects, comparable to the zooplankton, and the large animals, comparable to the nekton. Food carried down into the deeper layer, the middle zone and the ground, as fallen leaves, fruit, insect bodies, compares to the bodies of plankton organisms. This food source is utilized by the middle-zone birds and bats, corresponding to the nekton organisms of the deeper layer; and the middle-zone mammals, which might be considered as periphytic organisms. The small ground mammals and birds are equivalent to the benthic organisms.

Animal life in the tropical rain forest is largely hidden, either by the dense foliage of the upper strata or by the cover of night. Birds are largely arboreal, and although brightly colored, remain hidden in the dense foliage. Ground birds are small and dark colored, difficult to see. Mammals appear scarcer than they really are, for they are largely nocturnal or arboreal. Ground-dwelling mammals are small and secretive. Tree frogs and insects are most conspicuous at evening, when their tremendous choruses are at full volume. Insects are most diverse about forest openings and along streams and forest margins, where light is more intense, where temperatures fluctuate and air circulates freely. Highly colored butterflies, beetles, and bees are common. Among the unseen invertebrates, hidden in loose bark and in axils of leaves, are snails, worms, millipedes, centipedes, scorpions, spiders, and land planarians. Termites are abundant in the rain forest and play a vital role in the decomposition of woody plant material. Together with ants, they are the dominant insect life. Ants are found everywhere in the rain forest, from the upper canopy to the forest floor, although in common with other rain-forest life, the majority tend to be arboreal.

The savanna

Where the forests merge with grasslands, a distinctive type of vegetation, the savanna, may exist. Natural savannas, the halfway world between grassland and forest, occur on an environmental gradient between a pure grassland climate and a pure forest climate (Fig. 17-9). Savannas are dominated by grasses and sedges, and contain open stands of widely spaced short trees. The greatest extent of savanna in North America flourishes, or rather flourished, in a narrow belt between the prairie and the eastern deciduous forest. On the dry lower slopes of the Rockies and Sierras, where rainfall rarely exceeds 10 to 20 inches and evaporation is high, occurs other savannalike vegetation, the piñon-juniper woodland. Elsewhere natural savanna existed in scattered areas throughout the forested region from Kentucky and Texas to the seaboard, places which today may still carry the name savanna on the map.

True savanna exists only where climate is favorable. Elsewhere savanna has been created, either by fire, by grazing, or by a combination of both. The oak

Figure 17-9 *Juniper–pinyon pine–grassland community. Note the overbrowsed cliff rose in the foreground.* (Photo courtesy Arizona Game and Fish Department.)

savannas of Michigan, Minnesota, and Wisconsin originated largely from fire. Bur oak and black oak were the trees; and once the land was protected from fire, they began to claim the grassland (Curtis, 1959). In other areas, over-grazed grasslands, lacking a thick sod cover, are invaded by woody species to form a savannalike cover, such as the mesquite of the southwestern United States.

Best known of all are the tropical savannas of Africa, dominated by grasses and sedge, which put out new growth in the rainy season and die down in the dry. The short, flat-crowned trees are uniformly scattered or form a gallery forest along the river banks. Just as in the temperate zone, the tropical savanna in places is increasing as the forest cover is destroyed; in other areas trees and shrubs invade overgrazed grassland. The African savanna is inhabited by the richest and most diverse ungulate fauna in the world, including the gazelle, the impala, the eland, the buffalo, the giraffe, the zebra, and the wildebeest. In contrast, the seral and geologically more recent South American savannas lack these conspicuous mammalian herds.

SUMMARY

Coniferous, deciduous, and tropical rain, these three kinds, to a great extent, dominate the forest cover of the earth. Confined to the northern hemisphere, the coniferous forest is typical of regions where the summers are short and the winters long and cold. The deciduous forest, which is richly developed in North America, western Europe, and eastern Asia, grows in a region of moderate precipitation and mild temperatures during the growing season. The tropical rain forest, which grows in equatorial regions, is the vegetative cover where the humidity is high, the rainfall is heavy, especially during at least one season of the year, seasonal changes are minimum, and the annual mean temperature is about 80°F. Of the three, the tropical rain forest is the most highly stratified and contains the greatest diversity of ecological niches. A well-developed deciduous forest is the next most highly stratified, while the coniferous forest is the least. Accompanying this vegetative stratification is a stratification of light, temperature, and moisture. The canopy receives the full impact of the climate and intercepts light and rainfall; the forest floor is shaded through the year in most coniferous and tropical rain forests, and in late spring and summer in the deciduous forest. The coniferous and deciduous forests hold different species of animal life, but animal adaptations are similar. The greatest concentration and diversity of life is on and just below the ground layer. Other animals live in various strata from low shrubs to the canopy. The tropical rain forest has pronounced feeding strata from above the canopy to the forest floor, and many of its animals are strictly arboreal. Whatever the forest, the different trees that compose it create different environments, which ultimately dictate the kind of plants and animals that can live within it.

SUGGESTED FIELD ACTIVITIES

The forest is the most complex terrestrial ecosystem and perhaps the most fascinating. It lends itself to a wide variety of studies, including the ones suggested below. These are given in general terms and are applicable to both the coniferous and deciduous forest.

1. Determine the composition of the stand by the methods outlined in Appendix C. Consider only trees over four inches in diameter (breast height). Express data as per cent composition for each species, number of trees per acre, basal area per acre. If a number of stands are compared, work up the importance values and arrange stands on a continuum.

2. Study the horizontal subdivisions of the community. Examine the low tree, shrub, and herb layers. By sweep net, sample the arthropod populations of each. Sort out distinctive species; compare biomass.

3. Determine the dominant species for each stratum.

4. Predict the future of the forest by the seedlings and saplings present in the understory and herb layer.

5. What influence does the forest opening have on animal life, with emphasis on birds and small mammals?

6. Study the microclimate of the forest. Compare the microclimate of a coniferous forest, a deciduous forest, and open land.

7. Compare the vegetation and microclimate of north-facing and south-facing slopes. Such a study should include chemical and physical properties of the soil, and the soil profile. Pay close attention to moisture.

8. Compare the physical and chemical properties of the upper soil layers of a coniferous and deciduous forest. Compare the litter fauna, even if only in a general way.

9. Investigate recent burns, logging areas. Study the vegetation. Determine the effect of fire on the soil, on the nature of ground vegetation and shrubs, on litter and nutrients, on seedling survival.

10. By studying old stumps (including the identity of the species), the residual trees, dendrochronology, etc., reconstruct the past history of the stand.

11. Study the animal life of the forest including:

   a. Relation of wildlife populations to mast-bearing trees and the presence of den trees.

   b. Stratification of bird life. Determine the niches of various species. Do they feed, nest in different parts of the forest or in different parts of the stratum?

   c. Distribution of small mammals in relation to litter and ground vegetation.

   d. The impact of deer on the forest.

   e. Relation of deer movements through the seasons to types of forest cover.

CHAPTER 18

The tundra

North of the coniferous forest belt lies a frozen plain, clothed in sedges, heaths, and willows, which encircles the top of the world. This is the arctic tundra. At lower latitudes similar landscapes, the alpine tundra, occur in the mountains of the world. But in the Antarctic a well-developed tundra is lacking. Arctic or alpine, the tundra is characterized by low temperatures, a short growing season, and low precipitation, since cold air can carry very little water vapor.

The tundra—the word comes from the Finnish *tunturi,* meaning a treeless plain—is a land dotted with lakes and transected by streams. Where the ground is low and moist, there are extensive bogs. On high, drier areas and places exposed to the wind, vegetation is scant and scattered, and the ground is bare and rock covered. These are the fell-fields, an anglicization of the Danish *fjoeld-mark,* or rock deserts. Lichen covered, the fell-fields are most characteristic of the highly exposed alpine tundra.

Frost molds the tundra landscape. Alternate freezing and thawing, and the presence of a permanent frozen layer in the ground, the permafrost, create conditions unique to the tundra alone. The sublayer of soil is subject to annual thawing in spring and summer and freezing in fall and winter. The depth of thaw may vary from a few inches in some places to one to two feet in others. Below this, the ground is always frozen solid and is impenetrable to both water and roots. Since the water cannot drain away, flat lands of the Arctic are wet and covered with shallow lakes and bogs. This reservoir of water lying on top of the permafrost enables plants to exist in the driest parts of the Arctic.

The symmetrically patterned land forms so typical of the tundra result from frost. As the surface freezes, the fine soil materials and clays, which hold more moisture, expand while freezing and then contract when they thaw. This action tends to push the larger material upward and outward from the mass to form the patterned surface.

Typical nonsorted patterns associated with seasonally high water tables are frost hummocks, frost boils, and earth stripes (Fig. 18-1). Frost hummocks are small earthen mounds up to five feet in diameter and four feet high, which may or may not contain peat. Frost boils are formed when the surface freezes across the top, trapping the still unfrozen muck beneath. As this chills and expands, the mud is forced up through the crust. Raised earth stripes, found on moderate slopes, appear as lines or small ridges flowing downhill. They apparently are produced by a downward creep or flow of wet soil across the surface of the permafrost.

Sorted patterns are characteristic of better-drained sites. The best known of these are the stone polygons, the size of which is related to frost intensity and the size of the material (Johnson and Billings, 1962). The larger stones are forced out to a peripherial position, while the smaller and finer material, either small stones or soil, occupies the center. The polygon shape may result from an accumulation of rocks in desiccation cracks formed during drier periods. These cracks appear as the surface of the soil dries out, in much the same way as cracks appear in bare, dry, compacted clay surfaces in temperate regions. On the slopes, creep, frost-thrusting, and downward flow of soil change polygons into sorted stripes running downhill. Mass movement of supersaturated soil over the permafrost forms solifluction terraces, or "flowing soil." This gradual downward creep of soils and rocks eventually rounds off ridges and other irregularities in topography. This molding of the landscape by frost action is called *cryoplanation* and is far more important than erosion in wearing down the arctic landscape.

Permafrost in the alpine tundra exists only at very high elevations and in the far north, but the frost-induced processes—small solifluction terraces and stone polygons—are still present. The lack of a permafrost results in drier soils; only in alpine wet meadows and bogs do soil-moisture conditions compare with the Arctic. Precipitation, especially snowfall and humidity, is higher in the alpine region than in the arctic tundra, but the steep topography results in a rapid runoff of water.

Arctic and alpine vegetation

Tundra vegetation begins at the tree line. In appearance, it suggests a short-grass plain, but it is actually a land of lichens and mosses, sedges and rushes, grasses and low-growing shrubs, chiefly heaths. Although the vegetation may appear homogeneous over wide areas of the tundra, the pattern of vegetation is often complex. Large differences exist across the tundra, which reflect changes in

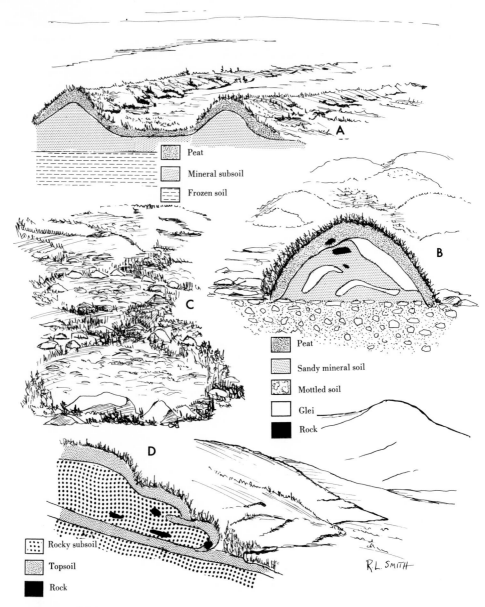

Peat

Mineral subsoil

Frozen soil

Peat

Sandy mineral soil

Mottled soil

Glei

Rock

Rocky subsoil

Topsoil

Rock

Figure 18-1 *Patterned ground forms typical of the tundra region.* (A) *Unsorted earth stripes;* (B) *frost hummock;* (C) *sorted stone nets and polygons;* (D) *solifluction terrace.* (Cross-sectional diagrams adapted from Johnson and Billings, 1963.)

the macroclimate and microclimate, land form, history, time, and substrate. The relatively permanent instability of the substrate plays a primary role in influencing tundra vegetation, physically dislodged by the movements of the surface soil. In fact the timber line may be regarded as a zone of transition from relatively stable to instable soils (Raup, 1951) rather than a purely climatic phenomenon. Thus climate would have only an indirect effect through its influence on soil movements.

Although the environment of the arctic and alpine regions are somewhat similar, the vegetation of the two differs considerably (Bliss, 1956). Both, however, do have some features in common. Because the environment is especially rigorous, the number of species tends to be few and their growth form is low. The plants are rarely able to take a sufficient hold on the surface to have any sort of control over the immediate soil environment. The complications of snowbanks, microrelief, aspect, snowmelt, frost heaving, and so on produce an almost endless change in plant associations from spot to spot (Polunin, 1955). Because of frequent and drastic disturbances, plants are often shortlived and successional cycles are fragmentary.

The growth rate of both arctic and alpine species is reduced and appears to be controlled to some degree by soil and air temperatures. In Greenland, for example, plant growth begins when the mean daily soil-surface temperatures pass 0°C (32°F) (Krog, 1955). The influence of temperature near the surface of the ground is illustrated by a study of the alder, *Alnus crispus* (Bliss, 1956). This shrub leafed out two to four days earlier at the base of the clump than at the top, one meter above; and leaves opened on the south side of the clump six days earlier than on the north side. Another plant, *Arctagrostis latifolia*, increased and decreased its growth with corresponding temperature changes. The greatest stem elongation took place during high-temperature periods. The cessation of growth in tundra plants, however, is completely independent of temperature and is probably due to physiological changes during the latter part of the growing season.

There are adaptative differences between the plants of the arctic and alpine regions, associated in part with the photoperiod. The alpine sorrel, found both in the arctic and alpine tundras, produces an increasing number of flowers in the southernly portions of its range and a decreased production of rhizomes (Mooney and Billings, 1960). Northern populations of the plant have a higher photosynthetic rate at lower temperatures and attain a maximum rate at a lower temperature. Alpine plants reach the saturation point for light at higher intensities than arctic plants, which are adapted to lower light intensities. Arctic plants require longer periods of daylight than alpine plants. The further north the geographic origin of the plant, the more slowly the plant grows under short photoperiod. Arctic plants propagate themselves almost entirely by vegetative means; alpine plants propagate themselves by seedlings. The adventitous roots of arctic plants are short and parallel to the rhizomes and short-lived. Those of the alpine species are long, penetrate to considerable depths, and are long lived.

Arctic vegetation

In the Arctic only those species able to withstand constant disturbance of the soil, buffeting by the wind, and abrasion from wind-carried particles of soil and ice can survive. On well-drained sites, heath shrubs, dwarf willows and birches, dryland sedges and rushes, herbs, mosses, and lichens cover the land. On the driest and most exposed sites—the flat-topped domes, the rolling hills, and low-lying terraces, all usually covered by coarse, rocky material and subject to extreme action by the frost—vegetation is sparse and often confined to small depressions. Plant cover consists of scattered heaths and mats of mountain avens, as well as crustose and foliose lichens growing on the rocks. Willows, birch, and heath occupy well-drained soils of finer material, and between them grow grasses, sedges, and herbs.

But over much of the Arctic the typical vegetation is a cotton grass–sedge–dwarf heath complex (Hanson, 1953). Hummocks may support growths of lichens, willow, blueberry, and Laborador tea. Depressions are covered with sedge-marsh vegetation, and over the rest grows tussocks of cotton grass. The spaces between the tussocks may be filled with sphagnum, on top of which dwarf shrubs grow; in other places sphagnum may overgrow the sedges and cotton grass. On mounds and hummocks in fresh-water marshes, on well-drained knolls and slopes, in areas of late-melting snowbanks, along streams and on sandy and gravelly beaches, grassland types develop.

Topographic location and snow cover delimit a number of arctic plant communities. Steep, south-facing slopes and river bottoms support the most luxuriant and tallest shrubs, grasses, and legumes, while cotton grass dominates the gentle north and south slopes, reflecting higher air and soil temperatures and greater snow depth. Pockets of heavy snow cover create two types of plant habitats, the snow patch and the snowbed. Snow-patch communities occur where wind-driven snow collects in shallow depressions and protects the plants beneath, particularly the aerial stems of shrubs. As a result, snow patches support rather tall growths of willow, birch, and heaths, in contrast to the shorter vegetation surrounding them. Snowbeds, typical of both arctic and alpine situations, are found where large masses of snow accumulate because of certain topographic peculiarities. Not only does the deep snow protect the plants beneath, but the melt water from the slowly retreating snowbank provides a continuous supply of water throughout the growing season. Snowbed plants, usually found only here, have an extremely short growing season but are able to break into leaf and flower quickly because of the advanced stage of growth beneath the snow. In unfavorable seasons, the snowbank may melt so late that the plants do not have sufficient time to ripen the fruit or perhaps to open the flower. Thus vegetative propagation is important in these species. In fact the gradual retreat of the snow may result in zonation of vegetation across the snowbed, with lichens along the exposed edge, to sedges and hairgrass, to shrubs such as willow. Where the snow cover is very deep and extremely late in melting, only mosses grow (Hanson, 1953; Polunin, 1934–35).

Because of the cold climate, short summers, low soil temperatures, sparse vegetation, and slow decay of organic matter, arctic soils are poor and deficient in nitrates, phosphates, and other salts. Where these nutrients are added to the soil, as around bird cliffs, animal burrows, goose nesting grounds, and present and past areas of human habitation, the vegetation is lush and green, in contrast to the less colorful surrounding expanse. These local areas are the "arctic oases," for they contain not only species common to the region but also some species confined to these habitats (see Bank, 1953; Wiggans and Thomas, 1962).

Alpine vegetation

In general the alpine tundra is a more severe environment for plants than the arctic tundra; and the adaptation of plants to the physical environment is probably more important than the interrelations of one species with another.

The alpine tundra is a land of strong winds, snow, and cold, and widely fluctuating temperatures. During the summer the temperature on the surface of the soil ranges from 40°C (104°F) to O°C (32°F) (Bliss, 1956). The atmosphere is thinner in the alpine tundra, and because of this, light intensity, especially ultraviolet, is high on clear days.

The alpine tundra of the Rocky Mountains is a land of rock-strewn slopes, bogs, and alpine meadows, and shrubby thickets. In spite of the similarity of conditions, only about 20 per cent of the plant species of the Arctic and Rocky Mountain alpine tundra are the same, and these are different ecotypes. Heaths are lacking in the tundras of the Rockies, as well as the heavy growth of lichens and mosses between other plants. Lichens are more or less confined to the rocks, and the ground is bare between plants.

Cushion and mat-forming plants, rare in the Arctic, are important in the alpine tundra. Low and hugging the ground, they are able to withstand the buffeting of the wind. The cushionlike blanket traps heat and the interior of the cushion may be 20 degrees warmer than the surrounding air, a microclimate that is utilized by insects. Thick cuticles, which increase the plant's resistance to desiccation, and the abundance of epidermal hairs and scales are characteristic of alpine plants. The significance of this is still debated. These hairs appear to absorb and reflect the bright light of the alpine environment. At the same time, the hairs may act as a heat trap and perhaps prevent cold injury when air temperatures drop to freezing (Krog, 1955), and enable the plants to develop and bloom while the air is still cold.

Alpine vegetation and its associated soils vary on a rather complex gradient or continuum controlled by topographic site and snow cover, both of which interact with wind (Fig. 18-2). The vegetational pattern has been worked out for the Beartooth Plateau of Wyoming (Johnson and Billings, 1962) and serves as an example of the high alpine areas of the Rocky Mountains. The high, windswept areas, rocky and free of snow, support only lichens, which may completely cover the sheltered side; but on the windward side they are short, no higher than the depth of snow, and they may be completely lacking on the most exposed sites. Below the lichen growth are the xeric cushion-plant communities, which extend further downslope on the windward side than they do on the lee. This land of rock, lichens, and cushion plants is the alpine rock desert. In somewhat more protected sites grows the geum turf, a sodlike covering of geum and associated plants, such as sedges, lupines, polygonums, and mountain avens. Alpine meadows develop on well-drained soils of sheltered uplands and lower mesic slopes and basins. Hairgrass, *Deschampsia*, often growing in pure stands, is the dominant species. These meadows are subject to considerable disturbance both from frost activity and from pocket gophers. Alpine bogs, communities quite similar to those of the arctic tundra, support a growth of sedge and cottongrass. Willow thickets, dense and uniform in height, grow along drainage channels and in alpine valley bottoms.

The alpine tundra of the high Appalachians is not nearly so cold and windswept as that of the Rockies. Tundra areas are small and lack the diversity of species found in the western mountains. Indeed little floristic similarity exists between the regions. There is a much closer affinity between the flora of the eastern alpine tundra and that of the arctic and of the alpine communities of Scandinavia and central Europe.

Nine plant communities are recognized in the tundras of the Presidential Range in New Hampshire (Bliss, 1963). These occur on two gradients, one of increasing snow depth, the other of increasing moisture (Fig. 18-3). On exposed windswept sites where winter snow cover is thin or nonexistent, *Diapensia,* a dwarf, tussock-forming shrub, grows. Over those widespread areas where snow cover is variable a dwarf-shrub-heath-rush community occupies the sites. Dwarf shrub heaths—bearberry, bilberry, Lapland rosebay—dominate where the deep

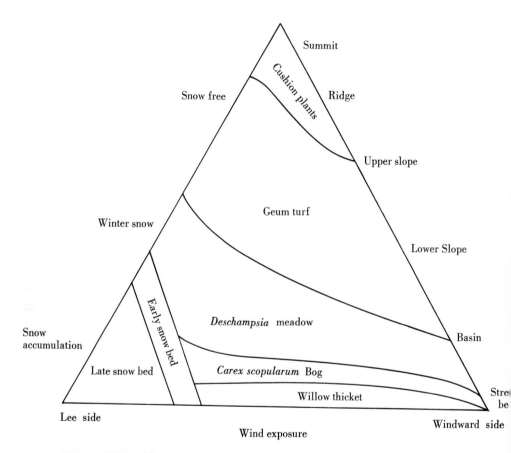

Figure 18-2 *Relationship of major vegetation types to slope cover and slope position in the western alpine tundra on Beartooth Plateau, Wyoming.* (After Johnson and Billings, 1962.)

snow cover melts early. Snowbank communities are most prevalent on the east- and southeast-facing slopes, in the lee of the prevailing winds. The second gradient, one of increasing summer atmospheric and soil moisture and fog, is largely restricted to north- and west-facing slopes on the higher peaks. Sedge meadows at the highest elevations give way downslope to a sedge-dwarf-shrub-heath community. At lower elevations this is replaced by a sedge–rush–dwarf-shrub-heath type. Two other communities, the streamside and the bog, are common at low elevations.

Krumholtz

At the tree line, where the forest gives way to the tundra, lies an area of stunted, wind-shaped trees, the krumholtz or "crooked wood." The krumholtz in the North American alpine region is best developed in the Appalachians. In the west it is much less marked, for there the timber line ends almost

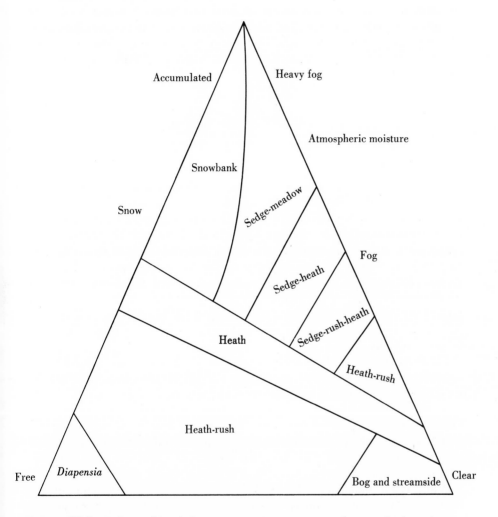

Figure 18-3 *Relationship of alpine communities to snow and atmospheric moisture in the Presidential Range of New Hampshire.* (After Bliss, 1963.)

abruptly with little lessening of height; the trees for the most part are flagged—branches remain only on the lee side. On the high ridges of the Appalachians, particularly in the White and Adirondack Mountains, the trees begin to show signs of stunting far below the timber line. As the trees climb upward, stunting increases until spruces and birches, deformed and semiprostrate, form carpets two to three feet high, impossible to walk through but often dense enough to walk upon. Where strong winds come in from a constant direction, the trees are sheared until the tops resemble close-cropped heads, although the trees on the lee side of the clumps grow taller than those on the windward side. While the wind and cold generally are regarded as the cause of the dwarf and misshapen condition of the trees, Clausen (1965) has demonstrated that the ability of some species of trees to show a "krumholtz" effect is genetically determined. Eventually conditions become too severe even for the prostrate forms, and the trees drop out completely except for those that have taken root behind the protection of some high rocks, and tundra vegetation then takes over completely. On some slopes the trees might be able to grow on better sites at higher elevations, but they appear to be eliminated by competition from sedges (Griggs, 1946).

Animals of the tundra

Arctic tundra

The tundra world holds some fascinating animals, even though the diversity of species is small. Like the plants, the animals of the arctic and the alpine tundras are of two distinct groups. Except for the caribou and the pipit, there are no important species in common. The animals of the arctic tundra are mostly circumpolar, and those species of the North American tundra which are not have close relatives in the Eurasian tundra. The North American barren ground caribou, for example, has the European reindeer, and the North American wolverine is matched by the glutton. Musk-ox, arctic hare, arctic fox, and arctic ground squirrels are or have been common to both. In addition, some 75 per cent of the birds of the North American tundra are common to the European tundra (Udvardy, 1958).

The arctic tundra with its wide expanse of ponds and boggy ground is the haunt of myriads of waterfowl, sandpipers, and plovers, which arrive when the ice is out, nest, and return south before winter sets in.

Invertebrate life is scarce, as are amphibians and reptiles. Some snails are found in the arctic tundra about the Hudson Bay. Insects, reduced to a few genera, are nevertheless abundant, especially in mid-July. The insect horde is composed of black flies, deer flies, and mosquitoes (Shelford and Twomey, 1941).

White is the dominant color of the animals of the arctic tundra. In the high arctic, white coloration is universal and maintained the year round, as in the polar bear, arctic fox, and greater snow goose. Others are dimorphic. The gray falcon is white in the high arctic, gray in the low arctic, and dark in the subarctic. Some animals alternate a white winter color with a dark summer color, and again there is a relation between the winter climate and the degree of whiteness. The rock ptarmigan of the low boreal mountains, for example, never quite acquires a full white winter plumage, for the back is marked with dark; the ptarmigans of the high and low arctic are pure white in winter. The snow bunting, too, exhibits the same relationship. Those birds wintering in Siberia have creamy white edges to the feathers, while those that winter in central Europe and North America have the feathers edged in buff. The reason for the white color is not fully known. It does conceal both predator and prey in winter and was believed capable of reducing the amount of heat radiating from the body, but recent experiments indicate that this apparently is not true. (Hammel, 1956).

Animal activity in the arctic tundra is geared to short summers and long winters. The only hibernator is the ground squirrel, although the female polar bear does den up in the snow where she gives birth to her cub. The ground squirrel is active only from May to September. It mates almost as soon as it emerges from the burrow in spring, and the young are born in mid-June, after a 25-day gestation period. The young are self-sufficient by mid-July, attain adult weight and are ready to hibernate by late September and early October (Mayer, 1960). A similar speed-up in the life cycle is found among some of the arctic birds. Because of the long days, the northern robin feeds the young for 21 hours per day and the young may leave the nest when a little over eight days old, in contrast to 13 days or more in the temperate region (Karplus, 1949). The larger mammals and the few overwintering birds, such as the ptarmigan and the redpoll, and the marine mammals have heavy layers of fat beneath the skin, long dense fur, or long dense feathers. Ptarmigan and snowy owls have feathers on their tarsi; the caribou and the musk-ox have winter coats of extremely heavy, wooly underfur overlaid with a thick fleece that is almost air tight. Small rodents and weasels tunnel beneath the snow, itself a good insulator. Those species unable to withstand the severe cold migrate to warmer or more protected areas. Few birds remain behind over winter, and even the caribou leaves the high arctic tundra for the southern portions, even south of the tree line. Invertebrates usually pass the winter in the larval and pupal stages. A few, however, such as rotifers and diving beetles, may be frozen in the ice; while others pass the season as adults.

Alpine tundra

The alpine tundra, which extends upward like islands in the mountain ranges of the world, is small in area and contains few characteristic species. The alpine regions of western North America are inhabited by pikas, marmots, mountain goat—not a goat at all but related to the South American chamois— mountain sheep and elk. The sheep and the elk spend their summers in the high alpine meadows and winter on the lower slopes. The marmot, a mountain woodchuck, hibernates over winter, while the pika cuts grass and piles it in tiny haycocks to dry for winter. Some rodents, such as the vole and the pocket gophers, remain under the ground and snow during winter. The pocket gopher is important, for its activities influence the pattern of alpine vegetation. The tunneling gophers kill the sedge and cushion plants by eating the roots and by throwing the soil to the surface, smothering plant life. Other plants then take over on the wind-blown, gravelly soil. These pioneering plants are rejected by the gopher. The rodent moves on, the cushion plants move back in, organic matter accumulates again. Slowly the sedges recover, and when they do, the gophers return once more.

The alpine regions contain a fair representation of insect life. Flies and mosquitoes are scarce, but springtails, beetles, grasshoppers, and butterflies are common. Because of the ever-present winds, butterflies fly close to the ground;

other insects have short wings or no wings at all. Insect development is slow; some butterflies may take two years to mature and grasshoppers three.

A major problem for mammals of the alpine tundra is low oxygen pressure. Birds obviously are able to live at high altitudes where oxygen pressure is low, but mammals that wander into high places are not, unless they live there permanently and have become adapted to rarefied air. Normal air pressure for most mammalian life is 15 pounds per square inch. At high alpine elevations this pressure may drop to 10 pounds at 10,000 and even lower higher up; at 18,000 feet, air pressure is reduced by one half. In such a rarefied atmosphere the mammal, including man, has a difficult time securing sufficient oxygen. Mammals can temporarily adapt themselves to high altitudes by increasing the heart beat and the rate of respiration. Mammals permanently adapted to high altitudes have blood richer in red cells and hemoglobin.

SUMMARY

The alpine tundra of the high mountain ranges in lower latitudes and the arctic tundra that extends beyond the tree line of the far north are at once similar and dissimilar. Both have low temperature, low precipitation, and a short growing season. Both possess a frost-molded landscape and plant species whose growth form is low and whose growth rate is slow. The arctic tundra has a permafrost layer; rarely does the alpine tundra. Arctic plants require longer periods of daylight than alpine plants and reproduce vegetatively, while alpine plants propagate themselves by seedlings. Over much of the Arctic, the dominant vegetation is cotton grass, sedge, and dwarf heaths. In the alpine tundra, cushion and mat-forming plants, able to withstand buffeting by the wind, dominate the exposed sites, while cotton grass and other tundra plants are confined to protected sites. At the tree line lies the krumholtz, a land of stunted, wind-shaped trees, a growth form that may be genetically determined. Animal life in the arctic tundra, except for the caribou and the pipit, is distinct from that of the alpine and is circumpolar in distribution. White is the dominant color of tundra birds and mammals, especially in winter. For mammals of the alpine tundra a major problem is low oxygen pressure, a situation that animals of the arctic tundra generally do not face. The tundra region, arctic and alpine, is a rigorous environment for plants and animals; but in spite of it, the tundra, contrary to its implied barrenness, is a land rich in life—if not in variety, then in seasonal abundance.

SUGGESTED FIELD ACTIVITIES

Opportunities for work with alpine and arctic tundra is rather limited for most, except those who happen to live in or close by the limited areas of the eastern alpine tundra and the western mountain ranges. Even for these, opportunities may be limited because of other seasonal activities.

Soil

Some time might be spent exposing, examining, and analyzing the soil profile, as well as studying cross sections of hummocks, frost boils, stripes, and even solifluction terraces. Note the distribution of stones, gravel, peat, and top soil. Active frost boils and hummocks can be studied by (1) inserting stakes into them and keeping a record of movements of the stakes, or (2) by painting spots on surfaces of bare polygons or marking lines across sorted stripes. Disruption of paint marks indicates frost-caused movements. Direction of movements can be determined by arranging painted stones in grid patterns on the surface at a known depth. Painted stones should be approximately the same size as those replaced. Photographic records come in handy here.

Environmental analysis

Where possible, records should be made of rainfall, air and soil temperature, light, etc. The erosive force of the wind can be determined by placing wooden stakes into the ground, and after several years measuring the height of maximum abrasion. This will be related to snow cover.

Vegetation

Vegetation should be studied in relation to soil features. Description of vegetation growing on top of and along borders of frost hummocks in and around polygons, and on stripes and solifluction terraces should be carefully noted. After some of the principal communities have been determined, they can be further analyzed by means of randomly located square plots, by listing all species occurring, by cover estimates of at least the most important species. This method is perhaps most useful for studying microhabitats associated with patterned ground. Wide expanses of plant cover, such as meadows and bogs, may be more rapidly sampled by using the point quadrat method. This method is particularly useful where cushion plants are involved, for it is difficult to determine where one plant begins and another ends. Pins with sharpened points should be spaced at 1-decimeter intervals in a frame, the vegetation first contacted by each pin recorded. Vegetation data can be obtained either on a transect laid out in the direction of maximum vegetation change or samples may be centered on homogeneous, randomly selected points in the form of two intersecting 5-meter transects, one in the direction of the slope, the other across the slope.

Snowbank vegetation

Snowbank vegetation is particularly interesting, for the distribution and life cycles of plants are closely related to the retreat of snow and to moisture conditions. Weekly patterns and rates of snow melt can be recorded by marking the outlines of snowbanks on rocks with paint. Use a different color paint for each week. Snow depth can be measured and a photographic record of the retreat can be taken. The vegetation within each weekly segment can be recorded by means of 2- by 5-decimeter quadrats along transects at both the upper and lower edges of the snowbank. Data should show density and cover value for each species. Weekly phenological notes should be made at the same time, these to include: start of growth, leaf expansion, flowering, set of seed, seed dispersal, and leaf coloration.

Production

Productivity may be determined by clipping weekly all vegetation in 4-decimeter quadrats along a transect above and below the bank, oven drying the material, and weighing it. Clip quadrats should be made where the vegetation cover is 100 per cent. Productivity values can be assigned to quadrats by adjusting them to the average percentage of vegetation cover per square meter.

Animal life

As elsewhere animals are more difficult to study and to measure. Observations should be made as to the species present, the locations of bird nests in relation to vegetation, the influence of pocket gophers and voles on vegetation patterns, browsing activities and preferences of deer, elk, mountain sheep. Marmot populations and pika populations might be estimated roughly by locating dens and hay piles. Special studies related to the movements and migrations of large mammals might be undertaken.

CHAPTER 19

Distribution of communities

Biomes

Grasslands, the desert, the forest, the tundra, the major terrestrial ecosystems discussed in the previous pages, can be classified into broad natural biotic units, called *biomes* (Fig. 19-1). Each biome consists of a distinctive combination of plants and animals in the fully developed or "climax" community; and each is characterized by a uniform life form of vegetation, such as grass or coniferous trees. The biome is identical with the major plant formations recognized by the plant ecologist, except that the biome is the total community of plants and animals and not just plants alone. It also includes the developmental stages, which may be dominated by other life forms. Because the species that dominate the seral stages are more widely distributed than those of the climax, they are of little value in defining the limits of the biome.

The major terrestrial biomes include the *temperate deciduous forest*, which occupies regions of abundant, evenly distributed rainfall and moderate temperatures that vary seasonally, and the *coniferous forest*. The latter stretches as a broad belt across North America and Eurasia and extends southward in the mountains of eastern and western North America. The temperate deciduous forest originally covered eastern North America, all of Europe, eastern China,

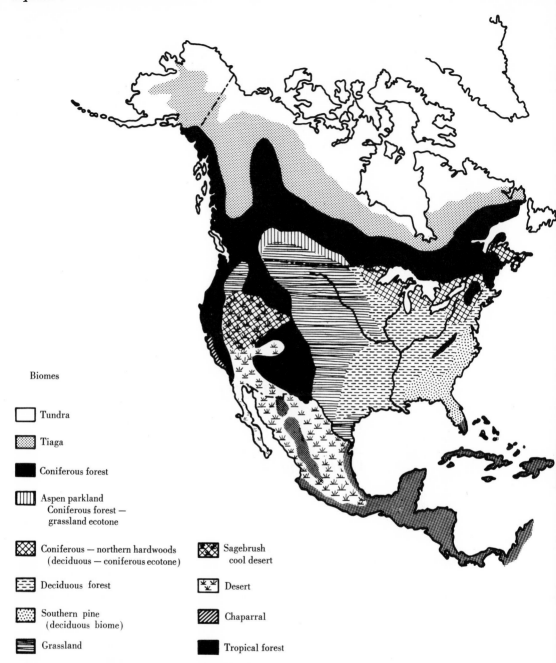

Biomes

☐ Tundra

▦ Tiaga

■ Coniferous forest

▥ Aspen parkland
Coniferous forest —
grassland ecotone

▧ Coniferous — northern hardwoods   ▨ Sagebrush
(deciduous — coniferous ecotone)   cool desert

▤ Deciduous forest   ⚶ Desert

⣿ Southern pine   ▧ Chaparral
(deciduous biome)

▤ Grassland   ■ Tropical forest

Figure 19-1 *A schematic map of the major biomes of North America.* (Prepared after several sources, including F. A. Pitelka, Distribution of Birds in Relation to Major Biotic Communities, *Am. Midl. Nat.,* 25: 113–137; A. S. Leopold, Vegetation Zones of Mexico, *Ecology, 31:* 507–518; E. N. Transeau, et al., *Textbook of Botany,* Harper and Row, New York, 1953.)

and Japan. The *tundra* covers large areas of North America and Eurasia north of the coniferous forest belt, as well as high mountain peaks of lower latitudes. Where rainfall is too low to support extensive forests, the *grassland* biome occurs, generally within the interior of continents. The *desert* biome exists in western North America, in North Africa, and Australia, in central Asia, and in Chile, Argentina, and Bolivia. Tropical regions embrace the *tropical rain forest* and *tropical savanna* biomes. The tropical rain forest occupies the region extending from the Amazon of South America north to lower Mexico, as well as the Congo of Africa, parts of India, southeast Asia, New Guinea, and other Pacific Islands. The tropical savanna reaches its best development in eastern and southern Africa.

In addition, there are several other extensive plant and animal communities that cannot be included in any of the major continental biomes. These are given equal rank by themselves. One is the *woodland,* which consists of an open stand of trees evergreen in habit and tolerant of low moisture. In western North America this biome includes the pine-oak woodlands of central and northern Mexico; the broadleaf evergreen–oak woodlands, most highly developed west of the Sierra Nevada mountains; the pinon-juniper woodlands, which extend from the eastern slopes of the Sierras and Cascades across the Great Basin to Wyoming and New Mexico. Similar woodland is found around the Mediterranean Sea in Eurasia and Africa. A second is the *chaparral,* consisting of broadleaf evergreen shrubs and small trees. It is best developed in southern California, in Baja California, in a narrow belt on the Sierra Nevada and southern Rocky Mountains, along the shores of the Mediterranean, and along the southern coast of Australia. A third is the *tropical scrub* and *deciduous forest biome,* which occupies areas where moisture conditions are intermediate between the desert and savanna and the rain forest. It is represented by the thorn forests of Africa, Australia, and Brazil and by the monsoon forests of tropical Asia. The wet and dry seasons of approximately equal length give these regions the seasonal appearance of "winter" and "summer."

These major biomes do not begin and end abruptly. Like the communities found within them, the biomes gradually blend one into the other; rarely is there a sharp line demarking each one. So between each biome there is a broad transitional belt, or *ecotone.* The aspen parkland of north-central Canada is an ecotone between the coniferous forest and grassland; the tiaga is an ecotone between the tundra and the northern coniferous forest; and as a final example, the northern mixed hardwood–coniferous forest is a transition between the northern coniferous forest and the central hardwoods forest of North America.

The biome concept developed gradually over the years. It probably began back in 1877, when Mobius in a report of the U.S. Fish Commission on oysters and oyster culture described the oyster bed as a "community of living beings, a collection of species and a massing of individuals which find here everything necessary for their growth and continuance." For such a community, Mobius proposed the word biocoenosis. Similar ideas arose in other parts of the world, and the whole concept was further expanded and discussed by Frederick Clements and Victor Shelford. Today the biome is more or less recognized as the major natural unit of plants and animals throughout the world, although in Europe it is more apt to go by the name "major life zone."

Biogeographical regions

Encompassing larger areas and embracing a number of biomes are the biogeographical or faunal regions. The idea of faunal regions is older than that of the biome. For centuries naturalists and explorers had penetrated deeper and deeper into the unknown parts of the world, and they brought back specimens and tales of new and strange animals and plants. Gradually the fact that different kinds of animals occupied different regions of the world became quite clear. By the beginning of the twentieth century, naturalists had accumulated the basic facts of worldwide animal distribution. All they needed to do—and this was a great enough task—was to arrange the facts and draw some general conclusions. This was done for birds by Philip Sclater in 1878;

Figure 19-2 *Polar projection map of the world, showing major biogeographical realms.* (From M. F. Guyer and C. E. Lane, *Animal Biology,* Harper and Row, New York, 1964.)

but the master work in zoogeography was done by Alfred Wallace, who is also known for reaching the same general theory of evolution as Darwin (see Chap. 22). The *realms* of Wallace, with some modification, still stand today.

There are six biogeographical regions, each more or less embracing a major continental land mass and each separated by oceans, mountain ranges, or desert (Fig. 19-2). They are the Palearctic, the Nearctic, Neotropical, Ethiopian, Oriental, and Australian. Because some zoogeographers consider the Neotropical and the Australian regions to be so different from the rest of the world, these two often are considered as regions or realms equal to the other four combined. They are classified as Neogea (Neotropical), Notogea (Australia), and Metagea, the main part of the world. Each region possesses certain distinction and uniformity in the taxonomic units it contains, and each to a greater or lesser degree shares some of the families of animals with other regions. Except for Australia, each at one time or another in the history of the earth has had some land connection with another, across which animals and plants could pass.

Two regions, the Palearctic and the Nearctic, are quite closely related; in fact the two often are considered as one, the Holarctic. The Nearctic contains the North American continent south to the Tropic of Cancer. The Palearctic region contains the whole of Europe, all of Asia north of the Himalayas, northern Arabia, and a narrow strip of coastal North Africa. At various times a continuous land mass across the Bering Sea connected Eurasia and North America; and over this bridge plants and animals freely passed. Both regions are similar in climate and vegetation; both contain coniferous and deciduous forest biomes, tundra, desert, grassland, and chaparral. Both are rather alike in their faunal composition, and together they share, particularly in the north, such animals as the wolf, the hare, the moose (called elk in Europe), the stag (called elk in North America), the caribou, the wolverine, and the bison.

Below the coniferous forest belt, the two regions become more distinct. The differences are more pronounced among birds and reptiles than among mammals. The Palearctic is not very rich in vertebrate fauna, most of which it shares with the Nearctic, the Oriental, and the Ethiopian regions, and very few of which are endemic, restricted to the region. The latter include the mole rats and the hedge sparrows. Palearctic reptiles are few and usually are related to those of the African and Oriental tropics. The Nearctic, in contrast, is the home of many reptiles and has more endemic families of vertebrates, including the pronghorned antelope, pocket gophers, and pocket mice. The Nearctic fauna is a complex of New World tropical and Old World temperate families; the Palearctic is a complex of Old World tropical and New World temperate families.

South of the Nearctic lies the Neotropical, which includes all of South America, part of Mexico, and the West Indies. It is joined to the Nearctic by the Central American isthmus and is surrounded by the sea. Long isolated (until 15 million years ago), the fauna of the Neotropical is most distinctive and varied. At the time of the great interchange of animal life between North and South America over the Central American corridor, such ancient North American forms as the tapirs and llama moved into South America and survived, while the same forms disappeared from North America. In fact about one-half the South American mammals are descendants of the North American invaders, while the only South American mammals to survive in North America are the armadillo, opossum, and porcupine. Lacking in the Neotropical is a well-developed ungulate fauna of the plains, so characteristic of North America and Africa.

The Neotropical, however, is rich in endemic families of vertebrates. Of 32 families of mammals, excluding bats, 16 are restricted to the Neotropical. Of these, three make up the order Edentata, the anteater, sloth, and armadillo. In addition, five families of bats, including the famous vampire, are endemic. Nearly one-half the bird fauna consists of restricted families, and two orders, the rheas and the tinamous, are confined to the region. The reptile fauna is shared with the Nearctic and, to a limited extent, with the Oriental and Ethiopian regions.

The Old World counterpart of the Neotropical is the Ethiopian, which includes the continent of Africa south of the Atlas Mountains and Sahara Desert, and the southern corner of Arabia. It embraces tropical forests in central Africa and in the mountains of East Africa, savanna, grasslands, and desert. During the Miocene and the Pliocene, Africa, Arabia, and India shared a moist climate and a continuous land bridge, which allowed the animals to move freely among them. This accounts for some similarity in the fauna between the Ethiopian and the Oriental regions. Both have the elephant and the rhinoceros, but they differ at the generic level. Also shared are the great apes. The Ethiopian region has the gorilla and the chimpanzee; the Oriental owns the orangutan and the gibbon. Later an ocean barrier developed; East Africa and Arabia dried out and interposed an arid grassland and desert between the tropical forests of Africa and India. On these drier lands exist the finest but disappearing examples of tropical savanna in the world with their remarkable herds of grazing ungulates.

Of all the regions the Ethiopian contains the most varied vertebrate fauna; and in endemic families it is second only to the Neotropical. Its fish, amphibians, and reptiles resemble both the Oriental and Neotropical, but its birds and mammals exhibit strong affinities with the Oriental region.

Lush forests cover much of the Oriental region, which includes India, Indochina, south China, Malaya, and the western islands of the Malay Archipelago. It is bounded on the north by the Himalayas and on the other sides by the Indian and Pacific Oceans. On the southeast corner, where the islands of the Malay Archipelago stretch out towards Australia, there is no definite boundary, although Wallace's line is often used to separate the Oriental from the Australian regions. This line runs between the Phillipines and the Moluccas in the north, then bends southwest between Borneo and the Celebes, then south between the islands of Bali and Lombok. A second line, Webers', has been drawn to the east of Wallace's line; it separates the islands with a majority of Oriental animals from those with a majority of Australian ones. Since the islands between these two lines is a transition between the Oriental and the Australian regions, some zoogeographers call the area Wallacea.

Of the tropical regions, the Oriental possesses the fewest endemic species and lacks a variety of widespread families. In many ways it resembles the Ethiopian region, as already discussed. It is rich in primate species, including two families confined to the region, the tree shrews and the tarsiers. Like Africa, it has few parrots, but the Oriental does possess an abundance of pigeons and pheasants. Reptiles are abundant, including the poisonous snakes and the pythons, and the slender-nosed fishing crocodilian, the gavial, which is restricted to the region. Unlike the Ethiopian, the Oriental has its share of bears, moles, tapirs, and deer.

Of all the regions, perhaps the most interesting and the strangest, and certainly the most impoverished in vertebrate species is the Australian. This includes Australia, Tasmania, and New Guinea, and a few smaller islands of the Malay Archipelago. New Zealand and the Pacific Islands are excluded, for these are regarded as oceanic islands, separate from the major faunal regions. Partly tropical and partly south temperate, this region is noted for its lack of a land connection with other regions, the poverty of fresh-water fish, amphibians, and reptiles, the absence of placental animals, and the dominance of marsupials. Endemic to the region are eight families of mammals, excluding the bats. Included are the Monotremes with the two egg-laying species, the duck-billed platypus, and the spiny anteater. The marsupials have become diverse and have evolved ways of life similar to those of the placental animals of other regions.

Birds of the region, however, belong to families of wide range; and its reptilian fauna, of which only two families are endemic, show close affinity with the Oriental region.

Life zones

Before the biome became generally accepted by ecologists, Merriam's life zones were commonly used to divide North America into several vegetational and faunal units. Although not widely used today, many vestiges of the life-zone concept still remain, enough to warrant some consideration.

Back near the close of the last century, C. Hart Merriam, then chief and founder of the United States Bureau of Biological Survey (later to become the Fish and Wildlife Service), proposed the idea of *life zones*. These are transcontinental belts running east and west. The differences between them, expressed by the animals and plants living there, supposedly are controlled by temperature. Merriam published his ideas first in 1894 in a paper entitled "Laws of Temperature Control of the Geographic Distribution of Terrestrial Plants and Animals," in the December *National Geographic* magazine. Later he summarized and expanded still further this idea in a U.S. Department of Agriculture bulletin, *Life Zones and Crop Zones of the United States*. Merriam developed this life-zone system after observing the sharp zonation of life on San Francisco Mountain in Arizona. Impressed with the importance of temperature as an influence on plant and animal distribution up the mountain, he formulated his two laws of temperature control. The first law states "that the northward distribution of terrestrial plants and animals is governed by the sum of the positive temperatures for the entire season of growth and reproduction." In determining the sum of positive or effective temperatures, Merriam assumed that a minimum of 6°C (43°F) marked the beginning of the period of physiological activity in plants and the reproductive activity in animals. The second law states "that southward distribution is governed by the mean temperature of a brief period during the hottest part of the year."

Merriam divided the North American continent into three primary transcontinental regions, the Boreal, the Austral, and the Tropical. The Boreal region extends from the northern polar seas south to southern Canada, with extensions running down the three great mountain chains, the Appalachians, the Rockies, and the Cascade–Sierra Nevada Range. The Austral region embraces most of the United States and a large part of Mexico. The Tropical region clings to the extreme southern border of the United States and includes some of the lowlands of Mexico and most of Central America. Each of these regions Merriam further subdivided into life zones.

The Boreal region he subdivided into three zones. The Arctic-Alpine zone, characterized by arctic plants and arctic animals, lies north of the tree line and includes the arctic tundra as well as those parts of mountains further south that extend above the timber line. The Hudsonian zone, the land of spruce, fir, and caribou, embraces the northern coniferous forest and the boreal forests covering the high mountain ranges to the south. The Canadian zone includes the southern part of the boreal forest and the coniferous forests that cloak the mountain ranges extending south.

337

The Austral region is split into five zones. First is the Transition zone, called the Alleghanian in the East, which extends across northern United States and runs south on the major mountain ranges. It is a zone in which the coniferous forest and the deciduous forest intermingle. Extending in a highly interrupted fashion across the country from the Atlantic to the Pacific is the upper Austral zone. It is further subdivided into the Carolinian area in the humid east and the upper Sonoran of the semiarid western North America. The lower Austral embraces the southern United States from the Carolinas and the Gulf States to California. In the humid southeast, it is known as the Austroriparian area and in the arid west as the Lower Sonoran.

Once widely accepted, the life zones are rarely used today, although they creep now and then into the literature on the vertebrates. They were supplanted by the biome, for the life zones oversimplified the real situation. In the first place a life zone is not a unit that can be recognized continent-wide by a characteristic and uniform faunal or vegetational component. There are wide differences in the Transition zones of the East, with its hardwoods, of the Rocky Mountains, with the yellow pine, and of northeastern California, with the redwoods. Thus the Transition covers too many types of vegetation and too many different animals to be useful. The life zones south of the Arctic and Canadian are not transcontinental; thus the Transition and Upper and Lower Austral of the East are totally different from those of the West. Then the temperatures at times of the year other than the season of growth and reproduction influence the distribution of plants and animals. However, recent studies on the relationship of metabolism to climate and distribution of three finches, the Cassin, the purple, and the house finch, in western North America indicate some correlation with Merriam's first law (Salt, 1952). In summer, Cassin's finch is found in the arid Canadian zone of the Great Basin; the purple finch inhabits the humid transition zone forest; and the house finch lives in the dry, warm Sonoran zones. Temperature and humidity seem to control the summer distribution of these birds. Daily maximum temperatures, rather than daily mean temperatures, are more important in limiting the southern distribution of some animals. Temperature fluctuations may have little effect on the physiology of an animal, but one high maximum temperature may not be endurable. Even the selection of 43°F as the threshold for physiological activity for plants and animals is too arbitrary, for organisms differ widely in this. Temperature may be quite important in controlling animal and plant distribution, but differences in moisture, topography, geological history, and evolution of species from stock isolated from the main parent population play an active role in determining the biotic community of a given region.

In spite of all this there is something evocative about the life-zone terminology. The Arctic-Alpine zone recalls the cold, windswept mountains above the timber line; and the name Sonoran, slowly spoken, sings of the sun-baked desert, cactus, mesquite, horned lizards, and roadrunners.

Biotic provinces

A third approach to the subdivision of the North American continent into geographical units of biological significance was the biotic-provinces concept, defined and mapped by Dice in 1943. It differs from the others in that a province embraces a continuous geographic area that contains ecological associations distinguishable from those of adjacent provinces, especially at the species and subspecies level. Each biotic province is further subdivided into ecologically unique subunits, districts, or life belts, based largely on altitude, such as grassland belts and forest belts.

Basically the biotic-province concept is an attempt to classify the distribution of plants and animals, especially the latter, on the basis of ranges and centers of distribution of the various species and subspecies. But the regions themselves and their subdivisions are largely subjective. The boundaries more often than not coincide with physiographic barriers rather than with vegetation types; and the regions never occur as discontinuous geographic fragments. Although a number of species may be confined to some biotic province, others occur over several provinces, since their distribution is determined more by the presence of suitable habitat, which is rarely restricted to a single region. Since the boundaries of biotic provinces and the ranges of subspecies of animals with a wide geographic distribution do coincide, this system is used at times by mammalogists, ornithologists, and herpetologists in the study of a particular group.

SUMMARY

Through the years, a number of attempts have been made to classify life into meaningful distributional units. Most of these attempts are faunistic in their approach, but one considers both plants and animals together. The first division of the world into distributional units was the biogeographical or faunal regions and realms. Of the latter, three are recognized and are further subdivided into six regions. Each region is separated by a barrier of oceans, mountain ranges, or deserts, which prevent the free dispersal of animals; and each possesses its own distinctive forms of life. Each region is further subdivided by secondary barriers, such as vegetation types and topography. These subdivisions have been recognized as life zones, biotic provinces, and biomes. The life-zone concept, restricted to North America, divides the continent into broad transcontinental belts, the plant and animal differences between which are governed chiefly by temperature. The biotic-provinces approach divides the North American continent into continuous geographic units that contain ecological associations different from those of adjacent units, especially at the species and subspecies level. The biome system groups the plants and animals of the world into integral units, characterized by distinctive life forms in the climax, the stage or point of development at which the community is in approximate equilibrium with its environment. Boundaries of biomes, or "major life zones," as they are known in Europe, coincide with the boundaries of the major plant formations of the world. By including both plants and animals as a total unit that evolved together, the biome permits the recognition of the close relationship that exists among all living things. The biomes today have been greatly disturbed by man. The preservation of samples of the original climax communities of each biome as indicators of the natural potential and limitations of a given region would provide a reference point against which man's influence on the natural environment can be assessed.

PART **IV**   *Population ecology*

CHAPTER **20**

Relations within a population

The community consists of populations of various interdependent species of plants and animals. The term population, like so many others, has come to mean many things. Considered ecologically, a population is a group of organisms of the same species occupying a particular space. But more than this, a population is a self-regulating system. It exists because new matter continually replaces that which it must inevitably lose. A population has a birth rate and a death rate, a growth form, density, and age structure, and a numerical dispersion in time and space. The study of the numbers of organisms and what determines their abundance and distribution is population ecology. As one might imagine, even in its simplest form, the laboratory population, the field is extremely complex.

Density

The size of a population in relation to a definite unit of space is its *density*. Every 10 years the Census Bureau counts the number of people living in the United States. Wildlife and fishery biologists determine the number of fish and

341

game in areas with which they are concerned. A forester cruises a timber stand to determine the volume and number of trees. These people may express their results as so many thousand per square mile, per acre, or per square meter. This is *crude density*. But populations do not occupy all the space within a unit, since all is not suitable habitat. A biologist might estimate that 500,000 deer live in a 40,000-square-mile area. The deer, however, will not utilize all the land within this area because of human habitation and land-use practices. A sample of soil may contain 2,000,000 arthropods per square meter. These arthropods do not inhabit the entire substrate, since they live only in the pore spaces in the soil. No matter how uniform a habitat may appear, it is in fact heterogeneous. There are microdifferences in moisture, light, temperature, exposure, to mention a few conditions. Each organism occupies only those areas that can adequately meet its necessary requirements, resulting in a patchy distribution. To be accurate, the density of organisms should refer to this amount of area available as living space. This would be *ecological density*. Determining just what area is available to any one particular kind of organism and just how suitable it is represents one of the most important problems in modern ecology.

The density of organisms on any area varies. It may change with the seasons, with weather conditions, with food supply, and many other influences. There is, however, an upper limit to the density of a population within a unit area, imposed by size and trophic level. Generally the smaller the organism, the greater its abundance per unit area. A 100-acre forest will support a greater number of woodland mice than deer. A forest stand will contain many more trees 2 to 3 inches dbh (diameter breast height) than trees 12 to 14 inches dbh. The larger its size or the higher its position on the trophic levels, the less is the numerical density of an organism.

The first problem a biologist faces in population studies is the determination of density. A demographer periodically can make a *total count* of the population of a nation, state, or city. Occasionally the biologist can do the same. Total counts of elk, deer, and caribou can be made, usually from the air, where these animals live in relatively open country or are concentrated in a small area. The number of waterfowl in concentrated areas can be counted from aerial photographs. Trees and other plants can be tabulated on selected study areas. For most organisms, animals especially, a total count of individuals is impossible, because of the nature of the habitat, habits of the animals, size of the area, and so on.

But some estimate of the population can be obtained by *sampling* a part of the population. By taking into account the variability within the population, one can make some general inferences about the population as a whole. To be valid, the samples must be completely random, that is all combinations of sampling units must have an equal probability of being selected. To characterize the population as a whole, certain constants called *parameters* are used. The proportion of males in a population is a parameter; so is the mean value per plot. The objective of sampling is to estimate some parameter or a function of some parameter. The value of a parameter as estimated from a sample is the *estimate*, which is hoped to be *accurate*—close to the true value. But often the estimate is *biased*. This is a systematic distortion due to some flaw in the measurement, or to the method of collecting the sample. It should be avoided, but often it cannot be. In any case the important thing is to recognize the source of bias and take it into account. A biased account can never be accurate, although it may be *precise.* Precision refers to a clustering of sample values about their own average.

Sampling may involve plots, quadrats, transects, or other means (Fig. 20-1). Foresters, for example, may sample a forest stand by measuring all trees in fifth-acre plots established along random cruise lines. More recently a plotless method involving the determination of basal area has been developed. Here a prismatic sighting gauge is used to count trees within a distance not more than 33 times their diameter. Plotless methods have been modified further by plant ecologists. One of the most useful is the quarter method (Cottam and Curtis, 1956). The distance from the sampling point to the nearest individual in each quadrat is measured (see Appendix B for details). The quadrats are determined by running a line at right angles through a point located on a transect line. Plot methods are used in invertebrate work, especially in the study of aquatic bottom fauna and soil fauna. The results from any of the samples taken are multiplied by an index figure to arrive at an estimate for a larger unit of area.

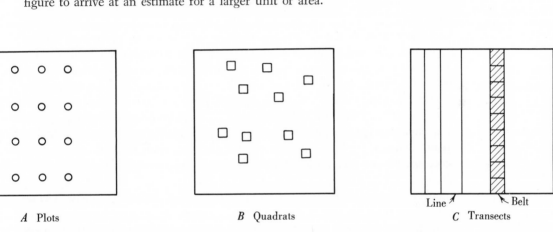

A Plots *B* Quadrats *C* Transects

Figure 20-1 (A) *Plots, rectangular and circular, established systematically;* (B) *quadrats, random and systematic;* (C) *transects: line and belt.*

Sampling procedures are full of difficulties. An adequate sample must be taken. This is influenced by the size of the area, the availability of the species, and the time involved. Areas being sampled must be large enough to include various levels of abundance. A student of animal populations has the added difficulty of fluctuating numbers because of the movement and individual susceptibility to trapping.

A method widely used in the study of animal populations is the *mark-recapture,* or *ratio.* This is widely known in wildlife work as the Lincoln index and in fisheries work as the Petersen index. The method was first described by C. G. J. Petersen in 1896 for fish. In 1930 F. C. Lincoln described its use in estimating waterfowl populations. The method involves the release of a known number of marked animals (banded birds, tagged rabbits or fish, toe-clipped rodents) into a given population. These animals supposedly redistribute themselves in the original population as they were before they were withdrawn. Then after an appropriate interval of time, a sample of the population is taken. An estimate of the total population is then computed by the ratio of marked to unmarked individuals (see Appendix C).

343

$$N : T \; : \; : \; n : t \quad or \quad \frac{T}{N} = \frac{t}{n}$$

where T = number marked in the precensus period
   t = number of marked animals trapped in census period
   n = total animals trapped in census period
   N = population estimate

The mark-recapture method has shortcomings. It assumes (1) that marked animals are as subject to sampling as unmarked ones; (2) that mortality of the two groups are the same; (3) that none of the marked animals lose their identification; and (4) that the population remains relatively stable between the two trapping periods. To increase the reliability of this method, biologists have resorted to complicated statistical calculations. In fact biometrics, or statistical analysis of populations, is assuming great importance in population sampling and estimation.

Indirect methods involve the use of signs such as tracks, droppings, browse, songs and calls, and hunting and fishing success as criterions of population size. These are not censuses, since they do not arrive at any density figure. They are useful in determining an index of abundance of an organism. This information is useful to compare one area with another. Such methods are used in wildlife work, where population information must be considered in determining seasons and bag limits. One example of the indirect method is the call index for bobwhite quail (Bennett, 1951). Routes are established along roads in quail country with stops spaced one mile apart. Starting an hour after sunrise, the observer drives the route for one hour. He stops at each station for 2 to 3 minutes, counts the number of birds calling, and drives to the next station. From this data an average number of birds per stop is computed and corrected by a factor for temperature. A number of such counts is taken over a state or region. Such information collected year after year indicates population trends.

Rarely can populations in nature be measured accurately enough so that density figures have any real meaning. Instead, indexes of relative abundance are often used. This is usually the case in studies of plant populations, since numbers alone do not indicate the relative importance of a particular species. Density counts in plants are most useful when measuring natural reproduction and the effects of fire, seeding, spraying, and the like.

One of the most useful measurements of plant populations is *cover,* the area occupied above ground by leaves, stems, and flowers as viewed from above. Since tall plants overtop smaller ones, each layer of vegetation is considered separately.

Coverage is best expressed as basal area, the ground actually covered by the crowns or by the stems penetrating the soil. Because basal area will differ when measured at different heights above ground, the values must be obtained in a standardized way. In forest ecology, basal area is the cross-section area of a tree measured at 4.5 feet above the ground (breast height). In grassland and range ecology, the basal area refers to the area at the height at which the grass is normally utilized (see Appendix C). This is usually one inch for sod grasses and three to five inches for bunch grasses. Measurements such as this have considerably more meaning and more stability than the total spread of the foliage, which varies within and between years and under different weather, grazing, and management conditions (Fig. C-4).

Coverage is obtained by a number of methods, including charting by hand, by estimating the area occupied by plants on a square-foot basis (Cain and Castro, 1960), by line intercept and point contact (see Appendix C).

Height, which reflects a plant's condition or vigor, is used as an indicator of the success or potential success of plant species in various habitats. Height measurements are most useful in forestry and range management. Foresters use height or *site index* to indicate the quality of a habitat to grow trees (Fig. 20-2). Range managers determine from height studies of herbage the time to start grazing in spring and the effects of clipping or grazing on grass species at different heights and frequencies.

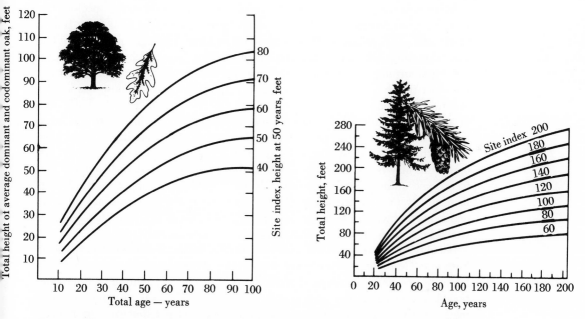

Figure 20-2 *Site index of white oak and sitka spruce. The site index of white oak is based on the height of the tree at 50 years of age; that of sitka spruce, at 100 years. A site index of 40 for white oak means that the trees on that particular area should grow to a height of 40 feet in 50 years; those growing on a site with an index of 80 should reach 80 feet in 50 years. The higher the index of the area for a particular species, the better the site. Commercial production areas for white oak usually are located on sites of 60 or better. (Oak index from G. L. Schnur, Yield, stand and volume tables for Even-aged Upland Oak Forest, U.S. Department of Agriculture Tech. Bull., 560, 1937. Spruce index from W. H. Mayer, Yields of Even-aged Stands of Sitka Spruce and Western Hemlock, U.S. Department of Agriculture Tech. Bull., 544, 1937.)*

Natality and mortality

Population density and increase depend upon the number of individuals added to the population and the number leaving or dying. In other words, the number of organisms depends chiefly upon the difference between the birth rate and the death rate and the balance between immigration and emigration.

345

Natality

The greatest influence on population increase is usually natality, the production of new individuals in the population. Natality often is described in two ways, as *maximum* or *physiological natality* and *realized natality*. Physiological natality represents the maximum possible births under ideal environmental conditions, the biological limit. Since this is rarely achieved in wild populations, it is of little value to the field biologist. It is somewhat theoretical but nevertheless is a useful yardstick against which to compare realized natality. Realized natality is the amount of successful reproduction that actually occurs over a period of time.

Maximum natality varies with the species and even within the species. The bluegill, a fish common in lakes and ponds, produces 4000 to 61,000 fry from a single nest. The pelagic codfish produce up to 61 million eggs per female. The ground-nesting bobwhite quail lays about 15 eggs per clutch, while the tree-nesting mourning dove lays only two eggs per clutch. The white-tailed deer has one or at the most twin fawns once a year; the white-footed mouse has a litter of four to six young four times a year. Lack (1947) suggests that the birth rates of animals are adjusted through natural selection (see Chap. 24) to the maximum rates at which the offspring are destined to reach adulthood. For some species this is the largest number of young the parents can rear successfully. For others this may be the maximum number the parents can feed, or brood and protect. Some animals, such as many fish and amphibians, simply lay their eggs in relatively unprotected masses. With these, the number of eggs laid probably represents that which the animal is physiologically able to lay. Here, too, selection would favor those that laid sufficient eggs to assure some survivors.

Natality, measured as a rate, may be expressed either as crude birth or specific birth rate. *Crude birth rate* is expressed in terms of population size, as for example 50 births per 1000 population. *Specific birth rate,* more accurate in its interpretation, is expressed relative to a specific criterion, such as age or condition. The most usual form is the number of offspring produced per unit time by females of age x, since reproductive success varies with age. Females of reproductive age are divided arbitrarily into age classes, and the number of births for each age class is tabulated. From this, an age-specific schedule of births can be constructed (Table 20-1). Since population increases are a function of the female, the age-specific birth schedule can be modified further by determining only the mean number of females born in each female age group. This information is known as the *gross reproductive rate,* in contrast with the *net reproductive rate,* which includes adjustments for mortality of females in each age group.

The reproductive rate is measured on the basis of mature females and omits the males and immature females. Useful for comparative purposes, the reproductive rate summarizes information on the frequency of pregnancy, the number of females born, and the length of the breeding season. Since the simplest methods of obtaining reproductive rates involve the counting of embryos, placental scars, the number of eggs and unfledged young in birds, the reproductive rate incorporates a measure of mortality of the original group of ova. In field work with wild populations, the reproductive rate may have little more than academic interest, since the important point is the number of offspring per unit female that survive to fledgling stage, or independence.

Mortality

The second great influence on population size is mortality. Like natality, mortality varies with age groups. In fact mortality is distributed according to age even more dramatically than births.

TABLE 20-1. Age-specific Birth Rates of Female Cottontail Rabbits

AGE CLASS	AVERAGE LITTER SIZE	PREVALENCE OF PREGNANCY	GROSS REPRODUCTIVE INDEX
Juvenile	4.72 ± 0.79	0.31	1.46
1 year	5.44 ± 0.80	0.77	4.19
2 years	5.87 ± 1.20	0.70	4.11
3 years	6.00 ± 1.12	0.68	4.08

From Lord, 1961.

Mortality, which begins even in the uterus and the egg, can be expressed either as the *probability of dying* or as a *death rate* (Davis, 1960). The death rate is the number of deaths during a given time interval divided by the average population, and is an instantaneous rate (see Appendix D). The probability of dying is the number that died during a given time interval divided by the initial population, the number alive at the beginning of the period. The complement of the latter is the probability of living, the number of survivors divided by the initial number in the group. Since the number of survivors is more important to the population than the number dying, mortality is better expressed in the terms of survival, or *life expectancy,* the average number of years to be lived in the future by members of a population.

To obtain a clear and systematic picture of mortality and survival, a life table can be constructed. The life table, first developed by students of human populations and widely used by actuaries of life insurance companies, is simply an account book of deaths. It consists of a series of columns, headed by standard notations, each of which describes mortality relations within a population when age is considered. It always begins with a certain size group, usually 1000, at birth or hatching (Tables 20-2 and 20-3). The columns include X, the units of age; d_x, the number dying in the stated interval; l_x, the number surviving in the stated interval; q_x, the probability of dying; e_x, the life expectancy at the end of each interval.

At first data for life tables could be obtained only for laboratory animals and humans. As census methods and age-determination techniques became more and more refined, data necessary for the construction of life tables for wild populations could be acquired. Deevey (1947) compiled data and constructed life tables for a number of wild species. Hickey (1952) constructed life tables for a number of birds, based on data obtained from banding recoveries.

Basically there are two kinds of life tables. One is the cohort type, the data for which are obtained by following a given group from birth until death. The other type is constructed from a sample of animals taken at one place at one time. It involves the assumptions that the birth and death rates are constant and

TABLE 20-2. LIFE TABLE FOR COTTONTAIL RABBITS

AGE INTERVAL IN MONTHS	OF 10,000 RABBITS IN UTERI			
	Number alive at beginning of month of age	Number dying during month of age	MORTALITY RATE[1]	COMPLETE EXPECTATION OF LIFE[2]
X	l_x	d_x	$1000q_x$	e_x
0–4	10,000	7,440	744	6.5
4–5	2,560	282	110	6.6
5–6	2,278	228	100	6.5
6–7	2,050	246	120	6.5
7–8	1,804	307	170	6.4
8–9	1,497	150	100	6.4
9–10	1,347	175	130	6.3
10–11	1,172	164	140	6.3
11–12	1,008	212	210	6.3
12–13	796	143	180	6.3
13–14	653	98	150	6.2
14–15	555	55	100	6.0
15–16	500	65	130	5.8
16–17	435	31	70	5.6
17–18	404	24	60	5.3
18–19	380	49	130	5.0
19–20	331	36	110	4.9
20–21	295	47	160	4.6
21–22	248	20	80	4.4
22–23	228	39	170	4.2
23–24	189	32	170	4.0
24–25	157	13	80	3.7
25–26	144	7	50	3.4
26–27	137	30	220	3.1
27–28	107	12	110	2.9
28–29	95	13	140	2.6
29–30	82	32	390	2.4
30–31	50	7	140	2.3
31–32	43	9	210	2.1
32–33	34	11	330	1.9
33–34	23	16	700	1.9
34–35	7	3	350	2.3
35–36	4	—	—	2.0
36–37	4	—	—	1.5
37–38	4	—	—	1.0
38–39	4	4	1000	0.5

[1] Number dying per 1,000 alive at beginning of month.
[2] Average number of months of life remaining at beginning of month of age.

Lord, 1961.

TABLE 20-3. LIFE TABLE FOR THE SPRUCE BUDWORM

x	$N(1_x)$	MF	$M_x(d_x)$	100 M/N	S_x
AGE INTERVAL	NO.[1] ALIVE AT BEGINNING OF x	FACTOR RESPONSIBLE FOR M_x	NO.[1] DYING DURING x	M_x AS PERCENTAGE OF N_x	SURVIVAL RATE WITHIN x
Eggs (to Instar I)	200	Parasites	18.0	9	
		Predators	12.0	6	
		Other	8.0	4	
		Total	38.0	19	.81
Instar I	162	Fall and spring dispersal, etc.	132.8	82	.18
Instar III	29.2	Parasites	11.7	40	
		Disease	6.7	23	
		Other[2]	6.7	23	
		Total	25.1	86	.14
Pupae	4.10	Parasites	0.53	13	
		Predators	0.16	4	
		Other[2]	0.70	17	
		Total	1.39	34	.66
Moths	2.71	Sex (46.5% females)	0.19	7	.93
Females × 2	2.52	Reduction in fecundity	0.50	20	.80
Normal females × 2	2.02	(No adult mortality or dispersal)			
Generation			197.98	98.99	.010
Normal females × 2	2.02	Adult mortality ± dispersal	0.99	49	.51
Actual females[3] × 2	1.03				
Generation			198.97	99.49	.005

[1] Number per 10 square feet of foliage.
[2] Minus interaction among all factors.
[3] A mutual egg density of 103 eggs in generation $n + 1$ divided by 200.

From Miller, 1963, in Morris, 1963.

the population size has long been stationary. The age of the individuals involved is determined by tooth wear, lens weight, or other means (see Appendix D). Approximate life tables can be developed for a wild population if the age of death for individuals is known from a random and adequate sample of a population or if the age structure of the living can be obtained at intervals. The d_x column, or number dying, can be estimated from the shrinkage between each successive age class.

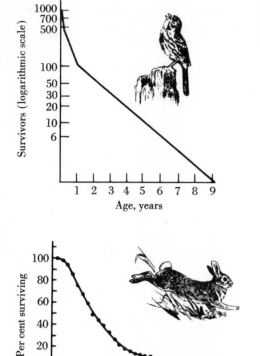

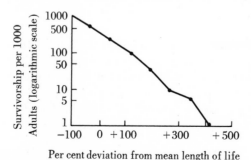

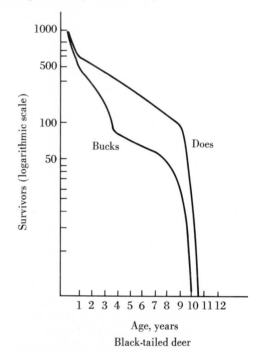

Figure 20-3 *Survivorship curves for the song sparrow* (from Johnston, 1956), *the cottontail rabbit* (Lord, 1960, courtesy the Illinois Natural History Survey), *and the black-tailed deer* (Taber and Dasmann, 1957). *The difference between the survivorship curves of bucks and does reflects the hunting seasons for bucks only.*

Black-tailed deer

From life tables, survivorship curves can be plotted. This is done in two ways. One is to plot the data from survivorship or l_x column against time, with the time interval on the horizontal coordinate and survivorship on the vertical coordinate (Fig. 20-3). The other method is to plot the data with the time interval plotted as per cent deviation from the mean length of life (Fig. 20-4). When plotted in this manner, survivorship curves for different species can be compared.

Survivorship curves fall into three types (Fig. 20-5). If mortality rates are constant at all ages, the survivorship curve will be a diagonal line (if plotted on semilog paper). Such a curve is characteristic of hydra and adult stages of many birds and mice. If mortality rates are extremely high in early life, as in oysters,

Figure 20-4 *A survivorship curve for the American robin,* Turdus migratorius, *expressed as a percentage deviation from the mean length of life.* (Adapted from Deevey, 1947.)

fish, and many invertebrates, the survivorship curve is concave. When individuals of a population tend to live out their physiological life span and when there is a high degree of survival throughout life and a heavy mortality at the end of a species life span, the survivorship curve is typical of man, deer, mountain sheep, and many other mammals (Fig. 20-3). Two weaknesses of all survivorship curves are the lack of data on the survival of young and the assumption that the curves are independent of crowding.

Age and sex ratios

Age ratio

Crude natality and mortality rates of a population are influenced considerably by age distribution within a population. Even density of a population is without much meaning until age structure is considered (Fig. 20-6).

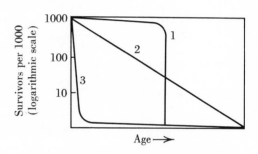

Figure 20-5 *Three basic types of survivorship curves. The vertical scale may be graduated arithmetically (see Fig. 20-3) or logarithmically. If graduated logarithmically, the slope of the line will show the following rates of change. (1) Curve for animals living out the full psysiological life span of the species. (2) Curve for animals in which the rate of mortality is fairly constant at all age levels—a more or less uniform percentage decrease in the number that survive. (3) Curve for animals with high mortality early in life.*

Populations may be divided into three ecological periods, prereproductive, reproductive, and postreproductive. The ratio of these three ages may vary, although the density remains the same. Theoretically at least, populations tend toward a stable age distribution; that is, the proportion of age classes in a closed population, where no immigration or emigration is taking place, tends to become constant when mortality equals natality. If this stable situation is disrupted by any cause, such as a natural catastrophe, exploitation, or emigration, the age composition will tend to restore itself upon the return of normal conditions.

Since reproduction is limited to certain ages and mortality is most prominent in others, the ratio of age groups is important to the future of the population. Changes in age-class distribution reflect changes in production of young, their survival to maturity, and the time when most losses occur. Hunting and fishing an unexploited population immediately alter the life expectancy of members of the population. Some age groups, particularly the young and old, are more vulnerable than others. Fish are selected by the size of the gill net. Such exploitation causes age ratios to shift, because of changes in age specific death rates (Fig. 20-7). This in turn affects the population birth rate. Age ratios are influenced continually by management subsequently applied to the exploited population. In

351

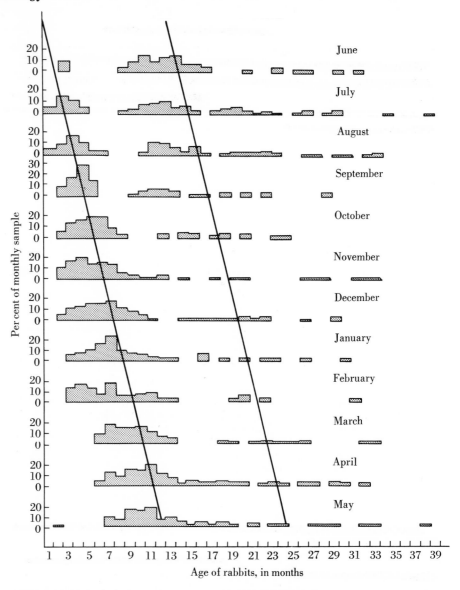

Figure 20-6 *Monthly changes in the age composition of a cottontail rabbit population in east-central Illinois. The black lines follow one age group. Note how rapidly the proportion of an age class declines as that age group grows older.* (From Lord, 1960; courtesy Illinois Natural History Survey.)

populations where life expectancy for the oldest ages is reduced, a higher proportion falls into the reproductive class, automatically increasing the birth rate. Conversely, if life expectancy is extended, a greater proportion of the population falls into the postreproductive age, reducing the birth rate (Fig. 20-7). This is true both of natural and human populations.

Basically a population can do three things: increase, decrease, or remain stationary. The ratio of young to adults in a relatively stable population is approximately two to one in most populations of game animals. A normally

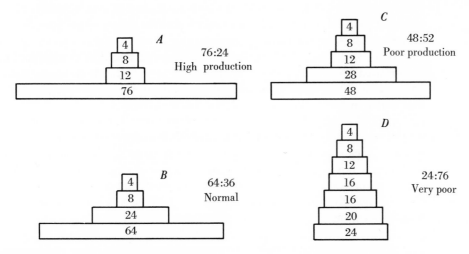

Figure 20-7 *Theoretical age pyramids for* (A) *a population with high production of young;* (B) *normal production;* (C) *low production;* (D) *very poor production. Note how the pyramids flatten out with high production of young. Pyramid D is typical of an aging population. These figures are based on the assumption that the life table is the same from* A *through* D.

increasing population should have an increasing number of young; a decreasing population a decreasing number of young (Fig. 20-8). Within this framework there are a number of variations. A population may be decreasing, yet showing an increasing percentage of young. Or a population might be stationary with a decreasing percentage of young. By combining information on population density, age ratios, and reproduction, a biologist can correlate changes in population structure with habitat changes, and ecological and human influences.

An example of the use and application of age structure in the management of natural populations can be found in the work on deer herds. One such

Figure 20-8 *Age pyramid of a black-tailed deer population in California chaparral. This pyramid is broken down by sex, showing sex ratio by age classes. The black skulls indicate mortality in each group.* (Redrawn from Taber and Dasmann, 1958, California Fish and Game Bull. No. 8.)

study concerned the deer herd of the northern Kaibab Plateau (Swank, 1958). Wildlife biologists found that fawn mortality over the winter varied from 20 to 56 per cent of the total fawn crop. They were able to correlate this with winter precipitation, which controlled the amount of forage produced in that area. If the precipitation were high enough to encourage an abundance of winter forage, fawn survival was good. Biologists also examined the reproductive tracts of does and found that the conception rate among yearlings varied from 27 to 70 per cent and among older does from 78 to 99 per cent. Since mature does made up the greater proportion of the doe herd, their conception rate was very important. They also discovered that the general trend in the conception rates of yearlings was a good indicator of herd vigor and range conditions. Thus a knowledge of age distribution and density, combined with information on habitat changes and other ecological conditions, can lead to an effective management program for game.

Sex ratio

The sex ratio at birth is often slightly in favor of males in vertebrates. By adulthood the sex ratio may favor either male or female, depending upon the species, mortality, and habitat. A study of muskrat populations in Wisconsin showed that the sex ratio is about equal at birth, but as early as three weeks the ratio shifts to about 140 males to 100 females (Beer and Traux, 1950). There is little or no change after this until the following breeding season. Then mortality from intraspecific strife brings the sex ratio back to equality again. Sex ratios of gray squirrels in West Virginia (Uhlig, 1955) and fox squirrels in Michigan (Allen, 1943) show a predominance of females, ranging from 51 to 60 per cent of the population. Among white-tailed deer, the males outnumber the females at birth and maintain their predominance the first year. By adulthood the ratio shifts strongly in favor of females, as much as 42 males per 100 females (Dahlberg and Guettinger, 1956). This apparently reflects the selective hunting of bucks (Fig. 20-8).

Males tend to be excessive among birds, particularly adult waterfowl (Bellrose et al., 1961). Fall and winter sex ratios of prairie chickens show a preponderance of males in adult groups (Ammann, 1957). Apparently there is some selective mortality of females of this species at an early age, which may be counterbalanced by a selective mortality of males during and prior to the breeding season. Sex ratios of the rusty lizard, on the other hand, are unbalanced in favor of females of older age classes (Blair, 1960).

The sex ratios of a population of some species may change with a change in population density. Snyder (1962) removed females from a population of woodchucks and then compared the sex ratio of the progeny to that of a control group in which the sex ratio was not disturbed. In the experimental area the sex ratio of captured young males to females was 100 to 222, while the ratio on the control areas was 100 young males to 97 females. The sex ratio of the fetuses in the experimental area was also heavily in favor of the females, in contrast to the control, where male ratio was higher. Increasing populations of gray squirrels and fox squirrels are associated with a predominance of females (Allen, 1943; Uhlig, 1955). Low populations of cottontail rabbits are associated with large populations of males (Linduska, 1947). Among polygamous species, such as the ring-necked pheasant and white-tailed deer, a large proportion of males can be killed off without affecting the population. This is considered in harvesting deer and pheasants, where the males can be distinguished from the females. But a continual harvest of males from such populations may permit females to increase to the point that the numbers grow beyond the carrying capacity of the range. In such cases it is necessary to harvest both sexes until a favorable sex ratio is established.

In any population of sexually reproducing animals in which a group of all males contribute as much to the ancestry of future generations as a group of all females, the sex ratio is the result of natural selection (see Chap. 24) (Fisher, 1929; MacArthur, 1961; Kolman, 1960). To rear young to independence, the parents must expend as much energy, time, and nutrients on the male fraction as the female fraction of the population. Other things being equal, the sex that is in short supply has the greater value per individual and will tend to be favored by selection pressures. For example, if males in a population suffer heavy mortality during the period of parental care, they are more expensive per individual to produce, since an expenditure is involved not only for those that survive but also for those that die prematurely. Thus there is a greater expenditure for each male reared, but less for each male born than for females at corresponding stages. Natural selection would tend to favor more males at birth. Because of a higher death rate, they would become less numerous, and by the end of the period of parental care, the sex ratio would be the result of differential mortality. In the end approximately the same expenditures would be involved for both the male and the female groups, but this equal expenditure does not imply equal sex ratios.

Population growth

Births, deaths, and movements influence both the number of organisms inhabiting a given area and the growth of the population. Like the individuals that make it up, a population grows from a small beginning until it arrives at some form of equilibrium with the environment. When a population first colonizes an unoccupied habitat, the environmental conditions in which it finds itself are, for all practical purposes, rather constant and the resources excessive. Under these conditions, the population increases geometrically in proportion to its numbers (Fig. 20-9). The rate at first is influenced largely by such hereditary features as litter or brood size, length of egg development and pregnancy, and length of the breeding season. As the population increases, the detrimental effects of increased density begin to slow down the growth until it reaches *carrying capacity,* the maximum number that can be supported in a given habitat. Once a population has reached or approached this level, it tends to fluctuate about it; but in some species it may be followed by a population crash before the numbers reach some sort of equilibrium with the habitat (Fig. 20-9). Only a certain density of any species can be supported by the resources available in any environment.

This concept was popularized by the English clergyman and economist Thomas Robert Malthus in 1798. The same idea, however, was expressed a number of times in a 200-year period before Malthus (Cole, 1957). In 1588, Giovanni

Botero suggested that human populations did not grow, because the environmental resources were insufficient to support a larger population. Sir Walter Raleigh in 1650 noted that although Spain sent large numbers of men to war, the size of the country's population remained stationary. This he attributed to the fact that Spain's population was adjusted to what the country could nourish. Later, in 1713, a Reverend William Derham asserted in a book *Psyciotheology* that the surface of the globe could support only a limited number of creatures. If they should multiply by doubling or tripling their numbers, they would starve or devour one another. This, he said, was prevented by balancing the number of individuals of each species in their environment. The balance

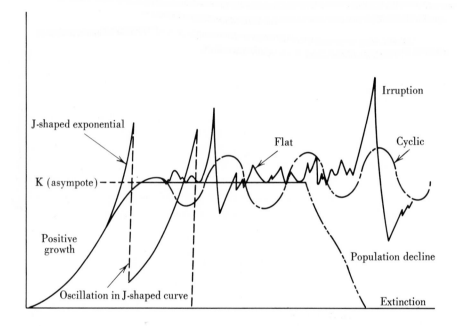

Figure 20-9   *The growth curve showing variations.*

was maintained since the length of life in each species was adjusted to its ability to increase.

The famous French naturalist Buffon in 1756 stated in his book that populations of plants and animals, including man, were subject to some type of control by physical forces. He noted that field mice populations were controlled in part by disease, spread by crowded conditions, and by intraspecific strife, fighting to death among one another when food was scarce. He also regarded predation as a powerful agent in checking population growth of rabbits and herring. He arrived at the concept that populations fluctuate between size limits, the fluctuations being compensated by variations in fecundity and mortality.

These concepts remained unnoticed until Malthus produced his essay on principles of population. His work was noticed at that time because England was suffering from overpopulation, while its Prime Minister, William Pitt, was urging an increase. Because Malthus did not foresee the tremendous technological advances that would, in effect, enlarge the environment, his principles fell into some disrepute.

Although Malthusian principles, temporarily at least, do not appear to apply to human populations in parts of the western world, they are nevertheless still biologically sound. The basic fact that population increase is checked by environmental limitations, including food, or the lack of it, disease, predation, strife, and lack of space is supported by a mass of data collected from natural and even local human populations. Ultimately human populations must stabilize at some number and at some level of subsistence, since there is an ecological limitation to the number of any species the earth can support.

Rate of increase

When births exceed deaths, the population increases; when deaths exceed births, the population declines. This can be expressed by a simple formula: $r = b - d$, where r is the difference between births and deaths, or the rate of increase. As long as b exceeds d, r is positive; when d exceeds b, r is negative. At a particular point in time, a population has a certain age distribution, which influences the schedule of births and deaths. If the age distribution is biased in favor of ages having the highest reproductive values, the rate of increase would be high, temporarily. In such a situation, r represents the actual rate of increase. But if within a population each age category remains constant and each age category is increasing at the same rate in an unlimited environment, then the population will have a constant age schedule of births and deaths and a stable age distribution (which rarely happens in nature, but is a point toward which all populations tend to go). Under these conditions, r reaches a certain value, which is the *intrinsic rate of increase*. It represents the rate of compound interest at which a population in an unlimited environment would grow.

Life history events, especially the physiological aspects, influence r (Cole, 1954). In general, r is increased in a continuously reproducing population by a reduction of the age at which a female first produces young, the average size of the litter, and longevity. Of these the age when a female produces her first young probably has the greatest influence on r. It takes two young to replace the parents, but the consequences of producing more than two young per lifetime varies greatly with the age at which reproduction takes place. Offspring from young females enter the reproduction period while the mother may still be producing young herself. In contrast, the offspring of those whose first reproduction came much later in life would not become a part of the reproductive population until the mother was in late reproductive or postreproductive stage. Thus the female who produces early begins to compound interest in the population much sooner. In man, for example, if a first birth occurred when the mother was 13, an average of 3.5 children per female would contribute as much to the future growth of a population as an average of six children would if the first birth came when the mother was 25 years old (Cole, 1954). The effect of increased litter size per female lifetime is very small if the initial reproductive age is very young. Again using man as an example, if human females on the average produced their first offspring at the age of 20 and had a total of five children spaced at one-year intervals, they would be contributing

357

almost half as much to the population growth as would hypothetical females capable of living forever producing a child every year. On the other hand, if the reproductive life of the female is short, or if initial reproduction does not occur until a relatively late age, an increase in longevity would significantly increase r.

Determination of r often is of more academic than practical interest. To do this, not only must the birth rate be determined, a difficult task in wild populations, but age-specific life tables must be constructed for the species in question. But there are situations in which r is useful. One is the investigations of granary pests, which typically exhibit "boom and bust" situations, in which the species suffers frequent exponential expansion (discussed below) in artificial environments. The index r can also be of limited use in the study of wild populations, especially while the population is in the lower portion of the growth curve. At this time the environment is changing little from the impact of the population; and because of the lack of crowding, age-specific fecundity and mortality rates are fairly stable. The rate of increase can be used to compare the differences in growth rates of two populations of the same species under different environmental conditions, and can serve as an indicator of the suitability of the environment and of the relationship between populations and their environment.

The growth curve

If a population were suddenly presented with an unlimited environment (as occasionally happens when an animal is introduced into a suitable but unoccupied habitat), it would tend to expand geometrically. In the beginning, the number of animals in the first age category would increase (because of births), while those of the older age groups would remain stationary. But as time goes on, the age categories increase as the survivors of the initial age groups grow older. As more animals enter into the reproductive stage, greater numbers of young are produced. Eventually after several generations the population will grow at a fairly steady rate. If the number of animals is plotted against time, the points will fall into an exponential-increase curve (the first part of the curve in Fig. 20-9); and if the logarithms of the numbers of animals are plotted against time, the points will fall in a straight line.

This exponential growth is expressed in a familiar equation,

$$\frac{dN}{dt} = rN$$

or, in its integrated form,

$N_t = N_0 e^{rt}$ where N_0 = the population at some arbitrary initial time
N_t = the number of animals at t time units later
e = the base of Naperian or natural logarithms
r = the intrinsic rate of increase

This in mathematical terms represents the increase of a population at geometric rates.

But the environment is not unlimited, nor does the age structure remain stable; and rarely do real populations reach the point of constant rate increase. As each category grows older, the ratio of its future offspring to those of its past, and the rate of increase for that group declines to zero. In 1838 the French mathematician Verhulst formulated an equation as a model of population growth in a limited environment. In 1920 Pearl and Reed in a classic paper plotted the growth of the population of the United States by years and fitted it to a curve described by the Verhulst equation. Mathematically the Verhulst-Pearl equation states:

$$\frac{dN}{dt} = rN\frac{K-N}{K} = rN\left(1 - \frac{N}{K}\right)$$

or, integrating,

$$N = \frac{K}{1 + e^{a-rt}} \qquad \text{where} \qquad a = r/K$$

where K is the maximum population size possible under environmental conditions. In words, the equation simply states that the rate of increase of a population is equal to the potential increase of the population times the proportion of the carrying capacity of the habitat that is still unexploited. It describes a logistic or sigmoid (S-shaped) growth curve (Figs. 20-9 and 20-10). The rate of increase, slow at first, grows until it reaches a maximum, the inflection point. The rate becomes progressively less as the density increases; the curve then flattens out as the population reaches the carrying capacity.

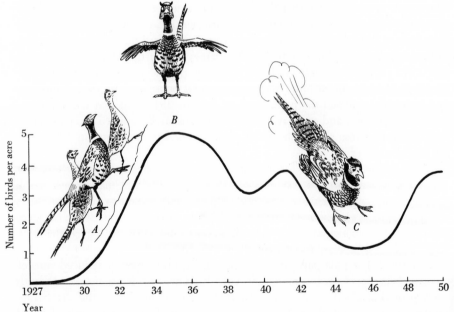

Figure 20-10 *A growth curve for the ring-necked pheasant on Pelee Island, Ontario.* (Curve redrawn from Stokes, 1955.)

359

This logistic equation has been criticized as unrealistic (Smith, 1952; Slobodkin, 1962), for it involves several assumptions that tend to simplify the situation. It assumes that all animals in the population have an equal chance to give birth or to die, to eat or be eaten, which eliminates the concept of age structure; that all animals respond instantaneously to changes in environment, when in fact adjustments often lag; and finally that there is a constant upper limit to the population in any particular situation. Furthermore it tempts investigators to try to fit empirical data to a predetermined curve.

The growth of a number of laboratory and natural populations is roughly sigmoid, especially if introduced in unfilled environments. As the density increases, population growth departs from the logistic and fluctuates. This is particularly true of animals with complex life histories, where different life stages may compete with or prey upon one another; or where each stage depends upon different environmental conditions and foods. As populations grow, age structure changes, causing population growth curves to fluctuate. For this reason it is very dangerous to predict the future of population trends from such a curve.

Another population growth form is the J-shaped, or exponential, curve (Fig. 20-9). This is similar to the sigmoid curve except that as the population approaches the asymptote, a sudden limiting effect, such as weather or space, causes the population to drop sharply. Such a growth curve often is found among insects as well as such mammals as the deer (see Mohler et al., 1951). The two growth forms may be combined or modified in a number of ways, depending upon the species and environmental conditions.

As indicated by the growth curves, the rate of increase or population growth is at a maximum where there are neither too many nor too few individuals. When the population falls below or exceeds this point, the rate of increase falls off. Increasing sparseness is associated with a reduction in rate of increase, the population may become so low that the rate of increase r becomes negative and the population dwindles to extinction. The heath hen is a classic example. Formerly abundant in New England, this eastern form of the prairie chicken was driven eastward by excessive hunting to Martha's Vineyard, off the Massachusetts coast, and to the pine barrens of New Jersey. By 1880 they were restricted to Martha's Vineyard. Two hundred birds made up the total population in 1890. Conservation measures increased the population to 2000 by 1917. But that winter, a fire, gales, cold weather, and excessive predation by goshawks reduced the population to 50. Numbers rose slightly by 1920, then declined to extinction in 1925. The last bird died in 1932.

There are several causes for the decline of sparse populations. When only a few animals are present, the females of reproductive age may have a small chance of meeting a male in the same reproductive condition. Many females remain unfertilized, reducing average fecundity. A small population also faces the prospect of increased death rate. The fewer the animals, the greater may be the individual's chance of succumbing to predation.

Overcrowded populations, on the other hand, often have a reduced rate of increase because of strife among individuals. This results in increased death rates, poor reproduction, aberrant maternal behavior increasing the death rate among the young and physiological derangement typified by low levels of blood sugar and liver glycogen. Disease and parasites spread rapidly through dense populations, often dramatically reducing numbers.

Life equations

A picture of the limitations of the growth of a population, seasonal gains and losses, and other important events occurring throughout the year can be summarized in a life-equation table (Table 20-4). Since slight changes in reproduction, survival, or sex ratios can influence the rate of increase considerably from year to year, the wildlife biologists, especially, finds the information summarized in the life equation highly useful.

The life equation is a modification of the life table. The life table is a

TABLE 20-4. Life Equation of a Black-Tailed Deer Population on a 36,000-Acre Area from 1949 to 1954

TYPE OF GAIN OR LOSS	MALES			FEMALES			Total
	Adults	Yearlings	Fawns	Fawns	Yearlings	Adults	
1949 Prehunting population	312	140	456	475	274	1,003	2,690
Legal hunting kill	204	3	—	—	—	—	− 207
Crippling loss and illegal kill	10	11	8	8	8	38	− 83
Winter losses	13	19	304	229	40	135	− 740
1950 Prefawning population	85	107	144	238	226	860	1,660
Fawning season gain	192	144	+707	+589	238	1,098	2,968
Summer mortality	2	1	221	83	12	52	− 371
Prehunting population	190	143	486	506	226	1,046	2,597
Legal hunting kill	125	25	71	86	43	160	− 510
Crippling loss	6	12	21	26	13	50	− 128
Winter losses	2	6	80	61	10	37	− 196
1951 Prefawning population	57	100	314	333	160	799	1,763
Fawning season gain	157	314	+617	+515	333	959	2,895
Summer mortality	2	3	311	195	17	48	− 576
Prehunting population	155	311	306	320	316	911	2,319
Legal hunting kill	96	9	—	—	—	—	− 105
Crippling loss	5	10	3	3	6	15	− 42
Winter loss	2	8	89	67	9	42	− 217
1952 Prefawning population	52	284	214	250	301	854	1,955
Fawning season gain	336	214	+762	+601	250	1,155	3,318
Summer mortality	3	2	436	260	12	58	− 771
Prehunting population	333	212	326	341	238	1,097	2,547
Legal hunting kill	178	80	62	64	55	205	− 644
Crippling loss	9	20	19	20	17	70	− 161
Winter loss	5	6	71	54	8	30	− 174
1953 Prefawning population	141	106	174	203	158	786	1,568
Fawning season gain	247	174	+608	+506	203	944	2,672
Summer mortality	2	2	338	225	10	47	− 624
Prehunting population	245	172	270	281	193	897	2,058
Legal hunting kill	85	26	38	36	18	70	− 273
Crippling loss	4	9	8	8	7	27	− 63
Winter loss	5	7	71	53	7	29	− 172
1954 Prefawning population	151	130	153	184	161	771	1,568

Adapted from Brown, 1961.

mathematical expression of the dynamic processes only, the vital statistics of a population. The life equation on the other hand illustrates changes within the population. The life equation involves a census or inventory of an identifiable population. Age in the life equation is referred to as stages in the life history of a population within one breeding cycle, instead of within a day, a month, or a year.

Life equations, like life tables, begin with a given population, usually 1000, broken down into sex and age categories. If a game animal is involved, the table begins with a prehunting population. Hunting losses then are subtracted, according to sex and age, leaving a posthunting population. The number left

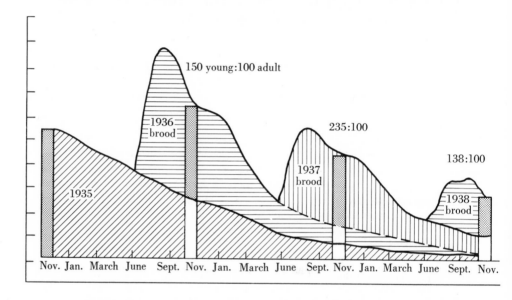

Figure 20-11 *Changes in a population of California quail. The bars indicate the ratio of mature to immature birds in November. This is a diagrammatic life equation.* (After Emlen, 1940.)

after winter losses comprise the prebreeding season population. To this is added the breeding-season gains. Finally a new prehunting-season population estimate is obtained one year later.

This tabular data of gains and losses can be presented as a sort of survival curve (Fig. 20-11). Curves of several years can be joined to illustrate numerical changes over a period of years. In addition, changes in age structure can be indicated by showing the proportions of several age classes (Fig. 20-8).

Life equations are not very accurate nor are they intended to be. Some categories in the equation cannot be measured accurately; other items are based more on estimates than on facts. At the same time other information might be quite correct. Properly constructed, the life equation shows the magnitude of population losses to several causes and where and when the heaviest losses occur. The life equation also indicates the extent and importance of production of young to the future of the population, gaps in knowledge of population behavior of the species involved, and the most important research problems for future study.

Regulation of populations

No animal population increases indefinitely. Eventually it arrives at some continuing state of balance, about which it fluctuates. The nature of the regulatory processes of animal numbers is a major problem of population ecology.

Basically population numbers are influenced by some force outside the population itself or by some force generated within the population. The former, extrinsic in nature, often is termed density independent, since the action or effect is constant, regardless of the size of the population. The latter, intrinsic in nature, is called density dependent, because the intensity of action varies with the density of the population. In natural situations, however, it is difficult, if not impossible, to separate the effects of each, for the two acting together influence nearly all population fluctuations.

Density-independent influences

In general, population fluctuations influenced by annual and seasonal changes in the environment tend to be irregular and correlated with variations in moisture and temperature. But how much these density-independent effects control or regulate animal populations is debatable.

The small insect *Thrips imaginis* of Australia lives as nymph and adult almost exclusively in flowers. It sucks sap from stamens, pistils, and petals, but especially the contents from pollen grains, without which it cannot grow nor lay eggs. The thrips population reaches a minor peak in August, the southern winter, increases during September, and reaches a peak in spring, November and December. During the long, dry summers, flowers are scarce; winter, a time of growth in southern Australia, finds a few flowers, but in spring, flowers grow in profusion. As a result of this abundance of food and living space, survival rates and birth rates of thrips are high. The flowers increase more rapidly than the thrips, so there is little chance of a food shortage; the environment, in effect, is unlimited. With the coming of summer, conditions change. Drought sets in, the flowers die, and the few blooms available to the thrips are scattered. The thrips that fly off to seek new flowers have little chance of finding food and die without reproducing. Yet there is no real shortage of food, for the number of thrips on the remaining flowers is still low. The population, large in November, declines as summer advances and, except for a slight respite in autumn, continues its decline through the winter, until the trend is reversed in the spring. Thus according to Davidson and Andrewartha (1948*a,b*) the seasonal changes in the abundance of thrips are related to the seasonal change of the accessibility of food (not an absolute shortage of food). Based on this, Andrewartha and Birch (1954) argue that yearly abundance of thrips and many other animals is determined by the previous year's density and the influence of weather, rather than by some density-dependent regulator. This viewpoint is severely criticized by some ecologists (Solomon, 1957; Nicholson, 1958; F. Smith, 1961). They argue that if peak numbers are highly correlated with weather conditions, then

363

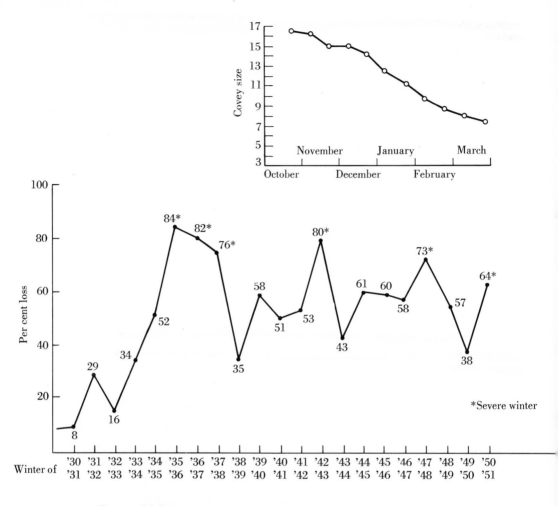

Figure 20-12 *Annual winter loss, expressed as a percentage, of bobwhite quail at Prairie du Sac, Wisconsin, showing the effects of severe winters. The years run from 1929 to 1951, inclusive. The inset shows the shrinkage of quail covies at Prairie du Sac during the winter. The graph is based on an average for 15 years, 1937–1951. (After Kabat and Thompson, 1963.)*

even these weather-induced changes must take place each year from some approximately constant number determined by some other other influence, undoubtedly density dependent.

This latter argument is supported by studies of the population of bobwhite quail in Wisconsin, a bird sensitive to severe winter weather. Data gathered over a 22-year period indicated that winter losses fluctuated directly with the number of months the ground remained covered with more than three inches of snow (Fig. 20-12). Losses ranged as low as 4 per cent during winters having less than one month of snow cover to 80 per cent during winters having a ground cover of snow lasting three months (Kabat and Thompson, 1963). However, only the most severe winter had any apparent direct effect on the population size the following fall. More important in controlling the population was the interrelation between winter losses, spring density, and summer and fall losses. When the spring population was low because of heavy winter mortality, the quail approached their full reproductive potential (intrinsic rate of increase). This resulted in a high summer gain and an increased fall population. Conversely, when the spring population was high, an intolerance developed between birds that significantly affected breeding behavior. Summer gains were suppressed and the fall population leveled off. There exists over the years a fairly stable level of population size about which the population fluctuates (Fig. 20-13). An adverse winter may cause a sharp decline in the population one year, but from this the population quickly recovers.

Too much or too little moisture can temporarily reduce populations. Drought can be a time of crisis for muskrat populations, as water levels of marshes become low (Errington, 1939, 1943, 1951, 1963). Muskrat burrows and entrances to lodges are exposed. Muskrats are forced to leave the area and take up residence in such unlikely places as corn cribs and woodchuck burrows. With water gone, foxes are able to reach the houses and feed on the stranded animals. When dry weather happens in late fall and early winter, muskrats are forced to channel below the frost line to seek retreats against the cold; and when food is frozen under, muskrats are forced to wander across the ice to seek another source. In doing so they expose themselves to the lethal dangers of cold, exposure, and predation, especially by mink. When the weather is extremely cold, muskrats may not be able to plug completely lodge and burrow openings for the lack of unfrozen mud and other material. As a result, many freeze to death. On the other hand, late spring floods drive muskrats out of burrows and lodges and drown the young. When wet years turn marshes into lakes, muskrats are forced

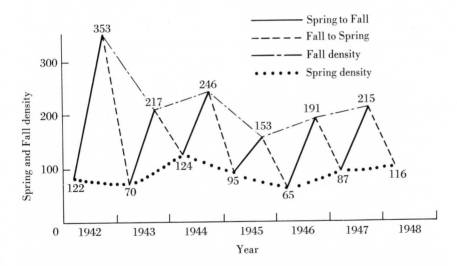

Figure 20-13 *Spring and fall densities, 1942 through 1947, of bobwhite quail at Prairie du Sac, Wisconsin. Note the seasonal fluctuation of population density from spring to fall back to spring again. Fall densities fluctuate far more than spring densities, which are fairly stable in this territorial species. (After Kabat and Thompson, 1963.)*

to live in danger close to shore and to seek shelter in woodchuck burrows, grain shocks, culverts, and cavities beneath tree roots (Errington, 1937*b*). After conditions return to normal, the population rises to its previous level, provided the habitat itself was not destroyed.

Heavy rains in May and June appear to be important in determining hatching success and juvenile survival among ring-necked pheasants (Stokes, 1955), as well as rabbits, quail, and other animals. Survival of the spruce budworm, which causes enormous damage in northern forests by consuming the flowers and leaves of spruce, balsam fir, and other conifers, is influenced by an interaction of temperature and moisture (Greenbank, 1956). Overwinter larval survival is high when temperatures fluctuate between freezing and thawing. Wet summers are inimical to active stages of budworms. Outbreaks usually start at times when the summers are clear and dry.

Man exerts one of the greatest influences on population rate of increase. Market hunting for hides, meat, and feathers exterminated or greatly reduced many species over the world. Man's ability to change environments has benefited some species, reduced others. Destruction of virgin forests in the South exterminated the ivory-billed woodpecker; cutting of the northern beech forests combined with market hunting caused the extinction of the passenger pigeon. Drainage of potholes in the prairie regions has seriously reduced waterfowl populations. Clearing of the forests and subsequent cultivation of land in eastern North America increased the habitat for open field birds and species of the edge. It permitted the eastward spread of such prairie life as the dickcissel and the coyote. In one way or another, whatever man does to the land, he influences populations.

Population growth of Oregon juncos is stimulated by timber harvesting in Douglas fir. As the cutover areas pass into weed and brush stages, the populations of this bird become two to three times as great as they were in the virgin forest. Other birds, like the red-breasted nuthatch, disappear (Hagan, 1960). A corresponding increase also takes place in the populations of white-footed mice. Three months after the timber is felled and the slash burned, the number of mice is equal to that of the uncut forest. In summer, when weedy vegetation covers the ground, the mice exhibit a high rate of increase. Two to three years later, as the area passes into the brush stage, the mice erupt. From the fourth to the tenth year the mice are three to four times as abundant as in the forest. After this the number of mice steadily declines to the original level (Tevis, 1956).

One of man's more recent influences is the widespread use of pesticides. Numerous studies point out the effects of pesticides on wildlife populations not only by direct killing but also by lowering fecundity (see Rudd and Genelly, 1956). At East Lansing, Michigan, annual spraying of elm trees to control Dutch elm disease resulted in a heavy mortality of robins. They died from DDT poisoning caused by feeding on earthworms that had built up a concentration of DDT, obtained from soil and fallen leaves, in their tissues. Reproduction failed almost entirely in those robins that survived. Treetop and trunk-feeding birds virtually disappeared from the spray areas (Wallace, 1959). Spraying elms in Wisconsin caused songbird density to drop 38 to 90 per cent below that of unsprayed areas. Robin populations declined 69 to 98 per cent below those in unsprayed communities (Hunt, 1960). Use of heptachlor and dieldrin to control fire ants in several southern states resulted in heavy mortality of vertebrate life, including birds, reptiles, amphibians, and mammals. On treated areas, bobwhite quail mortality was nearly 100 per cent (Clawson, 1958). Nesting success of red-winged blackbirds was reduced 50 per cent on areas treated in March and 100 per cent on areas treated in May (Lay, 1958).

The use of pesticides also affects populations by interfering with the food chain. Food organisms may be killed off, resulting in mass starvation of animals dependent upon them. Pesticides accumulate at low levels in tissues of organisms low in the food chain. As the material passes up through the food chain, it becomes more concentrated, until the final feeding organisms die from lethal doses. Clear Lake in California received repeated treatment of DDD (dichloro-diphenyl-dichloroethane) to control gnats. The first treatment, made in 1954, appeared harmless to other life; but after the second treatment in 1954, breeding western grebes disappeared. In seven years hundreds of migrant grebes died from DDD poisoning. Fish upon which they fed contained amounts of DDD stored in body fat ranging from 40 to 2500 parts per million. Four to five times as much DDD was found in 7-year-old bass as in yearlings. Plankton collected in the lake contained 5.3 parts per million of DDD, although no trace of DDD was found in water samples except shortly after spraying. Thus the fish apparently built up a concentration of DDD above residual tolerance level by consuming insects and other small organisms killed by or containing the pesticide (Hunt and Bischoff, 1960).

Since this study, further evidence of the detrimental effect of DDT and related pesticides on animal life has accumulated (see, for example, Pesticides, *Wildlife Studies,* Fish and Wildlife Circular 199, 1963; Rudd, 1964). The bald eagle, the osprey, the duck hawk of North America, and the peregrine falcon of Europe have declined alarmingly in the past 10 years. The first two are fish-eating birds; the latter two feed on birds that are fish eaters. All exhibited impaired fertility and mortality. Examination of eggs, remains of fish about the nest, and carcasses of the birds revealed accumulations of DDT and other chlorinated hydrocarbons. A declining lake-trout fishery in areas of high DDT use in New York state prompted an investigation of the cause. DDT was extracted from the oil of spawning females; and a direct relationship existed between parts per million of DDT in the ether-extracted oil of eggs and the mortality of fry (Burdick et al., 1964).

Density-dependent effects

Among most species the mechanism for the regulation of populations within the limits imposed by the environment are largely density dependent. Through such mechanisms, animals avoid the hazard of destroying their environment and even bringing about their own extinction. It appears that this regulation of animal populations is a homeostatic process, that there is an automatic governor or self-regulator that keeps population density and resources in balance. As population grows too large, some density-dependent effect acts to reduce the population. If a population falls below a certain level, the density-dependent processes fade and the population builds up. Such a feedback system results in oscillations, or regular fluctuations. In general these oscillations will move

367

about an equilibrium density, the level at which the production of offspring precisely compensates for the loss of adults by death. Any departure from this level brings compensating reaction or self-regulation into play, which ceases as soon as an equilibrium density is obtained again. Since a time lag is involved in these oscillations, an equilibrium density is rarely attained; for animals take a significant time to grow up and join the reproductive segment of the population.

Intraspecific competition. When a number of animals utilize a common resource that is in short supply, they are said to compete. Intraspecific competition is considered one of the major processes in the regulation of population (see Nicholson, 1954), although some ecologists disagree (see Andrewartha and Birch, 1954; Andrewartha, 1961). While the over-all effect of competition in a natural population may be debated, the fact does remain that some sort of competition exists within a population. Of the various components of the environment, the two that are apt to be in short supply in relation to population density are space and food.

In a long-term experiment involving the sheep blowfly, *Lucilia cuprina,* Nicholson demonstrated the influence of intraspecific competition in a population. Although the experimental population lacked all the complex interactions one would expect to find in nature, the work does show what might or could happen.

In one experiment, Nicholson fed to a culture of blowflies containing both adults and larvae a daily quantity of beef liver, plus an ample supply of dry sugar and water for the adults. The number of adults in the cages varied with

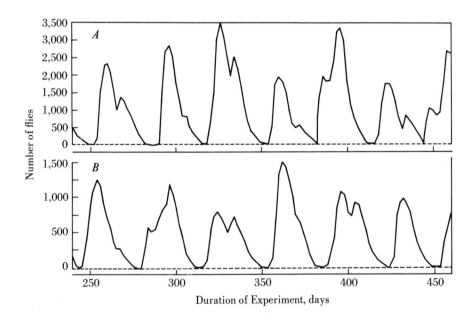

Figure 20-14 *Fluctuations in the number of adult blowflies,* Lucilia cuprina, *in cultures subjected to constant conditions but restricted to a daily quota of food: 50 grams of food in A, 25 grams in B. (Redrawn with permission from Nicholson, 1957,* Cold Spring Harbor Symposia on Quantitative Biology *22:156.)*

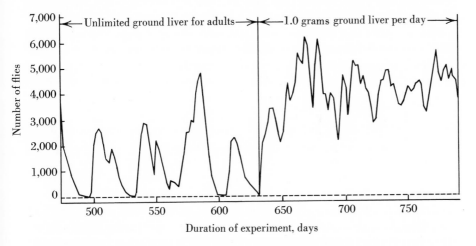

Figure 20-15 *Fluctuations produced by restricting the daily quota of ground beef for adult sheep blowflies to 1.0 grams after a period of ample supply, in a population governed by larval competition for a daily quota of 50 grams of meat.* (Redrawn by permission from Nicholson, 1957, *Cold Spring Harbor Symposia on Quantitative Biology, 22:158.*)

violent oscillations (Fig. 20-14). When the number of adults was high, they laid such a vast number of eggs that the resulting larvae consumed all the food before they were large enough to pupate. As a result, no adult offspring came from the eggs laid during that period. Through natural mortality, the number of adults progressively declined and few eggs were laid. Eventually a point was reached where the intensity of larval competition was so reduced that some of the larvae secured sufficient food to grow to a size large enough to pupate. These larvae in turn gave rise to egg-laying adults—after a developmental period of about two weeks. Meanwhile the population continued to decline, further reducing the intensity of larval competition and permitting an increasing number of larvae to survive. Eventually the adult population again rose to a very high level and the whole process started over again.

Competition for limited food held this blowfly population in a state of stability and prevented any indefinite increase and indefinite decrease. But the time lag involved between the addition of egg-laying adults by the way of larval survival to the declining population resulted in an alternate over- and under-shooting of the equilibrium position, causing an oscillating population density.

In a second part of the experiment, Nicholson supplied the adults with a surplus of suitable food, which was unavailable to the larvae. As a result of the enormous quantity of eggs laid by the adults, larval competition intensified and eventually the density of adults decreased in a manner comparable to the experiment described above (Fig. 20-15).

In another variation, the larvae were supplied with a surplus of food and the adults were given a constant daily quota of protein food. Again the adult population oscillated. The adults produced a high number of eggs which, because of the lack of larval competition, nearly all developed into adults. The adults competed intensively for a limited amount of food. Lacking sufficient protein

369

needed for the production of eggs, the adults laid fewer eggs; and for the lack of replacements the adult population declined. Competition was gradually relaxed to a point that some of the flies obtained enough protein to produce eggs. After a two-week lag the adult population began to build up again.

From these results Nicholson felt that the magnitude of the oscillations would be reduced if the larvae and the adults each competed for a limited quantity of food not available to the other. This assumption was confirmed experimentally. Under the conditions described not only were the fluctuations slight, but they had lost their periodicity, and the mean population level was nearly quadrupled.

In these competitive situations, the larvae and the adults were seeking food, the rate of supply of which was not influenced by the activity of the flies. In effect the resource, or food available, could be subdivided into many small parts to which the competitors, the larvae and the adult flies, had general access. The individuals "scrambled" for their food, which under gross crowding resulted in wastage. Each competitor got such a small fraction of the food that it was unable to survive and take a part in sustaining the population. "Scramble" competition tends to produce violent oscillations in the population not caused by environmental fluctuations. It limits the average density of the population far below that which the food supply could support if there were no wastage.

In contrast to the scramble type of competition is the "contest" type, in which each successful individual claims a supply of requisites sufficient for self-maintenance and reproduction. Since unsuccessful individuals are denied access to food or space by the successful competitors, the deleterious effects of shortage are confined to a fraction of the population. This either eliminates or greatly reduces the wastage of food, permits the maintenance of a relatively high population density, and prevents violent oscillations in numbers.

The end result of intraspecific competition is an increasing mortality rate as the population increases. This mortality usually is the heaviest among the young and directly influences the recruitment of new reproductive members to the population. The effect of density-dependent mortality upon this recruitment or addition is in part a function of the number of parents that produce the offspring. This relationship can be shown graphically by plotting net reproduction (mature progeny) against the density of the stock that produced them. The resulting graphs are known as reproduction curves (Ricker 1954, 1958a,b) (Fig. 20-16).

Reproduction curves consist of two parts: a diagonal 45-degree line and a domed curve. The 45-degree line represents the replacement level of the stock, reproduction in which density-dependence is absent. The filial generation tends always to be equal to the parental except for density-independent deflections under such conditions. Such a stock has no mechanism for the regulation of its numbers. Eventually by chance it would decrease to zero. The domed curve plots the actual recruitment in relation to the density of parent stock. As indicated by the sigmoid growth curve, maximum recruitment occurs at some intermediate level of abundance. The ascending limb is steeper than the descending limb. The apex of the domed curve lying above and to the left of the diagonal line represents the maximum replacement reproduction. The curve must cut at least once and usually only once the 45-degree line and must end below and to the right of it. Where the curve and the diagonal intersect is the point at which the parents are producing just enough progeny to replace current losses from the reproductive units. Basically any curve lying wholly above the 45-degree line would describe stock that is increasing without limit, something that does not exist in nature. A curve below the 45-degree line would describe stock headed for extinction.

There are, of course, many kinds of reproduction curves. Four of them are shown in Figure 20-16, *A, B, C,* and *D.* In these curves recruitment rises to a maximum as the density of the parental population increases and then falls off. They differ in the size of maximum recruitment and in the size of the parental stock necessary to reproduce the maximum. Curve *B* represents a population in which scramble competition exists and in which a low density of parental stock is not very productive. This contrasts with the other curves in which the maximum

Figure 20-16 A set of reproduction curves. In curves A, C, and D, reproduction rises to a maximum as the density of parental stock increases, but they differ in the magnitude of maximum reproduction relative to replacement level and in the size of the parental stock that produces the maximum. Curve A is typical of territorial animals, a contest type of competition; curves B and C with a steep right climb are characteristic of scramble competition. B represents a situation in which the lowest stock densities are not very productive. Curve E represents a stock-reproduction relationship in which there is an oscillation equilibrium. This curve will generate the cycle shown in the lower right-hand square when the population consists of single-age parental stock. The values of the ordinate and abscissa represent fractions or multiples of replacement level of stock. For the mathematical determination of these values, see Ricker, 1958a,b.) (Based on Ricker, 1958a,b.)

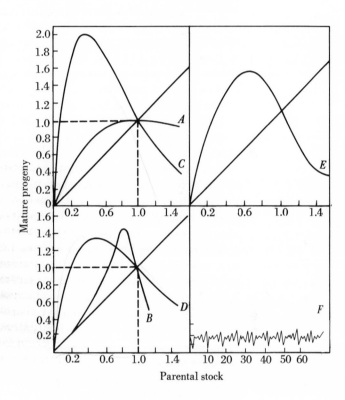

production for the parents occurs when density is low. The flatter dome and more gently inclined limbs of curve *A* are typical of territorial animals (contest competition) whose populations are divided into partially distinct units, so that the effects of density are not uniformly felt through the stock. In curves *C* and *D* substantial reproduction takes place only over a narrow range of stock densities considerably below the equilibrium level.

An interesting aspect of these reproduction curves is that they generate cycles within a single-species population in a constant environment, just as happened in Nicholson's blowfly experiments. In curves *C* and *D,* for example, the increasing density of stock exceeds and precedes the replacement number. In such a situation a population tends to oscillate in abundance. If the reproduction curve crosses the 45-degree line with a slope between -1 and $-\infty$, as it does in curve *E,* a population of single-age parental stock will have an irregular but permanent cycle of abundance (Fig. 20-16F); if the parental stock is multiple aged, the cycle is more regular. On the other hand, if the right-hand slope of the curve is between 0 and -1, the cycles are damped and eventually disappear.

Social behavior: territory. Intraspecific competition expresses itself in the social behavior of animals (see Chaps. 26 and 27) as the degree of tolerance and intolerance between individuals of the same species. As Wynne-Edwards (1962, 1965) points out, social behavior is a mechanism that regulates population by controlling the number of animals permitted to breed and by influencing the number of young each breeding pair is conditioned to produce.

Social behavior, as expressed by territoriality and hierarchy, limits the number of animals to a habitat, food supply, and reproductive activity, and excludes the surplus. This right to food, the right to space, and the right to reproduce are the greatest competitive situations in which an individual animal can engage. It is a contest type of competition in which violence is minimized and in which conventionalized display is used to intimidate rivals.

Territoriality exists when an individual animal claims a certain area and defends it against others of the same species and perhaps even against others of different species. It is most conspicuous during the critical breeding season.

Territoriality is a system that results in the parceling out of the habitat into a mosaic of breeding and feeding areas. It spaces the animals more uniformly over the area. Surplus individuals are forced into poor habitats to form a sort of a floating population reserve. Kluyver and Tinbergen (1953) studied wild populations of three species of titmice (Paridae) in two kinds of woodland, mixed and pine. One of these birds, the great tit, preferred mixed woodland. As the population increased to the limits of territorial compressibility, the surplus was forced to live in the less acceptable pine woodland. In such situations, the animals living in the poorer habitat are available to fill in territories vacated by mortality. Stewart and Aldrich (1951) counted 148 territorial male birds in a 40-acre spruce forest in Maine from June 6 to June 14, 1947. From June 15 to July, they shot from the area 302 territorial males, 84 adult females, 34 adults for which sex was not determined, and 35 young birds. The large number of males over the census count undoubtedly represented new birds that moved into the area to occupy the vacated territories. Hensely and Cope (1951) returned the following year. The area then was occupied by 154 territorial males. A subsequent removal of all birds this time included 352 territorial males.

A similar situation exists in red grouse, a game bird of the Scottish moors (Jenkins et al., 1963). When the breeding habitat is occupied, surplus birds without territories disperse to marginal habitats. As a result there are three social components: mated and unmated territorial owners, surplus nonterritorial residents on marginal interspaces, which form the floating reserve, and surplus transients for whom long-term survival is impossible. These birds eventually succumb to disease, parasites, and predation.

Autumn territoriality appeared to control the population of song sparrows on Mandarte Island off the coast of southern British Columbia (Tompa, 1962, 1964). Because of a homogeneous and simple vegetational community of grassland and shrubs, the island lacked a diversity of bird life but provided an optimum habitat for song sparrows. The population density was high and low mortality of young during the breeding season produced a large gain in the fall population. Autumn territorialism coincided with major population movements of the young. Adult males were aggressive towards territorially active young. As the young males began to space themselves, they were hostile to one another. Those unable to settle in fall territories left the island. Final status of the new recruits to the population was determined by territorial clashes in the spring.

Territoriality then appears to control both under- and overpopulation. Since excess animals are forced into less suitable habitat to form a "floating reserve," overpopulation of better habitat is avoided. When mortality creates openings, the vacated territories are reoccupied by individuals moving in from marginal areas. In addition to stabilizing the population, territoriality also assures resident animals of isolation. The territory provides a place for courtship and mating without interference from others of the same species. At the same time the losers are excluded from breeding. Their sexual development may be inhibited; they contribute nothing to posterity; and in most cases they even forfeit their right to survive. (The behavioral aspects of territory are discussed in detail in Chap. 27.)

The size and shape of territories vary widely among animals (Fig. 20-17). The size of territory is usually larger at the beginning of the breeding season but becomes compressed because of pressures from other members settling in the area. Territories tend to be larger when the population density is low; but as the density increases, territories may be greatly compressed, although there is a limit to the minimal size acceptable. When members of a population occupy minimum-sized territories, the density has reached the saturation for the area. Territories of passerine birds vary from one-third to three acres. The Iowa darter defends a territory 30 to 60 centimeters, and the greenside darter from 80 to 100 centimeters (Winn, 1958*a*, *b*); the vicuna defends a territory from 20 to 130 acres (Koford, 1957). Size of territory among salmon and other fish appears to be correlated with the size of the fish. As the fish increases in size, it intensifies its territorial defense. Smaller, less dominant fish relinquish territory and locate in areas less favorable for food and thus for further growth.

The shape of the territory varies, influenced by topography and other environmental features. Generally the territory is roughly circular, except among stream dwellers, whose territories usually are linear. Territories among birds have not only width and depth but also height, which is regulated by the height of the canopy where the bird sings and feeds (Fig. 20-18) (Martin, 1960; Stenger and Falls, 1959).

Social dominance and hierarchy. A tendency exists among many animals to band together in flocks, herds, or schools. Many of these animal aggregations, especially among the vertebrates, have some form of social organization based on intraspecific aggressiveness and intolerance and on the dominance of one individual over another. Two opposing forces are at work in these social groups. One is a mutual attraction toward one another—gregariousness, the impulse of individuals to be in and remain with some group. At the same time the animals exhibit a degree of social intolerance, a negative reaction against crowding. This aggressiveness limits the size of a herd or a flock. In small groups, aggressiveness may be minimal, but as the population grows more dense, as space becomes less, aggressiveness increases. Each individual occupies a position in the group based on

373

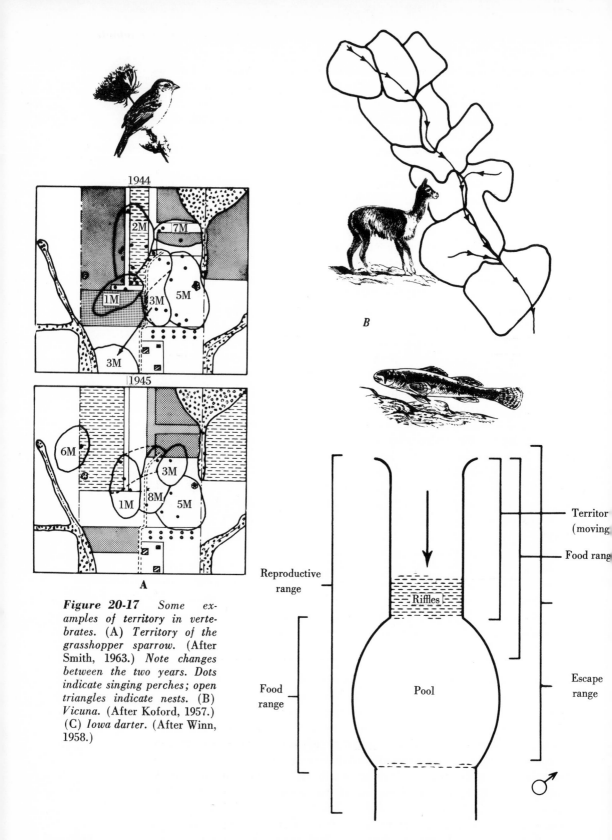

Figure 20-17 *Some examples of territory in vertebrates.* (A) *Territory of the grasshopper sparrow.* (After Smith, 1963.) *Note changes between the two years. Dots indicate singing perches; open triangles indicate nests.* (B) *Vicuna.* (After Koford, 1957.) (C) *Iowa darter.* (After Winn, 1958.)

dominance and submissiveness. Social rank is determined by fighting, bluffing, and threat at initial encounters between any given pair of individuals or at a series of such encounters. Once social rank is established, it is maintained by habitual subordination of those in lower positions, reinforced by threats and occasional punishment meted out by those of higher rank. Such organization results in social harmony by stabilizing and formalizing intraspecific competitive relationships and by resolving disputes with a minimum of fighting and consequent waste of energy.

Figure 20-18 *Territories of birds have height as well as width and depth. The bars indicate the height of territorial defense by several birds in a spruce-cedar forest.* (A) *white-throated sparrow;* (B) *magnolia warbler;* (C) *yellow-bellied flycatcher;* (D) *red-breasted nuthatch;* (E) *golden-crowned kinglet;* (F) *olive-sided flycatcher.* (Adapted from Martin, 1960.)

Home range. Contrasting with territory is home range, the area over which an animal habitually travels while engaged in its usual activities. Among some species, home range and territory are the same. Among others only a part or none of it is defended. The two sexes may have the same or different home range; however, these overlap and the home range of the male may embrace those of several females.

The home range is highly variable, even within a species. Seldom is it rigid in its use, its size, its establishment. The home range may be compact, continuous,

375

and usually circular, especially in uniform habitat. Or it may be broken into two or more disconnected parts reached by trails and runways. Irregularities in the distribution of food and shelter produce corresponding irregularities in the home range and in the frequency of animal visitation. The animal does not necessarily visit every part daily. Its movements may be restricted to runways or its activities may be concentrated in the most attractive parts. These centers of activity vary with the season, the age of the occupant, and the intraspecific and even interspecific competition. Woodchucks may move between five to seven different dens throughout the year (Merriam, 1960). And the beach mouse may have as many as 20 holes, only five of which may be in continuous use (Blair, 1951). These holes may be abandoned and replaced by new ones. But the most heavily used area at any given time is about the home site, which is not necessarily in the middle of the home range.

Variations in home range are associated with the species, sex, and age of the animal, with the season, and with such ecological conditions as available food, cover, and intraspecific strife (Fig. 20-19).

The size of the home range is rather closely related to the body weight of the animal (McNab, 1963). This influences the rate of energy expenditure and the amount of food needed by the animal. Also involved are the feeding habits of the animal—whether it is a "hunter" or a "nonhunter." Rabbits, which are nonhunters, have small home ranges relative to their body size, while the tree squirrels, essentially the same weight, require a much larger home range. They must "hunt" for and store the acorns, nuts, and seeds that form the major part of their diet. Deer, too, have a relatively restricted home range. The white-tailed deer under normal conditions remains in about a one-half-square-mile area. The mule deer spends its life in about 250 acres. Tagged white-tailed deer in New York State moved only three-quarters of a mile (Severinghaus and Cheatum, in Taylor, 1956), while in Texas, tagged deer remained within a radius of a mile (Hahn and Taylor, 1950). In fact the home range of croppers or nonhunters is about four times smaller than that of the hunters, since there is a greater concentration of food material for the former in a given area.

The kind of food utilized also influences the size of home range. Large predators that feed on large prey, such as the mountain lion preying on deer, require a large home range to maintain a prey population high enough to support the predator. The lynx, for example, has a home range of six to eight square miles (Saunders, 1963). Some predators have a restricted home range, since they utilize a diversified food source and use the area more efficiently. One such efficient carnivore is the fox, whose home range is about one square mile. This contrasts with the smaller pine marten, which feeds largely on red squirrels and snowshoe hares and has a home range of around seven square miles (Marshall, 1951). It follows that such species, because of their food choice and energy requirements, cannot maintain locally dense populations.

Other influences on the area of the home range are the sex and age of the animal. In general the home range of females is smaller than that of the males. When females are preoccupied with young, their home range is quite restricted and even defended against both sexes and all age groups, as in the case of the female gray squirrel (Bakken, 1959) and the chipmunk (Burt, 1940). The male snowshoe hare has a home range of around 25 acres and the female about 19 acres (Adams, 1959). The larger home range of the male may be associated with his increased curiosity and his search for mates. Juveniles tend to have smaller home ranges than adults.

Like territory, the home range provides the animal with its necessities of life—food, cover, water, a place to rest and to rear the young. By remaining within a restricted area the animal becomes extremely familiar with the environment where the food is located and knows where the best shelter is located and where to escape from its enemies. Such familiarity places the animal at a great advantage over its enemies and any newcomers in the area. The ability of an animal even as large as a fox or deer to outwit a hunter in a restricted area attests to the animal's extraordinary knowledge of its immediate surroundings.

Endocrine balance. Associated with behavioral regulation is a physiologic control mechanism. Evidence suggests that social stresses act on the individual through a physiological feedback involving the endrocrine system. In vertebrates, this feedback is most closely associated with the pituitary and adrenal glands (Christian, 1963; Christian and Davis, 1964). Increasing populations of mice held in the laboratory resulted in the suppression of somatic growth and curtailment of reproductive functions in both sexes. Sexual maturation was delayed or totally inhibited at high population densities, so that in some populations no females reached normal sexual maturity. Intrauterine mortality of fetuses increased, especially in the fetuses of socially subordinate females. Increased population density resulted in inadequate lactation and subsequent stunting of the nurslings. The same effect appeared again to a lesser degree in the animals of the next generation, even though the parents were not subject to crowding.

Studies of some wild populations under stress seem to support this hypothesis. When the density is high, snowshoe hares suffer from severe physiological stress, typified by a low level of blood sugar and liver glycogen, producing a shock disease (MacLulich, 1947). Chitty (1952) found that a decline or crash of a vole population in Wales was characterized by strife during the breeding season, causing the death of young and a psychological derangement among adults. Young that survived from these parents were abnormal from birth. In Germany, Frank (1957) found that when the number of voles exceeded supportable density, a population crash occurred. This crash, brought on by psychological stresses induced by crowding and physiological stresses from food shortages, was triggered off by cold, wet weather. The die-off was characterized by the exhaustion of adrenal and pituitary functions, liver degeneration, convulsions, and cannibalism. Before this happened, mass emigration and reduced reproduction took place. In years when a high percentage of gray and fox squirrels survive, the population may be reduced by a weakened physical condition that inhibits reproduction.

Further information on the role of psychological stress on population crashes is furnished by studies of Sika deer by John Christian and associates (1960) on the 280-acre James Island in the Chesapeake Bay, Maryland. Four or five deer were introduced onto the island in 1916. By 1955 the population reached a high of 280 to 300, a density of one per acre. In 1958, 60 per cent of the population, mainly young and females, died during January and February, even though all deer appeared well nourished and free of parasites. Growth, however, was inhibited at the time of the die-off but returned to normal afterwards. The dead deer, particularly the young, had one characteristic in common, an increase in adrenal weight. Accompanying the adrenal weight increase were degenerative

377

changes in the adrenal *zona glomerulosa,* suggestive of overstimulation and severe imbalance of fluid-electrolyte metabolism. But these changes appeared to be secondary to the overstimulation and exhaustion of adrenal cortex metabolism. This resulted from psychological stress induced by high density and such social pressures as dominance and subordination. Accompanying these physiological derangements were two diseases, hepatitis and nephritis, or edema and swelling in the glomeruli of the kidneys. Both are closely related to adrenal malfunctioning.

Thus evidence continues to accumulate that the die-offs from overpopulation are caused not so much by disease or malnutrition but by adrenocorticular and other metabolic responses known to occur during increased density and social strife.

Genetic feedback. Between 1956 and 1959 the population of the western tent caterpillar collapsed in southern Manitoba. Wellington (1960), who was studying the population dynamics of this species, noted certain qualitative changes in the behavior of individuals in the caterpillar colonies. Some caterpillars were active, others sluggish. A colony with active caterpillars built a number of long clavate tents, dispersed them widely, and foraged some distance away from them. A colony with sluggish individuals seldom constructed more than one compact pyramidal tent and fed nearby. These sluggish colonies were less viable than active colonies in harsh environments and some were too sluggish to survive even in favorable situations.

As the infestation aged, even the active colonies decreased in size and activity. By 1959, fourth-instar colonies along 156 miles of roadway had decreased from 74,000 to 251. In years of minimal density colonies increased in size and vitality, suggesting that the resurgence was due to the elimination of the least viable portion of the population.

The reason behind this, Wellington suggests, is that although the strongest and most active moths may oviposit locally, they are apt to fly some distance away from their birthplace to lay their eggs. On the other hand, less active adults are incapable of sustained flight, and thus all these females able to oviposit must do so near their birthplace. Thus there is a partial emigration of viable stock and a complete retention of the poorer quality, but still viable, stock which hastens the decline of population quality in that locality. As long as the favorable environment permits the survival of poorer and poorer colonies produced by increasingly sluggish resident populations, the latter increase to a point where the sluggish colonies outnumber the active, produced by strong adults that remained or immigrated from the outside. The ultimate result is the presence of numerous colonies too sluggish to reproduce or even to survive under the most favorable circumstances. When they die, the local population decreases abruptly. The decline or "crash" is followed by a sudden recovery, after its least viable portion had been eliminated. In such a manner does colony life lead to the rapid deterioration of local population quality at a time when survival is maximum and the colonies are functioning most effectively.

In his work with voles, Chitty (1960) found that a decline in the number of these rodents can take place even though the environment appears to be favorable. In fact a high density of population is insufficient to start a decline, and a low density is insufficient to stop it. A majority of animals die from unknown causes, males more rapidly than females. However, the adult death rate is not abnormally high during years of maximum abundance. Since Chitty observed that individuals in a declining vole population were intrinsically less viable than their predecessors, any changes in the cause of mortality were insufficient to account for the increased probability of death among the voles.

Based on his studies of voles, Chitty (1960) suggests that under appropriate circumstances, a deterioration in the quality of the population prevents an indefinite increase in the population. This hypothesis assumes that a self-regulating mechanism, adapted to a more or less limited range of the environment, has evolved through natural selection; and it implies that population density has an effect on the physiology of the individual and the genetics of the population. It also assumes that disease, psychological derangement, and responses to climatic changes become more severe as the numbers rise and the quality of the population falls. The hypothesis recognizes that a genetic feedback operates through density pressure, selection pressure, and genetic change within the population. Large increases in the population brought about by a changing environment increase the variability in the population, and many inferior genotypes survive. When conditions become more rigorous, these inferior types are eliminated and the population is reduced, often abruptly. This hypothesis has the distinction of bridging the two opposing arguments: the one that populations are regulated by density-dependent mortality, and the other that populations are controlled by climatic changes.

Cycles

Oscillations of most natural populations are damped by combined action of density-dependent and density-independent influences, so that variations in population density often appear as irregular fluctuations. But the fluctuations of some populations are more regular than one would expect by chance. These are commonly called cycles (Fig. 20-9). The two most common intervals between oscillations are three to four years, typified by lemmings (Fig. 20-20), and nine to ten years, typified by the snowshoe hare and lynx. These cyclic fluctuations, as far as is currently known, are confined to the simpler ecosystems, such as the tundra and the desert.

A number of theories have been advanced concerning cycles. These can be divided into two main schools. One maintains that something in the physical environment, in the ecosystem, or in the population itself is able to cause rhythmic fluctuations. Predation has been singled out as a cause, but predators usually are not abundant enough when rodents are at a peak to bring about a decline. Although epidemic disease is characteristic of snowshoe hare cycles, it is not associated with every decline. Food shortages, perhaps brought on by overpopulation, have been considered as a cause. Lack (1954) suggests that cycles are caused by a combination of food shortages and predation. As rodents increase with an abundance of food, the predators also increase. The high rodent population depletes its food supply and declines. The predators lose their staple food supply and turn to gallinaceous birds, causing a decline of these species. Excess predators starve or move southward in search of food. Few, if any, ever return north. Another school of thought, represented by Cole (1951, 1954*b*) and Palmgren (1949), holds that cycles simply represent random fluctuations of a population. Since populations are affected by a variety of environmental forces,

379

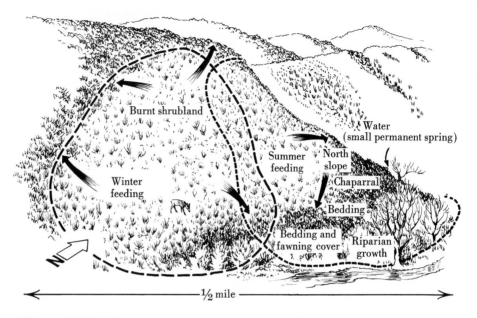

Figure 20-19 *Home range of the black-tailed deer. Note the shift in the range from summer to winter, as well as the use of several types of cover.* (Redrawn from Taber and Dasmann, 1958, California Fish and Game Bull. No. 8.)

random oscillations are the result. Cycles then simply reflect random oscillations or fluctuations in environmental conditions.

The most famous of all cyclic animals are the lemmings, which follow a three to four year oscillation. Occasionally among the European species, the numbers become so great that mass emigrations take place. These begin as seasonal movements down the mountains from one vegetation type to another, from the preferred lichens to the willows to the birch forests, and finally to the conifers (Curry-Lindahl, 1962). Breeding as they move slowly down from higher elevations, the lemmings build up to new population highs at lower elevations. If the rodents' slow progress is stopped by a long lake, by the meeting of two rivers, the continuing accumulation of lemmings becomes so great that panic breaks out, resulting in a reckless movement that follows no special direction, that flows north or south, east or west, uphill or down, across rivers and lakes, and sometimes ending disastrously in the sea. The cause of this behavior appears to be caused by endocrine malfunctioning, particularly of the adrenal gland, but this is questioned by Clough (1965a,b).

Fluctuations of the brown lemming, which inhabits the high artic grass and sedge communities of the North American tundra, suggest a vegetation-herbivore cycle. This is brought about by a short growing season and by dependence of herbivores upon a year-long food supply. At high densities, which occur every three years, the numbers are so great that they literally eat themselves out of house and home over winter. With the spring thaw, the lemmings are exposed to excessively heavy predation. Lemming numbers are reduced so severely that the animals require two years to build up to peak numbers again (Fig. 20-20) (Pitelka, 1957).

The vegetation-herbivore hypothesis for lemming cycles is not supported by recent studies of the brown lemming in northern Canada (Krebs, 1963, 1964). There, no extensive depletion of forage or evident starvation took place during the four-year cycle. Neither was there any macroscopic evidence of a deficiency disease nor any relationship between adrenal weight in summer and population density. Similar results are also reported for voles by Clough (1965a). Instead the cycles seemed to be associated with changes in the quality and behavior of the animals during changes in abundance, an observation that supports the genetic feedback hypothesis discussed above. The role of endocrine-behavioral response, however, cannot be dismissed, even though there appeared to be no relationship between adrenal weight and population density. The conclusion has been criticized (Christian and Davis, 1964), since the above studies failed to

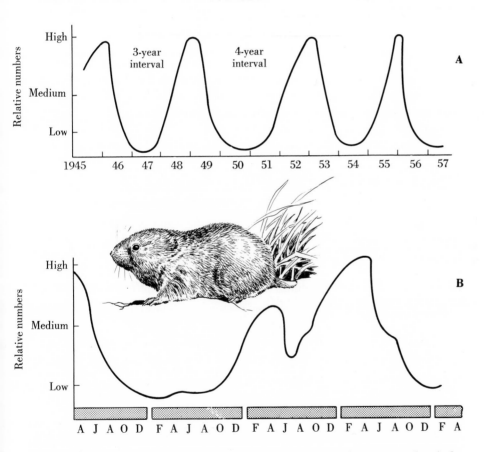

Figure 20-20   (A) *A generalized curve of the three- to four-year cycle of the brown lemming near Barrow, Alaska.* (B) *A generalized curve of a single oscillation in a short-term cycle showing subordinate fluctuations.* D, *December;* O, *October;* J, *July;* A, *April.* (After F. Pitelka, *Some Characteristics of Microtine Cycles in the Arctic,* 18th Annual Biology Colloquium, Oregon State College, Corvallis, 1957.)

include a critical evaluation involving a consideration of microscopic changes and the age and maturation of the animals.

Further south in the coniferous forest biome the snowshoe hare follows a nine- to ten-year cycle. Since the hare is the chief food supply of the lynx, the lynx population is also cyclic, with its peaks and depressions somewhat behind those of the hare, traceable through fur reports back to 1735. The ruffed grouse, too, is supposed to follow a similar cycle; but there is some dispute as to whether any animal south of the tundra is truly cyclic. Some biologists think these are merely statistical pseudocycles.

Cycles do not appear to affect migratory species in the region, only permanent residents; nor do they appear on a continental level. Only local and regional populations are affected, although the 10-year cycle of the snowshoe hare and the lynx are broadly synchronized from Quebec to the Northwest Territory (Keith, 1963).

Patterns of population distribution

Territoriality results in a rather uniform distribution of a population over an area, if environmental conditions are favorable. Uniform distribution also occurs among plants when competition is severe for crown and root space, as among forest trees, and for moisture, as among desert plants. But for the vast majority of organisms, uniform distribution is not the rule. Very rarely individuals of a population may be distributed at random, every individual occurring purely by chance. Among forest invertebrates, spiders are the only ones so far shown to have a random distribution (Cole, 1946).

The most common pattern is clumped or contagious distribution, producing spots of greater or lesser abundance or spots of presence and complete absence (Fig. 20-21). Clumping produces aggregations, the result of response by plants and animals to habitat differences, daily and seasonal weather changes, reproductive patterns, and social behavior. Among plants, aggregations often are influenced by the nature of the seed or other propagative means. Nonmobile seeds, like those of oak and cedar, are clumped near the parent plant or where seeds are

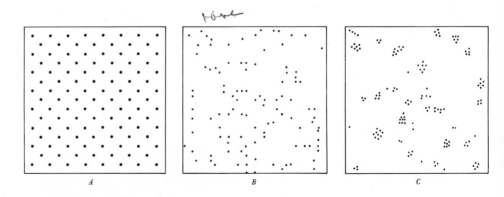

A   *B*   *C*

Figure 20-21 *Patterns of distribution. Note the difference between uniform,* A; *random,* B; *and clumped or contagious,* C.

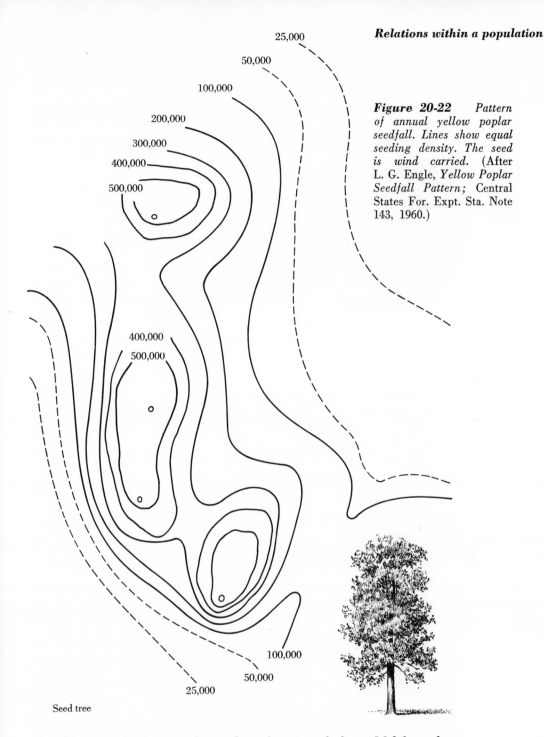

25,000
50,000
100,000
200,000
300,000
400,000
500,000

400,000
500,000

100,000
50,000
25,000

Seed tree

placed by animals. Runners also produce clumping of plants. Mobile seeds are more widely distributed, but even here the number of individuals is greater nearer the parent plant (Fig. 20-22) or along natural barriers like fencerows, where seeds are dropped by deflection of the wind. Some animal aggregations are purely accidental, brought about by environmental conditions, as aquatic organisms washed ashore in concentrations along the beach line. Individuals may be drawn together by a common source of food, water, or shelter, or by favorable moisture

383

Figure 20-23 *A doe deer that died of starvation, the result of a population too high for the available food supply.* (Photo courtesy of the Michigan Conservation Department.)

conditions. Other aggregations reflect a varying degree of social tolerance. Moths attracted to light, earthworms congregated in a moist pasture field, barnacles clustered on a rock, all reflect a low level of social interaction. The individuals do not aid one another, yet they do not prevent other members of the same species from sharing the conditions that brought them together.

Aggregations on a higher social level reflect some degree of response by population members. Prairie chickens congregate on "leks" for communal courtship. Birds flock together for migration flights; with geese these flocks are organized with a leader. Elk band together in herds with some social organization, usually with a cow as the head (Altmann, 1952). Birds may congregate on feeding grounds away from territorial sites, yet show intolerance for each other about the nest. Aggregations of the highest social structure are found among insect societies, such as ants and termites, where individual members are organized into social castes according to the work performed.

Aggregations result in competitive or cooperative situations. White-tailed deer gather in severe winter weather. Often too many are gathered in an area of limited food supply. After low browse is eliminated, only the larger, stronger deer are able to browse the higher limbs; the smaller, weaker deer die of starvation (Fig. 20-23). Fewer deer in the yard would have extended the food supply and permitted more to survive the winter. On the other hand, aggregation may improve group survival. An animal may have a greater chance of survival if it is one of a large organized band or flock rather than solitary or in a small group. Pronghorned antelope herds of more than 15 will stand ground when attacked by wolves and bunch into a defense unit, while smaller herds will stampede and scatter (Leopold, 1933). Schooling of fish apparently serves as a protection against predation (Brock and Riffenburgh, 1960). Any increase in the size of the school over and above the quantity a predator can consume on a single encounter reduces the frequency of predator-prey encounters. Fish appear to condition water with a growth-promoting substance secreted in the slime of skin glands. Fish raised in such water grow much better than those reared in water frequently changed. Green sunfish in groups of four grew faster than single individuals in one fourth the volume of water (Allee et al., 1948). Covies of bobwhite quail mass in a tight circle at night during winter, some even perching on top of another. This maintains a high temperature on cold nights. Small covies and lone individuals succumb to low temperatures.

Among most aggregating organisms there is an optimum density, illustrated graphically in Fig. 20-24. Among some species the optimum population is the smallest possible; among others, it lies between too many and too few.

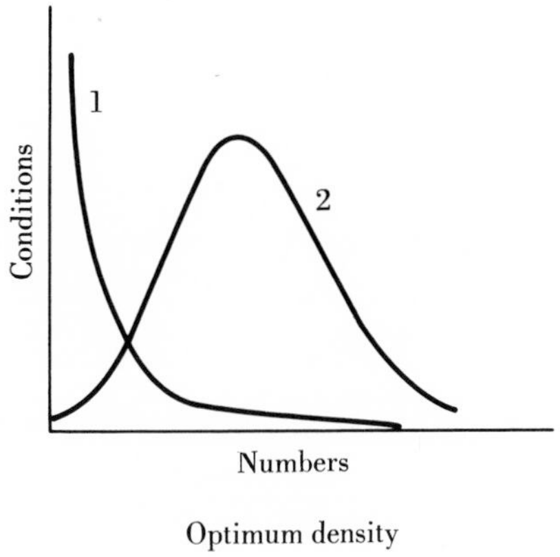

Figure 20-24 *Optimum density for some organisms is the smallest possible; for others, somewhere between the two extremes.*

Numbers

Optimum density

Population dispersal

Natural populations rarely occur as isolated units, since living organisms at one time or another in their life cycle possess mobility, enabling them to move away from population centers (Fig. 20-25). Such dispersal is a constant phenomenon, regardless of whether a population is dense or sparse. Movement results in the scattering of some members of a population into surrounding regions. Most of these emigrés probably perish in unsuitable habitats. But some may establish new breeding colonies in unexploited habitats and leave far more progeny than they could have done in their original home. This is probably the selective basis for dispersal; but it also facilitates the interchange of genetic material between populations, of great importance for the evolution of the species as a whole.

Population dispersal may take three forms, (1) emigration, or outward movement with no return; (2) immigration, or inward movement to a new area; (3) migration that involves a return movement to the area vacated.

385

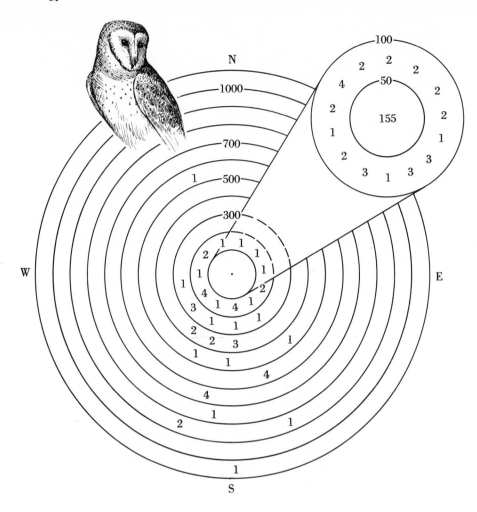

Figure 20-25 *Dispersal of banded barn owls from their hatching places. The concentric circles indicate the miles; the numbers within the circles give the number of birds moving in any given direction.* (After Stewart, 1952.)

Emigration and immigration

Emigration and immigration, both of which involve one-way movements, are closely related. Their chief difference lies in the viewpoint from the area involved. The emigrants of one region are the immigrants to another. Emigration and immigration are taking place constantly, although the peaks are seasonal. Dispersal among gray and fox squirrels takes place in the fall, when the mast crop (acorns and nuts) is ripe. The movement of fox squirrels begins in late August, reaches a peak in late September, and is over by December (Allen, 1943). Up to one-half of the juvenile population of ruffed grouse emigrated in the fall from a study area in Pennsylvania (Chambers and Sharp, 1958). Young birds moved as far as 7.5 miles from the original area (Fig. 20-26). Spring dispersal is common among some mammals, especially the muskrat. As much as 60 per cent of the wintering population of muskrats may leave for other suitable habitat (Errington, 1940).

If populations in an area are fairly stable and are at or near the carrying capacity, dispersal movements have little influence on population density and may only slightly influence age structure. But emigration movements induced by overpopulation and food shortages reduce populations and may greatly influence age structure and the reproductive rate of the remaining population. Immigration into rapidly growing populations can increase the growth rate not only by the addition of new members but also by an increase in the birth rate. Immigration into sparsely populated areas can bolster greatly the reproductive potential of a population and halt the reduction of r, characteristic of very low population densities. This principle is involved in wildlife management, where restocking programs with wild trapped individuals are undertaken to build up low populations; this has been very successful with wild turkey and deer.

Plants have many means of dispersal, including gravity, water, animals, man, and the plants' own mechanical power. The seeds of violets and jewelweed and others are shot some distance from the seed pods. Coconuts are carried from island to island by tidal movements and ocean currents. Many plants indigenous

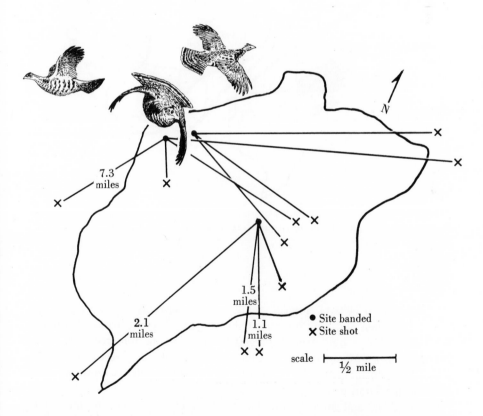

Figure 20-26 *Dispersal movement of 17 ruffed grouse banded as juveniles on a pine oak–barrens study area in central Pennsylvania. Distances outside of study area not to scale, as indicated. (Adapted from Chambers and Sharp, 1958.)*

387

to the Great Lakes have been carried by water to the banks of the St. Lawrence River. Winds carry balloonlike seeds, those with silky attachments like milkweed and dandelion, and the winged seeds of maples and conifers. Some weeds and grasses, like witchgrass and other tumbleweeds, break off near the ground when their seeds are ripe and roll before the wind on their springy stems and branches. Other seeds, such as those of enchanter's nightshade, bur marigolds, and beg-

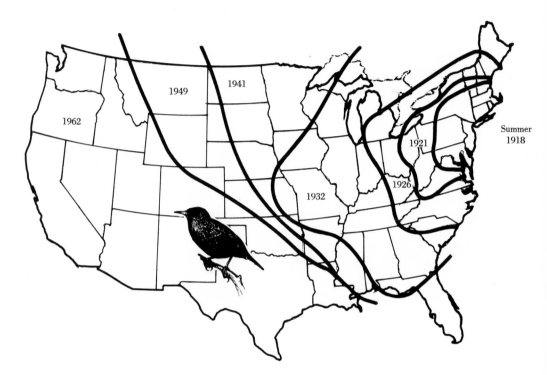

Figure 20-27 *The spread of the starling across the United States.* (After Kessel, 1953.)

garticks, stick to pelts of animals, while others, especially aquatic plants and berries, are eaten and pass unharmed through the digestive tracts of animals. Squirrels and jays hide acorns. Forgotten, these sprout into seedlings. Man intentionally or unintentionally has aided plant dispersal by direct introductions or by carrying plant seeds with other cargo in the ballast of boats, on trains, or on other means of transportation.

Exotic plants and animals introduced into a new environment often take hold and spread with extreme rapidity, an example being the European starling. Introduced in New York City in 1890 and 1891, the bird expanded its range southward and westward until, in 59 years, its range included southern Canada, all of the United States except southern Florida, and northeastern Mexico. Its breeding range extends from British Columbia, Washington, California, Arizona, and Utah to Mississippi and eastward (Fig. 20-27). In addition it has established migratory habits essentially the same as those it had in Europe (Kessel, 1953).

Similar stories could be written for the European pine shoot moth and the gypsy moth, as well as for some North American animals that have migrated into other lands. The gray squirrel and the muskrat have become serious pests abroad. And of course there is the well-known introduction of the European rabbits to Australia.

The direction and rate of dispersal often are influenced by man. Plants of the Great Plains moved eastward along railroad rights-of-way; and eastern plants have invaded the prairies by the same route. Other vast invasion and dispersal movements have been induced by biotic changes caused by man. The horned lark, a prairie bird, extended its range eastward with the clearing of the forest; the cardinal has moved north to Massachusetts; and the opossum is found as far north as northern New York, even though the ears of many individuals freeze off during winter. Clearing of the forest and development of agriculture on the plains about the Great Lakes and St. Lawrence River have allowed the eastward spread of the coyote to the forested mountains of the Adirondacks and Berkshires. Here the coyote is filling up a niche made vacant by the extermination of the wolf. Range extension, however, by these animals following artificial changes in their habitat is not explosive like the spread of exotics introduced into a new region (see Elton, 1958).

Migration

Migration is a two-way movement, involving a return to the area originally vacated. Migratory movements occur among highly mobile species, particularly vertebrates and some insects. Migratory movements usually are seasonal or periodic in nature and may or may not follow traditional pathways.

Insect migrations are more widespread than commonly believed, cover tremendous distances, and even involve specific flyways. The most famous insect migrant in North America is the monarch butterfly, which each fall migrates south in huge flocks, roosting at night in selected trees. The return trip the following spring, however, appears to be made by the progeny of these autumn migrants, that apparently breed on the wintering ground (Beall, 1941*a,b*; 1946). In the desert regions of the Middle East and North Africa the migratory movements of locusts have been famous since Biblical times. Locust migrations are governed to a large extent by the wind and temperature. The temperature must be warm enough to cause upward convection currents strong enough to get the insects on wing, and the wind strong and steady enough to carry them great distances (Rainey and Waloff, 1951). Compared to migrations of other insects, locust movements largely are involuntary, but they do show regularity, since they take place in areas where seasonal and trade winds and monsoons occur. These migrations lead the insects only by chance to suitable breeding places. When they arrive at a moist area, the locusts develop to sexual maturity and lay eggs (Rainey and Waloff, 1948).

Migrations are common among vertebrates, especially birds. In autumn, birds

Figure 20-28 *Migration routes of four vertebrates. (1) Ring-necked duck. Clear arrows indicate fall migration; dark arrows spring migration. (After Mendall, 1958.) (2) Canvasback duck; fine lines represent minor routes; the broad path the major route. (After Stewart et al., 1958.) (3) California gray whale. (After Pike, 1962.) (4) Barren-ground caribou. (After Banfield, 1961.)*

flock and move south, to return in the spring. Most of these migrations follow regularly used paths or flyways (Fig. 20-28). The movements and times of departure usually coincide with weather conditions. Southward migrations appear to be timed to start after the passage of a cold front with its flow of continental polar air coming in from a northerly direction. Northward migration in spring usually is timed with the onset of a warm front, with barometric pressure dropping and warm moist air moving up from the Gulf of Mexico and the Caribbean. When a cold front arrives, migratory movements stop, not to resume again until high-pressure areas have passed. In fact radar studies (Drury et al., 1961) show that a cold front in spring may start immediately a steady reverse southward movement. Radar has revealed a similar reverse migration in autumn, when the birds meet a warm tropical air mass moving north.

Migration among birds does not take place until the urge is released by a stimulus. The proper release of this stimulus requires that the bird be in a proper physiological state. Before migrating in the fall, birds put on a heavy deposit of fat. In spring, the increased photoperiod (see Chap. 5) stimulates the pituitary gland, in turn stimulating gonadal activity. Increasing temperatures reduce energy requirements. This, plus the lengthening day, causes nightly unrest among the birds, which results in increased rate of feeding, beyond the ordinary need for existence. Fat accumulates, providing the reserve needed for northward flight. This nightly unrest, both spring and fall, continues until it reaches a threshold that responds to the environmental change, usually temperature, that triggers off migratory movement. Birds not in proper physiological condition fail to migrate (see Farner, 1955; Kendeigh et al., 1960).

The migratory habit is also highly developed among many fish. Some make short journeys; others, like the salmon and eel, make long, spectacular journeys. Fish that make these long migrations may be *catadromous,* those that migrate from fresh water to the ocean to breed, or *anadromous,* those that return from the ocean to fresh water to breed.

The eel is a catadromous fish, which lives in fresh water streams but migrates to the area of the Sargasso Sea to spawn. The eggs hatch in late winter or early spring into quarter-inch larvae. The two populations, American and European, both drift with the Gulf Stream to their respective shores. In one year's time the American, and in three years' time the European eels arrive along the coast, both as two- to three-inch larvae. They metamorphose into "glass eels," or elvers, and swarm up streams. In eight to ten years the eels mature; then, come autumn, they return downstream to the ocean, swim to the Sargasso Sea, where 1000 feet below the surface they spawn and die.

The Pacific Coast salmon spawn in cold headwater streams of the northwest river systems. The fry return to the sea, where they mature. They then return up to 1000 miles inland from the ocean to the home stream where they were spawned. If a population is prevented from reaching its home stream by a dam, the fish will not spawn and the population will perish.

More restricted migrations are made by a number of fish. Lake-dwelling salmonid fish like the rainbow trout and lake trout may ascend streams to spawn, then return to the lake (Hartman, 1957; Loftus, 1958). Young rainbow trout of the Finger Lakes in New York may live several years in the stream before moving into the lakes. A similar situation exists in the rainbow trout of the Pacific Coast. They migrate upstream to spawn, but spend their adult life in

391

salt water. These rainbows are called "steelheads." Stream-dwelling trout move upstream to spawn and return to the home area downstream sometime later (Schuck, 1943; Shetter, 1937). A migratory race of walleyed pike inhabits the Muskegon River, Michigan, along with a resident population. During the summer, fall, and winter they spread out over 250 miles along the eastern shore of Lake Michigan. In spring they return to the Muskegon River (Eschmeyer and Crowe, 1955). Smallmouth bass in Cayuga Lake aggregate in a particular area in the southern end of the lake during winter, disperse north during spring and summer, and return to their wintering area about the rock ledges of the southern end (Webster, 1954). Migrations also occur among some ocean fish, such as tuna and herring.

The ability of birds and fish to return to the same place they occupied the previous year has been the subject of considerable research, and the final explanation has yet to be learned. Many theories have been advanced to explain direction finding in certain birds and fish. Those currently supported by research hold that these organisms can determine direction by the sun and compensate for daily change in the sun's position relative to the earth, local time (as indicated by the animals' "internal clock"—see Periodicity), and season (Hochbaum, 1955; Braemer, 1960; Hasler, 1960). Experimental evidence seems to indicate that these animals possess some sort of "computing" mechanism that indicates to them that every 24 hours the sun makes a revolution around the horizon. Even when reared under sunless conditions, fish and starlings still possess the ability to calculate the sun's movement (Kraemer, 1960). When, however, fish trained to compass direction under the sun at Wisconsin were transported to the equator and southern hemisphere, they did not adapt to the radically different daily sun movement. Instead they continued to compensate for the azimuth curve of the sun that would have been correct for Wisconsin.

Although the sun compass explains direction finding in the day, the explanation of how birds can navigate at night is still a problem. Results of experiments carried out by Sauer (1955) and Sauer and Sauer (1960) suggest that both the azimuth and altitude of the starry skies influence the directional choice made by the birds. This presupposes that the birds have the ability to perform actual navigation, the ability to find the way directly from one place to another that lies outside the immediate range of perception. Recent work with bobolinks by W. J. Hamilton, III (1962), suggests that both immature birds, who have never migrated, and adults can tell directions by some feature of the night sky (see Fig. 20-29). Direction choice seems to be based on the stars and an internal clock, although other orientating clues such as terrain may provide additional information. The birds failed to respond to direction on overcast nights.

While investigators of this problem generally agree that birds, fish, and some arthropods, including the bee, do determine direction by the sun and stars, some question the true nagivational ability of birds, or in other words the ability to establish position as well as direction. This would require a very precise and stable internal clock, more exact than any biological clock already known. The birds would have to be able to measure the sun's altitude within a few seconds of arc. They would have to be able to estimate exactly the time of day and the time of year; and they would have to possess a nautical almanac that gives exact information on the daily and seasonal paths of the sun (Wallraff, 1960). This, these investigators conclude, is too much to expect from an organism. Thus

392

many problems still remain to be solved in this very fascinating field of animal navigation.

Once the animals arrive in the general home vicinity they find their exact location by random search and probably recognize the area by familiar landmarks, although even this is open to question (Wallraff, 1960). Salmon locate their home stream by a sense of smell, the odors serving as guideposts. Young salmon are conditioned to the organic odor of the home stream during the finger-

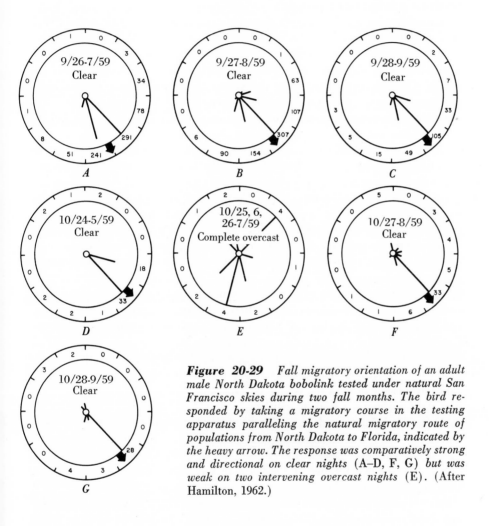

Figure 20-29 *Fall migratory orientation of an adult male North Dakota bobolink tested under natural San Francisco skies during two fall months. The bird responded by taking a migratory course in the testing apparatus paralleling the natural migratory route of populations from North Dakota to Florida, indicated by the heavy arrow. The response was comparatively strong and directional on clear nights (A–D, F, G) but was weak on two intervening overcast nights (E). (After Hamilton, 1962.)*

ling period. Then when as mature salmon they reach the mouth of the home river, they are stimulated to enter by the characteristic of that water alone. They swim upstream against the current past one tributary, then another, until they detect the strong traces of the home stream and enter it. Occasionally faulty choices are made, but the fish backtrack until the correct spawning or home tributary is located (Hasler, 1960).

The first warm spell of spring initiates migration of many amphibians to ponds where they mate and deposit their eggs in the water. A few consecutive warm days in March and April, accompanied by rain or by rapidly melting snow, stimulate the annual migration of Jefferson's and spotted salamander to their breeding ponds. After mating they return to damp retreats beneath logs and stones and in the soil. Spotted newts approaching sexual maturity migrate to water in autumn or spring. In the fall newly transformed individuals, the efts, move out of the ponds to remain on land until sexually mature. Wood frogs, toads, and others leave their terrestrial habitats to make the annual journey to ponds for a brief mating period.

Among the reptiles, the journey of young green turtles from their nest far back on the sandy beach to the sea is outstanding (Carr, 1962). Although navigation per se is not involved, the short trip to the ocean seems to be based on a tendency of the turtles to move toward a better-illuminated sky or a horizon free of obstacles. The journey begins when the young green turtles have worked their way up out of their nest. Once on the surface the hatchlings, after a few false starts, move toward the ocean, although it is often hidden from their view behind dunes, driftwood, and other obstructions. No matter what the obstacle, they scramble on. They find it day or night, in sunlight or moonlight, in overcast or rain. Once they arrive on the smooth, hard, flat beach, they are stirred on; and when they reach wet sand, they slide into the furthest reach of the breakers and burst into flurries of swimming strokes. When they are picked up by the water they begin to swim ahead in earnest. Finally they reach the heavy breakers and, diving beneath the crests, head out to sea.

Migration among North American mammals generally is confined to the more northern forms and those that spend a part of the year in an area not offering a year-long food supply. The gray whale spends the winters along the bays and lagoons of the lower coast of California, where the young are safe from killer whales, and return, in summer, to the Arctic Ocean (Fig. 20-28). Females, pups, and young males of the fur seal winter as far south as the waters off southern California, while adult males winter south of the Aleutians and in the Gulf of Alaska. As the breeding season approaches, the bulls return to the Pribilof Islands; meanwhile the females migrate 3000 miles, arriving at the islands a few hours or days ahead of the birth of the young. By November the females with grown pups start the long journey back to southern waters. Caribou migrations are anticipated by the Eskimos and Indians, who depend upon these animals for food. Caribou in the Mount McKinley area of Alaska spend the summer on the grassland of the southern slopes of the Alaskan Range (Murie, 1944). In the winter they shift to the lichen range on the northern side, where the snowfall is lighter. Caribou tend to shift their ranges to new areas after passing over one route a number of years. This enables the range plants and lichens to recover from grazing. Nearly as famous are the migrations of elk in the Jackson Hole country, Colorado, and Yellowstone Park. Here elk make regular journeys from the snow-covered highlands to winter in the lowest valleys and sagebrush plains (Anderson, 1958). They return to the mountains in spring, following the snowline. Mule deer of western United States spend their summers well back in the mountain meadows and along the higher ridges, from 4000 to 12,000 feet up, and winter in the oak-covered foothills, from 300 to 1500 feet up. Mule deer of the chaparral country are more restricted but move from south-facing slopes in late spring to cool northern exposures in late summer (Taber and Dasmann, 1958).

SUMMARY

Mule deer in the mountains, thrips in spring flowers, quail in brushy land, all living organisms live in groups of the same species or populations. These populations occupy a particular space, have a density and age structure, a birth rate and a death rate, a growth form, and numerical dispersion in time and space. The size of a population in relation to a definite unit of space is its density. Population density depends upon the number of individuals added to the group and the number leaving, the difference between the birth rate and the death rate, and the balance between emigration and immigration. Birth rate usually has the greatest influence on the addition of new individuals. Mortality is a reducer and is greatest in the young and old. It is usually stated in terms of survivorship rather than as a rate of mortality. Age and sex ratios influence the natality and mortality rates of populations. Reproduction is limited to certain age classes; mortality is most prominent in others. Changes in age-class distribution bring about changes in the production of young. The sex ratio tends to be balanced between males and females but may change with a change in population density. If mortality is high in one sex before the animals are on their own, the sex in short supply tends to be favored by selective pressures.

When births exceed deaths, the population increases; and the difference between the two represents the rate of increase, r. In an unlimited environment, an animal population expands geometrically, a phenomenon that occurs when a small population is introduced into an unfilled habitat. But since the environment is limited, population growth eventually slows down and arrives at some point of equilibrium with the carrying capacity of the habitat, about which it fluctuates.

A number of mechanisms appear to influence or regulate animal numbers. Inclement weather can reduce populations; but since it is density independent, that is its effect is constant regardless of the size of the population, it rarely regulates density. Among density-independent influences, man is the most important. By his activities he can increase or exterminate whole populations. The regulatory process seems to be controlled by some intrinsic, or density-dependent, mechanisms. Among these is intraspecific competition, in which animals compete for some resource often in short supply—food, space, a mate. There are basically two types of competition; the first is scramble, in which the resource is subdivided into many small parts to which all have access. Individuals "scramble" for the resource, which results in wastage. Each individual obtains such a small amount that it is unable to survive. A second is the contest type, in which each successful individual claims a part of the resource and the unsuccessful are denied any access to it. Contest competition shows up in territoriality and social dominance and hierarchy. Such stresses often result in endocrine imbalances, especially in the pituitary-adrenal complex, which results in abnormal behavior and growth and in degeneration and infertility. Also involved in this behaviorally-related regulation may be a genetic feedback, which results in a deterioration of population quality. These mechanisms produce oscillations in population density, which are damped, or become irregular, through the combined action of density-dependent and density-independent influences.

When oscillations are more regular than one would expect by chance, they are called cycles. The most common intervals between oscillation are three to four years, typified by the lemmings, and nine to ten years, typified by the snowshoe hare and lynx. Two major groups of theories have been advanced to explain cycles. One is that something in the environment or within the population itself produces the cycles; the other is that they simply reflect random oscillations in environmental conditions.

Populations are distributed in some kind of pattern over an area. Territoriality results in uniform distribution. Most organisms exhibit a clumped or contagious distribution, which results in aggregations. Some aggregations reflect a degree of sociality on the part of the population members, which may lead to cooperative or competitive situations.

Members of a population, especially those under social pressure and crowding, move away from the area of their birth. This dispersal takes the form of emigration and immigration. These are one-way movements, which may result in the establishment of new breeding colonies in unexploited habitats. Migrations are round-trip movements involving a return to the area originally vacated. Often these migrations follow regularly used routes or flyways. Along these, animals find their way by some navigational mechanism associated with the biological clock. This clock seemingly enables some animals to orient themselves to the sun, or in a few instances perhaps even the stars.

Relationships
between
populations

Animal and plant populations of the biotic community ex-
hibit a wide range of relationships to one another. Some populations have little
influence on one another, except in the indirect and often distant roles they play
in energy exchange. Other populations, such as parasites and their hosts and predators and prey, have a very direct and immediate relationship. From an individual
standpoint these relations often are detrimental; from a population standpoint
they may act either as a depressant or as a stabilizer of population numbers. Such
interactions influence the growth curve of a population.

Mutualism

Situations in which a close and often permanent and obligatory contact exists
between two species is called *mutualism*. Such relations are mutually beneficial
to both species involved. A classic example is the lichen fungi. The basic fungal
structure is the hypha, usually white or colorless. Within the lichen thallus is a
thin zone of algae, which usually forms colonies of 2 to 32 cells. The hyphae
support the plant while the algae supply the food. Without the algae component

397

the lichen could not survive. Similar relationships exist between algae and lower invertebrates. The hydra has green algae living within its gastrodermal cells (Muscatine and Lenhoff, 1963). The algae photosynthetically incorporates CO_2, and about 10 per cent of this is released to the hydra, which assimilates it into its cellular components. Evidence suggests that the symbiotic algae are nutritionally significant to the host, but how the material is used is still a subject of study.

Another well-known example of mutualism is the nodule growth of nitrogen-fixing bacteria on the roots of legumes. Less well known are the fungi that form mycorrhizal structures either inside or outside the roots of other plants. Such fungal growth is found on the outside of roots of pines, oaks, beech, and other trees. The fungi, taking the place of root hairs, aid in the uptake of water and nutrients from the soil. Conifers depend on these mycorrhizae for growth in soils deficient in essential nutrients.

An outstanding case of plant-animal mutualism is the yucca moth and the yucca plant. The female yucca moth carries pollen from the stigma of one flower to the pistil of another. At the same time the female moth, which does not feed, lays her eggs in the undeveloped seed pods. When the larvae hatch they feed on some but not all the seeds. Thus the plant is fertilized and the moth larvae have a source of food.

Mutualism is often termed symbiosis. Actually symbiosis means "living together" and includes mutualism, commensalism, and parasitism.

Commensalism

Often a one-sided relationship between two species exists, in which only one benefits and the other is neither benefited nor harmed. Such a relationship is called *commensalism*. Among the commensals are epiphytes, such as orchids. These plants grow up in the branches of trees where they are nearer to light source; their roots draw nourishment from the humid air. Other epiphytes are the lichens, "Spanish moss," which festoons southern live oaks, and "old man's beard" of the northern coniferous forests. All these epiphytes depend upon the trees for support only. They manufacture their own food by photosynthesis. Animal commensals include the barnacles, which attach themselves to the backs of whales and shells of horseshoe crabs. The remoras attach themselves to the bellies of sharks by means of a dorsal fin highly modified into a suction disk on the top of the head. Not only do they obtain a free ride but they also feed on the fragments of the shark's prey. In Arizona the elf owl nests in the hole made by the Gila woodpecker in the stems of Saguaro cactus. The burrows of many animals may be occupied by others. Woodchuck burrows are used by cottontail rabbits; muskrat bank dens by mink.

Amensalism

Contrasting with commensalism is *amensalism*, a situation in which one population definitely inhibits the other while remaining unaffected itself. Various species of algae produce extracellular by-products, which inhibit the growth of other algal species, usually within the same phylum. Thus a species of alga that begins its development first in a body of water quickly assumes dominance. A sudden crash of this dense algae population is believed to be the result of the inability of the algae to tolerate an accumulation of its own extracellular products. The alga *Chlorella vulgaris,* for example, produces chlorellin, which is toxic to other species of algae. Such action, where an organism produces an injurious compound that inhibits the growth or destroys other organisms, is termed *antibiosis* and the specific chemical compound an *antibiotic.* The inhibitory effect of algal antibiotics may extend beyond algae. A subalpine lake just outside Glacier National Park received a drainage from a small farm and barnyard. This raised the nitrogen and phosphorus content enough to support a bloom of *Aphanizomenon flos-aquae.* Each year this bloom develops, mudpuppies die by the scores, while others are sluggish and roll about on the bottom (Prescott, 1960). Another alga, *Anabaena flos-aquae,* has killed Franklin gulls and mallard ducks, which suffered from symptoms of botulism. And the dinoflagellate *Gymnodinium veneficium* has caused the wholesale death of fish by depolarizing nerves and muscle systems (Abbot and Ballentine, 1957). Molds, actinomycete fungi, and bacteria also produce antibiotics. Soil fungi in particular secrete antibiotics that even in small amounts can inhibit life processes of other susceptible organisms. Such an association between organisms is exploited in medicine, where these chemical substances are used to combat bacterial and virus infections.

Parasitism

It is only a short step from commensalism to *parasitism,* a condition where two animals live together but one derives its nourishment at the expense of the other. Parasites, strictly speaking, draw nourishment from the tissues of their larger hosts, a case of the weak attacking the strong. Typically, parasites do not kill their hosts as predators do, although the host may die from secondary infection or suffer from stunted growth, emaciation, or sterility. A strict line cannot be drawn here, since many parasitic larvae of insects draw nourishment from the tissues of their hosts; but by the time of metamorphosis the larvae have completely consumed the soft tissues of the host. These parasites act in much the same way as predators and are discussed later as such; such parasites are used in the biological control of insects.

Parasites exhibit a tremendous diversity in ways and adaptations to exploit their hosts. Parasites may be plants or animals; they may parasitize plants, animals, or both. They may occur on the outside of the host (ectoparasites) or live within the body of the host (endoparasites). Some are full-time parasites; others, only part time. The latter may be parasitic as adults, free-living as larvae, or they reverse. They have developed numerous ways to gain entrance into their hosts, even to the point of using several hosts to disperse their kind. They have evolved various means of mobility, ranging from free-swimming ciliated forms to dependence upon other animals and have developed ways of securing themselves to the host to maintain their position. Some, like the tapeworm, have become so adapted to the host that they no longer require a digestive system. They simply absorb their food directly through their body wall. Parasites that live within the body of plants and animals possess cuticles or develop cysts resistant to the digestive enzymatic action of the host.

399

Figure 21-1 *Liver flukes in the white-tailed deer. This is an important parasite of the white-tailed deer, especially in northern herds, where the incidence is very high.* (Photo courtesy of the Michigan Conservation Department.)

Parasites may be restricted to one host. Some parasites of birds, especially the tapeworm, can live only on one particular order or genera (see Baer, 1951). This fact is utilized by the taxonomist as evidence of relationships between species, genera, or families. Others may be restricted to special habitats within the host (Fig. 21-1). The roundworm lives near the duodenum of the digestive tract and the soil nematodes live in the rootlets of plants. Some parasites live their entire life cycle on one host; others may require more. An example of this is the "black grub," or black spot infection of minnows and sunfish (Fig. 21-2). This is caused by the small white larvae of a fluke. Once infected, the fish host lays down a black pigment around the thick-walled cysts, causing black spots on the body wall of the fish. The adult stage is attached by suckers to the mucosa of the intestine of the kingfisher. The eggs pass through the intestine of the kingfisher into the water where the miracidia hatch. These miracidia, moving through the water by cilia, seek an intermediate host, a snail. They gain entrance by secreting a tissue-dissolving substance. Within the snail, the miracidia transform into saclike sporocysts, which eventually give rise to a tailed larval stage called cercariae. These free-swimming larvae emerge from the snail and seek the next host, a fish, which they must find within two days or die. The cercariae penetrate the fish and encyst. The fish in turn is consumed by the kingfisher, the cercariae are released and mature in the bird's intestinal tract, and the new adults start laying eggs, to repeat the cycle.

Among the plant parasites, rusts require secondary hosts. White pine blister rust, which infects the five-needled pines, enters through and grows in the needles until it reaches the bark, where it forms spindle-shaped cankers. In two to five years orange-yellow spore-bearing blisters appear on the bark and release millions of spores, which infect only the leaves of gooseberry. Here the fungus forms brownish-yellow spots, in which are produced spores capable of infecting pines only. These spores, unlike those produced on the pine, are delicate, short-lived, and can travel only up to 900 yards. Control of parasites requiring more than one host can be accomplished by eliminating one of the intermediate hosts, such as the gooseberry.

Social parasitism in various stages of development is found among some higher vertebrates. Outstanding is egg parasitism among birds, both nonobligatory and obligatory. Nonobligatory egg parasites lay their eggs in nests of other birds, although they have nests of their own. Among these are the pied-billed grebe, black-billed and yellow-billed cuckoos, the bobwhite, and ring-necked pheasant. The ring-necked pheasant is notorious for dumping eggs in the nest of another, and even in dump nests in which the eggs are not incubated. Equally notorious

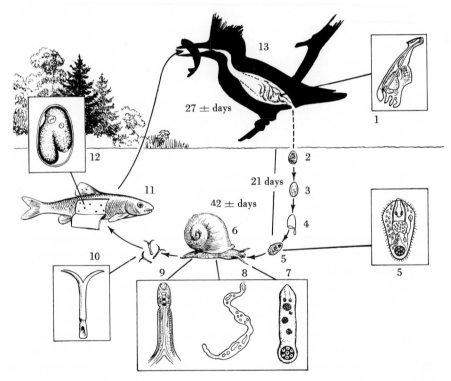

Figure 21-2 *Life cycle of the "black grub,"* Uvulifer ambloplitis. *(1) Adult trematode attached to the mucosa of the kingfisher intestine; (2) immature egg; (3) mature egg; (4) empty shell; (5) miracidium; (6) the first intermediate host, the snail; (7) and (8) sporocysts; (9) cercaria; (10) free-swimming cercaria, which penetrates beneath the scales or into fins and encysts, producing black spots in about 22 days; (11) minnow with skin cut away to show black grubs; (12) sketch of parasite within inner cyst; outer cyst removed; (13) kingfisher. (Adapted from Hunter and Hunter, 1934, New York State Conservation Department.)*

401

are waterfowl, especially the redhead and ruddy duck. Twenty-one species of ducks are known to lay eggs in nests other than their own (Weller, 1959). An estimated five to ten per cent of female redhead ducks are nonparasitic and nest early. All others lay eggs parasitically at one time or another. More than half of these are semiparasites and nest themselves. The remainder are completely parasitic.

Egg parasitism has been carried to the ultimate by the cowbird and European cuckoos, both of which have lost the instinct for nest building, incubating the eggs, and caring for the young. These are obligatory parasites who pass off these duties to the host species by laying eggs in their nests. The cowbird removes one egg from the nest of the intended victim, usually the day before laying, and the next day lays one of her own as a replacement. The young cowbird does not eject its nestmate, a practice carried out by nestling European cuckoos. Another form of social parasitism is robbery or pirating of food from other species. The bald eagle forces the osprey to drop its prey in flight and catches the dropping fish before it hits the water. Jaegars and skuas, dark, hawk-like birds of the sea, force gulls to give up their catch of fish.

Successful parasitism represents something of a compromise between two living populations. Parasites and hosts that have lived together over a long period of time have developed a sort of mutual toleration with a low-grade, widespread infection, as long as conditions are favorable for both host and parasite. But if conditions become favorable for the parasite or the host, or if a host is exposed to a new parasite against which it has no defense, then conditions worsen for one or the other.

Such a situation has developed with the Kirtland warbler (Mayfield, 1960), a relict species that inhabits extensive jack pine stands in a compact central homeland of about 100 square miles in northern lower Michigan. Before the white man arrived, Kirtland warbler apparently was isolated by 200 miles of unbroken forest from the parasitic brown-headed cowbird of the central plains, a bird closely associated with grazing animals. When settlers cleared the forest and brought grazing animals with them, the cowbirds spread eastward and northward in the jack pine country. Unlike other birds, Kirtland warblers had no real defense against the cowbird, such as egg ejection, building a new nest over the old, or rearing young successfully along with the cowbird. The warbler has a short nesting season and an incubation period a day or two longer than other songbirds, so that the young cowbird already is out of the egg when the warblers hatch. The result of this parasitism, which involves 55 per cent of the nests, is a 36 per cent reduction in the number of warbler fledglings produced, below the level attained without cowbird interference. Since the annual survival rate of adults is about 60 per cent from one June to another, 57 per cent of the 1.41 fledglings produced per nest (in contrast with 2.2 under normal conditions) must survive the first year to replace the adult loss, nearly an impossibility.

Disease

Parasites usually are not the primary cause of the death of a host, but they may so weaken it that it succumbs to other causes. Or the animal may be so weakened from other causes that it is highly susceptible to parasitism. Even at its best, a parasitized animal is not in a state of health, that condition in which all vital processes function harmoniously. Any disturbance to this finely adjusted balance that results in an abnormal function is termed a disease. There are a number of causes of diseases. Parasites are one, physiological stress is another, as well as nutritional deficiency and poisoning. But most commonly, disease is considered as bacterial, viral, or fungal infections. Disease organisms either are present in animals at all times, becoming active only when body resistance is lowered; or they are absent and highly virulant only when they enter the body. Single attacks of some diseases confer immunity on the organism, an adaptation that enables the animal to withstand any further attack.

Disease, although prevalent, becomes important only when epidemics or epizootics occur. These usually come about when the host populations are high. Disease, when rampant, can reduce populations, but it may not be the primary cause. An increasing population may result in a depression within the animal of antibody formation and other body defenses, an increase in inflammatory processes, and in an increased susceptibility to disease. Thus disease may be the consequence of a high population, rather than a cause of population decline.

Diseases among plants are caused largely by fungi; and certain diseases, such as chestnut blight have spread rapidly through a species population, wiped it out, and thus changed community composition. This rapid and fatal spread of a disease is especially characteristic when an exotic infection is introduced into a population that has had no prior adaptation to it.

Several diseases, only partially understood, are prevalent in eastern forests and are potential threats to a number of tree species. Maple, ash, and black cherry are subject to dieback. Beech, particularly in northeastern North America, is subject to a near epidemic of beech bark disease spread by the woolly beech scale. In the oak forests of the upper Mississippi Valley and the southern Appalachians, oak wilt threatens the hardwoods stands. The disease is caused by a fungus, *Ceratocystes fagacearium,* which appears to be spread by root grafts and nitidulid beetles, especially *Glischrochilus* and *Colopterus* (True et al., 1960). Affected trees have wilted or defoliated tops, a brownish discoloration to the leaves, bark cracks, and pressure cushions caused by fungal mats. Loss of oaks would be more disastrous than the loss of the American chestnut, not only from an economic but also an ecological viewpoint, for a wide spectrum of animal life relies on oaks for food, and the gaps in the plant community would be occupied by lesser species.

Bacteria and viruses are causal agents of important animal diseases. Bacteria may produce localized inflammatory changes in tissue, enter the blood stream, or produce powerful poisons known as toxins. Viruses cause diseases that may be complicated by secondary invaders. Some diseases, both bacterial and viral, may be transmitted from wild to domestic animals, by direct contact or by insect vectors.

One such disease, widespread among rabbits and squirrels, beaver and muskrats, is tularemia, a bacterial disease transmitted from animal to animal by the bites of ticks and flies, particularly the rabbit tick, and carried to man by ticks (especially the wood tick, *Dermacentor* spp.) and deerflies, or by direct contact through a break in the skin. Contraction of the disease while cleaning an infected animal is the cause of 90 per cent of the cases in man (Yeatter and Thompson, 1952). Infected animals in advanced stages will not move from cover; and if

403

they do, they stagger, stop, and perhaps fall over. Internally the liver and spleen are swollen and studded with tiny white discolorations.

Another important bacterial infection of wild animals, leptospirosis, is caused by the spirochetes of the genus *Leptospira*. Since they do not always produce morbid reactions in infected animals, the presence of the disease is hard to detect except by laboratory methods. Leptospirosis occurs in a wide variety of animals, from rats, mice, and opossums to skunks, armadillos, and deer, from which it can be transmitted to cattle, horses, swine, and dogs. Rats, mice, and skunks have a high rate of infection.

Possibly the greatest natural drain on waterfowl populations is botulism, or western duck sickness, caused by *Clostridium botulinum,* which produces a toxin in purifying animal and vegetable matter that it inhabits. When toxin is consumed, particularly during late summer when water levels are low and exposed aquatic vegetation begins to decay, ducks develop paralysis of the neck and a looseness of feathers, which is followed by death.

Viruses are the causal agents of two wildlife diseases important to man, encephalitis, or sleeping sickness, and rabies. Encephalitis is harbored by a host of avian species, from bluebirds, jays, and warblers to herons and ibis and is transmitted by the mosquitoes *Culex* and *Culeseta*. Among birds, only the ring-necked pheasant succumbs to the disease, which is transmissible to both animal and man. Rabies, also highly contagious to man, is a viral disease, which follows the nerves from the infection point to the spinal column and brain before symptoms appear. The symptoms are both behavioral and physical. Infected animals are restless, excitable, exhibit convulsions, wander aimlessly, and show no fear of man. Physically they are emaciated, exhausted, partially paralyzed. Among wild animals, rabies occurs most commonly in coyotes, foxes, raccoons, and skunks, although no species is immune. Foxes, together with domestic dogs, are the primary causes of the spread of the disease. Rabies may reach epidemic proportions, as it did in New York State in 1954. Severe reduction of fox populations will control the disease, although it can never be entirely eliminated.

Fungal diseases are common among wild animals. Aspergillosis, common in domestic fowl, is caused by a fungus that invades the air sacs of the lungs, developing pneumonialike symptoms; the infection is found among waterfowl. Fish are susceptible to *Saprolegnia,* or water mold. This whitish growth often begins on lesions caused by some injury, from which it spreads.

Predation

No phase of population interaction is more misunderstood (or hotly debated, especially by sportsmen) than predation. Predation in natural communities is a step in the transfer of energy. It is commonly associated with the idea of the strong attacking the weak, the lion pouncing upon the deer, the hawk upon the sparrow. But this idea must be modified, for predation grades into parasitism or vice versa. Between the two exists the broad gray area of the parasitoid and the host, which sometimes is called parasitism and sometimes predation. In this situation, one organism, the parasitoid, attacks the host (the prey) somewhat indirectly by laying its eggs in or on the body of the host. After the eggs hatch, the larvae feed on the host until it dies. Ultimately the effect is the same as that of predation; and in this discussion the two shall be considered as one.

From the viewpoint of the population ecologist, predation in its actions and reactions is more than just the transfer of energy. It represents a direct and often complex interaction of two or more species, of the eaters and the eaten. Perhaps the numbers of some predators depend upon the abundance of their prey, and predation may regulate the numbers of the prey. Both these ideas are debatable; certainly the same generalizations cannot apply to all groups of predators and prey.

Theory of predation

The influence of predation on population growth of a species received the attention of two mathematicians, Lotka (1925) and Volterra (1928). Separately they proposed formulas to express the relationship between predator and prey populations. They attempted to show that as the predator population increased, the prey decreased to a point where the trend was reversed and oscillations were produced.

Later the biologist Gause (1934) attempted to prove this experimentally. He reared together under constant environmental conditions a predator population, *Didinium,* a ciliate, and its prey, *Paramecium caudatum.* The predator always exterminated the prey, regardless of the density of the two populations. After the prey was destroyed, the predators died from starvation. Only by periodic introductions of prey to the medium was Gause able to maintain the predator population and prevent it from dying out. In this manner he was able to maintain populations together and produce regular fluctuations in both, as predicted by the Lotka-Volterra models. The predator-prey relations were ones of overexploitation and annihilation, unless there was an immigration from other prey populations.

In another experiment Gause introduced sediment in the floor of the tube. Here the prey could escape from the predator. When the prey was eliminated from the clear medium, the predators died from the lack of food. The paramecium that took refuge in the sediment continued to multiply and eventually took over the medium.

About a decade later, an ecologist, Nicholson, and a mathematician and engineer, Bailey, developed a mathematical model for a host-parasitoid relationship. This model predicted increasingly violent oscillations in single-predator and single-prey populations living together in a limited area with all external conditions constant.

Essentially both the Lotka-Volterra and the Nicholson-Bailey models state that as predator populations increase, they will consume a progressively larger number of prey, until the prey populations begin to decline. As the prey diminishes, the predators are faced with less and less food, and they in turn decline. In time the number of predators will be so reduced by starvation that the reproduction of the prey will more than balance their loss through predation. The prey will then increase, followed shortly by an increase of predators. This cycle, or oscillation, may continue indefinitely. The prey is never quite destroyed by the predator; the predator never completely dies.

Predator-prey systems

In an experiment, Huffaker (1958) attempted to learn if an adequately large and complex laboratory environment could be established, in which predator-prey relations would not be self-exterminating. Involved were the six-spotted mite *Eotetranychus sexmaculatus* and a predatory mite, *Typhlodromus occidentalis*. Whole oranges, dispersed on a tray among a number of rubber balls the same size, provided the food (and cover) for the spotted mite. Such an arrangement permitted the experimenter to change both the total food resource available, by covering the oranges with paper and sealing wax to whatever degree desired, and by the general distribution of oranges among the rubber balls. The experimenter could manipulate conditions to simulate a simple environment where the food of the herbivore was concentrated, or a complex universe where the food was widely dispersed, partially blocked by barriers, and where refuge areas were lacking.

In both situations, the two species found plenty of food available at first for population growth. The density of predators increased as the prey population increased. In the environment where the food was concentrated and the dispersion of the host population was minimal, the predators readily found the prey, quickly responded to changes in prey density. and were able to destroy the prey rapidly. In fact the situation was self-annihilative. On the other hand, in the environment where the primary food supply and thus the host were dispersed, the predator and the prey population went through two oscillations before the predators died out. The prey recovered slowly.

Several important conclusions resulted from this study. For one, predators cannot survive when the prey population is low. Second a self-sustained predator-prey relationship cannot be maintained without immigration of the prey. Finally the complexity of prey dispersal and predator-searching relationships, combined with a period of time for the prey population to recover from the effects of predation and to repopulate the areas, had more influence on the period of oscillation than the intensity of predation.

The degree of dispersion and the area employed were too restricted in the above experiment to perpetuate the system. But in another experiment, Pimental, Nagel, and Madden (1963) attempted to provide an environment with a space-time structure that would allow the existence of a parasite-host system. Used in the study was a wasp (*Niasonia vitripennis*) parasite and a fly (*Musca domestica*) host. For the environment the experimenters used a special population cage, which consisted of a group of interconnected cells. A system of 16 cells died out; but a 30-cell system persisted for over a year. Increasing the system from 16 to 30 cells decreased the average density of parasites and hosts per cell and increased the chances for the survival of the system. The lower density was due to the breakup and sparseness of both parasite and host populations. The greater number of individual colonies that remained following a severe decline of the host assured the survival of the system, since these colonies provided a source of immigrants to repopulate the environment. Moreover the amplitude of the fluctuations of the host did not increase with time, as proposed by the model of Nicholson. Apparently the fluctuations were limited by intraspecific competition.

There are in nature a few studied examples that these laboratory experiments support. Perhaps the most famous is the *Cactoblastis* story. Sometime before

1839 the *Opuntia,* or prickly pear, cactus was introduced from America into Australia as an ornamental. As is often the case with introduced plants and animals, the cactus escaped from cultivation and rapidly spread to cover eventually 60 million acres in Queensland and New South Wales. To combat the cacti, a South American cactus-feeding moth, *Cactoblastis cactorum,* was liberated. The moth multiplied, spread, and destroyed the cacti to a point that the plants existed only in small sparsely distributed colonies with wide gaps between them.

But the decline of the prickly pear also meant the decline of the moth. Most of the caterpillars coming from the moths that had bred on the prickly pear the previous generation died of starvation. And because of the low number of moths, not many of the plants were parasitized. In some areas the moth survived; and as the prickly pear increased, so did the moth, until the cactus colony was again destroyed. In other places the moth was absent and the prickly pear spread once more. But sooner or later it was found by the moth and the colony eventually destroyed. Meanwhile seed scattered in new areas established new colonies that maintained the existence of the species. The rate of establishment of prickly pear colonies is determined by the time available for the colonies to grow before they are found by the moth. As a result, an unsteady equilibrium exists between the cactus and the moth. Any increase in the distribution and abundance of the cactus leads to an increase in the number of moths, and a subsequent decline in the cactus. The maintenance of this predator and prey, or more accurately herbivore-plant, system depends upon environmental discontinuity. The relative inaccessibility of the host or prey in time and space limits the number of parasites and predators.

The rise and decline of a predator population as its prey population rises and falls suggest that some density-influenced relationship exists between them. The nature of this relationship depends a good deal on whether the prey species is vagile or sedentary, territorial or nonterritorial. Among invertebrates, especially the insects, and nonterritorial animals, intensity of predation is independent of prey density but directly related to predator density. Under such conditions predators may respond to changes in the density of prey in two distinguishable ways. As the density of the prey increases, each predator may take more of the prey or take them sooner. This is a functional response (Holling, 1959, 1961). Or the predators may become more numerous through increased reproduction or immigration, a numerical response.

Functional response

In general the predator or the parasite will take or affect more of the prey, as the density of the prey increases. However, there is also a tendency for the number of prey taken or the number of hosts affected to increase in less than a linear proportion to the total number of host or prey available (Fig. 21-3). The functional response of parasites to hosts is usually curvilinear (Fig. 21-4). The slope decreases as the host density increases, until the curve levels off. When vertebrate predators are involved, the functional response curve is S-shaped (Fig. 21-9). This is caused by the behavior of the predator—its response to hunger, its hunting ability, its frequency of contact with the prey species, and the stimulation it provides.

407

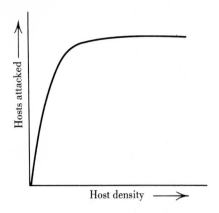

Figure 21-3 *A functional response curve. The number of prey taken is related to the density of the prey population. This curvilinear relationship is typical of parasite-host relations.*

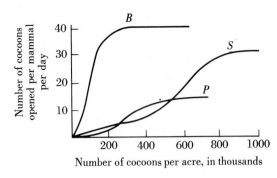

Figure 21-4 *A functional relationship between small-mammal predation and the density of sawfly cocoons. Curve B is the curve for the short-tailed shrew, Blarina; curve S for the common shrew, Sorex, and P, for the white-footed mouse, Peromyscus. (After Holling, 1959.)*

This latter type of functional response is well illustrated in a study by L. Tinbergen (1960) of the relation between woodland birds and insect abundance. According to Tinbergen's hypothesis, when a new prey species appears in a given area, its risk of becoming prey is low at first. The birds as yet have not developed a "searching image" for that species. Once the birds have acquired this image for the prey, intensity of predation increases suddenly. However, the relation between the density of the prey species and its percentage in the food of the predator cannot be explained from the probability of encounters alone.

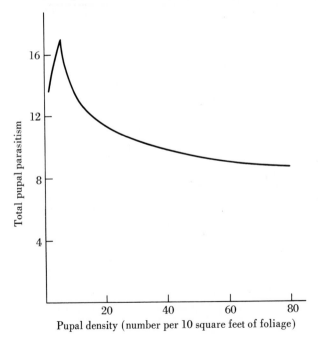

Figure 21-5 *Predator and parasitoid populations may show an inverse density relationship to prey and host population. The predators cannot keep up with the prey and host populations during a time of outbreak. (After Miller, 1963, in Morris, 1963.)*

When prey density is low, predatory consumption is lower than would be expected on a density-dependent basis. At moderate densities, predation is unexpectedly high. At high densities, predation drops again. Tinbergen explains this on the assumption that when the prey species is low, the birds lack a searching image for it. At high densities, the birds become satiated or stop using that particular searching image when the prey concerned forms more than a critical percentage of the food. This may be the reason for the S-shaped curve of functional response.

Numerical response

As the density of the prey increases, the numbers of predators may also increase. But the response is not immediate. There is necessarily a time lag between the birth and the appearance of an active predator, and this time lag may prevent the predator or the parasite population from catching up with the prey. As a result

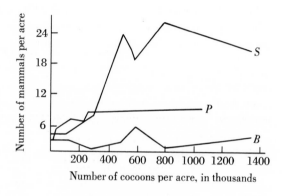

Figure 21-6 Numerical response of small mammalian predators to a sawfly cocoon population. The only mammal that shows any strong response is the shrew, Sorex. *(After Holling, 1959.)*

an inverse relationship often exists between numerical response and prey density (Figs. 21-5 and 21-6). This is well illustrated in the long-term study of the spruce budworm in Canada (Morris, 1963). The response of parasites to an increasing density of budworms was sharp at first, then declined rapidly as the pupal density of the budworm increased.

Outstanding as examples of a numerical response to prey density are several warblers, especially the Tennessee, the Cape May, and the bay-breasted, whose abundance is dictated by outbreaks of the spruce budworm. During such periods the population of the bay-breasted warbler has increased from 10 to 120 pair, per 100 acres (Mook, 1960; Morris et al., 1958), Cape May and bay-breasted warblers have larger clutches during budworm outbreaks than associated warbler species (MacArthur, 1958). In fact the Cape May and possibly bay-breasted apparently depend upon occasional outbreaks of spruce budworms for their continued existence. At these times the two species, because of their extra large clutches, are able to increase more rapidly than other warblers. But during the years between outbreaks, these birds are reduced in numbers and are even extinct locally.

Sparrows prey heavily on the larch sawfly, a serious defoliator of tamarack, in and near the bogs of Manitoba, Canada. These birds were far more important **409**

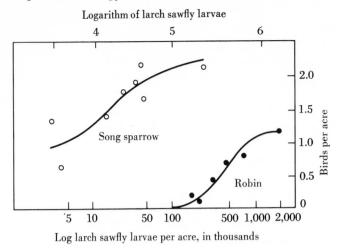

Logarithm of larch sawfly larvae

Song sparrow

Robin

Birds per acre

Log larch sawfly larvae per acre, in thousands

Figure 21-7 *Numerical response of song sparrows and robins to larch sawfly larvae. (After Buckner and Turnock, 1965.)*

predators of the adult sawfly than the insectivorous warblers and showed a strong numerical response to prey density (Fig 21-7) (Buckner and Turnock, 1965). The sparrow population increased largely by immigration, which involved family flocks, adults and subadult birds, and premigratory flocks.

Total response

In analyzing the relationship between predator density and prey density, functional and numerical responses may be combined to give a total response, and predation is plotted as a percentage. If this is done, predation falls into two types. In one the percentage of predation declines continuously as the prey density rises (Fig. 21-8). In the other the percentage of predation rises initially and then declines. The latter results in a dome-shaped curve (Fig. 21-8P) produced by the S-shaped functional response to prey density and by direct numerical response.

The predation discussed so far has been recognized by Ricker (1954) as types *A* and *B*. In type *A*, predators of any given abundance take a fixed number of prey species during the time they are in contact, usually enough to satiate themselves. The surplus prey escape. Trout feeding on an evening hatch of mayflies would come under this category. There is a functional response but no numerical response. Type *B* predation exists if predators of any given abundance take a fixed fraction of a prey species, as though the prey were captured at

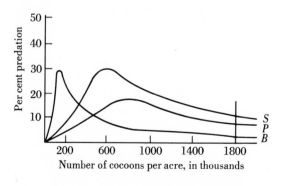

Per cent predation

Number of cocoons per acre, in thousands

Figure 21-8 *Total response of predators to prey density expressed as a percentage of predation to prey density. These graphs are based on the graphs in Figs. 21-4 and 21-6. (After Holling, 1959.)*

random encounters. In other words, the amount of prey eaten is proportional to the abundance of the predator and the abundance of the prey. There is both a functional and a numerical response.

Compensatory predation

Among many vertebrate populations, the response of predator to the prey does not quite follow the functional and numerical response just described. Predators take most or all the individuals of the prey species that are in excess of a certain minimum number, as determined by the carrying capacity of the habitat and social behavior. The prey species compensates for its losses through increased litter and brood size and greater survival of young. For this reason this type of predation, type C of Ricker, is called compensatory. The population level at which predators no longer find it profitable to hunt the prey species has been called the "threshold of security" by Errington (1946). As prey numbers increase above this threshold, the surplus animals are no longer tolerated in the area (see Chap. 20) and become vulnerable to predation. Below the threshold of security,

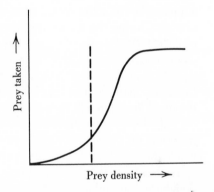

Figure 21-9 *Compensatory predation as illustrated by a functional response curve. There is no response to the left of the vertical line.*

functional response of the predator is very low (Fig. 21-9) and numerical response is nonexistent. Above the threshold, functional response is marked, and numerical response could occur. An outstanding example of compensatory predation is detailed by Errington (1963) in his notable study of the muskrat.

Predation and vertebrate populations

Some modification in the relationship between predator and prey exists when predation is compensatory. In this situation several variables influence predation. They include natural food preferences of the predator, physical condition of the prey and escape facilities, the abundance of alternate foods, and the density of both the prey and the predator populations (Leopold, 1933). These variables can be examined from two viewpoints, that of the prey and the predator.

Prey. The many variables that make up the odds that an animal will be captured by a predator—the prey risk—is determined in part by the availability of food and cover to the prey, its movement, activity, habits, size, strength, age, and escape reactions.

411

As suggested already there is a very strong interaction between predation and cover. Prey that occupy secure habitats with good cover are much less vulnerable to predation. A sunfish hiding in a mass of pondweed is relatively safe, but once the fish moves into clear water, it exposes itself to a number of predacious fish. Young salmon living in clear shallow streams are easy prey for kingfishers and mergansers while those living in deep pools are safe. Meadow mice are secure in heavy cover, but after the spring thaw, when the grass cover has been destroyed by the mice and flattened by winter snows, the mice are exposed to heavy predation.

Habitat preferences that bring predator and prey into close contact increase prey risks. Predatory rainbow trout in Paul Lake, British Columbia, move into the shoals when their prey, the redside shiner, are most heavily concentrated there. A complex pattern of seasonal movements of the shiner governed by water temperatures brings prey in contact with the predator in the midsummer. During winter the shiners move into warmer, deep water, where they are isolated from the predatory trout (Crossman, 1959a,b).

Movement, activity, and habits affect an animal's chances of falling to a predator. During periods of territorial establishment and courtship, passerine birds are more active and less wary, increasing their conspicuousness. Nocturnal animals like the white-footed mice are less susceptible to diurnal predators than to owls. During the winter the same mice run along the top of the snow while meadow mice tunnel beneath. The dark pattern against the white makes the white-footed mouse highly vulnerable while the meadow mouse is relatively safe. Concentrations of prey may make them highly vulnerable to predation. Covies of quail are the target of Cooper hawks in winter; during summer, when the quail are scattered, they are less subject to attack. On the other hand, ring-necked pheasants are relatively secure in winter cover. Spring dispersal takes them into the range of additional predators; and increased daily activity at a time when there is little background cover makes the pheasants more conspicuous (Craigheads, 1956). Speed, agility, and escape reactions vary between species. Songbirds and rabbits possess considerable agility and maneuverability to escape. Bobwhite quail, on the contrary, have little speed or agility and must rely on acute awareness of danger, cover, and protective coloration. Animals that harmonize with their immediate surroundings are much less subject to predation, while animals with striking coloration may be targets of predators, especially when they venture into the open. Predation by trout on redside shiners in Paul Lake was heaviest on clear hot days in July and August, when visibility through the very calm water was exceptional. Then the shiners were very conspicuous because of the sun's reflection on their silvery scales (Crossman, 1959a).

Age, size, and strength vary the prey risk. The young and immature, the feeble and the sick of all prey species are less wary and have not developed a rapid response to predatory danger. Larger animals are better able to escape predation than smaller ones. Adult fox squirrels, for example, are relatively invulnerable to predators because of their size and toughness.

Predator. The chances of a particular prey species being captured vary with the kinds of predators present on the area. As the most numerous prey species declines, it becomes less vulnerable to those predators most poorly adapted to capture it. Specialized predators, those adapted to hunt only a few species, are forced to move when the vulnerability of a staple prey item drops to a point where the predator population cannot support itself. Generalized predators, not so restricted in diet, adjust to other food sources. The horned owl and buteo hawks have a large range of collective prey available. Foxes can shift to a vegetable and carrion diet, should conditions require it. In general, adaptations of predators are such that small rodents are vulnerable to more species of predators than small birds and game.

Hunting ability and food preferences of predators vary widely between species and between individuals of the same species. Cooper hawks will return time and again to harass a covey of bobwhite quail. Other predators will hunt favorite areas. Individual foxes develop excellent skill in hunting rabbits and appear to concentrate on them. Some predators may acquire a taste for certain prey items and seek them out. Peales falcon, a subspecies of the peregrine falcon found along the northwest Pacific Coast, show a marked preference for duck or pheasant and will eat gulls and crows only when necessary (Beebe, 1960).

From this it is apparent that predation is a highly complicated phenomenon, which must be studied from a community and not an individual predator or prey viewpoint. This has been done in an interesting manner by the Craigheads (1956) for an area in Michigan. During fall and winter, predation was exerted on peak small-rodent populations and tended to be proportional to prey densities. Heaviest pressure on rodents occurred in winter, when populations and cover were at a minimum. By mid-March, breeding hawks, as well as foxes, had settled, and breeding territories were established. As a result, predation no longer was distributed according to density of the prey species. Ring-necked pheasants were especially vulnerable because of the lack of cover and increased activity. By April pressure on warm-blooded prey was relieved in part by the appearance of snakes and frogs. In late April and early May young mice and rabbits were abroad. In May, small birds were as readily available for food as meadow mice. Predation on young pheasants and fox squirrels began in May and increased gradually as the offspring increased. Then from June to mid-July the young of small birds became the major source of food. White-footed mice did not become important food items until fall and winter. Hawks migrated south and other birds in late August and September. With the return of winter, rodents again absorbed the predatory pressure.

The situation just described emphasizes another important aspect of predation, that of the facultative predator and alternate prey. Although the predator may have a strong preference for a particular prey, it can turn in the time of relative scarcity to an alternate, more abundant species, which provides more "profitable" hunting. If rodents, for example, are more abundant than rabbits and quail, fox and hawks will concentrate on them instead of the game animals. These alternate prey species then are often called "buffer species" since they stand between the predator on one hand and the game species on the other. If the buffer population is low, then the predators will turn to the other source of food, the rabbits and the quail, if populations of these animals are high.

Regulatory effect of predation

The question of whether predation can regulate populations is an old and debated one, especially among hunters and fishermen, who too often think mammalian predators, hawks, owls, and fish-eating birds are reducing game and fish populations.

It is almost impossible to generalize about the influence of predation upon a prey population, for as already pointed out, the effect depends in part upon the interaction of many variables. Theoretically at least, a predator can regulate or control a prey population if it can increase its density or effectiveness as the abundance of prey increases, and vice versa. Or to state it somewhat differently, regulation results only if the average risk of each prey individual increases with an increasing density of prey (Nicholson, 1954). As long as the predator or parasitoid feeds only on the "interest" of the prey population and does not touch the "capital," both predator and prey populations will tend to remain fairly stable. This is typical of compensatory predation. If the predator cuts into the capital stock, then the prey declines. In this situation, in which the predator must have a high rate of increase and an ability to disperse, predation may act to limit or may virtually exterminate local prey populations. The predator population tends to overshoot that of the prey. The decrease in prey results in a sharp decline in the predator population through starvation. If a portion of the host or prey is not available because of environmental discontinuity, then the oscillations will be damped, and under certain conditions the predator-prey system will be self-regulating. On occasions the host or prey do overcome any controlling influence the parasitoids and predators may have upon them and reach outbreak proportions. Under this condition it would be unusual for a parasite or a predator to overtake a prey while it is abundant and cause it to crash.

This is nicely illustrated by the predator-prey relationships among the cicadas. Among the nonperiodical cicadas, some adults, after a long developmental period, appear above ground every year. Their eggs are attacked by parasitoids, the adults by predators. The cicada-killer wasp provisions nests with the bodies of adults, and even these paralyzed adults may be attacked and devoured by sarcophagid and tachinid flies before the wasp larvae can complete their own development (Damback and Good, 1943). As far as is known, these predators and parasities have yearly life cycles and move from year class to year class of their cicada hosts. The predatory population, in theory at least, could build up and bring any nonperiodical cicada population under control. But the periodical cicadas, by becoming periodical and possessing a long developmental period underground, have been able to escape the delayed density-dependent effects of predation. The large number of cicadas appearing about the same time satiate the predators and parasites. A fixed number of prey are taken, depending upon the density of predators, and the rest go free. The predators and parasitoids may be able to increase their population as a result of the increased food supply provided by the periodical cicadas, but the effect will be dissipated before the next generation emerges (Lloyd and Dybas, in press).

Among the ungulates, predation may hold down the population when the predator is one of the highly skilled canids, the coyote or wolf, or a big cat, such as the mountain lion. The depressant effects of predation on the Kaibab deer illustrate how predators can regulate certain populations, although in such instances it is probably to the best interests of the prey. Because of the desire to protect the deer on a newly established game preserve, lions and wolves were eliminated. The deer population increased tremendously from the original 4,000 in 1907 to 100,000 in 1924. The range was insufficient for such high numbers;

within two years it was overbrowsed. From 1924 to 1930, 80,000 deer died of starvation. After that the population declined another 10,000 until the herd leveled off at around 10,000 animals (Rasmussen, 1941). Such is the story when man attempts to correct a predator-prey relationship.

Predation is least effective in limiting populations when the prey is territorial or is subject to intraspecific strife. Here the predators feed upon the surplus, those animals no longer tolerated in the area and forced to settle in poor habitat or to wander in search of a place to live. Such animals are extremely vulnerable to predation and are doomed to die, if not by predation, then by disease, exposure, or starvation. With these animals, apparently excessive predation simply reflects excessive numbers of prey; the predators have only a negligible influence on prey abundance.

Genetic feedback and predator-prey systems

Environmental discontinuity, predator density, alternate prey—these and other influences may not be acting alone in the maintenance of an equilibrium, however unstable, in a predator-prey system of nonterritorial animals. In recent years increasing attention and thought have been given to the idea that evolution acting through genetic feedback systems may integrate the herbivore-plant, parasitoid-host, and predator-prey systems in the community.

A possible example of genetic feedback is the prickly pear–*Cactoblastis* moth relationship already discussed. Although the moth in general reduced the prickly pear population, some types of the cactus grow that are not readily destroyed by the moth (Dodd, 1959). One, *Opuntia inermis*, has thickened segments of such high mucilaginous and starch content that the moth larvae are unable to survive in them. But this advantage for the plant is offset, since the plant produces terminal cladodes, which are attacked by the moth larvae. Stimulated by the larval feeding, the prickly pear continues to produce terminal cladodes until the stored resources of the plant are depleted. A second resistant species, a nitrogen-deficient yellow prickly pear, grows on basalt soils at higher elevations. Because of a lack of food of adequate quality and suboptimal temperatures, the larvae grow slowly, are small in size, and fail to control the cactus. In fact, of 26 species of prickly pear and other cacti naturalized in Australia, the moth feeds primarily on two species, *Opuntia inermis* and *O. stricta.*, and cannot support itself on the other existing species. Both *inermis* and *stricta* possess different levels of resistance to the moth, and of these the former is the most abundant and embraces most of the resistant strains. The abundance and distribution of species and strains and the corresponding decrease in susceptible plant species available act to control the moth population.

Another example of genetic change functioning to adjust a natural parasite-host system is the myxomatosis outbreak in the European rabbit population in Australia. To control the rabbit, the Australian government introduced myxomatosis into the population. The first epizootic of the disease was fatal to between 97 and 99 per cent of the rabbits; the second resulted in a mortality of 85 to 95 per cent; the third, 40 to 60 per cent mortality (Fenner et al., 1953). The effect on the rabbit population was less severe with each succeeding epizootic, suggesting that the two populations were becoming integrated and adjusted to one another in the ecosystem. In this adjustment, attenuated genetic strains of virus,

415

evolved by mutation, are tending to replace virulent strains (Thompson, 1954). Also involved is passive immunity to myxomatosis, conferred to the young born of immune does. Finally a genetic change has occurred in the rabbit population, providing an intrinsic resistance to the disease.

But this is not the whole story. The transmission of the myxomatosis virus is dependent upon *Aedes* and *Anopheles* mosquitos, which feed only on living animals. Rabbits infected with the virulent strain live for a shorter period of time than those infected with the less virulent strain. Because the latter live for a longer time, the mosquitoes have access to that virus for a longer period. This gives the nonvirulent strain a competitive advantage over the virulent. In those regions where the nonvirulent strains have a competitive advantage, the rabbits are more abundant. This means that more total virus is present in those regions than in comparable areas where the virulent strains exist. Thus the virus with the greatest rate of increase and density within the rabbit is not the one selected for. Instead the virus whose demands are balanced against supply has the greatest survival value in the ecosystem.

These two examples suggest how a genetic feedback mechanism through genetic evolution might integrate the herbivore-plant, the parasite-host, and predator-prey systems in the community. It functions as a feedback system through the dynamics of density pressure, selective pressure, and genetic change in the interacting populations (Pimentel, 1961). In a herbivore-plant system, animal density influences selective pressure on plants. This selection influences the genetic make-up of plants, and the genetic make-up of plants determines the quality of food they provide the herbivores. Since the birth rate and the death rate of herbivores are in part a function of the quality of food they consume, the plants influence animal density. This same action and reaction follow through the food chain. Density influences selection; selection influences genetic make-up, and in turn genetic make-up influences density, all of which result in the evolution and regulation of animal populations.

Cannibalism

A rather special kind of "competitive interference" or predation that exists within a species population or between populations of closely related species is cannibalism. Distasteful as it may seem, cannibalism is a method of population control common to a wide range of animals, including fish, rodents, birds, and primitive human societies, although in the latter (and in today's society) infanticide, abortion, and war are more commonly employed violent methods of intraspecific population control. Of all the methods of population control, canni-

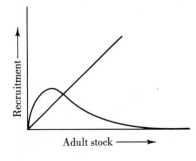

Figure 21-10 *A reproductive curve illustrating cannibalism. Note how the population dwindles to zero.*

balism is the one in which the abundance of the control agent is inseparably linked to that of the population controlled. With cannibalism, an increase in parental stock not only increases the number of eggs laid and young born in a given reproductive season; it is also accompanied by a decreasing survival of young. If the breeding stock is large enough, cannibalism reduces reproduction to practically zero (Fig. 21-10), in spite of the greatly increased production of young. However, cannibalism as a form of population control is probably important only in a minority of populations.

Exploitation

A form of highly selective, intensive predation, which often is not related to the density either of the predators or the prey, is exploitation by man. Over-

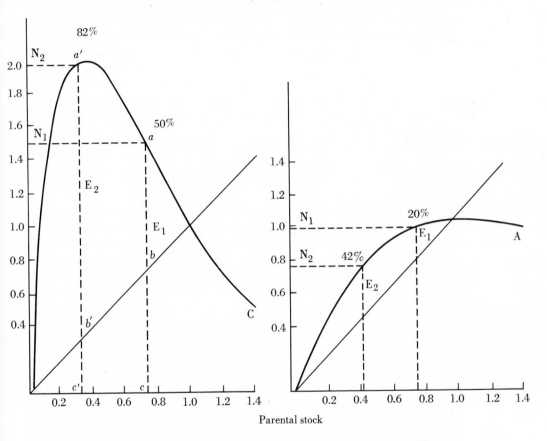

Parental stock

Figure 21-11 *Reproductive curves illustrating rates of exploitation. The perpendicular line ac cuts the 45-degree line at b (see text). On curve C, the 82 per cent point represents the maximum surplus reproduction and the maximum rate of exploitation possible for this population. Other figures in the population indicate the position on the curve for other rates of exploitation. Segment ab (E) is harvest; bc is the stock left for recruitment. Note the differences between the two curves. In curve C, $E_2 > E_1$, and $N_2 > N_1$. Under these conditions the greater the standing crop, the greater is the sustained yield. In curve A where $E_2 > E_1$, yet $N_1 > N_2$, a high standing crop does not result in greater sustained yield. A knowledge of parent-progeny relations is essential for the wise exploitation of natural animal populations.*

exploitation of wild populations, especially if coupled with the loss of habitat, has resulted in a serious decline and even local and total extermination. The history of the buffalo, the great auk, the herds of African ungulates, and the current overharvesting of whales are examples of such short-sightedness on the part of man. On the other hand, such valuable wildlife populations as the white-tailed deer are underharvested in many places, especially since their natural predators have been eliminated. In the wise exploitation of any natural population, the object is to maintain some sort of equilibrium between recruitment and harvest.

This can be illustrated by means of some reproductive curves, as shown in Fig. 20-16. For any position of the stock to the left of the 45-degree line there is a rate of exploitation that will maintain the stock at that position. Maximum sustained yield does not necessarily require a large standing crop. In the curves in Fig. 21-11 let *a* be any position on the curve and *c* a perpendicular line that cuts the 45-degree line at *b*. At equilibrium, the portion *bc* of the recruitment must be used for the maintenance of the stock, for *bc* = *oc*; *ab* can be harvested. There is however a limit to exploitation, a limit that is influenced by the inflection point of the curve. For curve *C*, maximum rate of exploitation is about 82 per cent; for curve *A*, 42 per cent. In these curves the size of the reproductive stock that will give maximum sustained yield will not be greater than half of the replacement of the reproductive population. The greater the area of the reproduction curve above the 45-degree line, the greater is the optimum rate of reproduction.

Interspecific competition

When two species in the same community seek the same resources, such as food and space, which are in short supply (in relation to the number seeking it), or interact in such a way that it affects their growth and survival, they are said to compete with one another. Few concepts have had such an impact on ecological and evolutionary thinking; yet basically the nature of interspecific competition and its effects on the species involved is one of the least known and most controversial fields of ecology.

The idea of competition, or the "struggle between species," was emphasized by Darwin. Later Lotka and Volterra separately developed mathematical formulas describing relationships between two species utilizing the same food source. Essentially these formulas indicate that eventually only one species, the least susceptible to food shortage or most adaptable to changed environmental conditions, will survive.

Gause (1934) set out to test these formulas experimentally. He introduced two species of Paramecium, *P. aurelia* and *P. caudatum*, in one tube containing a fixed amount of bacterial food. *P. caudatum* died out. The success of *P. aurelia* resulted from its higher rate of increase. But in another experiment *P. caudatum* occupied the same solution with *P. bursaria*. Here both species were able to reach stability, since *P. bursaria* confined its feeding to bacteria on the bottom, while the other fed on that suspended in the solution. Although the two used the same food supply they occupied different parts of the culture, thus utilizing food essentially unavailable to the other. Later Crombie (1947) confined two beetle populations, one *Trilobium confusum* and the other *Oryzaephilus suri-*

namensis, in flour. The *Oryzaephilus* population died out, chiefly because *Trilobium* ate more eggs of *Oryzaephilus* than the latter did of *Trilobium.* In a second experiment he reared another population of two beetles, one *Oryzaephilus* and the other *Rhizopertha dominica,* in a culture of cracked wheat. *Rhizopertha* lived and fed outside the grain and *Oryzaephilus* lived and fed inside the grain. Since they occupied different niches they were able to exist together even though they utilized the same food.

These experiments seemed to bear out in part at least the mathematical models devised by Lotka and Volterra. From this developed the concept that two species with identical ecological niches cannot occupy the same environment. English ecologists called this "Gause's principle," although the idea was far from original with him. More recently the concept has been called the "competitive exclusion principle" (Hardin, 1960), which can be stated briefly as: "Complete competitors cannot coexist." Essentially this principle means that if two noninterbreeding populations occupy exactly the same ecological niche, if they occupy the same geographic territory, and if population *A* multiplies even the least bit faster than population *B,* then *A* eventually will occupy the area completely and *B* will become extinct.

Empirical evidence of competition, although often difficult to determine and prove in nature, seems to support competitive exclusion. No two species, as far as is known, possess identical ecological requirements. Each species faces the chance that reproduction and survival will fail and thus permit a competitor to step in. Subtle differences in the ecology of each species, which might escape notice at first, may tip the scales in favor of one species or the other. Thomas Park (1948, 1954) studied the relationship of laboratory populations of two flour beetles, *Trilobium castaneum* and *Trilobium confusum.* He found the interaction between the two species to be quite complex. The fate of the two competitors depended considerably upon environmental conditions such as temperature and humidity, upon the presence or absence of parasites, and the fluctuations of the total number of eggs, larvae, pupae, and adults. Often the final outcome of competition was not determined for generations. Frank (1952), working with two water fleas with overlapping niches, *Daphnia pulicaria* and *Simocephalus vetulus,* found that eventually *Daphnia* won out, although *Simocephalus,* better adapted to yeast food, put up a good struggle. In nature, however, under less severe crowding conditions, the two species probably could exist together.

Similar species or members of the same genus are able to exist together in normal numbers in the same community because of ecological adaptations that permit them to occupy different ecological niches, to possess different feeding methods, to utilize different foods, or if the food is the same, to feed at a different time or place. (Fig. 21-12). In other cases competition is avoided because normally there is a superabundance of food. Here competition would be evident only when the shared resource was in short supply.

There are many examples to illustrate these situations. The hermit thrush and the olive-backed thrush both occur in the coniferous forests of eastern North America. However, the olive-backed thrush inhabits the forest interior and feeds in the trees, while the hermit thrush prefers interior forest edges and feeds on the ground. They can exist together because they occupy different ecological niches (Dilger, 1956).

The myrtle warbler, the black-throated green warbler, and the Blackburnian warbler all inhabit the same forest and all have similar feeding habits; but each feeds in a particular part of the forest canopy with a minimum of overlap. Two other species, the bay-breasted warbler and the Cape May warbler, are competitors whose abundance varies with the superabundance of food. The Cape May warbler, in particular, depends upon the spruce budworm. During years between outbreaks of this insect, this warbler is reduced in numbers or eliminated locally (MacArthur, 1958).

Animals that depend on the same food source in identical areas will in times of food shortage come into direct competition. In Newfoundland the moose and snowshoe hare share the same habitat and food (Dodds, 1960). Of the 30 woody plants consumed by the moose, 27 are utilized by the hare. Both browse most heavily on plants under six feet tall. When moose feed on balsam fir reproduction on cutover areas, they retard the growth of cover for hares, preventing them from inhabiting the area during the early years after cutting. Birch is the most important hardwood browse for both moose and hares. Competition for this food begins when hares move into the cutover areas. Where forest reproduction is predominantly fir and birch, moose may cause a winter food shortage for hares. On the other hand, spruce forests with an understory of heaths provide the hares with palatable foods not utilized by moose.

When two strongly competing species do chance to occupy the same habitat, one simply may relinquish all or part of its territory or living space to the intruding competitor. Such a situation exists among the blackbirds—the red-wing,

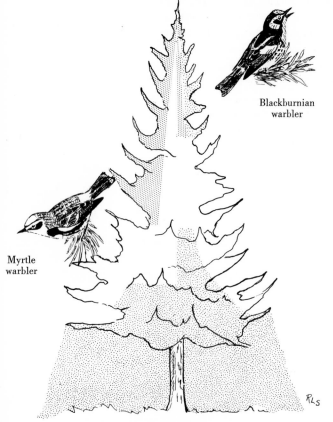

Blackburnian
warbler

Myrtle
warbler

Figure 21-12 *The feeding niches of two species of warblers, the myrtle and the blackburnian. The shaded areas represent that portion of the trees in which the birds forage over 50 per cent of the time.* (Adapted from MacArthur, 1958.)

Blackburnian warbler

Myrtle warbler

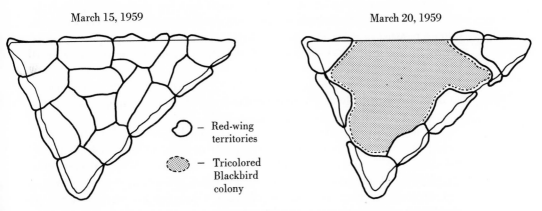

Figure 21-13 *Interaction between red-winged and tricolor red-winged blackbirds at Hidden Valley Marsh, Ventura County, California, in 1959. The tricolor is colonial.* (After Orians and Collier, 1963.)

the tricolor red-wing, and the yellow-headed. The ubiquitous red-wing blackbird and the restricted tricolor red-wing occupy the same range in the lowlands of California and adjacent Oregon and Baja California. Morphologically they are similar; behaviorally they are different. Male red-wings establish moderately large territories of 500 to 30,000 square feet early in winter in the California marshes. Within these territories, the females establish subterritories and build their nests. Male red-wings take no part in caring for the nest and young; the females stay partly on the territory and partly on the adjacent dry land. The tricolor red-wing is nomadic and is the most colonial of the North American passerines. Colonies of less than 50 nests are rare; and in such optimum habitats as the California rice fields, there may be as many as 200,000 nests. Male territories are about 35 feet square, and in them, one to three females construct the nests. The males do not assist in incubation and may even leave the area during the incubation period. But once the eggs have hatched, the males take an active role in feeding the young. Unlike the red-wing, the tricolor red-wing feeds off the territory and may range as far as four miles from the colony. The colonial system of the tricolor red-wing is more demanding of energy than the territorial system of the red-wing. Since the birds have to travel some distance to obtain food for the young, the tricolor red-wing requires a rich food supply that can be gathered quickly when the birds arrive. This results in an unpredictable breeding distribution.

Because of early territorial establishment, the red-wings have usually filled the marsh by the time the tricolored red-wings start to establish their colonies. When large numbers of the tricolor red-wings move into a marsh occupied by red-wings, the male red-wings act aggressively, but the tri-color red-wings simply through superior numbers usually are successful, without offering counteraggression (Orians and Collier, 1963). The red-wings either desert their territories (Fig. 21-13) or if they remain on them, cease to defend them. Because the tricolor red-

421

wings do not necessarily breed in the same place year after year, the red-wings do not desert the area but continue to remain aggressive toward the tricolor.

Still another competitive relationship exists between the red-wing and the yellow-headed blackbirds, both of which occupy the marsh habitat. The two birds differ somewhat in the food delivered to the nestlings. The red-wing is not a food specialist; the yellow-headed blackbird is, and preys on a comparatively small number of insects available for only a short period of time. The yellow-headed blackbird then utilizes the marsh only during time of maximum emergence of aquatic insects, usually only a single brood is raised, and renesting is rare. If the large insects fail, the nestlings may starve.

Although the two blackbirds differ in the food delivered to the nestlings, their diets apparently are similar enough to preclude the possibility of their exploiting the same simple vegetation in different ways. This limits the population intra-specifically and interspecifically. The total number of birds in an area is limited and territorial conflicts are interspecific. The yellow-headed blackbirds occupy the deeper water areas, while the red-wings are restricted to shallow water near shore. The size of the territories of each is influenced by the presence of individuals of the other species. The early-arriving red-wings contract their territories when the yellow-headed blackbirds arrive; and if the red-wings are not there, the yellow-headed blackbirds expand shoreward.

There are other examples that might be noted briefly. When brook trout and rainbow trout occupy the same stream, they treat each other as if they were the same species (Newman, 1956). The largest fish occupy the deepest and darkest parts of the stream and the smaller ones are forced to live in less favorable parts. Seven species of darters defend territories against other species as well as against individuals of their own species (Winn, 1959). The marine intertidal zone off the Scottish coast is inhabited by two barnacles, *Chthamalus stellatus* and *Balanus balanoides*. The upper limits of the intertidal zone inhabited by the two species are set by physiological tolerances. Of the two, *Chthamalus* grows higher up on the rocks. When young *Chthamalus* settle in the *Balanus* zone, they seldom survive unless the area is kept free of *Balanus*. The *Balanus* colonize an area in greater numbers and grow so much faster than *Chthamalus* that they undercut, smother, or crush the latter. The *Chthamalus* that do survive are small and produce few offspring (Connell, 1961). Thus, the *Chthamalus'* degree of success in colonizing the lower limits is set by competition.

In general when even partial competition exists, the immediate effect is depressed population levels of one or both populations, reduction in rate of increase, or reduction in individual growth rates. Trout, for example, grow more rapidly to a larger size when other trout species and forage species are low or absent (Cooper, 1959). Shiners in Paul Lake were serious competitors with smaller trout for food, even though they were a food source for larger trout (Crossman, 1958*b*). A rise in the shiner population in this lake caused a drop in production and a decrease in the growth rate of trout. A more extreme response occurs among two species of butterflies, the monarch and the queen monarch in Florida (Brower, 1961). Both are attracted to the flowers of the same milkweed plant, upon which they both feed and lay eggs and on which the larvae feed. The nonmigratory queen monarchs, however, avoid some species of milkweed that the migratory monarchs utilize. But after the monarchs have flown northward, the queen monarch oviposts on this milkweed. Thus the disappearance of the monarch coincides with a population increase in the queen monarch.

A population may be less than the carrying of the habitat because it has to share a limited environmental resource with another species. In such situations, natural selection (Chap. 24) will favor any new gene in the population that will eliminate or reduce sharing. It will promote the spread of those genes that will enable the population to exploit an unfilled ecological niche. In other words real competitors are dropped along the evolutionary wayside.

Many species tolerate a wide range of habitat conditions, from optimum to marginal. If the population expands, the surplus individuals may settle in marginal habitat. This same habitat also may be marginal for another similar species and be occupied by it. If the new colonizer is a strong competitor, the original occupant is forced to narrow its ecological range by contracting it to the optimum habitat. Here the species remains, until the marginal range again is unoccupied by its competitor, when the species again may expand into the area. Such a situation is called *ecological overlap.*

A similar situation exists among plants. Under optimum conditions, some plants will dominate, and suppress their associates. During moist years the prairie grass, little bluestem, dominates the grassland, but during dry years it almost disappears, while two associates, side-oats grama and blue grama, two grasses of the same species associated with each other become dominant.

In fact competition among plants is more conspicuous than that among animals. From the time seedlings germinate and develop, the demand for growing space, light, moisture, and nutrients increases. Those plants that utilize resources in short supply most efficiently have the best chance for survival. Plants whose root systems are in the same horizon compete for limited moisture and nutrients. In western North America the shallow-rooted annual grass *Bromus tectorum* grows early in spring and often reduces moisture so much that slow-growing annuals, perennials, and even shrubs are unable to withstand the competition (Holmgren, 1956). In drier regions, plants that develop roots rapidly after germination have the competitive advantage. The weaker plants are overtopped and eventually crowded out by more vigorous and aggressive individuals.

Like animals, plant species existing together in a community occupy different niches or grow at different times (see Hanson and Churchill, 1961). Plants with high light requirements occupy the top strata of the community. Some plants of the lower strata are very tolerant and carry on adequate photosynthetic activity at low light intensities. Other plants, particularly herbaceous species, develop and flower before the forest leaves and other plants shade the ground.

The composition of a plant community may be influenced by the competitive advantage of one species over another. Two grasses are common to pastures of Australia, *Bothriochloa ambigua*, of low grazing value, and *Danthonia* spp., a better pasture grass. If the seeds of both are disseminated on a bare area, *Bothriochloa* becomes established as a dominant because of its more vigorous root growth. But in native pastures already occupied by *Danthonia,* invasion by *Bothriochloa* rarely occurs, unless the former has been weakened by overgrazing (Moore, 1959). In other communities, taller plants may gain the upper hand, receive most of the light, and occupy the greatest root space, and only those plants able to grow and develop in their shade will survive underneath. If the dominant plants are intolerant they will be unable to replace themselves and the more tolerant invaders will assume dominance.

Most plants are not too exacting in soil requirements as long as competition is absent. But this is rarely the case in nature. On deep fertile sites poorer competitors often can coexist only if they can produce more viable seeds and occupy a situation within their range of tolerance. Otherwise the species is swamped. Thus on better sites the inefficient competitor, the intolerant plant, is eliminated. But on poorer sites competitive ability may take second place. The chestnut oak, a prolific seeder, will grow very well on fertile soil; but it is most abundant on poorer sites since it is excluded on the better sites by more vigorous competitors, such as red or white oak.

The competitive exclusion principle is based on the assumption that the competing species themselves and their biotic environment remain genetically constant. Since this is not the case, a situation might arise in which two competitors could coexist. The interspecific competitors may change genetically, so that both could live together and utilize the same food, space, and other necessary resources in the ecosystem (Pimentel et al., 1965). It might happen in this manner. Assume that two species A and B are fairly evenly balanced, populationwise, but species A is slightly superior to species B. As the numbers of the stronger species increase, the weaker species declines and becomes sparse. At this point the individual of A contends largely with intraspecific competitive selection. Concurrently species B, still contending primarily with interspecific competitive pressure, would evolve and improve its ability to compete with the more abundant A species. As B improves as a competitor, its numbers increase, until finally B becomes the abundant species. The original trend is reversed. After many such oscillations, a state of relative stability should result.

SUMMARY

The interrelations between populations of different species are as important in population regulation of a species as intragroup relations. In many cases the two relationships are so intertwined that it is difficult to separate them. Disease may decimate a population, yet it usually reaches epidemic proportions only when the population density is high and individuals are under stress. Much the same is true in parasitism, a condition in which two animals live together but one derives its nourishment at the expense of the other. Also rather common is social parasitism, in which one bird, the parasite, lays its eggs to be hatched in the nest of another, the host. Successful parasitism represents something of a compromise between two populations. The hosts and the parasites have developed a sort of mutual toleration with a low-grade, wide infection. Also the products of a long evolutionary process are the predator-prey and parasitoid-host systems. A close relationship exists between both populations of the system. Among many animal populations, especially invertebrates, the intensity of predation is independent of prey density but related to predator density. As the density of the prey increases, the predators may take more of the prey, a functional response; or the predators may become more numerous, a numerical response. These interactions may result in oscillations of both predator and prey populations. If a portion of the prey is not available because of environmental discontinuity, then the oscillations will be damped, and under certain conditions the predator system will be self-regulating. In other predator-prey systems in which the predators take most of the individuals of a prey species that are in excess of a certain minimum number, as determined by the carrying capacity of the habitat and social behavior, the relationship is compensatory. The prey reproductively compensate for their losses; and since only surplus prey is taken, the predators have little regulatory effect on the prey population.

Still another interrelationship exists between population of different species, interspecific competition. This phenomenon has given rise to the competitive exclusion principle, which states, simply, "complete competitors cannot coexist." If two non-interbreeding populations occupy the same ecological niche, occupy the same geographical area, and if one population multiplies the least bit faster than the other, the former will occupy the area and the latter eventually will disappear. This concept has had a great impact on ecological thinking; it is basic to the theory of natural selection and evolution of species.

Photo courtesy U.S. Department of the Interior

PART **V**

*Natural selection
and speciation*

C H A P T E R **22**

Natural selection: an introduction

In 1831, on the 27th of December to be exact, young Charles Darwin, 22 years old, shipped aboard the HMS *Beagle,* a surveying ship of the British Navy, as a naturalist. The *Beagle* sailed from Plymouth, England, to the eastern coast of South America, through the Strait of Magellan, past Tierra del Fuego, up the west coast to Peru, and then across the water to Galapagos Islands. From here the ship sailed to the South Sea Islands, New Zealand, and Australia, across the Indian Ocean, around the Cape of Good Hope, and on to England. Five years later Darwin returned, his notebooks filled with observations, boxes filled with specimens of rocks, plants, and animals, and his head filled with ideas on evolution. On this trip he explored the jungles and pampas of South America and climbed the Andes. On the pampas he unearthed the fossil remains of prehistoric creatures, the glyptodon, the megatherium, and the guanaco, and he noted the similarities and differences between these and the existing species, the armadillo, the sloth, and the llama. He wondered that two such similar forms, one living and the other extinct, should exist in exactly the same part of the world. About this, Darwin later wrote: "The wonderful relationship in the same continent between the dead and the living will, I do not doubt, hereafter, throw more light on the appearance of organic

427

beings on our earth, and their disappearance from it, than any other class of facts."

During frequent stops along the South American coast, Darwin noticed that although individuals of the same species were identical or nearly so in one locality, they were slightly different in another. The nearer the locations were, the more closely did the two populations resemble each other. The more distant they were the greater was their divergence. So often did Darwin observe this subtle difference within so many different species that he was convinced that it was a general rule.

When Darwin reached the Galapagos Islands, uninhabited and visited only by buccaneers and whalers, he found the clues he needed to explain his observations. Volcanic in origin, the main islands were grouped close to one another, separated by not more than 30 miles of water from their nearest neighbor. Here he stumbled onto a living laboratory of evolution. Most of the specimens he collected were new to science; most were found only on the Galapagos. More remarkable to him, he found that each island had its own species of plants and animals, although living under similar conditions.

Darwin pondered on these similarities and differences between fossil and living representatives, and between populations of animals separated by space. He eventually came to the conclusion that species gradually became modified with the passage of time, an idea already advanced by the French biologist Lamarck. In a similar manner, he reasoned, when a species consisting of a homogeneous group increased its range into new habitats, the organisms would evolve or change in different ways, resulting in slightly different races in each region.

In this manner, Darwin thought, the different species developed on Galapagos Islands. Some mainland forms reached the islands in the distant past. Separated by a great distance from the mainland, which precluded any appreciable migration to the islands, they evolved in isolation to produce the unique types that Darwin observed. Distinctive species on each island, all of which Darwin assumed to be only one species originally, could have resulted in the same way. Once it reached the island the species followed a different evolutionary course. Various island populations diverged so much that they became different species.

But the questions "How did evolution occur?" and "What are its mechanisms?" still remained unexplained. Then in October, 1838, Darwin happened to read "An Essay on Population" by Malthus, which considered the relationship between population size and food supply. Malthus wrote: "Through the animal and vegetable kingdoms, nature has scattered the seeds of life abroad with the most profuse and liberal hand. She has been comparatively sparing in the room, and nourishment necessary to rear them. The germs of existence contained in this spot of earth, with ample food, and ample room to expand in, would fill millions of worlds in the course of a few thousand years. Necessity, that imperious all-pervading law of nature, restrains them within prescribed bounds. The race of plants, and the race of animals shrink under this great restrictive law. And the race of man cannot, by any efforts of reason, escape from it. Among plants and animals its effects are waste of seed, sickness, and premature death. Among mankind, misery and vice."

From this Darwin developed his concept of "the struggle for existence," which forms an important part of his hypothesis for the mechanism of evolution.

Darwin reasoned from his observations on the differences among living things that some variations were more advantageous than others, that some variations enabled the organisms to occupy an area or to survive. Since only a few animals would survive, Darwin argued, then those with more favorable variations would have better odds to survive. "Under these circumstances," wrote Darwin, "favorable variations would tend to be preserved, and unfavorable ones to be destroyed. The result of this would be the formation of a new species. Here then I had at last got a theory by which to work. . . ."

This process that resulted in a greater survival of individuals possessing advantageous characteristics over those which less advantageous ones Darwin called *natural selection*. As a result of it, favorable variations will be retained in the population and will increase. Through time, this will result in a population better adapted to its environment; if continued long enough, new and different species will evolve.

Although this theory is in essence accepted today, Darwin hesitated to publish his theory of evolution. He started to develop his hypotheses in 1837, and in 1842 he wrote a penciled 35-page abstract of his ideas, which he enlarged to 255 pages in 1844. He still withheld publication but discussed his ideas with two friends, the geologist Sir Charles Lyell and the botanist Dr. J. D. Hooker. In 1856 Lyell urged him to publish his material and by 1858 he had his book half completed.

Then in the summer of that year, Darwin received a letter from a fellow naturalist, Alfred Russel Wallace, who was exploring the Malay Archipelago. Its contents shocked Darwin, for with the letter Wallace sent an essay entitled "On the Tendency of Varieties to Depart Indefinitely from the Original Type." This essay contained an excellent summary of Darwin's own theory of evolution by natural selection.

After much reflection by Darwin over the dilemma and the intervention of Lyell and Hooker, the two men, who independently had arrived at the same conclusion, presented their views jointly through Lyell and Hooker, to the Linnaean Society of London on July 1, 1858, and subsequently published in the Society's journal.

Darwin pointed out that animals as well as plants produce more offspring than necessary to maintain the species. He concluded that the number of organisms must be held in check either by their own struggle with other individuals of the same species or different species or against "external nature." "Now, can it be doubted," wrote Darwin, "from the struggle each individual has to obtain subsistence, that any minute variation in structure, habits, or instincts adapting that individual better to new conditions would tell upon its vigor and health? In the struggle it would have a better *chance* of surviving; and those of its offspring which inherited the variation, be it ever so slight, would also have a better *chance*. Yearly more are bred than can survive; the smallest grain in the balance, in the long run, must tell on which death shall fall, and which shall survive. Let this work of selection on one hand, and death on the other, go on for a thousand generations, who will pretend to affirm that it would produce no effect, when we remember what, in a few years, Blakewell effected in cattle, and Western in sheep, by this identical principle of selection?"

Wallace stated much the same theory, except that he emphasized population control largely by food supply. Like Darwin, Wallace concluded that forms best adapted to their environment evolved through selection on the individual.

429

Wallace argued that if any environmental change made existence difficult, then "of all the individuals composing the species, those forming the least numerous and most feebly organized variety would suffer first, and, were the pressure severe, must soon become extinct. The same causes continuing in action, the parent species would next suffer, would gradually diminish in numbers, and with a recurrence of similar unfavorable conditions might also become extinct. The superior variety would then alone remain, and on a return to favorable circumstances would rapidly increase in numbers and occupy the place of the extinct species and variety."

Darwin further expounded his theory of natural selection and evolution in the *Origin of Species,* published in November, 1859. Darwin received, as he should, the major credit for arriving at a theory of evolution, while Wallace is best known for his fundamental studies of the distribution of animals.

Darwin's theory of evolution can be summarized briefly. Variation exists among individuals of sexually reproducing species that affects their chances of survival and reproductive rates. In addition many species have such a high potential rate of increase that if unchecked they would exhaust both food and living space. Since both food and space are limited, those with the most advantageous variations will have the better chance to survive. Constant selection of the better adapted and the elimination of the less fit result in the evolutionary change of populations. This is "survival of the fittest."

Neither Wallace nor Darwin could explain adequately or fully understand the nature and origin of variation or how these variations were transmitted from parent to offspring, although they realized that they were inherited. Had they known, much of the storm of controversy over the theory might never have developed. Ironically the answers to Darwin's most pressing questions on variation and a basis for understanding the mechanisms of evolution were being discovered in a monastery garden by a contemporary, an Austrian monk, Gregor Mendel. His finding on the laws of inheritance, presented as a lecture to the Natural History Society of Brunn in 1866 and published in the *Transactions* of the Society, were unappreciated by the scientific world at that time and remained lost in the obscure journal until 1900, when he was discovered independently by three biologists, deVries, Correns, and Tschermak.

CHAPTER 23

The basis
of
natural selection

The community, aquatic or terrestrial, consists of many different, locally defined groups of individuals similar in structure and behavior. Individuals within these groups interbreed, oak tree with oak tree, white-footed mouse with white-footed mouse, largemouth bass with largemouth bass. Collectively, individuals within each group make up a genetical population, or deme. Beyond one local population may be other similar demes. They may be separated by distance, or they may be only indistinctly separated—the populations may be more or less adjacent and continuous over a wide area. Whatever the situation, hereditary material to a greater or lesser degree passes from one population to the other. Some adjacent demes may interbreed so freely they become essentially one. If a local population of a plant or animal dies out, it will, if conditions are favorable, be replaced by individuals from surrounding populations (see Chap. 20). Individuals that die are replaced by their offspring, so that the population tends to persist down through the years; the inheritable features pass from one generation to the next.

Individuals that make up the deme are not identical. Just as a wide individual variation exists between and among human populations, so the same variation exists among individuals of sexually reproducing plants and animals. This variation is the raw material of natural selection.

The variability evident, and that perhaps not so evident, may be inherited or noninherited. Some of the conspicuous individual variants, such as shortened tails or missing appendages, malformed horns, enlarged muscles, or other features, which are the result of disease, injury, or constant use are not inheritable. These are acquired characteristics, which the early evolutionist, Lamarck, hypothesized, erroneously, were passed down from one generation to the next. On the other hand some acquired characteristics, environmentally induced, are inherited; or to say it more accurately, the ability of an organism to acquire these characteristics appears to be inherited.

Genetic variation

Of major importance to natural selection and adaptation are genetic or inherited variations within a population, variations that arise from the shuffling of genes and chromosomes, especially in sexual reproduction. That variation exists within a population can easily be demonstrated. All one needs to do is to select some 100 or so specimens from a local population and observe and record the variations of a single character: the tail length of some species of mouse, the number of scales on the belly of a snake, the shapes and sizes of sepals and petals, the rows of kernels on ears of corn. These observations can be tabulated as frequency distributions (Fig. 23-1). Many of the specimens will have the same numerical value; since this is the most common, it is called the *mode*. Others will vary above and below the mode. The frequencies of these values fall off away from the mode—fewer and fewer individuals are in each class. The frequency distribution of these variable characters tends to follow a bell-shaped curve, the normal curve of probability. In some situations the distribution may deviate from the normal bell-shaped curve. These differences may point out some facts on variation within a population. The variations may be due to heredity, to environment, or, more often than not, to an interaction of both. All tend to produce a bell-shaped distribution of the variations of the character within a population.

Species characteristics and their variants in bisexual organisms are transmitted from the parent to the offspring. Higher plants and animals bridge successive generations by the union of two germ cells, or gametes, the sperm of the male, the egg of the female. The resultant individual, or zygote, starts as a single cell. As it divides and grows, groups of cells differentiate into organs, and organs into systems, each with its own physiological functions. In coordination with each other, these systems control the functioning of an organism. The underlying control system, found in the fertilized egg and later, as the result of cell division, in the nucleus of every cell within the organism, is deoxyribonucleic acid, DNA.

DNA, the template from which new life is patterned, is a complex molecule, ladderlike in its construction. The uprights are formed by an alternating sequence of deoxyribose sugar and phosphate groups, to which bases, adenine, guanine, cytosine, and thymine are attached. Pairs of bases make up the rungs. Because of the shape of the bases, the rungs are always formed by adenine with thymine, and by guanine with cytosine. The information of heredity thus is coded in terms of the sequential pattern in which the base pairs occur. Each

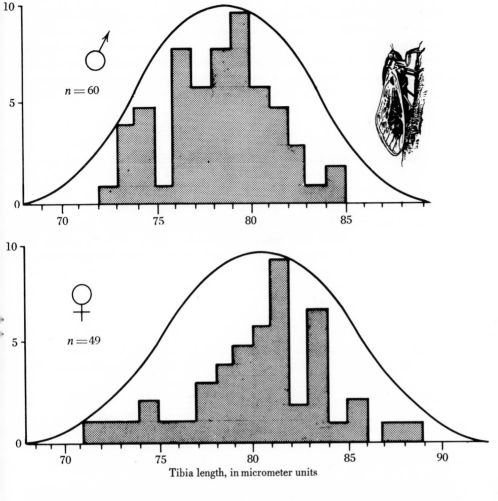

Figure 23-1 *A histogram showing the frequency distribution of hind tibia lengths of nymphal exuviae (shed skin) of the periodical cicada,* Magicicada septendecim. *The curve superimposed is a bell-shaped one (approximated). Such a bell-shaped curve of population variation in natural populations is usually the result of variation in both the environment and in individual genotypes.* (After Dybas and Lloyd, 1962.)

species, according to current theory, is unique in that its base pairs are arranged in a different order from every other species.

The egg and the sperm carry one of each member of every chromosome pair in a variety of combinations, brought about by random segregation at the time of meiosis. In man, for example, 23 haploid chromosomes (46 diploid, one-half contributed by each parent) may occur in 2^{23} possible combinations, somewhere over 8,000,000. When egg and sperm unite to form a new individual, the chromosomes recombine in any of a bewildering array of combinations. It is this segregation and recombination of chromosomes and the hereditary information existent for many generations that they carry that is the main immediate source of variation.

433

Each chromosome carries units of heredity, the genes, the informational units of the DNA molecule. Because chromosomes are paired, genes likewise are paired in body cells. The position a particular gene occupies on a chromosome is known as a locus. Genes occupying the same locus on a pair of chromosomes are alleles, and can be identical or different. During the formation of gametes, the alleles are separated as chromosomes separate; and at the time of fertilization, the alleles, one from the sperm and one from the egg, recombine as the chromosomes recombine. (This is all greatly simplified; the whole story must be sought in books on genetics.)

If genes occur in two forms, *A* and *a*, then any individual carrying them can *fall into three possible diploid classes: AA, aa,* and *Aa*. Individuals in which the alleles are the same, *AA* or *aa,* are called homozygous; and those in which the alleles are different, *Aa,* are heterozygous. The haploid gametes produced by the homozygous individuals are either all *A* or all *a*; those by the heterozygous, half *A* and half *a*. These can recombine in three possible ways (Table 23-1). Thus the proportion of gametes carrying *A* and *a* is determined by the individual genotypes, the genes received from the parents. Eggs and sperm unite at random, enabling the prediction of the proportion of offspring of different genotypes based on parental genotypes.

TABLE 23-1.   MIXING TWO HOMOZYGOUS POPULATIONS

		MALES	
		AA	*aa*
		.50	.50
		A	*a*
AA .50	*A*	*AA* .25	*Aa* .25
aa .50	*a*	*Aa* .25	*aa* .25

FEMALES

Assume that a population homozygous for the dominant *AA* is mixed with an equal number from a population homozygous for the recessive *aa*. Their offspring, the F_1 generation, then will consist of .25 *AA*, .50 *Aa*, and .25 *aa* (Table 23-1). These proportions, .25 of *AA*, .50 of *Aa*, and .25 of *aa*—are called genotypic frequencies. The gene frequencies, of course, are .5 of *A* and .5 of *a*. This proportion will be maintained through successive generations of a bisexual population (Table 23-2) if at least three conditions exist: reproduction must be random; mutations either must not occur or else they must be in equilibrium, that is, the rate of mutation from *A* to *a* is the same as *a* to *A*; and finally the

434

population must be large enough so that changes by chance in the frequency of genes are insignificant.

TABLE 23-2. PROPORTIONS IN THE F_2 GENERATION

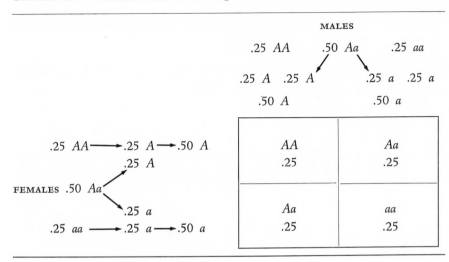

The equilibrium of these three genotypes can be expressed as a general statistical law, known as the Hardy-Weinberg law. Essentially it is this: If the frequency of allele A is p and the frequency of a is q, where $(p + q) = 1.0$, then $p^2 + 2pq + q^2 = 1.0$, in which p^2 is the genotypic frequency of individuals homozygous for A, q^2 is the frequency of individuals homozygous for a, and $2\,pq$ the frequency of the heterozygous, Aa. In the hypothetical population above, the proportion of the genotypes in the F_1 generation will be $(.5)^2 + 2(.5 \times .5) + (.5)^2$; and the same tendency can be demonstrated even if the ratio is not the classical Mendelian 1 : 2 : 1. Imagine a population in which the ratio of A alleles (p) to the a alleles (q) is .6 to .4. The frequency of the genotypes in the F_1 generation will be .36 AA, .48Aa, and .16 aa, and the gene frequency will be $(.6)^2 + 2(.6 \times .4) + (.4)^2$. From this one can conclude that all succeeding generations will carry the same proportions of the three genotypes (Table 23-3), provided that the assumptions mentioned earlier are fulfilled.

The stated assumptions are never perfectly fulfilled in any real population, so the Hardy-Weinberg law must be considered as wholly theoretical, a distribution against which actual observations can be compared. Nevertheless, the Hardy-Weinberg law is of fundamental importance in theoretical population genetics, since it means that one can state approximately what the genotypic frequencies will be from a knowledge of gene frequencies alone—provided that the population has discrete generations. In a population with overlapping generations, such as the human population, the Hardy-Weinberg law does not hold, even in theory.

Variation in a population seldom is constant from generation to generation. One reason is gene mutation, the ultimate source of genetic variation. Mutation is a change in chromosomes with a genetic effect. The change may involve a multiplication of chromosomes (polyploidy, discussed later), addition to or subtraction from one or more chromosome sets, gross structural changes, trans-

TABLE 23-3. An Illustration of the Hardy-Weinberg Law

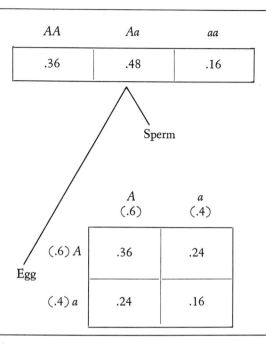

locations, and inversions (all discussed in detail in genetic books). Mutation, which can occur at all gene loci, produces new variation slowly, perhaps one in a million genes. Most common mutations involve the change of one allele into another. Even in a population homozygous for *A*, for example, *A* eventually will mutate to *a* in some of the gametes; and in a population having both genes, mutations may be forward to *a* or backward to *A*. If *A* mutates to *a* faster than *a* to *A*, then the frequency of allele *A* decreases over the other. This rarely occurs to a point where one of the alleles is lost to the population, for reversibility prevents a long-term or permanent loss. Eventually such mutations arrive at an equilibrium. Even if one allele is lost from the population, it will usually reappear by mutation.

But of more immediate consequence is nonrandomness of reproduction within a population. Not every individual is able to contribute its genetic characteristics to the next generation or to leave surviving offspring. It is this selectivity, this disparity between parents and the rest of the population, that is natural selection.

Before a given individual in a population can contribute to the succeeding generation, it must first survive to reproduce. Survival begins from the time of fertilization through the periods of development, growth, and sexual maturation. Fertilized eggs may fail to develop fully and die, either because of physiological or environmental reasons. Disease, predation, and accidents eliminate those young not quite as swift, as quick, or as strong as their siblings. In such survival, genetic variation plays a key role, for natural selection influences the frequency of alleles in a population. If a mutation arises that places its carrier at a disadvantage, selective pressures eliminate the individual; on the other hand an advantageous mutation is retained.

An example of such selection can be found among the flies. When DDT was first used as an insecticide against houseflies, the chemical was highly effective and destroyed the bulk of local populations. But among the flies were a few that did not die, that carried a mutation or a certain combination of genes that made them resistant to the spray. Resistance in one strain of flies was due to a recessive gene. Flies homozygous for this gene tolerated a high concentration of DDT, while homozygous dominants and heterozygotes were killed. These flies survived to multiply. Many of their offspring were as resistant to the sprays as the parents; some were even more resistant. The least resistant were selected against; the most highly resistant were retained in the reproductive population. Later applications of DDT continually selected for a combination of genes most resistant to the insecticide. As a result DDT became ineffective in fly control, and newer, stronger sprays were and are required. Eventually these sprays will select resistant strains of flies, which will become adapted to the new environmental conditions. But to acquire this resistance the flies pay a price. In the absence of DDT the flies are inferior competitors to the nonresistant flies, which have a shorter development time (Pimentel et al., 1951). If the spraying is stopped, evolution will be reversed and the resistance will largely disappear from the fly population.

Once they reach reproductive age, more individuals are eliminated from the parental population. The maintenance of genetic equilibrium infers random mating, but mating is not random. Many species of animals, particularly among birds, fish, and some insects (see Chap. 27) have elaborate courtship and mating rituals. Any courtship pattern that deviates from the commonly accepted pattern would be selected against, and the individual and its genes eliminated from the reproductive population. On the other hand, animals possessing a color pattern or movement that accents the typical pattern and increases its signal value or stimulus, especially to the opposite sex, would be selected for. Any new mutations that improved on courtship, mating signals and ritual would possess a favored position in subsequent generations. Among polygamous species, in particular, the majority of males go mateless, for the females mate with dominant males, that tolerate no interference from younger or less aggressive males (see Chap. 27). States of psychological and physiological readiness also are involved in mate selection. Unless both male and female are at the same state of sexual readiness, mating will not occur.

Neither is fecundity random. Even among human populations it is well known that some parents have many more young than others. The same is true throughout the living world. Some families or lines increase in number through time; others fade away. Obviously those who produce more offspring increase the frequency of their genes in a population and affect natural selection. For example, if individuals with allele A produce 10 offspring to every one produced by those with allele a, the proportion of A in the population will increase. There is a limit, however, for natural selection does not always favor fecundity. If an increased number of young per female results in reduced maternal care, survival of offspring may be reduced. This is true particularly among those animals whose chances of individual survival are high. Those organisms whose chances of individual survival are low—for example, ground-nesting game birds and oceanic fish—have become very fecund. A sort of general rule, already suggested (Chap. 21), applies to all organisms: high fecundity, low survival; low fecundity, high survival. Natural selection allows a wide range of interplay between these.

Genetic drift

Sexual reproduction is such that only a few gametes are ever involved in the formation of a new generation. In general, all an individual's genes will be represented somewhere among its gametes, but not in any two of them. Yet on the average, two gametes are all that an individual can leave behind, if the population size is to remain stable. For a heterozygote, *Aa,* there is a 50:50 chance that these two gametes will either be *A, A* or *a, a,* assuming no natural selection (and with selection the chance is even greater). Thus there is a 50:50 chance that a heterozygote will fail to pass on one of its genes. In a whole population, these losses will tend to balance each other, so that the gene frequencies of the filial generation will be a replica, but never an exact one, of the parents' gene frequencies. This is simply the familiar law of averages at work. The larger the population, the more closely will the gene frequencies of each generation resemble those of the previous one, the smaller the population, the greater will be the sampling error, or "genetic drift" (Wright, 1931, 1935). If the deme is very small, there is a good chance that the whole population may become homozygous for a particular allele in only a few generations. This is called "genetic fixation." Certain alleles are permanently lost until reintroduced by immigration or mutation. This loss of genetic variability is often maladaptative.

Theoretically, at least, the importance of genetic drift in natural selection and evolution may be considerable, especially since most species consist of partially isolated, small populations. Attempts, however, to demonstrate the importance of genetic drift in the field have been inclusive, owing largely to the difficulties of estimating effective deme sizes in natural populations.

Genetic assimilation

From a mathematical point of view, natural selection is regarded as a process that brings about changes in the frequency of genes within a population. But in actual operation, natural selection does not act on genes per se, but on the individual organism, especially as it affects the individual's ability to leave viable offspring. The receiving end of selection, then, is the phenotype, which throughout its development is exposed to the rigors of the environment. Any change in the environment that requires some adaptive change in the species will be lethal unless at least some of the organisms, by some somatic change, are able to weather the period of environmental stress, either until the environment returns to its previous norm or until some appropriate genotypic change occurs. This implies a certain amount of somatic or phenotypic flexibility (Bateson, 1963). This flexibility will involve some of the genotypes in such a way that they will produce a phenotype suitable for the new conditions. If the period is of long enough duration, then the somatic response in the form of acquired characteristics may, under appropriate conditions of selection, be replaced by similar characteristics that are genetically determined. The acquired characters would become "genetically assimilated" (Waddington, 1957). This genetic assimilation, which simulates Lamarckian inheritance, has considerable survival value when organisms must adapt to stress or change that remains constant over a generation. Through genetic assimilation, a species acquires the ability to respond through somatic changes to changes in the environment. Upon the return of the previous environmental norm, the changes in the individual produced in response to specific environmental conditions will follow with a diminuation or loss of characteristics (Waddington, 1957). But the ability to respond will be retained genetically.

Geographic variation

One fact that Darwin observed during his voyage aboard the *Beagle* along the South American coast was the variation between local populations of a given species over a geographical region. One local group may differ, more or less, from other local populations; and the greater the distance between populations, the more pronounced the differences become. These variations may be morphological, involving color, shape, and structure; physiological, involving body functions; or ecological, involving adaptation to elevation, light, humidity, or behavior.

Polymorphism

Geographical variations, especially discontinuous ones, frequently arise within local populations. The occurrence of several distinct forms of a species in the same habitat at the same time is *polymorphism,* which literally means "many forms." This may involve differences in color (such as the gray and black forms of the gray squirrel) and other morphological characters, and in physiology. The important feature about polymorphism is that the forms are distinct and the characteristic involved is discontinuous. There are no intermediates.

Although polymorphism is caused by differences in major genes, some are environmentally induced, the result of the environment modifying the action of genes. This is possible only when two environments, for example, background color, are present at the same time in the same place. Environmentally controlled polymorphism, favoring two or more forms, is the optimal expression of the characters concerned. All intermediates are at a disadvantage and usually are eliminated. The black swallowtail, a common butterfly in eastern North America, and the European swallowtail are good examples. Both swallowtails pupate either on green leaves and stems, or on brown ones. Each possesses two distinct colors to the puparium, one green, the other brown. Through natural selection both have acquired a genetic constitution that produces green pupal color in green environments, brown in brown. Green pupae would be quite conspicuous in winter; butterflies, however, emerge from these in late summer, while those in brown pupae do not emerge until the following spring (Sheppard, 1959).

There are times when environmental changes convert a disadvantageous allele or mutant gene to an advantageous one, permitting the latter to spread through the population. During this period, polymorphism will exist, only to disappear when the new advantageous form has completely replaced the original or has so swamped it that the original can be maintained only by recurrent mutation. Such a situation is known as *transient polymorphism.*

An excellent example is industrial melanism. In England, where most observations on transient polymorphism have been made, the appearances of more than 70 species of moths are being transformed by environmental changes in

Figure 23-2 *Normal and melanistic forms of the polymorphic peppered moth,* Biston betularia, *at rest on a lichen-covered tree. The spread of the melanic form,* carbonaria, *in industrial areas is associated with improved concealment of black individuals on soot-darkened, lichen-free tree trunks. Away from industrial areas the normal color is most frequent, since black individuals resting on lichen-covered trunks are subject to heavy predation by birds.*

the countryside caused by the spread of industrialization. The most famous case is the peppered moth, *Biston betularia.* Before the middle of the nineteenth century the moth, as far as is known, was always white with black speckling in the wings and body (Fig. 23-2). But in 1850 near the manufacturing center of Manchester a black form of the species was caught for the first time. The black form, *carbonaria* (Fig. 23-2), increased steadily through the years until the black form is extremely common, often reaching a frequency of 95 or more per cent in Manchester and other industrial areas. From these places *carbonaria* spread mostly westward into rural areas far from the industrial cities. The black form has come about by the spread of dominant and semidominant mutant genes, none of which are recessive. This increased frequency and spread has been brought about by natural selection. The typical form of the peppered moth has a color pattern that renders it inconspicuous when it rests on lichen-covered tree trunks. But the grime and soot of industrial areas carried great distances over the English countryside by prevailing westerly winds killed or reduced the lichen on trees and turned the bark of the trees a nearly uniform color of black. The dark form is very conspicuous against the lichen-covered trunk but inconspicuous against the black. A British biologist, H. R. D. Kettlewell (1961; see also Kettlewell, 1965) experimentally demonstrated that not only are the moths eaten by birds but the predation is selective. When melanistic and typical forms were released in woods with lichen-covered trees, the melanistic form was easily seen and subject to heavier predation. In polluted woodlands the typical form bore the brunt of predation. This explained why the typical form has virtually disappeared in polluted country and why it is still common in the unpolluted areas in western and northern Great Britain.

The most common type of polymorphism, however, is stable or balanced polymorphism, a condition in which an apparently optimum proportion of two forms exist in the same habitat and any deviation in one direction or the other is a disadvantage. This can result in several ways. One is when two opposing selective forces so operate that one allele is at a disadvantage when common and at an advantage when rare. There are several classic examples. One is the ladybird beetle. Individuals of this polymorphic European species possess two color phases, red and black, with a variety of spotting patterns. During the summer, black individuals increase and by fall outnumber the red. During the winter, selective mortality during hibernation is greatest among the black, so that by spring the red form is numerically superior. Thus a balanced selection works in favor of the red phase during winter and the black phase during the summer.

Another example is the banding and coloration in the European land snails *Cepaea nemoralis* and *C. hortensis* (Fig. 23-3). Both exhibit considerable variation in shell coloration and in the pattern of bands in a rather constant proportion within the population. This constancy has remained almost the same as that found among shells recovered from Pleistocene deposits. The color of the shell may be yellow, pink, and brown in varying shades; common band patterns are unbanded, one-banded, and five-banded. Nearly every population contains two different variants (Cain and Sheppard, 1954). When the background color in woodlands is a fairly uniform brown from decaying leaves, the unbanded brown and one-banded pink are the most common. On green backgrounds in hedgerows and meadows, yellow, five-banded snails are most common.

The fact that the yellow are less common on the brown background, and the brown fewer on the green suggests natural selection. Song thrushes prey upon the snails. The yellow forms are less vulnerable on green background, pink and brown on brown. In fact in the early spring woods, more yellow-colored snails fall prey to song thrushes than brown snails; but in late summer, when the woodland floor is green with herbs, the browns and pinks are taken. (Sheppard, 1951). This, of course, is not the whole story, for eventually, in some populations at least, one color form would replace the other; and such is not the case. Some other selective agency, possibly a situation where certain heterozygotes have higher viability or fertility than either homozygote, is involved in the maintenance of polymorphism.

Figure 23-3 *Some polymorphic forms of the land snail,* Cepaea nemoralis. *(A) Yellow shell with brown lip; (B) brown shell with light bands; (C) yellow shell with brown bands; (D) pinkish shell with faint bands.*

Polymorphism can be extended even further to embrace geographical regions in which each geographical district is characterized by a different proportion of several color phases. This is most pronounced among insular populations, the most widely studied of which are birds. The reef heron of the southwest Pacific, for example, possesses three color phases, gray, white, and mottled. On the Polynesian Tuamotu Islands, white birds make up 50 per cent of the population. This color phase comprises only 10 to 30 per cent over the rest of its range. White birds are absent or very rare in the Marquesas Islands and in south Australia, southern New Zealand, and New Caledonia. The mottled phase makes up 15 per cent of the population from Micronesia to the Solomon Islands and Fiji (Mayr, 1942). Ultimately one form may become dominant or even exclusive over a particular part of the animal's range. And from here it is only a short step to the formation of a well-defined subspecies (see Chap. 24).

Clines

In contrast to the discontinuous type of variation exhibited by polymorphic species is the continuous type of variation. Continuous variation is the result of the intergradation of gene pools between local populations. It is most prevalent among organisms with continuous ranges over a continental area.

One of the most familiar of all North American amphibians is the meadow frog, *Rana pipiens*. It has the largest range, occupies the widest array of habitats, and possesses the greatest amount of morphological variability of any North American ranid; and it is the only one successfully established throughout the

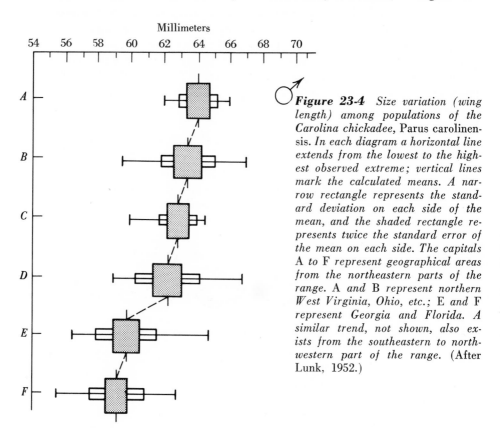

Figure 23-4 *Size variation (wing length) among populations of the Carolina chickadee,* Parus carolinensis. *In each diagram a horizontal line extends from the lowest to the highest observed extreme; vertical lines mark the calculated means. A narrow rectangle represents the standard deviation on each side of the mean, and the shaded rectangle represents twice the standard error of the mean on each side. The capitals A to F represent geographical areas from the northeastern parts of the range. A and B represent northern West Virginia, Ohio, etc.; E and F represent Georgia and Florida. A similar trend, not shown, also exists from the southeastern to northwestern part of the range. (After Lunk, 1952.)*

prairie country. But the variability and adaptability of the meadow frog are orderly, not haphazard. The species embraces a number of temperature-adapted races on a north-south gradient (Moore, 1949a,b). When the populations of the north and south extremes are compared, the differences are pronounced, yet between the two extremes, no break in variations occurs. Embryos of southern meadow frogs have an upper-limit temperature tolerance of 4°C above that of the northern embryos, although both survive equally well at low temperatures. Southern forms have smaller eggs and a slower rate of development at low temperatures. In fact so wide are these physiological differences that crossing the northern and southern forms results in defective individuals, although normal hybrids are produced when the meadow frog is crossed with either of the two gopher frogs, *Rana areolata areolata* and *Rana a. capito,* and the pickerel frog. This gradual change in a character along a gradient from one area to another is called a *cline* (Fig. 23-4 and Table 23-4). Clines, as said above, have distinctive extremes, but because such gradual changes exist from one population to another, it is impossible to group the demes into separate entities. Clines are usually

TABLE 23-4. Cline in Wing Length in the Hairy Woodpecker from North to South

LOCATION	WING LENGTH, IN MILLIMETERS ♂	♀
Maine and New Brunswick	125–129	123
New York and Pennsylvania	119–122	116–120
Maryland and District of Columbia	119	—
Virginia	117–118	118
North Carolina	119	115
South Carolina	116	113
Georgia	113	113
Florida	113	111

From Rand, 1961.

associated with an ecological gradient, such as temperature, moisture, altitude, and light. These changes may take place over a relatively short distance in response to some varying change in ecological conditions (ecocline) or they may take place over a much larger area, as is the case of the meadow frog. This phenomenon has resulted in a number of ecological rules, summarized in Table 23-5.

Some species of plants exhibit clinal gradation, some in size and other structural characteristics, others in time of flowering, in growth, or other physiological responses to the environment. Clinal differences in plants can be demonstrated by transplant studies in which a series of populations from different climates are grown together under one uniform environment in field and greenhouse. Further comparisons of differences can be obtained by growing such a series under several environmental conditions. Such studies have revealed that a number of prairie grasses, among them blue grama, side-oats grama, big bluestem, and switchgrass, flower earlier in northern and western communities and progressively later toward the south and east (McMillan, 1959). The goldenrod, *Solidago sempervirens,* flowers progressively later in the season from north to south along the Atlantic coast. The yarrow *Achillea* blankets the temperate and subarctic northern hemisphere with an exceptional number of ecological races. One species, *Achillea lanulosa,* which has been intensively studied (Clausen et al., 1948) occurs at all altitudes in the Sierra Nevada Mountains of California. It exhibits considerable variation, an adaptive response to different climatic environments at various altitudes. Populations at lower altitudes are taller and those at higher altitudes progressively shorter, although considerable variation in height exists within each population.

443

TABLE 23-5. RULES CORRELATING VARIATIONS WITH ENVIRONMENTAL GRADIENTS (Subject to frequent exceptions)

RULE	STATEMENT
Bergmann's rule	Geographic races possessing a smaller body size are found in the warmer parts of the range; races of larger body size are found in the cooler climate.
Allen's rule	The extremities of animals, the ears, tail, bill, etc., are shorter in the cooler part of the range than in the warmer part.
Gloger's rule	Among warm-blooded animals, black pigments are most prevalent in warm and humid areas, reds and yellows in the arid areas, and reduced pigmentation in the cool areas.
	Fish living in warm waters tend to have fewer vertebrae than those living in cool water.
	Races of birds living in the warmer part of the range lay fewer eggs per clutch than those races living in the cooler part of the range.

Protective coloration

Many animals are difficult to see or observe in the field because their coloration closely matches their surroundings, but aberrant-colored individuals stand out like "sore thumbs." Few abnormally colored individuals are ever seen, for being at a selective disadvantage, they are soon eliminated from the population. This was demonstrated experimentally by Dr. L. R. Dice (1947), who worked with two strains of white-footed mice, one with ivory-colored fur, the other with grayish, and an owl. Into two experimental cages, one containing sand that matched the ivory mice, the other a background matching the gray, he introduced an equal number of mice of each color and a hungry owl. In one group of experiments 192 mice were captured by the owl and of these 65 per cent were mice on nonmatching backgrounds. Under natural conditions the conspicuously colored mice would be eliminated rapidly; and those animals that blended with the landscape would have the best chance of leaving offspring. Such an adaptation is termed concealing or cryptic coloration (Cott, 1940). An animal so colored that it blends into the background of its normal environment is protectively colored. Protective coloration is common among fish, reptiles, particularly the lizard, and many ground-nesting birds, such as the woodcock. Countershading, or obliterative coloration, in which the lower part of the body is light and the upper part of the body is dark, reduces the contrast between the unshaded and shaded areas of the animal in bright sunlight. Object resemblance is common among insects. Here the animal, for example the walking stick and leaf insects, resembles some object, such as a twig or a leaf. Some animals possess "eyespot" markings, which intimidate potential predators, attract their attention away from the animal, or delude them into attacking a nonvulnerable

Figure 23-5 *Deflective and disruptive color patterns in the sparrow hawk. (A) The eyes are concealed by a prominent stripe crossing them. (B) From the rear the bird presents an owlish face, with a large pair of eyes with buffy iris and black pupils, between which is a slate-colored "beak."* (Adapted from a drawing by Mengel, from Clay, 1953.)

part of the body. Recent studies (Blest, 1957) suggest that eyespot patterns in Lepidoptera intimidate predators by imitating the eyes of large avian predators that attack small insectivorous passerine birds. Deflective eyespot coloration also is found in the sparrow hawk (Fig. 23-5). The markings on the rear of the head produce the likeness of an owlish face. The head of the sparrow hawk exemplifies disruptive coloration too, in which bold, contrasting color patterns break up the outline of the animal. Flash or dazzling coloration occurs among some species. Dull when at rest, the animal suddenly exposes brilliant, flashy colors in flight, then just as quickly returns to a dull pattern when it settles. Such action is highly confusing to predators and human observers alike.

Some unpalatable, disagreeable, or offensive animals are boldly colored, with patterns that serve as a warning to would-be predators. The black and white stripes of the skunk, the bright orange color of the inedible monarch butterfly, the yellow and black coloration of many bees and wasps serve notice to their natural enemies, all of whom apparently must have some unpleasant experience with the animal before they learn to associate the color pattern with unpalatability or pain. Together with these animals, other associated edible species have evolved a similar mimetic or false warning coloration. This phenomenon was described some 100 years ago by the English naturalist H. W. Bates in his observations on tropical American butterflies. This type of mimicry that he described, now called Batesian, is the resemblance of an edible species, the mimic, to an inedible one, the model. Once the predator has learned to avoid the model, it avoids the mimic also. An example among North American butterflies is the mimicry of the palatable viceroy butterfly to the monarch, definitely distasteful to birds (Brower, 1958). Both the model and the mimic are orange in ground color with white and black markings; both are remarkably alike. Yet the viceroy's nonmimetic relatives are largely blue-black in color. Another group of models and mimics involve the inedible pipe vine swallowtail and the palatable spicebush and black swallowtails (Fig. 23-6). Tests involving the Florida scrub jay

445

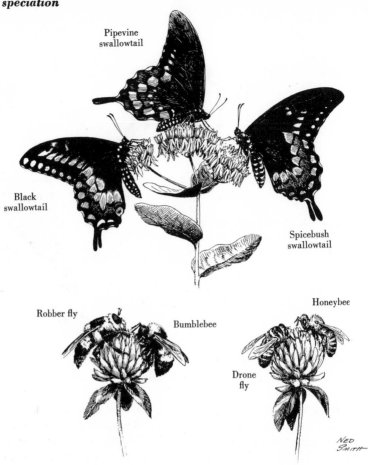

Figure 23-6 *Mimicry in insects. The model, the distasteful pipe vine swallowtail, has as its mimics the black swallowtail and the spicebush swallowtail. The black female tiger swallowtail, not shown, is a third mimic. All these butterflies are found together in the same habitat. The robber fly (left) is a mimic of the bumblebee, on which the robber fly preys. The drone fly, left, is a mimic of the honeybee. Characteristically, the model is much more common than the mimic, which is palatable to insect-feeding toads and birds.*

as the predator showed that this bird could not distinguish or confused the color pattern of the mimic with that of the model (Brower, 1958).

Bumblebees and honeybees have their mimics among the flies (Fig. 23-6). Of these perhaps the most interesting is the model bumblebee and the mimic robber fly, *Mallophora bomboides*. Not only does the robber fly benefit from reduced predation, but it also exploits the model as food. This robber fly, which preys on the Hymenoptera by preference, by resembling the bumblebee would not be noticed by the bee until it was too late to defend itself or flee. (Brower and Brower, 1962).

A second, less common type of mimicry is Müllerian, in which both model and mimic are unpalatable. The pooling of numbers between the two species reduces the losses of each, particularly when inexperienced birds are learning to avoid them (Sheppard, 1958).

SUMMARY

Mimicry and protective coloration represent a response, genetic in nature, by a species to the selective pressure of predation. As such it is one aspect of natural selection; essentially, it is nonrandom reproduction. This can come about in three different ways: nonrandom mating, nonrandom fecundity, and nonrandom survival. This nonrandomness, the basis for natural selection, lies in the variations contained in the gene pool of the deme or local population of interbreeding individuals, similar phenotypically and genotypically. Two sources of genetic variation are mutation and a recombination of genes provided by the parents in a bisexual population. Theoretically, in biparental populations the variations, as reflected in gene frequencies and genotypic ratios, remain in equilibrium if the conditions of random reproduction, equilibrium in mutation, and a relatively large population size exist. In nature, such conditions do not occur and there is a departure from genetic equilibrium. This departure is evolution, a continuing process. The direction evolution takes depends upon the genetic characteristics of those individuals in the population that survive and leave behind viable progeny. Thus natural selection, so often depicted as a desperate "tooth and claw" and "law of the jungle" sort of thing, is simply nonrandom reproduction. The successful are not those who just survive, but rather those who leave behind a sample of their genetic constitution.

CHAPTER 24

*Species
and
how they arise*

The species

One has little difficulty identifying a robin from a wood thrush or a white oak from a red oak. Each has certain morphological characteristics—ones most useful in field guides—that set them apart from other organisms. Each is an entity, a discrete unit to which has been given a name. This was the way that Carl von Linné, who gave us our system of classification, saw the great number of plants and animals. He, as did others of his day, regarded the many organisms as fixed and unchanging units, the products of special creation. Differences and similarities were based on color pattern, structure, proportion, and other characteristics, and from these criteria the species were described and separated and arranged into groups. Each species was monotypic, that is it contained only those individuals that fairly well approximated the norm or type for the species, the specimens from which the species was described. Some variation was permissible, but these variants were considered accidental, although some slight changes within the species were admitted possible. This is the *morphological species,* a classical concept still alive, useful, and necessary today for classifying the vast number of plants and animals.

Later the studies of Darwin on variation, of Wallace on geographical dis-

TABLE 24.1. Some Differences in the Sibling Species of the Seventeen-year and Thirteen-year Cicadas (Homoptera, Cicadidae, *Magicicada*)

	M. septendecim	*M. tredecim*	*M. cassini*	*M. tredecassini*	*M. septendecula*	*M. tredecula*
SIZE	No statistical difference in size between any of these					
BODY COLOR	Black above, reddish beneath, appendages reddish; pronotum reddish, prothoracic pleura reddish yellow	Same as *M. septendecim* except radial W in forewing heavily clouded	Black above; almost black below; appendages reddish; pronotum black; prothoracic pleura black		Pronotum black; prothoracic pleura black. Tibia reddish or with narrow black apical markings. In *M. tredecula* apical tarsal segments reddish all way to the tip. Abdominal sternites with prominent reddish bands.[1]	
BROOD	17 years	13 years	17 years	13 years	17 years	13 years
CALL	Low-pitched buzzing phrases, fairly even in intensity, ending with a drop in pitch. Phaaaaaaaraoh. 1–3 sec.		Rapidly delivered tick series, alternated with high-pitched, sibilant buzzes; noticeable rise and fall in pitch and intensity. Ticks: 2–3 sec; buzz: 1–3 sec.		High-pitched brief phrases in series of 20–40 at rate of 3–5 per sec. Entire call 7–10 sec.	
CHORUS	Even, monotonous roaring or buzzing; no regular fluctuations in intensity or pitch. Individual males not synchronized. Chorus most intense in morning.		A shrill, sibilant buzzing, rising and falling in intensity because of synchronization among individual males. Chorus most intense in afternoon.		More or less continuous repeating of short, separated buzzes produced without regular fluctuations in pitch or intensity. Individual males not synchronized. Chorus most intense around midday.	

[1] The only reliable way to distinguish *septendecula* from *cassini*, other than by song, is by morphometric characters. These color characteristics are very inconsistent. Where *cassini* occurs on the edge of its range in the absence of *septendecula*, some character displacement seems to take place. The abdominal sternites of *cassini* have reddish bands as prominent as those of *septendecula*.

Data from Alexander and Moore, 1962; M. Lloyd, personal communication.

tribution, and of Mendel on genetics upset the idea of special creation and emphasized that variation was the rule. Naturalists explored new lands, collected new specimens, and observed plants and animals in their natural communities. They found that some species were quite distinct and easily identified by structural or color characteristics; some, such as the song and savanna sparrows, had strong behavioral differences. But among some organisms the distinctions were much hazier. Many animals had only minute but constant morphological differences; some, such as mosquitoes, were morphologically indistinguishable as adults and were distinguishable only by the eggs. Others were structurally indistinguishable in all stages of life history but differed in their behavior (see Alexander, 1962), in ecology (see Dybas and Lloyd, 1962), in biochemistry, as determined by paper chromatography and electrophoresis (Sibley, 1960). These are *sibling species,* defined as "morphologically similar or identical natural populations that are reproductively isolated" (Mayr, 1963).

Examples of sibling species are widespread, especially among the insects. Some of the better-known cases occur in the genus *Drosophila* and in the malaria mosquito complex of Europe. Sibling species can be found in almost every family of beetles and are quite common in the Orthoptera (see Table 24-1). They also occur in snakes, in amphibians, particularly the frogs, in birds to a limited extent, and in fish, especially the whitefish and the salmonids (see Neave, 1944; Ricker, 1940). A characteristic common to all is the lack of a sharp division between ordinary species and the sibling species. The latter are at the far end of a broad spectrum or continuum of increasingly diminishing morphological differences. To the human eye the species may be virtually indistinguishable, but the differences are apparent to the animals themselves.

Biologists also realized, as Darwin observed, that many apparently closely related forms replaced each other geographically, and in doing so intergraded with one another. So smooth and gradual is the transition that it is often difficult to separate precisely one from another. The question "When does a robin cease to be a robin and become something else?" becomes very real and important. The robin, of course, is quite distinct, but the same cannot be said about some other species.

Eventually some biologists realized that the classical morphological or typological species, which emphasizes the individual, was incomplete. It was augmented by the population concept of the species—that species are not fixed, static units but are changing through long periods of time. The anatomical physiological and behavioral characteristics that clearly defined a species on a local basis are now regarded as a part of the sum of characteristics found throughout the entire population. The pattern of characteristics can be graphed as a frequency distribution of variants of different characters present in the population at a given time (Fig. 24-1). In other words, the species is multidimensional.

The species has been defined (Mayr, 1942) as "a group of actually or potentially interbreeding populations that are reproductively isolated from other such groups." This concept of the species, then, embodies a group of interbreeding individuals living together in a similar environment in a given region and under similar ecological relationships. The individuals recognize each other as potential mates. They interact with other species in the same environment. They are a genetic unit in which each individual holds for a short period of time a portion of the contents of an intercommunicating gene pool.

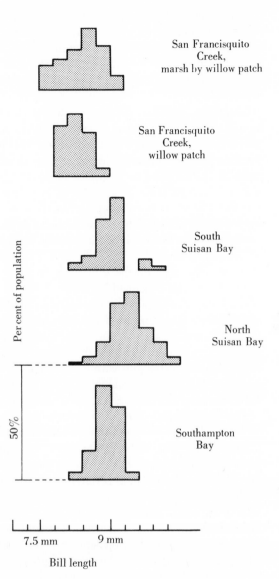

San Francisquito
Creek,
marsh by willow patch

San Francisquito
Creek,
willow patch

South
Suisan Bay

North
Suisan Bay

Southampton
Bay

Per cent of population

50%

7.5 mm   9 mm

Bill length

Figure 24-1 Geographic variation in the bill length of several populations of song sparrows in the San Francisco Bay region of California. (Adapted from Marshall, 1948.)

Such a definition of a species is applicable only to bisexual organisms. It is also limited to sympatric species, those occupying the same area at the same time. No allopatric species, those occupying an area separated by time or space, can be involved, since they never have the opportunity to meet other similar species. Thus there is no way of knowing whether they are reproductively isolated or not. The only direct evidence that an individual organism belongs to one species consists of observations in the wild that indicate that the organism is living with a specific population and functioning as a member of it. The individuals tend to possess the same morphological and physiological characteristics, since they belong to the same evolutionary population. This, then, is the biological species, in contrast to the static morphological concept—variable, constantly changing, splitting up, reuniting, almost impossible to define precisely.

451

Because of the widespread variation of many morphological, physiological, and behavioral characters in a widely distributed species, significant differences often exist between populations of different regions. One variant replaces the other geographically. The geographic variants reflect the environmental selective forces acting on various genotypes, adapting each population to the locality it inhabits.

Geographic variation shows up either as clines, as geographical isolates, or as hybrids. The cline has already been discussed in Chap. 23. It is the result of a phenotypic response to environmental selection pressures that vary on a gradient (continuum), as well as of the smoothing-out effect of a gene flow that tends to make all populations of a species identical (Mayr, 1963). The geographical isolate is a population or a group of populations that are prevented by some extrinsic barrier from effecting a free flow of genes with others of the same species (Mayr, 1963). The degree of isolation depends upon the efficiency of the extrinsic barrier, but rarely is the isolation complete. These geographical isolates, or races (or ecological races) (Fig. 24-2), and to some extent the clinal variants taxonomically make up the *subspecies,* in itself a very thorny problem.

The subspecies is defined by Mayr (1963) as "an aggregate of local populations of a species inhabiting a geographic subdivision of the range of a species, and differing taxonomically from other populations of the species." Here again the population is stressed, for while a whole population can be assigned to a subspecies, it is often very difficult to assign an individual to a subspecies because of the inherent variability within a population and the overlap of the curves of variations of adjacent populations. In reality the subspecies is an artifact of man, set up for practical reasons; it is not a unit of evolution.

The geographical races of a continental species are, more often than not, connected by intermediate forms or intergrades, so that it is virtually impossible to draw a line that will separate them. The differences between the races are greatest at the periphery of the species. Often these differences are so pronounced that the end races behave as perfectly distinct species. Such is the case in the cline of the meadow frog. The species differs so widely in its physiology on the ends of a north-south gradient that matings of individuals from two geographic extremes, Vermont and Texas and Vermont and Florida, produced young that died before complete development (Moore, 1949). Matings from two successive locations, however, produced normal offspring.

Sometimes a population of a species has diverged almost too far to be considered a race, yet not far enough to be considered a good species. This may result in a so-called ring of races. Sympatric populations that share the same habitat behave like distinct species, yet they are joined by a chain of allopatric races that smoothly intergrade. As a result, it is impossible to draw a line anywhere between the two, although for all practical purposes the end members are different species.

The classical example is the great tit, *Parus major,* of the Eurasian continent. This bird ranges from Ireland to Russia and on through central Siberia to the Pacific without change. The nominate race (the one first named) is *Parus major major,* and it has a dull green back and yellow belly. But in southern Europe some variation becomes evident. The great tit of Spain, Portugal, and North Africa, *P. major excelsus,* has a more vivid yellow on the belly and a reduced amount of white on the outer tail feathers. The variant on the Balearics, Cyprus,

Crete, and Greece, *P. m. aphrodite,* has a more grayish back and a paler yellow belly. The birds of Corsica and Sardinia are similar to *aphrodite,* except that they are grayer on the flanks and have been separated as *P. m. corsus.* The Palestinian subspecies, *P. m. terraesanctae,* is paler beneath and more yellowish on the back than any of the others mentioned, a condition even more pronounced in the birds of Persia and North Mesopotamia, which are known as *P. m. blanfordi.* However all the forms tend to intergrade except where separated by the sea, and all have the same basic coloration of gray back and yellow belly.

In India, Japan, and Manchuria live two other forms of the great tit, whose color variation is so pronounced that by morphological concepts they could easily be called two other species. The Indian bird, *P. m. cinereus,* has a gray back and a white belly; and the Japanese bird, *P. m. minor,* has a green back and a white belly. Both, however, are regarded as subspecies of *Parus major,* for through south-central China and along the coast of Indochina lives another form, *P. m. commixus,* which resembles the gray-backed form except that the tail is gray and the back green tinted; and where this form meets the Indian and Japanese birds, they intergrade. Where they come in contact with the Persian race, the Indian birds intergrade with it and thus connect *P. m. major* of Europe with *P. m. cinereus* and ultimately with *P. m. minor.* The white-bellied, green-backed form of the extreme eastern Asian coast extends northward from Japan to the northern border of Manchuria, the Amur River, where *P. m. minor* meets *P. m. major.* Here they coexist and breed without intermixing as separate species, although more recent information suggests that hybrid populations are formed (Delacour and Vaurie, 1950). Thus although two races, *Parus major major* and *Parus m. minor,* may behave as separate species in the zone of overlap they are connected with one another by a whole chain of intergrading geographic races. Where does one draw a line between the two? Where would one species, if so classified, begin and the other end? This is the problem that modern systematists face when they attempt to define a species. This is what is meant by the species problem.

This problem is not so pronounced among insular populations, for here the distribution is discontinuous, and because of natural barriers, zones of intergradation do not exist.

The concept of the biological species arose mainly in vertebrate systematics, where it has the widest application. The biological species is less generally accepted by botanists, for among plants, as well as among many small invertebrate animals, the biological species, as defined, is inadequate.

The biological species embraces only sexually reproducing organisms. But among plants and some invertebrates, asexual or vegetative reproduction is common. Many of the higher plants, even those in which cross fertilization occurs, reproduce in this fashion and others rely on it, by means of stolons, root runners, bulbs, and corms. The blue flag along the streamside and water lilies in a pond occupy the habitat not primarily through sexually produced seeds but through asexual propagation. In a somewhat similar fashion, the same is true for many annual plants, especially those that occupy extreme environmental situations and pioneering communities. These annuals are self-fertilized and, since they are short lived, they possess no effective means of vegetative reproduction. Selection has favored self-fertilizing forms most likely to produce a good crop of seeds.

453

Such organisms, which perpetuate their kind outside of sexual reproduction, are called *agamospecies*. They possess, as one may well imagine, very little genetic variability, and they have for the most part lost their capacity to adapt to environmental changes. Variability has been sacrificed for the ability to take the maximum advantage of a given environmental situation. Here they are preeminently successful.

Agamospecies possess for many generations the genetic constitution derived from parent stock. In fact they are the parent stock—genetic individuals on the whole immune to disease, fire, climate, age. These may destroy individual shoots, but separate vegetative parts capable of being carried considerable distances remain. The buffalograss of the western plains, some botanists believe, probably consists of the same genetic individuals that colonized the plains after the glacial retreat. They possess a sort of immortality.

Any changes in agamospecies are the result either of mutation or occasional reversal to sexual reproduction. Mutations involved are sudden and random changes with seemingly little relationship to the structure and needs of the individual in which they occur. Although small mutations may be tolerated, large ones have very little chance of being beneficial. But if mutations do persist, then they are maintained by the same vegetative reproduction, and a different form of the same species has arisen. Occasionally such plants may revert to sexual reproduction. Pollen from one may be transferred to another and some variability is introduced to the offspring, which propagate themselves either vegetatively or by self-fertilization. Eventually some forms may cross-pollinate and produce hybrids, which in turn are maintained and spread by self-pollination and vegetative reproduction. Hybridization may range from a slight blurring of distinctions between two or more species to the development of a huge complex of forms, in which the original species have become more or less lost. Such natural hybridization is the root of much of the "species problem" in plants and is involved in such "difficult" groups as hawthorns, blackberries, willows, and even some oaks. Certain groups of these are little more than aggregations of hybridizing semispecies (see Benson, 1962).

Agamospecies, however divergent from the biological species, still fit into the morphological species concept. They still can be associated typologically with their sexual relatives, yet they have no certain status.

How species arise

The great diversity of living things in the world causes one to wonder how all these species arose. Each is adapted to an ecological niche in the community to which it belongs, and each is genetically independent. The process by which this has come about, by which one form becomes genetically isolated from the other, is *speciation*, the multiplication of species.

Speciation is accomplished in most animals, at least, by an interaction of heritable variation, natural selection, and spatial isolation. Species formation under spatial isolation is described as geographical speciation (see Mayr, 1963).

The first step in geographical speciation is the splitting up of a single interbreeding population into two spatially isolated populations (Fig. 24-2). Imagine for a while a piece of land, warm and dry, occupied by species *A*. Then at some

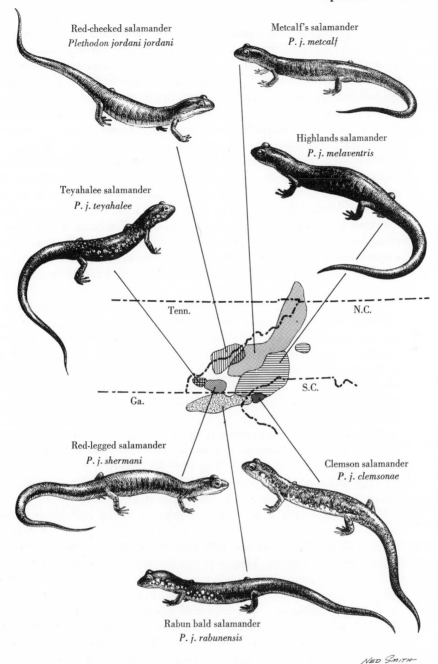

Red-cheeked salamander
Plethodon jordani jordani

Metcalf's salamander
P. j. metcalf

Highlands salamander
P. j. melaventris

Teyahalee salamander
P. j. teyahalee

Tenn.

N.C.

S.C.

Ga.

Red-legged salamander
P. j. shermani

Clemson salamander
P. j. clemsonae

Rabun bald salamander
P. j. rabunensis

NED SMITH

Figure 24-2 *Geographical races and sub-speciation in the* Plethodon *salamanders of the Appalachian Highlands. These salamanders of the* jordani *group resulted when the population of the salamander* Plethodon yonahlossee *became separated by the French Broad valley. In the eastern part, the separated population developed into Metcalf's salamander, which spread northeastward, being the only direction in which any group member could find suitable ecological conditions. South, southwest, and northwest the mountains end abruptly, limiting the remaining* jordani. *Metcalf's salamander is the most specialized and ecologically divergent and least competitive. Following separation of Metcalf's salamander, the isolation of Jordan's salamander from the red-legged and the rest of the group resulted from the deepening of the Little Tennessee River. Remaining members are still somewhat connected, especially around the headwaters of the Little Tennessee. (Information from Hairston and Pope, 1948; Hairston, 1949; distribution map based on data of latter and Checklist of Amphibians and Reptiles.)*

point in geological time mountains uplift, or land sinks and becomes flooded with water, or some great vegetational catastrophe occurs, which splits and separates by mountain, water, or ecological barrier, a segment of species *A* from the rest of the population. The newly isolated segment will now become species *A'*; and now occupies an area of cool, moist climate in our imaginary land.

The population of *A'*, because it represents only a random sample of the population of species *A*, will possess a slightly different ratio of genetic combinations. The climatic conditions are different, the selective forces are different. Natural selection will favor any mutation or any recombination of already existing genes that will result in a better adaptation to a cool, moist climate. Similar selection for a warm, dry climate will continue in population *A* on the original land mass. With different selective forces acting upon them, the two populations will tend to diverge. Accompanying this genetic divergence will be changes in physiology, morphology, color, and behavior, resulting in ever increasing external differences, until *A'* becomes a geographical race. *A'*, however, is still a part of the species *A* population, still capable of interbreeding if given the opportunity.

If geographical barriers break down at this point before isolating mechanisms (Dobzhansky, 1947)—those agents that curtail or prevent gene interchange between populations—are fully effective, then interbreeding takes place, and the individuals produced by the cross are fully fertile and viable. If these possess as high a reproductive potential as the parent stock, and if the latter has no other selective advantage, then the two gene pools will merge. The final result will be a population with increased variability over the original population prior to the split.

If the barrier, however, remains, further evolutionary diversification occurs, the two populations become increasingly different, and isolating mechanisms become more fully established. The time eventually is reached when normal interbreeding is no longer possible, even if the two populations do come together. Population *A'* has now arrived at the species stage.

If the barrier fails at this stage or prior to it, the individuals of the two populations may interbreed and produce hybrid offspring. Such hybrids among animals are less fertile and less viable than the parent stock because they contain discordant gene patterns. Their reproductive potential, if they are fertile at all, is low; they produce fewer offspring. They are at a selective disadvantage, while any color pattern, voice, behavior, etc., in the parent stock or any mutation or genetic recombination that reinforces reproductive isolation will be selected for. This selection against hybrids continues until gene flow between the two populations has stopped (see Sibley, 1957). Thus species *A* and new species *A'* can invade each other's territory, occupy suitable niches—in our example, a warm, dry environment and a cool, moist environment—and become wholly or partly sympatric (Fig. 24-3). This leads to a diversification of life (see also Ross, 1962).

Isolating mechanisms

In spring there is a rush of courtship and mating activity in woods and fields, lakes and streams. Fish move into their spawning grounds, amphibians migrate to breeding pools, birds are singing. During this frenzy of activity each

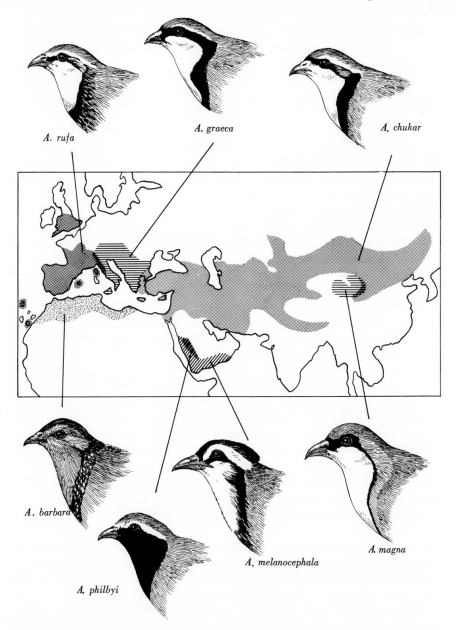

Figure 24-3 *Sympatry and allopatry in the* Alectoris *partridges. The overlap in ranges indicate regions of sympatry and ecological allopatry in the partridges (see text).* (Map redrawn from Watson, 1962a.)

species remains distinct. Song sparrows mate with song sparrows, trout with trout, wood frogs with wood frogs, and few mistakes are made even between species similar in appearance. The means through which the many diverse species remain distinct are *isolating mechanisms*. These include any morphological characters, behavioral traits, habitat selection, or genetic incompatibility that enables different species to remain apart.

457

Isolating mechanisms fall into four broad classes: ecological, which includes habitat and seasonal isolation; ethological, or behavioral; mechanical; and reduction of mating success (Mayr, 1942, 1963).

If two potential mates in breeding condition have little opportunity to meet, they are not likely to interbreed. Habitat selection can effectively reinforce this isolation. From North Africa and the Iberian Peninsula eastward through south-central Europe to Arabia and across central Asia to the Pacific are spread the *Alectoris* partridges, among them the chukar, well known as an exotic game bird in parts of North America (Fig. 24-3). Most of them are allopatric and separated by geographical distance. But in Thrace two very similar forms, the rock partridge, *A. graeca,* and the chukar, *A. chukar,* meet (Watson, 1962*a,b*). Here they are geographically sympatric. Both species inhabit rock-strewn hillsides and mountain sides with little cover and surface water. But the rock partridge is an alpine form found above 3000 feet; the chukar lives below 3000 feet. Otherwise their habitats, habits, and food are the same. In eastern Asia a parallel situation exists. Here the chukar and the great partridge, *A. magna,* both occur but are separated by altitude, the chukar being found at elevations below 7000 feet. In central Europe, there is a zone of sympatry between the redleg partridge, *A. rufa,* and the rock partridge. Again altitudinal allopatry separates the two forms. The redleg ranges on the lower, open, cultivated hillsides with their vineyards, cereal fields, and gardens. The rock partridge inhabits mostly the rocky mountain sides between the tree and the snow line. Thus among these partridges geological sympatry exists because of habitat isolation.

Four thrushes of the genus *Catharus*—the hermit, the gray-cheeked, the olive-backed, and the veery—all somewhat similar in appearance, inhabit the forests of eastern North America. They often occur together in zones of geographical overlap, especially where one species begins to replace the other. Typical replacement order from north to south or from low altitude to high is veery, hermit thrush, olive-backed thrush, gray-cheeked thrush. Each species differs somewhat in habitat, but often they share the same area with adjacent species. Both the gray-cheeked and the olive-backed thrushes prefer coniferous stands, but the gray-cheeked is most at home in the understory and in stunted conifers and feeds largely on the ground, while the olive-backed is an arboreal feeder. The hermit thrush occupies the interior edges of coniferous-deciduous forests and feeds on the ground, while the veery, living in the same habitat, occupies the forest interior and is an arboreal feeder (Dilger, 1956).

Habitat isolation on a very local basis is highly important among frogs and toads (see Bogert, 1960). Different calling and mating sites among concurrently breeding frogs and toads tend to keep the species separated. The barking tree frog typically calls while floating in open water, while sitting under water near shore, or when sitting on woody material projecting from the water. The closely related green tree frog calls from the ground or from low branches of trees or bushes near the breeding pool, but never in the water. Probably this is highly effective in preventing barking tree frog males from clasping green tree frog females. The upland chorus frog and the closely related southern chorus frog breed in the same pools, but ecological preferences tend to separate, partially at least, the calling aggregations of the species. The southern chorus frog calls from concealed positions at the base of grass clumps or among vegetational debris, while the upland chorus frog calls from more open situations.

458

Temporal isolation, differences in the timing of the breeding and flowering seasons, effectively isolates some sympatric species. The American toad, for example, breeds early in the season, while the Fowlers toad breeds a few weeks later (Blair, 1942). Brown trout and rainbow trout may occupy the same streams, but the rainbows spawn in the spring, the brown trout in the fall. Fluctuations in environmental stimuli can time mating seasons. Among the narrow-mouthed toads, *Microhyla olivacea* breeds only after rains, while *M. carolinensis* is little influenced by rain (Bragg, 1950). Since temporal isolation is incomplete, call discrimination also is involved (Blair, 1955); nevertheless some hybridization does occur.

Ethological barriers, differences in courtship and mating behavior, are the most important isolating mechanisms in animals. The males of animals have specific courtship displays to which, in most instances, only females of the same species respond. These displays involve visual, auditory, and chemical stimuli (see Chap. 27). Some insects, such as certain species of butterflies and fruit flies, and mammals possess species-specific scents. Birds, frogs and toads, some fish, and such "singing" insects as the crickets, grasshoppers, and cicadas have specific calls that attract the "correct" mates. Visual signals are highly developed in birds and some fish. Species-specific color patterns, structures, and display, which give rise to a high degree of sexual dimorphism among such bird families as the hummingbirds and ducks, have apparently evolved under sexual selection (Sibley, 1957). Among the insects, the light flashes sent out by fireflies on a summer night are the most unusual visual stimuli. The light signals emitted by various species differ in timing, brightness, and color, which may range from white through blues, greens, yellows, orange, and red (Barber, 1951).

Mechanical isolating mechanisms involve structural differences that make copulation or pollination between closely related species impossible, although evidence for such mechanical isolation among animals is very scarce. Even variations in body size and genitalic differences among insect species do not prevent cross-mating. Differences in floral structures and intricate mechanisms for cross-pollination within the species of many plants present mechanical barriers (see Grant, 1963). If hybrids should occur, especially among the orchids, they would possess such unharmonious combinations of floral structures that these would be unable to function together, either to attract insects to them or to permit the insects to enter the flower.

These three types of isolating mechanisms—ecological, ethological, and mechanical—are significant in that they prevent the wastage of gametes, diminish the appearance of hybrids, and permit populations of incipient species to enter each other's ranges and become partly or wholly sympatric.

The fourth type of isolating mechanism, the reduction of mating success, does not prevent the wastage of gametes, but it is highly effective in preventing crossbreeding. Male gametes of animals that are liberated directly into the water, as is the case of most fish, amphibians, and marine and fresh-water invertebrates, either are unable to fertilize eggs other than of their own kind, produce sterile eggs, or produce juveniles that fail to mature. If hybrids do mature, they may be sterile or at a selective disadvantage and thus eliminated from the breeding population. Among some F_1 *Drosophila* hybrids, the males are sterile and the females fertile only when backcrossed to either parental

459

stock, but the viability of the backcrossed progeny is low (Dobzhansky, 1947). Isolation through sterility is important only in organisms in which ethological isolating mechanisms are poorly developed.

Breakdown in isolating mechanisms: hybridization

The gaps between sympatric species are absolute. There is no crossing them when the species occupy the same habitat and are adapted to different niches. Between allopatric species, on the other hand, the gaps are relative only. There are no assurances that they are even good separate species; perhaps they are geographical races instead. The final test comes when the geographical barriers are broken and the two or more species in question meet. If the isolating mechanisms are not highly effective, if the populations are still diverging, then the organisms will hybridize freely. A more or less extensive hybrid zone is formed. Unlike the intergradation of subspecies, which involves a series of intermediate populations no more variable than neighboring populations, hybrid populations in the zone of secondary contact range from character combinations of species *A* to those of species *B*. Some hybrids may be indistinguishable from one or the other parent stocks; others may show a high degree of divergence.

If the hybrids are not at a selective disadvantage in competition with the parent populations, the genes of one species will be incorporated with the gene complex of the other. This resulting introgression leads to a swamping of differences between parental forms. There will be a period of increased variability in the rejoined populations, and new adaptive forms will be established. Eventually the variability will decrease to a normal amount, and once again there is a single freely interbreeding population.

Introgressive hybrids are more common in plants than in animals. One of the most conspicuous examples in animals is the golden-wing–blue-wing warbler complex, in which the hybrid forms, the Lawrence and Brewster warblers, are distinctive in color and song. Prairie chicken–sharp-tailed grouse hybrids are rather common, but whether these hybrids are capable of producing offspring among themselves or with either parent species is not known. However, the variety of types (Fig. 24-4) from one extreme to the other suggests that F_1 hybrids crossed with either parent species have reproduced (Ammann, 1957). There are numerous examples among plants. The white oak, for example, hybridizes with seven other members of the white oak group, including the chestnut, post, and overcup oaks (B). In plants, at least, two species may intergrade not only with each other but with still others to form chains or complex networks of partly segregated and partly interbreeding systems. These hybrids must compete with other plants selected by the environment and probably better adapted than they. Usually these hybrid swarms occupy permanent intermediate habitats somewhat removed from the parents or disturbed habitats where selective advantages to normal inhabitants are removed. If a hybrid population does survive, it may not retain all its members; through selection some members representing various genetic combinations may exploit special niches not suited for either parent.

If selected against, hybridization functions as a source of selection against individuals of both parental species that enter into mixed pairs. Any mechanism reducing the incidence of pairs then is selected for as long as the interaction continues. Any interaction between species that results in deleterious competition or in a wastage of gametes is selected against, reducing diversity in species-specific characters and reinforcing isolating mechanisms (Sibley, 1957).

The North American plains serve or served as an effective barrier to woodland

Figure 24-4   *Sharp-tail grouse, prairie chicken–sharp-tailed hybirds, and prairie chicken specimens. Dorsal and ventral views. (1) Sharptail, adult male; shot Oct. 3, 1941, near Sidnaw, Houghton County, Michigan; (2) prairie chicken–sharptail, adult male; shot Oct. 2, 1946, on Drummond Island, Chippewa County; (3) prairie chicken–sharptail, immature male; shot Oct. 17, 1947, near Ralph, Dickinson County, Michigan; (4) prairie chicken–sharptail, adult female; shot Oct. 28, 1950, near Sharon, Kalkaska County, Michigan; (5) prairie chicken, adult male, from Michigan. No additional data. Specimen no. 2 is in the University of Michigan Museum of Zoology collection. Others are in the Game Division collection, Michigan Department of Conservation.* (Photographs from Ammann, 1959; photos courtesy Game Division, Michigan Department of Conservation.)

species of animals, a barrier that has existed at least since the Pleistocene, when the ice sheet separated the populations of many animals. Woodlands stretched like fingers along the rivers, but only a few, the Platte in particular, provided a continuous woodland connection across the grasslands. Even these river-bottom forests may have been broken by prairie fires, by floods, and by trampling from buffalo. When the white man settled the plains, he destroyed the woodlands

461

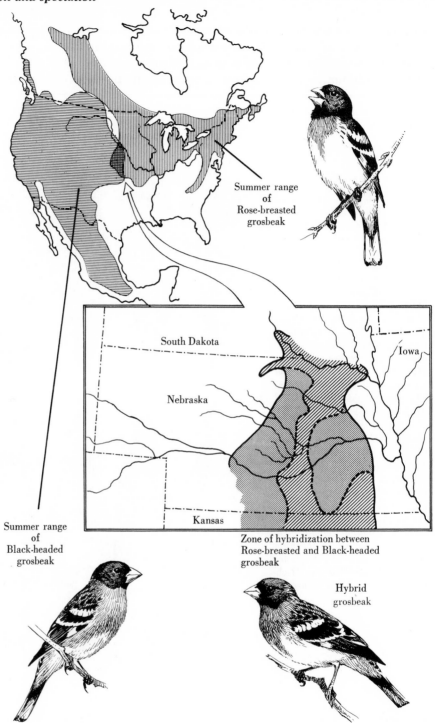

Summer range
of
Rose-breasted
grosbeak

South Dakota

Iowa

Nebraska

Kansas

Summer range
of
Black-headed
grosbeak

Zone of hybridization between
Rose-breasted and Black-headed
grosbeak

Hybrid
grosbeak

Figure 24-5 *Hybridization in the black-headed and rose-breasted grosbeak. The map of North America shows the summer range of both species; inset map shows the zone of hybridization between the two. Figure in the lower right is a hybrid grosbeak showing characters somewhat intermediate between the two parent stocks.* (Map based on West, 1962.)

for lumber. But importations of timber from the east, the control of fires, and the control of floods brought the riparian woodlands back. Trees and shrubs were planted in shelter belts around towns, farms, fields, and even along the rivers. These changes, which resulted in the development of suitable breeding sites, as well as "islands" of suitable resting places for migrants, permitted the woodland species of birds to move both east and west, to colonize the new habitat, and eventually to come in contact with one another. The red-shafted flicker of the west and the eastern yellow-shafted flicker were two species that spread into an area of contact on the plains, as well as the lazuli bunting and the indigo bunting, the Bullock and Baltimore orioles, and the black-headed and rose-breasted grosbeaks.

The two grosbeaks illustrate well what happens when two closely related allopatric species that have not yet diverged sufficiently to possess strong isolating

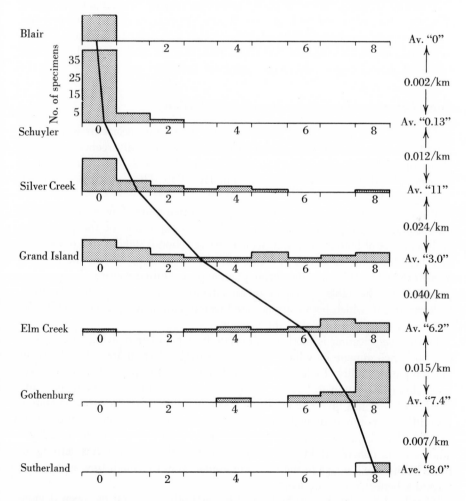

Figure 24-6 *Histograms of hybrid index scores for samples of grosbeaks from a Platte River transect. The shift per kilometer in average index is given. Localities are about 80 kilometers (50 miles) apart. (From West, 1962.)*

mechanisms come into contact (West, 1962). Both the black-headed and rose-breasted grosbeaks have essentially the same habitat preferences, build the same type of frail nest from twigs and rootlets, lay eggs that are almost indistinguishable, possess nearly the same vocalizations, and have nearly identical female plumages. Only in the male plumage do the two species differ widely (Fig. 24-5). On this basis the two have been considered separate species. Where the two come in contact, however, they interbreed, producing a variety of plumage combinations (Fig. 24-6). The variation found in the hybrids suggests that back-crossing, producing second-generation hybrids (F_2), is taking place. Differences in plumage that have evolved in the two under spatial isolation is insufficient to prevent the two from interbreeding. At present there is no indication that any selection against hybrids is operating. Possibly either the differences will be swamped or hybridization will stabilize, with a hybrid zone between the two "pure" populations, since by hypothesis the two species are ecologically too similar to become sympatric.

A similar situation arises in plants when geographic barriers are no longer effective. The eastern red cedar and the Rocky Mountain juniper are related and quite similar in appearance. Where the two come in contact from North Dakota south and east into Kansas and Nebraska, they, like the grosbeaks, hybridize and exhibit to varying degrees the characteristics of both.

Nongeographic speciation: disruptive selection

The idea that geographical isolation is necessary for speciation is not universally accepted. There is excellent evidence that racial divergence can come about through disruptive selection, even in the face of a high level of inter-crossing (Thoday, 1958; Millicent and Thoday, 1959; Thoday and Boam, 1959; Thoday and Gibson, 1962).

Within a population, selection may act in three ways. Given an optimum intermediate genotype, it may favor the average expression of the phenotype at the expense of both extremes, in which case selection is *stabilizing*. Or selection may be *directional*, in which one extreme phenotype is favored at the expense of all others. In this case the mean phenotype is shifted toward the extreme, provided that heritable variations of an effective kind are present. The third is *disruptive*, in which both extremes are favored, although not necessarily to the same extent, at the expense of the average.

Disruptive selection is most apt to occur in a population living in a heterogeneous environment in which there is a strong selection for adaptability or phenotypic flexibility. Increased competition within the population may select for a closer adaptation to habitat, with the result that the population may subdivide. This would give rise either to a polymorphic situation or to separation into different populations with different characteristics. The latter is most likely to take place in areas where selection is intense and where optimum habitat adjoins or is penetrated by less than optimum habitat. Organisms settling in these habitats will adapt to the local environment and through time will evolve toward a better and better adaptation.

That local populations can be formed by disruptive selection has been demonstrated experimentally by Thoday and his associates. One experiment involved at the start 80 flies of each sex of a wild-strain *Drosophila melanogaster*. From each sex, eight flies with the highest sternopleural chaeta number and eight with the lowest were selected. The 32 flies were permitted to mate at random during a 24-hour period, after which the eight high and eight low chaeta numbered females were separated. From their progeny, eight high and eight low flies of each sex were selected and mated at random. This process was repeated each generation. By the fourth generation of selection, almost all the high flies selected came from progeny of high females; and almost all the low flies from the progeny of low females. By the twelfth generation of selection, the distribution curves did not even overlap. In this experiment, mating was not enforced at any particular pattern and initially probably was entirely random. As the experiment progressed, reproductive isolation developed, limiting hybrids between high and low modes.

In another experiment (Millicent and Thoday, 1961) two populations of *Drosophila melanogaster* were exposed to disruptive selection with assortive mating and a 25 per cent gene flow between the half selected for high and the half selected for low sternopleural chaeta number. Divergence was greatly limited by 50 per cent gene flow between the two populations, but with 25 per cent gene flow, divergence, though slower, was as great as if the populations were completely isolated (0 per cent gene flow). The magnitude of divergence in the 25 per cent gene-flow lines offers strong evidence that random mating cannot prevent divergence under disruptive selection.

These experiments demonstrate that it is possible for ecotypes or biological races to diverge under the disruptive selection pressures that may be imposed by heterogeneous habitats and that the genetic differences involved are not "swamped" by random mating.

Polyploidy

Among plants, still another situation arises. New species can arise spontaneously. The most common method by which this takes place is through the alteration of the number of chromosomes. When a diploid cell divides, the chromosomes likewise must divide to produce a full complement in the two daughter cells. In rare instances the rest of the cell does not divide with the nucleus and the chromosomes, and the cell ends up with two times the normal complement of chromosomes. Thus a normal diploid cell becomes a tetraploid ($4n$) cells with more than a normal complement of chromosomes, and the individuals produced by them are called *polyploids,* to distinguish them from the normal diploid state. Polyploids, a type of mutant, usually have fewer but larger cells than the parent stock; often the individuals are larger and tend to be less fertile, because of the physiological upsets and abnormal pairing of chromosomes during the formation of gametes.

There are two types of polyploids, both important from the standpoint of plant speciation—autopolyploids and allopolyploids. The former, autopolyploids, are formed by the doubling of chromosomes in any individual of the species. Thus if the diploid species had *AA, BB, CC,* and *DD* chromosomes, its autotetraploid would have *AAAA, BBBB, CCCC,* and *DDDD.* When gametes are formed by meiosis, then groups of three and one, four, and two and two may be formed by each type of chromosome. Such irregularity in the chromosomes of the gametes results in few offspring. When a diploid gamete unites with a normal haploid

465

(1*n*) gamete, a hybrid triploid results. Although incapable of sexual reproduction, the triploid can reproduce and spread vegetatively.

The other type is the allopolyploid, which arises something like this. Suppose that species *A* has four chromosome pairs: *AA, BB, CC, DD,* and a second species *B* nearby has chromosome pairs: *RR, SS, TT, UU.* If the two plants hybridize, the offspring will have a complement of A, B, C, D, R, S, T, U. Since the chromosome pairs are very dissimilar, the hybrid will be infertile. But if during the development of one of the individuals, the chromosome number should be doubled, if it should mutate to a polyploid, then an allopolyploid (allotetraploid) with chromosome pairs *AA, BB, CC, DD, RR, SS, TT, UU* will be formed. Each chromosome now has one definite partner; pairing at meiosis once again is normal, and fertility is improved.

But there are other problems for the allopolyploid. Cross-fertilization with either parental species, both much more abundant, will produce sterile triploid offspring; and because of the small population of allopolyploids, few tetraploids will result, unless the plant is self-fertilized or relies on asexual reproduction. At such a competitive disadvantage, the polyploid is selected against and eventually disappears. If little cross-pollination takes place and asexual reproduction is the normal method of propagation, then the parental stock and the allopolyploid may coexist.

There is another alternative. If the allopolyploid colonizes an area unoccupied by either parent, then the allopolyploid may so completely dominate the area that the parents are excluded. The few that do gain a foothold are at a selective disadvantage since, being less common, they will receive more pollen from the polyploid than from the diploid stock. Thus the offspring of the parental stock will be sterile triploids, while only a few allopolyploid offspring will be in this condition. This is more than a remote possibility, since a number of polyploids thrive in areas different from the diploid ancestors. Because plants dispense with sexual reproduction under unfavorable conditions and multiply by rhizomes, bulbs, corms, etc., polyploidy is not at a disadvantage, particularly among perennial herbs. In fact this condition often enables plants to colonize and to tolerate more severe environments. Thus the availability of new ecological niches favors the establishment of polyploidy.

From polyploidy has arisen many of our common cultivated plants, potatoes, wheat, alfalfa, coffee, grasses, to mention a few. It likewise is rather widespread among native plants, in which polyploidy produces a complex of species as in the blackberries. The common blue flag of northern North America is a polyploid and is believed to have originated from two other species, *Iris virginica* and *I. setosa,* when the two, once wide ranging, met during the retreat of the Wisconsin ice sheet. The Sequoia is a relict polyploid, its diploid ancestors having become extinct, as are the willows and the birches. The whole fascinating subject of polyploidy and species formation in plants is a complex one that cannot be pursued any further here. For this one should turn to such sources as Stebbins (1950).

Intergroup selection

In general, selective pressures are considered as impinging upon individuals
of a species. But the idea has been advanced, first by Wright (1931, 1964)

and more recently by Wynne-Edwards (1963), that a social group or deme is an evolutionary unit. As pointed out previously, most species consist of small populations, typically self-regulating, persistent, strongly localized, and sufficiently (but not completely) isolated to permit some differentiation in sets of gene frequencies. On the other hand, there is sufficient contact between demes to allow a gradual spreading of an advantageous genetic complex to other demes and throughout at least part of the species. But gene flow is not fast enough to prevent local populations from acquiring some characteristics of their own. As a result some demes develop some selective advantages over neighboring demes and produce a greater surplus population. These immigrate into surrounding demes, which in time improve their own selective advantage. This process can spread among inferior demes. In effect the successful take over from the unsuccessful; one group is in sort of a passive competition with the other.

The resulting higher rate of reproduction through the populations could lead to overpopulation, which would threaten the existence of the group by an exhaustion of resources and poisoning of the environment. But long-time adaptation requires selection at a level that places a priority on a balance between population size and available resources. Involved in the regulation of the population are some kinds of adaptations that belong to and characterize the social group or deme as an entity rather than their members individually. Among many species this regulation is accomplished through territoriality and social dominance (see Chaps. 20 and 27). Such regulation operates through a conventional code of behavior, which subordinates the advantages of particular members to the advantage of group survival. In higher animals the number of progeny an individual leaves behind is closely related to its social status. Selection pressure of intragroup competition favors the social dominant and penalizes the less fortunate by preventing them from breeding and feeding or by forcing them out of the habitat. Social dominance, per se, however, is noninherited or is only of low inheritability, for it can change through the life of an individual (see Chap. 27). Rather, social dominance depends upon the summation of all the characteristics, inherited and environmental, that predicate health, vigor, and survival in the individual.

Thus superior demes can infiltrate inferior demes through intergroup selection, yet intrademe competition can regulate the size of the population. At the same time changes in gene frequency through gene flow, drift, and selection at the individual level tends to adapt individuals further, and through them the deme, to local selective pressures.

Adaptive radiation

The direction and degree to which a population diversifies is influenced by the preadaptability of the species population to a new situation, by selective pressures of climate and competition, and by the availability of ecological niches. All species of organisms are adapted to some particular environment, but since the environment is limited, overpopulation can result (see Chap. 20). This in itself is a selective force, for the time finally comes when those individuals that are able to utilize some unexploited environment and resource are at an advantage. Under lessened competition in the environment, these individuals have some opportunity of leaving progeny behind. By eliminating disadvantageous genes,

467

selection will strengthen the ability of the group to utilize the new niche or niches it has occupied.

Not every organism can adapt to a new environment. Before a species can enter a new mode of life, it must first have physical access to the new environment. Unless it is able to reach this new environment, the species cannot exploit it. And having arrived there, the species must be capable of exploiting the niches (preadapted). It must possess a certain level of physical and physiological tolerances to enable it to gain a foothold in the new locality. Here animals, particularly the vertebrates, have an advantage over plants. Most plants, although easily dispersed, are rather exacting in their habitat requirements; animals, while finding it difficult to cross barriers, are better able to cope with a new environment. Once the organism has established a beachhead, it must possess sufficient genetic variability to establish itself under the selective pressures of climate and competition from other organisms. The adaptations that permit the organism to gain a foothold are only temporary makeshifts, which must be altered, strengthened, and improved by selection before the organism can efficiently utilize the niche. Finally an ecological niche must be available for exploitation. Competition in a new habitat either must be absent or slight enough so that the new invader can survive in its initial colonization. Such niches have been available to colonists of some remote islands, such as the Galapagos, the Hawaiian, and the archipelagos of the South Pacific. The abundant empty niches available in these diversified islands when the first colonists arrived encouraged the rapid evolution of species. Darwin's finches are classical examples of colonization and diversification in an unexploited environment. The original finch population probably consisted of a few chance migrants from South America. Because of the paucity of invaders, on account of the great distance from the mainland, the successful immigrants were able to spread out in many evolutionary directions to exploit the islands' resources (see Suggested Readings at the back of this book).

A similar development took place among the honeycreepers, Drepanididae, in the Hawaiian Islands, which evolved into finchlike, honey eater-like, creeperlike, and woodpeckerlike forms (Fig. 24-7). They so completely occupied the diverse niches on the island that they prevented similar adaptive radiation by later colonists of thrushes, flycatchers, and honey eaters.

The ancestor of the honeycreepers was probably a nectar-feeding coerebidlike bird with an insectivorous diet somewhat similar to *Himatione* (Fig. 24-7*h*). After colonizing one or two islands, stragglers undoubtedly invaded other surrounding islands. Because each group was under a somewhat different selective pressure, the geographically isolated populations gradually diverged. By colonizing one island after another, and after reaching species level, recolonizing the islands (double invasion) from which they came, the immigrants enriched the avifauna, especially on the larger islands with a more varied ecology. At the same time, competition among sympatric forms placed a selective premium on divergence. The forms then became adapted to the somewhat different ecological niches available, survived by rigid specialization, or one or the other perished. Such divergence of one group into several different forms, each adapted to different ecological niches, able to exploit new environments or to tap a new source of food, is called adaptive radiation (Fig. 24-7).

This principle is nicely illustrated by the genus *Hemignathus* (Fig 24-7*e,f,g*), all members of which are primarily insectivorous. *Hemignathus obscurus,* whose

Psittirostrinae   Drapaniinae

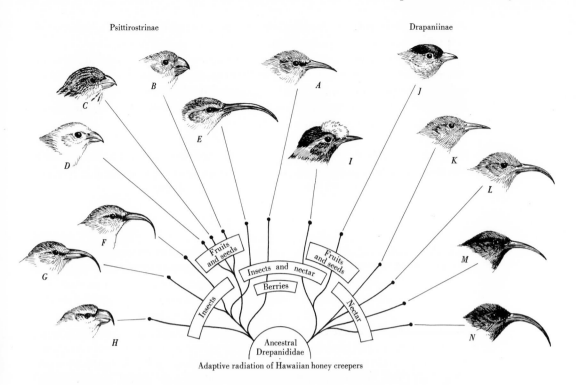

Adaptive radiation of Hawaiian honey creepers

Figure 24-7 *Adaptive radiation in the Hawaiian honeycreepers, Drepanididae. Selected representatives of the two subfamilies, Drepaniinae and Psittirostrinae, illustrate how the family evolved through adaptive radiation from a common ancestral stock. Both subfamilies show a certain degree of parallel evolution, based on diet. (A) Loxops viriens, which probes for insects in the crevices of bark and folds of leaves, as well as feeding on nectar and berries; (B) Psittirostra kona, a seed eater, extinct; (C) P. cantans, which feeds on a wide diet of seeds, insects, insect larvae, and fruit; (D) P. psittacea, a seed eater, feeding especially on the climbing screw pine, Freycinetia arborea; (E) Hemignathus obscurus, feeds on insects and nectar (see text); (F) H. ludicus, feeds on insects; (G) H. wilsoni, an insect feeder; (H) Pseudonester xanthophrys, which feeds on larvae, pupae, and beetles of native Cerambycidae, grips branch by curved upper beak; (I) Palmeria dolei feeds on insects and the nectar of Ohio (Metrosideros); (J) Ciridops anna, a fruit and seed eater; (K) Himatione sanganuine feeds on the nectar of Ohio and caterpillars; (L) Vestoria coccinae, feeds on nectar from a variety of flowers and on looper caterpillars; (M) Drepanis funera, a nectar feeder, extinct; (N) Drepanis pacifica, a nectar feeder, extinct. (Drawings based on Amadon, 1947, 1950, and other sources; evolutionary data from Amadon.)*

lower mandible is about the same length as the upper mandible, uses its decurved bill like forceps to pick insects from crevices as it hops along the trunks and limbs of trees. The bill of *H. ludicus* is also decurved, but the lower mandible is much shorter and thickened. The bird uses the lower bill to chip and pry away loose bark as it seeks insects on the trunks of trees. In *H. wilsoni,* the modification is carried even further. The lower mandible is straight and heavy. Holding its bill open to keep the slender upper mandible out of way, the bird uses the lower mandible to pound, woodpeckerlike, into soft wood to expose insects. The bill of genus *Hemignathus* was specialized at the start to feed on insects and nectar. **469**

Although the result of modification through competition in *H. wilsoni* is grotesque, it is the only species among eight surviving in fair numbers.

The honeycreepers also exhibit parallel evolution, adaptive changes in different organisms with a common evolutionary heritage in response to similar environmental demands. The long, thin, decurved bill of *Hemignathus obscurus* is adapted to a diet of insects and nectar; so too are the bills of several members of the subfamily Drepanidinae (Fig. 24-7*l,m,n*).

Similar adaptive radiation took place among the whales. Arising from a carnivorous creodent stock, they eventually radiated into filter feeders, the whalebone whales whose food is plankton, the great-toothed whales that feed on deep-sea mollusks, and the fish-eating porpoises and dolphins.

Convergence

Totally unrelated or distantly related groups of organisms occupying similar environments may evolve similar structures in response to selective pressures. Insects, birds, and bats all evolved totally different kinds of wings, but this structure enabled these animals to tap new sources of food, to acquire new modes of dispersal, and to escape the pressures of earthbound predators. Whales, porpoises, and to a certain extent seals all have acquired similar structures adapting them to a marine environment. The external morphology of the shark, the porpoise, and the extinct ichthyosaur is similar (Fig. 24-8), designed for swift movement through the water. The Australian marsupials, which evolved in the absence of competition from placental animals, include many highly diversified groups occupying niches comparable to those occupied by placental animals elsewhere. Thus there is the marsupial "wolf," "mole," "flying squirrel" (Fig. 24-8), and "anteater."

Evolution of species diversity

The wide range in species diversity among communities, especially on a latitudinal gradient, has long interested ecologists and evolutionary biologists. Alfred Wallace (1878) called attention to the fact that life is more varied and abundant in the tropics than elsewhere. Northward and southward from the tropics into the temperate and polar regions diversity declines. Although the number of organisms in the latter two may be high, the kinds of organisms are fewer (Fischer, 1960). A similar trend can be observed from high altitudes to the lowlands. As one comes down from a high mountain, the plant species increase. Also species diversity increases from a maritime climate in North America inland to a continental climate (Whittaker, 1965).

Why such a diversity exists is an area of current speculation. Tropical diversity, according to one hypothesis (Fischer, 1960), may be the consequence of a stable environment. Through evolutionary time, the tropics, of all regions of the earth, has probably remained the most constant and has been relatively free from severe environmental conditions that could have catastrophic effects on a population. Under tropical conditions, organic selection is strongly influenced by the competition of individuals against members of other species. At higher latitudes selection is influenced more by severe environment and by competitive relations of individuals with others of the same species.

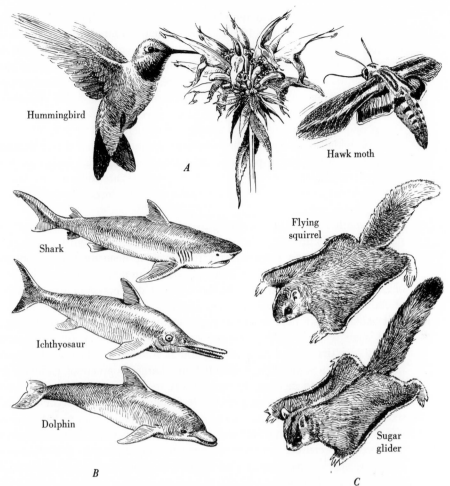

Figure 24-8 *Convergent evolution. (A) Convergent evolution in two highly dissimilar organisms, the hummingbird and the hawk moth. Both feed on the nectar of flowers; the bird by day, the moth by night. Both have adaptations of the mouth for probing flowers; both have the same rapid, hovering mode of flight. (B) Convergent evolution in three unrelated groups: the prehistoric marine reptile, the ichthyosaur; the modern shark; and the marine mammal, the dolphin. All have the same streamlined shape for fast movement through the water. (C) Convergent evolution in a North American rodent, the flying squirrel, and the Australian marsupial, the sugar glider. Both have a flat, bushy tail and an extension of skin between the fore leg and the hind leg that enables them to glide down from one tree limb to another.*

In the case of maritime and continental climates, the dry summers of the former may limit soil moisture, which is used by the dominants. Soil drought then may limit growth and diversification of subordinate plants (Whittaker, 1965).

In both severe and warmer, more constant environments, species diversity results in part from the utilization by subordinate species of environmental resources left over after the dominant organisms have fulfilled their requirements, and from niche differentiation by the subordinate species (Whittaker,

1965). A more stable environment, according to a hypothesis advanced by Klopfer and MacArthur (1961), favors among animals a more stereotyped feeding behavior, since energy demands are more easily met. This results in smaller, more restricted niches, less subject to change, and in an increase of similar coexisting species occupying these reduced but exclusive portions of species niches. A similar hypothesis involves plants. Small differences in the environmental requirements of plant species, expressed morphologically, but perhaps more often physiologically, may permit competing plant species to have widely overlapping distributions. Evolution of niche differentiation may enable many plant species to exist together as partial, rather than direct competitors (Whittaker, 1965). Such hypotheses are difficult to test, since they are based on the a priori premise that a niche is objectively definable, which it is not.

Still another and most interesting hypothesis for the development and maintenance of species diversity has been advanced by Connell and Orias (1964). In brief, this hypothesis proposes that the level of diversity of a community is determined by the amount of energy flowing through the food web. The rate of energy flow is influenced by the limitation of the ecosystem and by the degree of stability of the environment (Fig. 24-9).

If one assumes a hypothetical increase in the stability of the physical environment, then with increasing environmental stability, less energy is required for regulatory activities and more energy enters into net production. Increased net productivity can support larger populations. Larger populations maintain greater genetic variety and increase the opportunity for interspecific association. Greater productivity per unit area permits the less mobile animals to become even more sedentary, and the species tend to be broken into many semi-isolated populations, which may bring about greater intraspecific genetic variety. As a result speciation is favored, especially if semi-isolated segments are exposed to new environments. Any new species that arise would tend to be more specialized and initially to have smaller populations.

In the early stages of the evolution of a community, positive feedback would increase the rate of speciation, resulting in a faster cycling of nutrients and an increase in net productivity. As the number of species increases, the food webs become more complex and the community becomes more stabilized (see Chap. 6). But the tendency toward overspecialization and the smaller population per species would tend to decrease community stability and act as a negative feedback on the whole system.

Even within this hypothetical system and under stable conditions, there would be limitations. Diversity would be restricted by unfavorable physical conditions, by limitations of space, by the length of the food chain, by the evolution of large body size, by the degree of fineness into which a niche could be subdivided, by organic production, and by the random and cyclic variations that must continually be corrected by the homeostatic responses of the organisms. Because the niche is determined by more than the physical variations in the environment, the hypothesis implies that it is impossible to predict the number of niches and therefore the number of species from the complexity of the environment alone. The niche involves complex biological interactions that are not easy to determine and describe. Here the problem stands. Only by testing the hypotheses will some sort of answer to the question of species diversity be found.

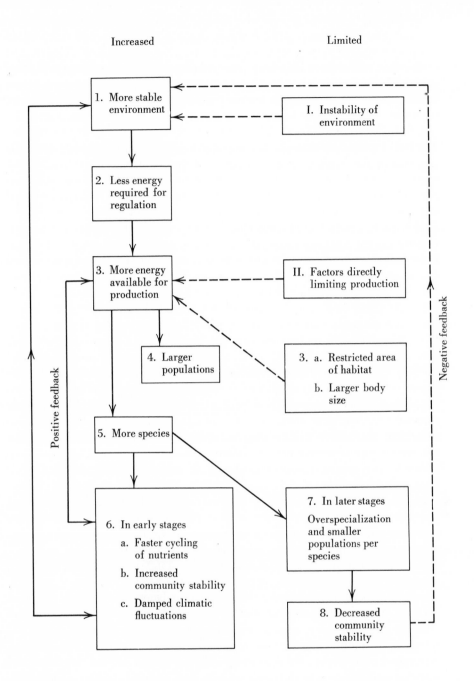

Increased   Limited

1. More stable environment

I. Instability of environment

2. Less energy required for regulation

3. More energy available for production

II. Factors directly limiting production

4. Larger populations

3. a. Restricted area of habitat
   b. Larger body size

5. More species

Positive feedback

Negative feedback

6. In early stages
   a. Faster cycling of nutrients
   b. Increased community stability
   c. Damped climatic fluctuations

7. In later stages
   Overspecialization and smaller populations per species

8. Decreased community stability

Figure 24-9 *Rate of production of new species.* (Adapted from Connell and Orias, 1964.)

Naming and classifying organisms

Scientific names have long been regarded as something mysterious and something quite unnecessary by the layman. Point out an organism and most people will demand a common name, one in the vernacular; a scientific name is unacceptable. Yet the scientific name is a necessity. In the first place, vernacular names are misleading. They differ from one section of the country to another. The ruffed grouse, for example, is a partridge in northeastern United States and a pheasant in the southern Appalachians. And the common mallard has 33 local names. But the scientific names *Bonasa umbellus* for the ruffed grouse and *Anas platyrhynchos* for the mallard clears all the confusion. Browse through a manual of plants or a manual of invertebrates and you will soon discover that only the most familiar plants and animals have common names. The rest do not. Even if every known organism could have a common name, no everyday language is large enough to meet the task. The scientific name, derived from the Latin and Greek, means something; it indicates relationships and it fits the organism into a definite slot in the catalog of living things.

Man has been naming and classifying animals and plants for a long time. Even early man probably had some sort of method for sorting out the plants and animals in the forests and grasslands about him. A scientific approach was made over 300 years before the birth of Christ. Often called the "Father of Natural History," the Greek philosopher Aristotle (384–322 B.C.) devised a natural classification scheme based on similarities in anatomy and reproduction. He divided all animals into two groups, those with red blood (the vertebrates), and those without red blood (the invertebrates). The former group he subdivided into those that gave birth to living young and those that lay eggs. Aristotle's classification served natural science for over 2000 years.

Much later others attempted to change or improve this classification to fit their own ideas. The earliest changes began with botanists. L'Obell (1538–1616), botanist to King James of England, attempted to classify plants along morphological lines, chiefly by the shape of the leaf; but this led to considerable confusion and difficulties. In Italy, Cesalapini (1519–1603) developed a system of plant classification based on fruits and flowers, a more reasonable approach. And next door in Switzerland, Kaspar Bauhin (1560–1624) revived Aristotle's concept of genus and species, as did the German botanist Joachim Jung, who taught at Lübeck. Always under the suspicion of heresy, Jung never published his work, but in 1660 a manuscript copy was picked up by John Ray, an English botanist. He compiled a catalog of British plants, which remained a standard reference for centuries. At the same time Ray published works on fishes, serpents, quadrupeds, and fossils. Attempts at animal classification around this same time involved artificial systems in which animals were grouped together according to some individual characteristic. Some attempted to use wings or power of flight and ended up with bats, birds, and insects all lumped together. Others had whales, a mammal, grouped with fish. Some early classifications were based on appendages, so that all birds with webbed feet were placed in one group, all those with long legs in another, and so on. But no one except Ray could improve on Aristotle; and because of his work, this Englishman paved the way for a young Swedish naturalist, Carl von Linné, who Latinized his name to Carolus Linnaeus (1707–1778).

Naturalists of Linnaeus' time and the years before that called plants and animals by a common name, often one used locally by the people. In their scientific works these naturalists used two or three Latin words to describe plants and animals, but there was no uniformity about it. Such a system, loose as it was, worked fine as long as the number of known plants and animals was small. But the 1700s was an era of exploration. Naturalists accompanying expeditions into the remote parts of the world brought back thousands of specimens of new plants and animals to the universities, museums, and royalty of Europe. The old system began to buckle under its own weight.

Carl von Linné was a Swedish naturalist and medical doctor who taught medicine and botany at the University of Uppsala. Just as some people like to collect coins or stamps for a hobby, so Linné had a passion for classifying things —plants, animals, diseases, minerals, and many other items that came to his attention. He explored in Lapland and northern Europe; he had collectors send him plants from other parts of the world. Out of this came a book in 1735, *Species Plantarum,* in which he listed and named all plants then known to science. He gave each plant two Latin names, a generic name and a species name. Later in 1758 he published a tenth edition, *Systema Naturae,* in which he consistently applied the same idea to animals.

Linné's great contribution to science was not his lists or even his classification of plants and animals. Rather it was his binomial, or two-name, system of naming plants and animals, a system that finally brought order out of chaos and led to a standardized method of naming all living organisms in Latin.

Why Latin? This is a question asked by nearly everyone unacquainted with the needs and methods of naming plants and animals. Why would not some other language do just as well? In the age of Linnaeus, the universal language in science as well as other scholarly fields was Latin. This had certain advantages. According to an old jingle:

> All are dead who wrote it
> All are dead who spoke it

(And to finish this parenthetically:

> All will die who learn it
> Blessed death, they earned it.)

So Latin for all practical purposes was a "dead" language. It would never change in grammar, syntax, or words. This gave the language a great degree of uniformity and stability, which served scholars well. Since all educated people of that day studied Latin, it was universally understood; and it still is today. In fact all formal descriptions of new plants written today must be done in Latin, although this procedure is not followed with animals.

To each organism, then, Linnaeus gave two Latin names. But before this he had to sort out his plants and animals into some broad general groups. First, all living things, he reasoned, belonged to two great groups, or kingdoms, plant and animal. The animal kingdom he subdivided into six parts: mammals, birds, reptiles, fishes, insects, and a catch-all group, vermes (or worms). Among the mammals, for example, he noted that some organisms were similar. It was not too difficult to identify a cat as such, or a dog, although there are many different kinds. All have certain identifying characteristics. Cats have retractile claws, rounded heads, and well-developed but relatively small, rounded ears. Some have long tails, others have short tails, ear tufts, and a ruff on the cheeks and throat. All the long-tailed cats then were placed in one group, or genus, to which Linnaeus gave the Latin name *Felis,* for cat; and to the short-tailed cats he gave the name *Lynx.* Doglike mammals, too, are readily distinguishable, and he could break them down into groups of animals similar in appearance: sharp-nosed little foxes, the very doglike wolves, and their descendants, the true dogs. To the wolves and dogs Linnaeus gave the name *Canis,* the Latin for dog. Each genus then contained a number of different animals, all with some broad structural characteristics in common, yet with differences in the finer details: color, size, thickness of hair, and the like. Thus the genus could be broken down into still finer groups, the individual species. To name this, Linnaeus gave another second name to the species. Thus the wolf became *Canis lupus,* the mountain lions *Felis concolor,* and the African lion *Felis leo.*

All catlike animals, according to the Linnaean system, are grouped together into a still larger classification, the family, which takes its name from one of the genera it embraces. In the case of cats, the genus *Felis* was used. By adding a standardized suffix "idae" onto the root word *Felis,* the cat family became Felidae; and by a similar process the dog family became Canidae. Dogs and cats, skunks and weasels (Mustelidae), the raccoons (Procyonidae), the bears (Ursidae), seals (Phocidae), and so on were classified into families. All have several general features in common: five toes with claws, shearing teeth, well-developed canine teeth or fangs, and other skeletal structures. These animals then were grouped together and placed in an even higher category, the order, in this case the order Carnivora. All orders of animals giving birth to living young, possessing body hair, and nourishing young with milk were placed in an even higher category, the class Mammalia. All animals having a backbone were grouped in a phylum, in this instance Chordata, belonging to the animal kingdom.

The final result was a hierarchical scheme of classification in which similar species were grouped together and placed in a genus, similar genera into families, similar families into orders. The complete hierarchical classification of a mountain lion looks like this:

Kingdom: Animal
Phylum: Chordata
Class: Mammalia
Order: Carnivora
Family: Felidae
Genus: *Felis*
Species: *concolor*

As time went on, the number of known animals swelled, and the need arose to refine this hierarchy even further. Phyla were divided into subphyla, classes into subclasses and infraclasses, orders into suborders, families into subfamilies (and even enlarged into superfamilies), and species into subspecies.

To take another example, the white-footed mouse would be classified as follows:

> Kingdom: Animal
>> Phylum: Chordata
>>> Class: Mammalia
>>>> Subclass: Theria
>>>>> Infraclass: Metheria
>>>>>> Order: Rodentia
>>>>>>> Suborder: Myomorpha
>>>>>>>> Superfamily: Muroidea
>>>>>>>>> Family: Cricetidae
>>>>>>>>>> Subfamily: Cricetinae
>>>>>>>>>>> Genus: *Peromyscus*
>>>>>>>>>>>> Species: *leucopus*

Note that the superfamily ends in *oidea,* the family in *idae,* and the subfamily in *inae.*

The principal categories used in plant classification are somewhat different:

> Kingdom: Plant
>> Division: Trachaeophyta
>>> Subdivision: Pteropsida
>>>> Class: Angiospermae
>>>>> Subclass: Dicotyledoneae
>>>>>> Order: Fagales
>>>>>>> Genus: *Fagus*
>>>>>>>> Species: *grandifolia.*

The plant classified here is the American beech.

Taxonomy and classification

That part of biology that has to do with the classification of organisms is taxonomy. It is one of the oldest, most basic, and necessary parts of the science of life. Before any serious work can be done in field biology, or for that matter even in physiology, morphology, and the like, organisms must be named and placed in some category that can serve as a reference point. Unless the organism is named and classified, any serious study of an unknown is virtually worthless.

A primary, but not the only task of the taxonomists is to name and classify organisms, plant and animal. Describing and naming the organism is the first step after the plant or animal has been collected. In the earlier day of the typological species, the taxonomist usually based his description on what he considered the typical individual, the type specimen. The modern taxonomist bases his description on measurements of and on evaluations of variations within a series of specimens from the population. In fact the typical specimen becomes mean values and ranges of variations. But when he comes to name the organism, the taxonomist still must select one specimen to be the *type,* the name bearer.

The statement is often made that nearly all plants and animals have been described, leaving the impression that taxonomic work is closed. Yet this is far from true. Relatively few of our plants and animals are really well known, taxonomically. Plants, taxonomists are discovering, that have been given the status of species, are often hybrids. Among many insects and some fish, males and females of a single species have been described as two separate species. Other organisms may be described as a single species, when in reality they are a complex of several species. In addition the relationships or phylogeny of most plants and animals is poorly known. So the task of naming and describing species is hardly completed.

Next the taxonomist must break up the confusing diversity of individuals into some recognizable groups. He must determine the significant characteristics that will separate out the individual species, seek similarities that will allow him to place groups of individual species into higher categories, and at the same time find differences that will separate one group from another at the same level. Usually these differences and similarities are summarized in identification keys.

These units or groups then must be given some appropriate scientific name and placed in a meaningful arrangement. The taxonomist usually attempts to place the units and groups in some natural order that will show relationships and phylogeny. This requires considerable study; and for many animal and plant groups a sound phylogenic arrangement is difficult to construct because of a paucity of information, anatomical, genetic, morphologic, behavioral.

Concepts of classification. Underlying the classification of organisms, or any phenomona for that matter, are a number of concepts (see Gilmour, 1951). Classification is based on the fact that objects or ideas can be assembled into groups, the groups into more inclusive groups, and so on. Thus objects are not placed into categories until they have first been placed into some sort of groups. Once this has been done, categories can be established consisting of objects, groups of objects, groups of groups, and so on. The categories then become the shelves upon which the groups are placed, and each shelf or category is a part of a hierarchy of categories. But always the basic category is the species.

How organisms are named

The only "legal" name for plants and animals is the scientific name. It designates a particular kind of organism and nothing else, recognized by biologists throughout the world. The binomial scientific name consists of two parts, the generic name—in the case of the lion, *Felis*—always capitalized, and the specific name, or species (*concolor*), with a lowercase initial letter. It is followed by the name of the authority who named the organism. In the case of the mountain lion, this was a taxonomist by the name of Kerr. This binomial name, *Felis concolor*, is used by zoologists to separate the mountain lion from other lions, much the way our own names distinguish us from other people with whom we are associated. Our last name corresponds (but not zoologically) to the genus, our first name to the species. Subspecies, on the other hand, have three names; added is the subspecies. A mountain lion found in the swamps of southern Florida is *Felis concolor coryi* Bangs. The use of three names sometimes results in an organism having a repetition of names. The bobcat of our eastern forests has this distinction. Scientifically his name is *Lynx rufus rufus* (Schreber). This indicates that this particular animal was the typical first-named subspecies.

When Linnaeus published his *Systema Naturae,* not all zoologists and botanists welcomed his system of naming and classifying animals and plants. Many refused to accept it and went about their own way of naming and describing organisms. Names were changed and changed again with great abandon. Eventually the situation became about as bad as if common names were being used. By 1840 a number of zoologists recognized the need for a set of international rules governing the names of animals. In that year the British Association for the Advancement of Science appointed a committee to draw up a set of rules for zoological nomenclature, the result of which was the Strickland Code (1842), named after one of the committee members. Between 1842 and 1895 half a dozen codes appeared, all of them in use. To resolve this confusion, the Third International Zoological Congress, held in Leyden in 1895, appointed a committee to draw up an international code, which was finally adopted by the Fifth International Congress, held in Berlin in 1901. From that year on, the International Rules of Zoological Nomenclature became the universal code for zoology.

Meanwhile botanists were also active. In 1867 the International Botanical Congress, meeting in Paris, adopted a set of rules suggested by Alfonse de Candolle and known as the Paris Code. It was universally accepted by all except the American botanists, who formulated their own code. This situation continued unresolved until 1930, when at the Fifth International Botanical Congress, Cambridge, England, all major disagreements were ironed out. The American Code was abandoned and an International Code was adopted.

The next logical step would seem to be a joint code between zoologists and botanists, but this probably will never come to pass. Although many similarities between the two codes do exist, confusion would result if the two were brought together, for accepted practices under one are not permitted under the other. Botanists, for example, require that all plant descriptions be written in Latin; zoologists do not. Zoologists can use the same word for a generic as well as a trivial name, a procedure forbidden by the botanical code. The same generic name can be used for one group of plants as well as one group of animals.

Both the botanical and zoological rules are long and technical, but there are a few interesting features about them that explain the whys and wherefores of scientific names. One of the rules is that all names must either be Latin in origin or be Latinized. The generic name is a singular noun, the species name usually an adjective or a substantive in the nominative or genitive case. The species name may be a descriptive one as it is for the mountain lion, whose species name *concolor* means "of one color," or the name may refer to some geographical location. The whistling swan is called *Cygnus columbanus,* meaning a swan of the Columbia River. At times the scientific name translated means the same as the common name. The whistling swan's relative, the trumpeter swan, bears the name *Cygnus buccinator,* which means a "trumpeter swan." Some of the species names are the Latinized names of some individuals. The Torrey pine, *Pinus Torreyana* Parry, of the California coast was named by its first botanical collector, Charles Parry, in honor of Dr. John Torrey. And often the scientific name even becomes the common name. Among animals some of these scientific common names are hydra, octopus, tarpon, and gorilla; and among plants forsythia, chrysanthemum, magnolia, and crocus.

Once you have been given a name it is legally yours. You can change it only by going through a court of law. The names given to plants and animals are just as binding. But during the early years of taxonomy communication was poor. The animal or plant may have been described once in some obscure journal and given a name. A number of years later another taxonomist, not knowing that the organism had already been described, may write up a description and give the animal a name. Later taxonomists discover that the organism has a number of aliases, as it were. Somehow the situation has to be cleared up.

To do this, the codes have what is called a law of priority. Briefly this states that the first name applied to a species has to be used as long as it is valid. The starting point for all zoological nomenclature is the tenth edition of Linnaeus' *Systema Naturae,* in which binomial nomenclature was first used systematically for animals. For botanical names the starting point is the 1753 edition of *Systema Plantarum.* All names used in these works and those since are considered valid. This does not mean that names cannot be changed. In fact a lot of reshuffling has taken place. Many names have been changed in response to the law of priority, others in the light of new knowledge.

All suggested name changes must be officially made and approved by the appropriate International Botanical or Zoological Committee on Nomenclature. These bodies meet regularly to settle arguments about names and to interpret the rules when they need some clarification. Since the codes on nomenclature have been established, names have been dropped for *synomony,* a case in which a species has been described more than once and given different names. In such cases the earliest valid name is retained. An example is the muskrat:

Muskrat   *Ondatra zibethicus zibethicus* (Linnaeus).

1766   *Castor zibethicus* Linnaeus, *Syst. Nat.* (**12**), 1:79. Type from eastern Canada.

1795   *Ondatra zibethicus* Link, *Beytrage zur Naturgeschichte,* 1 (2):76.

1808   *Ondatra americana* Tiedemann, *Zoologie,* 1:481. A renaming of *Mus zibethicus* Schreber and *Castor zibethicus* Linnaeus.

1829   *Fiber zibethicus* var. B, *nigra* Richardson. *Fauna Boreali Americana,* 1:119. No definite type locality.

1829   *Fiber zibethicus* var. C, *maculosa* Richardson. *Fauna Boreali Americana,* 1:114. No definite type locality.

1867   *Fiber zibethicus varius* Fitzinger, *Sitzungher k. Akad. Wiss.,* Berlin, 56:47. A renaming of *Fiber zibethicus maculosa* Richardson.

1867   *Fiber zibethicus nigra* Fitzinger, *Sitzungher k. Akad. Wiss.,* Berlin, 56:47. A renaming of *F. z. nigra.*

In this case the species name bestowed by Linnaeus was retained as valid, but the muskrat was moved to another genus, since Linnaeus had it placed in the same genus as the beaver, *Castor.*

In other instances the same name may have been given to two different species, a case of *homonymy.* The same name may have been used both for a genus of plants and a genus of animals; but, as it has already been pointed out, the same generic name is never permitted to appear twice within the plant or animal kingdom. Species or trivial names may be the same and a number of them are widely used, such as *virginianus.* In event two names are found to be homonyms, then the older name takes precedent, provided it meets all requirements of the rules.

As studies of species and genera increase and new knowledge of relationships emerges, some species may be transferred to the status of a subspecies or vice versa, or a species may be transferred from one genus to another. New genera may be erected, while others may be eliminated. All of these involve name changing. In such situations the generic name is changed but the trivial remains the same, except that the Latin ending may be changed to bring it into agreement with the generic name. In extreme cases the committees may suspend the rules if necessary to preserve the stability of a widely known name.

In order for a new species to be named properly, certain requirements must be met. The name must appear in a reasonably permanent publication placed on sale or made available to any interested person. The name must be accompanied by a description adequate enough that the species can be identified in the future. In addition taxonomists are urged to elaborate on the characteristics that separate the newly described species from previously described ones to which it is considered most closely related.

Authors of new species should designate and deposit in a museum a type specimen for the species and a type species for a new genera. At one time, when species were considered fixed entities, the type was regarded both as a typical representative of the species and as a standard for comparison. Today the type specimen is simply the name bearer. Although it has no biological significance, the type specimen is a legal device necessary to specify to which group of real organisms the name refers. No type specimen is really typical since, as already discussed, the species and subspecies are based on populations, and the typical specimens consist of mean values and ranges of variation.

In addition to the type specimen, or *holotype,* there are a number of other "types" employed in taxonomic work. The most important of these are the syntype, the lectotype, and the neotype. If the author of a new species fails to select a specimen as the holotype, then the several specimens upon which the author based his descriptions become the *syntypes* (or cotypes). If the author or even another taxonomist decides to select one of the syntypes upon which the original description was based as the definitive type of the species, then that specimen is called the *lectotype.* Its selection must be made known through publication. In the event that the original type specimens are destroyed, another specimen, known as the *neotype,* may be selected as a replacement.

The name of the author of the new species appears after the scientific name. Parentheses enclosing the name of the original author followed by the name of another indicates that either the species was transferred to a different genus or that the name was changed in some way after the species was described. So much for scientific names. For those who wish to dig deeper into this subject see Mayr, Linsley, and Usinger (1953), and Benson (1962).

SUMMARY

Naming and classifying plants and animals may be an old facet of biology, but it is as necessary today as it has been in the past. Before any serious work in ecology or in any phase of biology can be done with accuracy, the organisms must be described, placed into recognizable groups, named, and their relationships worked out. In spite of some opinions to the contrary, a considerable amount of work in the field of taxonomy remains to be done.

Because of its stability as a language, Latin is used in scientific names. Systems and methods of naming and classifying plants and animals are controlled by international botanical and zoological codes. The former uses as its starting point the 1753 edition of Linnaeus' *Systema Plantarum,* and the latter the tenth edition of *Systema Naturae.*

In the process of describing, naming, and classifying a plant or animal, it is usually treated as a morphological species, a discrete entity that exhibits little variation from the type of the species, the original specimen upon which the description is based. But organisms are not static; they are continuously changing through long periods of time. This fact has given rise to the concept of the biological species, a group of interbreeding individuals living together in a similar environment in a given region and under similar ecological relationships. This concept, limited as it is to bisexual organisms, is also filled with difficulties, such as the inability to distinguish, among some groups, just where one species begins and another ends. To get around this problem, some evolutionary biologists suggest that the species be retained to identify kinds of organisms, but as a concept the species should be regarded as evolutionary units.

It is through a long evolutionary process that species arise by an interaction of heritable variation, natural selection, and perhaps among most kinds, spatial isolation. Species formation under spatial isolation is known as geographical speciation. As one segment of the species is separated from another, it carries a somewhat different sample of the gene pool and faces different selective pressures. Eventually the population diverges so far from the original parent stock that interbreeding cannot take place even if the barriers are removed. At this point speciation is complete and the two populations could occupy the same geographical area (sympatry), yet remain distinct. This they accomplish by means of isolating mechanisms, which include any morphological character, behavioral trait, habitat selection, or genetic incompatibility that is species specific. If isolating mechanisms break down, hybridization results. Species may also arise in the absence of geographical isolation through disruptive selection in which the phenotypes of both extremes are favored at the expense of the average. Speciation in plants may also come about through alteration in the number of chromosomes—polyploidy.

Speciation often implies that selective pressures act only on individuals of the species. There is evidence that the local population, or deme, is also an evolutionary unit, that selective advantages exist between groups as well as between individuals. Superior demes can infiltrate inferior neighboring demes. If a new and unexploited environment is available and the deme is overpopulated, some individuals may be able to adapt to the new environment. If a sufficient number of groups from the parent population become adapted to somewhat different ecological niches available, they may diverge into several different forms. This divergence is called adaptive radiation.

The wide range of diversity of species in some communities, especially tropical ones, and the lack of diversity in others, has given rise to several hypotheses concerning species diversity. These involve the stability of the tropical environment, niches that are restricted because of stereotyped behavior brought about by the easy availability of food, and the control of the level of diversity by the amount of energy flowing through the food chain. The whole field of evolution, natural selection, and speciation is filled with such unsolved problems, about which one can speculate and explore. While biologists do this, evolution continues at the same slow steady pace.

PART VI

PART **VI**

*The behavior
of animals*

C H A P T E R **25**

Behavior:
some basic
considerations

A squirrel hurrying up a tree trunk and out across the limbs is a part of the forest in which it lives. It occupies a definite food niche in the community; it is a member and reproductive unit of a population of others of its own kind; and it contributes in its own small way to the gene pool of the population. The survival or nonsurvival of its young, indeed its own survival and ability to produce young over a period of several years, may influence in some small way the long-term evolution of the species. The ability of an animal to survive and leave offspring depends a good deal on how well the animal responds to its environment, to others of its own kind, to the whole world about it. The responses of an animal are caused by changes in the internal and external environment. How the squirrel reacts to or attempts to adapt to sudden changes in its environment is called its behavior.

Behavior is intrinsic to the ecology of an animal. It is involved in the success of the animal in caring for itself, in seeking appropriate shelter, in obtaining food, in escaping enemies, in courtship and mating, in caring for the young. It is a mechanism that, in part, reduces competition between animals and controls population densities. As F. Frazier Darling (1964) writes concerning the red deer, "social behaviour is an important ecological factor, a part of the environment as large to the deer as society and culture to us. If we interpret one face of ecology as the physiology of community, the inclusion of social behavior in our thinking helps us to understand."

The behavior of an animal, like its structure, is the result of natural selection. Perhaps more often than not, structure and behavior evolved together, structure influencing behavior, and behavior in turn influencing the development of the structure. To respond to environmental changes, physical and social, the animal must first receive a stimulus from the environment through its sensory system—sight, taste, smell, touch, hearing. From here the stimulus is transmitted to the motor organs, the muscular system, and finally the motor organs respond. The kind of sensory apparatus the animal possesses, the complexity and organization of its central nervous system, and the type and development of motor organs determine the manner in which the animal is able to respond to its environment. Thus how an animal perceives and reacts to the world about it is limited by what its eyes are built to see, its ears designed to hear, and its taste, hearing, and smell designed to respond to. Because of this, the world appears different to other animals than it appears to man. What is visible and important to them may be unperceivable to humans. Each animal lives, as Jacob von Uexkull put it, in its own phenomenal or self-world of perception and response, its *Umwelt*.

But the responses are not always completely controlled by structure. Species, and even individuals within a species, that appear to be structurally similar and live in the same physical environment may react differently to similar stimuli. Aggressiveness or tameness, vigor in courtship or defense, the ability to learn, these are not wholly associated with structure. Often behavioral patterns in the individual are genetically determined, and their appearance and retention and further development are influenced by the forces of natural selection. Behavior becomes a mechanism for survival, and through a period of time natural selection favors the best adapted behavior pattern for the species.

For centuries man has been interested in animal behavior, but mainly to attempt to gain some lesson or moral from the activities of lower animals. Thus the fox became a symbol of cunning and treachery; the ant, the acme of industriousness and foresight. The modern study of animal behavior did not really start until the age of Darwin. Darwin's theory of natural selection and evolution emphasized the increasing improvement of animals through adaptation. Since adaptation involves the animal's responses to a changing environment, Darwin called considerable attention to behavior, particularly in his work *Expression of Emotions in Man and Animals*. In his book Darwin argued that the difference in emotions between men and animals was one of degree and not of kind. This answer to his critics, who argued that human emotions were an unbridgeable difference between man and animals, marked the early beginnings of the comparative study of animal behavior.

Slowly the study of behavior of animals in their natural communities grew into the field of *ethology*, which is concerned primarily with determining how the behavioral processes work, how they develop during the life of an animal, and how behavior evolved. Ethology is replete with its own terminology and theory. Much of this is of little direct concern to the ecologist and field biologist. But to understand those aspects of behavior pertinent to the understanding of the ecology of animals, some exposure to ethological concepts is necessary.

Instinctive behavior

In the bright sunlight of an April morning, a male flicker taps out a drumming roll on the bone-gray limb of a dead oak tree. He is answered in the distance by another, and then suddenly he leaves his drumming perch and drops to the ground. Another flicker had flown into the territory. The two males face each other closely on the ground, point their bills into the air, wave them about for four or five seconds, utter a shrill *we-cup,* raise their bright red crests, and display the yellow-colored underwings. After several such dances, the birds fly into different trees. In the quiet of a summer evening a field cricket in a dark crevice in the base of the dead oak tree calls. He occupies the crevice alone and sallies forth for short distances for food and water, to challenge other males, and to court females. He is answered by other males, located in other dark corners, and the evening cricket chorus begins. Nearby female crickets respond to the chirps and travel in the direction of the source.

The response of each to a stimulus—in the case of the flicker the drumming and the moustache of the male, and in the case of the cricket, the chirping of the male—was stereotyped and automatic. Each performed as other individuals of their kind would perform under similar circumstances. The response was characteristic of the species and apparently inherited or genetically fixed. It is this internally "programmed" behavior, to use computer-age language, which ethologists refer to as innate or instinctive behavior.

The terms innate and instinct are often dangerous to use, for they are interpreted differently by different people. To some, innate implies that the behavior is "programmed" completely without any environmental influence or control. If an animal held in isolation from birth responds to a stimulus it never experienced in the way that normally reared animals would, then the behavior pattern is considered innate. But it is difficult to prove that no component of the environment influenced the "programming" as the animal developed. To others, the term innate refers to those complete behavioral patterns performed by an animal without prior practice or experience and with all senses fully functional. This latter interpretation is the one implied in this book.

An animal performs a specific innate behavior only when it receives the appropriate external stimulus or cue. Not all of the information gathered by the sense organs of the animal is meaningful. Somewhere between the sense organs and the motor centers that control the behavioral action much of the sensory input is rejected and the remainder is selectively admitted. What stimuli are admitted depends upon the internal condition of the animal. Only when a certain stimulus or stimuli are properly received by the animal is the behavior pattern discharged. This stimulus may be the appearance of a predator or prey, a sex partner, the presence or absence of a species-specific color pattern, morphological structure, or posture; it may be a chemical substance, such as the odor of a stream or a scent emitted by an animal; or it may be a specific

Figure 25-1 *The moustache of the male flicker (below) is the "releaser" that stimulates territorial defense in the male or courtship behavior in the female.*

call or song. Often the stimulus may be only a small part of the total object perceived, such as the moustache of a flicker (Noble, 1936) (Fig. 25-1), or the red breast feathers of a European robin (Lack, 1953). The essential features of an object or situation that elicit a particular innate behavior pattern are called the *sign stimuli*. And those structures of an animal that serve exclusively to send out sign stimuli and result in a high degree of response are called *releasers*.

Often the stimulus that normally triggers the behavior pattern is not always the one with the greatest triggering function. Supernormal or artificial objects may be chosen over the normal stimulus. The oystercatcher, for example, will choose a giant egg in preference to a normal one and will incubate a supernormal clutch of five eggs over the usual clutch of three (Tinbergen, 1952). This leads the way for the evolution of "releasing" structures, such as the conspicuous plumage patterns of birds used in territorial and courtship display.

The first phase of a behavioral pattern usually is spontaneous. Some internal change or stimulus in the animal, such as hunger or hormonal action, causes the animal to seek an external stimulus such as food or a sex partner. When the animal sights food or a potential mate, a series of behavioral acts is set in motion. The preliminary or searching phase is often called *appetitive behavior*. Internally controlled, this behavior in the right situation switches over to external stimuli. If the animal proceeds in a coordinated manner and in the right direction, the activity is self-stimulating and self-reinforcing until the "releaser" for the next stage is found.

An example of such a reaction chain of behavior and its control is the courtship of the queen butterfly (Brower, 1965). The appearance of the female is the stimulus that sets off the behavioral pattern or program (Fig. 25-2). When a female queen butterfly comes within the view of the male, he flies after her in aerial pursuit. The female flies off, but eventually the male overtakes her. As he passes a few inches over her back, he extrudes two bundles of hairs on either side of the abdomen. These are the abdominal hair pencils, which unfurled emit a strong, musky perfume. Changing to a bobbing flight, the male rapidly sweeps the hair pencils up and down her head and antennae. She responds to this by alighting in the herbage. The male then continues to "hair pencil" while still maintaining a bobbing flight. In response, the female folds her wings tightly over her back. This stimulates the male to retract the hair pencils and alight alongside of the female. The female acquiesces and the male in turn attempts to copulate. If successful, the male and female engage in a postnuptial flight, in which the male flies off carrying the female suspended at the end of his abdomen. If unsuccessful, the male induces the female to fly up again by hovering over her and striking her on the back. As she flies up, the male pursues her and starts the courtship over again.

Once a behavior is initiated, obviously some internal mechanism must exist to make the animal stop, to prevent the animal from carrying the behavior to

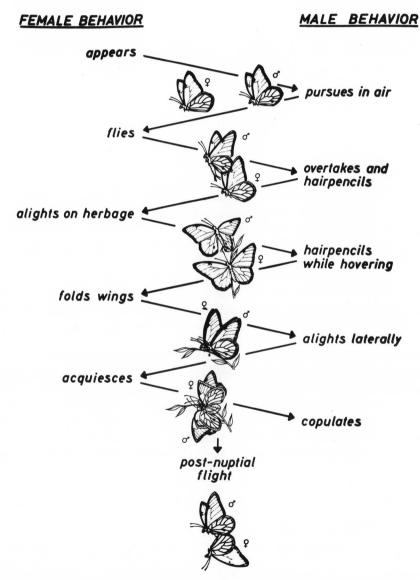

FEMALE BEHAVIOR   **MALE BEHAVIOR**

appears ⟶ pursues in air

flies ⟵ overtakes and hairpencils

alights on herbage ⟵ hairpencils while hovering

folds wings ⟵ alights laterally

acquiesces ⟵ copulates

post-nuptial flight

Figure 25-2 *Chain-reaction behavior in the courtship of the queen butterfly. The male behavior is shown on the right and the female behavior on the left.* (Drawing courtesy of Dr. L. P. Brower and the New York Zoological Society; from Brower, 1965.)

Figure 25-3 *Displacement feeding* (left) *and normal feeding* (right) *in the pectoral sandpiper.* (After Hamilton, 1959.)

an extreme. In the case of the queen butterfly, the behavior program ended with successful mating. Hunting behavior ends with the capture of a prey. And the entire program of feeding ends when the stomach of the animal is full and the animal's desire to eat is reduced. The concluding or *consummatory* act of a behavioral program may act as a sort of a negative feedback mechanism that reduces the effect of a stimulus and brings, if necessary, the behavior to an end.

Expression of conflict

The strong stimulation of one behavioral program apparently inhibits all others and allows only one particular behavior pattern to appear in an animal at one time. How this supression of one pattern by another is accomplished is unknown, but in some way it may be controlled through connections in the central nervous system. On occasions, however, an animal may be strongly stimulated in several ways at once. When neither of the two, or even three, behavior patterns suppresses the other, conflict behavior results. Such conflict behavior often arises when an animal is stimulated both to attack and to escape, and is expressed in the animal as behavior that is not quite appropriate to the situation (Figs. 25-3 and 25-4). For example, the black-headed gull will preen itself or go through the actions of nest building when its brooding drive is thwarted (Moynihan, 1955). During a fight with another male, the pectoral sandpiper, like other waders, will suddenly turn its head around, put its bill under its scapulars, and act as if it were going asleep (Hamilton, 1959). Such acts are called *displacement* or *irrelevant activities*. The still controversial theory behind displacement is that the energy of two opposing tendencies finds its outlet through another behavior pattern (see Iersel and Bol, 1958; Sevenster, 1961).

Figure 25-4 *Grass pulling, a displacement activity in the herring gull.* (Based on photos in Tinbergen, 1953.)

Another form of conflict behavior is *redirection activity,* a type of behavior elicited when some action directed toward an animal or object is suddenly redirected to another object (Tinbergen, 1952). Like displacement, redirection seems to occur when an activity or instinct is thwarted or conflicts with another (see Bastock et al., 1953). When its nest is disturbed by some human intruder, a falcon may direct its attack on some passing bird. Since both attack and escape drives are activated simultaneously, the escape drive may be strong enough to prevent the bird from attacking its adversary. Instead it finds an outlet for the thwarted attack drive through an unprovoked attack on some convenient scapegoat available at the moment.

Some of these displacement and redirection activities have become incorporated in display-behavior patterns, both hostile and courtship; both involve considerable conflict and thwarting.

Instinct versus learning

Although much of an animal's behavior may be "internally programmed," it may be "corrected and adjusted" by an external "programmer," experience and learning. Learning in animals enables them to adjust innate behavior patterns to changes in their lives. Individuals modify their behavior patterns as a result of experience and thus adapt themselves to a changing and unstable environment.

Learning is important in perfecting skills, even innate ones. Such behavior as walking, flying, feeding, courtship, nest building, vocal patterns, and others appear in the animal in species-specific form at some stage of maturation; many of them appear suddenly in complete form. But with experience, animals become more adept in performance. For example, nest building in birds is innate, although it improves partly with learning, partly with rising hormone levels. But the bird learns what materials are suitable for nest building, such as the size and type of twigs. Birds do not learn how to fly; they "know" how to fly once they have developed the proper motor coordinations. But what they do learn in flying are such things as a suitable landing place. Animals learn what is and what is not edible, and how to distinguish between social companions and enemies. They also learn not to respond to stimuli that tend to be insignificant in their lives. Invariably the self-protective tendency to flee is triggered by a wide range of generalized stimuli, ranging from moving objects and sudden movements to strange sounds and situations. Unless an animal is able to sort out those situations and movements that are meaningless to its existence, its life would be an impossible mess. Thus animals are able to get used to certain situations and sounds and ignore them.

Learning is a large and complex subject, which for our purposes need not be discussed any further here. For good reviews of the subject see Scott (1958) and Thorpe (1963).

Imprinting

The young of many precocial species, such as geese, ducks, and ungulates, possess a tendency during a restricted period after hatching or birth to orient toward or investigate an object, especially a moving one. Ducklings, goslings, and young gallinaceous birds shortly after hatching follow the first moving object to which they are exposed. In nature this obviously is their mother, and after following her for some time, the young will follow no other animal. Incubator-reared ducklings, goslings, and chickens, however, can be induced to follow an artificial or abnormal object, such as a wooden decoy or even a balloon. Once they have followed this for some time, they will continue to do so. This suggests that at the time of birth, the young possess an innate behavioral program that is incomplete and must be supplemented by some influence from the outside world. In other words, the object has to be "imprinted" upon the young before the young will respond to it. This phenomenon has been called *imprinting*.

Imprinting is the rapid establishment of a perceptual preference for an object and seemingly must take place during a limited and definite period of the life cycle (Klopfer and Hailman, 1964; Klopfer, 1964). The term was first suggested by Lorenz (1933) to explain his experiences with incubator-raised graylag geese. These young geese, deprived of a normal mother, attached themselves to Lorenz by following him and finally by accepting him as a substitute parent.

Imprinting presumably is confined to a definite and brief period in the life of an animal and to a particular set of environmental conditions. The "critical period" for imprinting varies among species and is linked to the rate of physical development. Young mallards are susceptible to imprinting somewhere between 13 and 16 hours (Hess, 1959), although this varies among individuals. The moose calf develops a heeling or following response to its dam around four days after birth (Altmann, 1960). If the following response is not elicited during this critical period, then the appetitive behavior for following fades. This is perhaps because of an increasing development of a competing fear or fleeing response. As a result, the older the animal becomes, the less likely it will follow strange objects (Hinde, Thorpe, and Vince, 1956). This rapid form of learning is highly adapted to those animals with rapidly developing motor abilities who must establish early and maintain contact with their parents and others of the same species.

Experimental studies have stressed visual imprinting, but there is growing evidence that imprinting also involves other perceptual stimulation. Young wood ducks, reared in a dark tree hole or nest box, are exposed to the call of their mother for a relatively long period before they are exposed to the sight of her. This auditory stimulation apparently plays a major role in the ducklings' recognition of their parent (Gottlieb, 1963). After fluttering to the ground, the young apparently rely on the calls of the mother to lead them to water (Klopfer, 1959). Olfactory imprinting apparently exists among mammals that recognize both species and individuals by body odor. Acceptance of newborn young by female sheep, goats, and cattle seems to depend upon the olfactory and tactile contact with the newborn young for at least a few minutes after birth (Collias, 1956). To separate the young and mother for even as short a time as one hour is sufficient to lead to rejection of that young. Immediately after giving birth, a female sheep or goat will accept any young lamb or kid but within a few hours will reject any strange young. This behavioral trait is utilized by some sheep raisers, who attempt to present orphaned young to a foster mother.

For a number of years, imprinting has been equated with the following response. As a result of recent experimental evidence (Klopfer, 1964; Polt and

Hess, 1964), imprinting is now being regarded as separate from the following response. Following may be an outcome of imprinting, but it is not imprinting itself. In experiments with chicks and ducklings, Klopfer and Heilman (1964) demonstrated that while these birds require exposure to a moving model during the critical period if they are to exhibit a following response, they did not necessarily attach to or permanently follow the original object or model. When two groups of chicks, one trained to a plain duck decoy and the other to a brightly painted decoy, were exposed to both models simultaneously, both groups showed a preference for the brightly colored one. In a second experiment, the chicks were trained as above, then exposed simultaneously to the two models, which were stationary rather than moving. This time each of the birds preferred the original model to which it was initially exposed. Another group, trained initially to a stationary model, later showed few responses and no preferences. Thus it appears that (1) while an imprinting experience with a moving object is necessary to activate the following response, the preferred characteristics of the object are fixed in some other way, perhaps independently of visual experience; (2) features other than movement may be involved in imprinting under different conditions; and (3) possibly imprinting may have a more limited effect than is commonly believed.

SUMMARY

If nothing else, the discussion on imprinting, the rapid establishment of a perceptual preference for an object, points out how meager our knowledge of it is. And much the same can be said of our knowledge of other behavioral processes. We can observe what an animal does in different situations; we can gain some insight into the animal's motivations; but as yet we can only theorize about the manner in which behavior is organized.

Behavior is essentially a stimulus-response phenomenon. Outside stimuli are selectively admitted, dependent upon the internal state of the animal. The sensory data are processed and integrated within the nervous system and the message sent out to the muscular system for appropriate response.

An animal is born with a number of inherited or innate behavior "programs," which respond to certain external stimuli and which may become modified through learning. Something within the system operates to permit only one behavior program to function at a time. But often two or more behavior programs may be active at once, none of which is dominant. Then conflict behavior, as expressed by irrelevant and redirection activities, results. Animals, however, are not automatic machines, responding only to certain stimuli and nothing else. They are able to modify their behavior through learning, which presumably is most highly developed in mammals. Innate or highly modified through learning, the behavior of an animal enables it to adapt to the changing environment in which it lives.

CHAPTER **26**

Egocentric behavior

The behavior of an animal is directed inward toward itself and outward toward others of its own kind and, in some, toward other species as well. The former will be called egocentric behavior. The latter is social behavior. Egocentric behavior includes those activities that relate to the individual animal's welfare. These include maintenance, feeding, shelter seeking, and escape and defense behavior. Social behavior includes flocking, sexual, parental, and agonistic relationships. Such a classification at its best is arbitrary, for often only a thin line divides the two. Both are important in the ecology of an animal and its ability to adapt to environmental changes.

Maintenance behavior

Anyone who has ever watched a cat, even for a few hours, is well aware that the animal spends considerable time caring for its body. The cat not only licks, scratches, and bites its body fur, but it also meticulously washes its face with pre-licked paws, especially after eating or rising from sleep. Similar maintenance

494

activities are widespread among animals and include such behavior as bathing, dusting, grooming and preening, head scratching, sunning, and anting.

Body care is most conspicuous among birds and mammals, probably because they are the most easily observed, especially the birds. Grooming is an activity frequently indulged in, but descriptions of this behavior for our most common birds and mammals are very meager. Grooming in birds consists mainly of bill wiping, feather settling, scratching, and preening, in order of decreasing frequency (Iersel and Bol, 1958; Rowell, 1961). Common preening movements involve nibbling of the feathers and drawing the full length of the feather through the bill. Preening often is done with oil from the uropygial gland. Even here different groups of birds distribute oil over their plumage in different ways (Fickens, unpub.). Songbirds (oscines) take oil from the gland with the tip of the bill, then scratch, first touching the tip of the bill with the claw of the second toe and then rubbing the claw over the top of the head. Ducks (Anatids) bite the oil gland, press the oil into the feathers around the gland, and then rotate the head against these feathers.

Grooming activity frequently follows feeding, drinking, bathing, and other activities. Variations in the length and composition of grooming movements usually are associated with the intensity and type of the stimulus and available time. The longest periods of grooming contain the greatest variety of action. These usually are undisturbed periods following bathing, for when the bird is wet, the stimulus to groom is at its maximum. Preening movements in chaffinches often are absent at the beginning of grooming and reach their peak about a third of the way through the grooming activity (Rowell, 1961).

Grooming and preening are such common activities that it is not unusual for these behavior patterns to appear in other situations. One is the so-called displacement preening, which appears when two primary conflicting tendencies are opposing and equal (see Displacement, Chap. 25). Preening movements also have become incorporated in the courtship display of herons and ducks

Grooming and comfort movements in mammals have received little attention. They are perhaps less involved, since the fur of mammals does not require the extensive care required by the feathers of birds. Rubbing, scratching, shaking, biting the fur and licking movements are common to most mammals. Dogs, while lying down, spend some time licking the soles of their paws and the skin between the toes. Cows, horses, and dogs roll in the grass; buffaloes and pigs wallow either in wet or dry mud holes, a movement analogous to dust bathing in birds.

Comfort movements in wild moose have been described by Valerius Geist (1963). When they rise from their beds, moose often stretch in several different ways. When stretching the body the moose draws in its belly, arches its back downward, and swings its head up and down (Fig. 26-1). These animals indulge in body shaking after exposure to water. The moose stands with its hind legs slightly spread, its head and neck held parallel to the ground to form a continuous line with the body, and raises the hair on the neck, withers, and rump. The shaking movement then begins at the head and spreads back. Rubbing new, growing antlers on the side of the hind leg is a common comfort movement in bulls. Moose scratch themselves with a raised hind leg on the nose, chin, cheeks, ears, and neck. The majority of these comfort movements, which vary with sex and season, take place mainly at the beginning or end of an activity period.

495

Sunbathing is common to both birds and mammals. During winter and spring, gray squirrels seek sunny areas where they can sun themselves. The squirrel will lie atop a limb and stretch outward from the trunk (Bakken, 1959). Among birds, two types of sunbathing are recognized (Hauser, 1957). One is voluntary, or normal, sunbathing, accompanied by preening, shaking, scratching, and the repeated resumption of the sunbathing posture. The second is compulsory sunning, exhibited when a bird is suddenly and apparently unexpectedly exposed to direct sunlight under extreme conditions of heat and humidity. This movement may be motivated by a sudden warming of the bird's immediate environment (Lanyon, 1958). Birds may assume a variety of positions in sunbathing (Hauser, 1957), but all are characterized by some form of feather fluffing, wing dropping, tail spreading, and often panting.

Figure 26-1 *Comfort movements in the moose. (left) Stretching; (right) rubbing antler knobs, typical among yearling bulls.* (After Geist, 1963.)

An unusual form of body maintenance among birds is anting, the application of foreign substances to the plumage and possibly to the skin (see Simmons, 1957a; Whitaker, 1957). Anting may be active, as when the bird applies crushed ants to the underside of the wings and tail with the bill; or it may be passive, as when the bird postures among the thronging ants and allows them to crawl in the plumage. If ants are unavailable, then some substitute material, such as fruits, foliage, millipedes, beetles, grasshoppers, and even burned matches are used.

Numerous reasons have been advanced to explain anting, including the repulsion of ectoparasites by ant predation and acids, the attraction of birds to the odor of ants, and the conditioning of the plumage. Recently there has come to light a three-volume work on feather mites by a Russian parasitologist, Dr. V. B.

Dubinin (Kelso and Nice, 1963), in which he describes some aspects and possible functions of anting. Birds typically are parasitized by feather mites (Analgesoidea), which lack mouthparts strong enough to chew feather substances. Apparently they feed instead on feather lipids, which exist in addition to those of the preen gland. Dubinin discovered that anting, which releases formic acid from the ants, may destroy the mites. He suggests that anting is performed to rid the bird of parasites and to treat or "nurse" the tail and flight feathers. Kelso and Nice (1963), however, suggest that "anting is an instinctive action present in many birds, perhaps aimed at the defense against feather mites. It appears to be 'triggered' by the acid or burning taste of ants and other substances and apparently may be performed *in vacuo*, i.e., in the absence of mite infestation."

Shelter seeking and habitat selection

All organisms, from the lowly paramecium to man, have one behavioral trait in common—shelter seeking. All seek optimum environmental conditions and avoid dangerous and injurious ones. Desert animals seek the shade of rock crevices or burrows in the sand during the heat of day. Deer and birds seek the cool of forest shade on a hot summer day. A bird escaping from a hawk darts into the thick underbrush. Shelter seeking can be divided into two broad groups, one in which the individual seeks a favorable situation for itself, and the other in which the individual seeks shelter from sudden danger.

TABLE 26-1. TYPES OF SHELTER OR COVER

WINTER COVER	Protection from snow and cold; a place to remain out of sight
ESCAPE COVER	Vegetation in which the animal is secure from predators and hunters
LOAFING COVER	Shade in summer; protection in winter
NESTING COVER	Protection for both nest and parents
ROOSTING COVER	Secure cover for sleeping

Based on Leopold, 1933.

Associated with shelter-seeking behavior is cover. Based on the behavior of the animal, Leopold (1933) recognized five different types (Table 26-1). Some time spent afield will reveal how well the behavior of animals is adjusted to their surroundings. The white-tailed deer, for example, has a predilection for coniferous cover during winter. During the winter of 1954–55 an intensive daily study was made of the use by deer of a 30-acre pine plantation in central New York State. Surrounded by woodland and open and brushy fields, the plantation and several small plantings were used almost exclusively as cover by deer. Here they bedded down, and on stormy days they always retired to its most protected and secluded depths. Only on warm sunny days did they bed down for afternoon rests in aspen and other hardwood cover (Smith, 1959). In northwestern Massachusetts the deer also showed a strong preference for bedding in coniferous cover

497

(Hosley and Ziebarth, 1935). Nearly half the beds observed were located in natural white pine stands 15 to 70 years of age, and a fourth of them were in 15-year-old Scotch pine.

Birds are rather selective of roosting cover, although this aspect of avian ecology has been somewhat neglected. The night-roosting habits of bobwhite quail have been rather intensively studied in southern Illinois (Klimstra and Ziccardi, 1963). The covies showed a strong preference for bare ground protected by low, sparse, open canopy of vegetation. The majority of roosting headquarters were located at medium to low elevations on well-drained soil and faced to the south or southwest. Occasionally the covies shifted their roosting headquarters, and most of the shifts were made from lower to higher elevations. Shifts down to poorly drained sites and low elevations were made usually in response to wind and inclement weather.

Considerable selection also is involved in the choice of nesting sites by birds and denning sites by mammals. Insects often are highly selective. Nesting substrate, access, cover, song and observation posts, all are involved in the selection of sites for the reproductive season.

Suggestive of roosting cover is loafing cover, a place where animals spend restful minutes during the day. In New York conifer plantations, white-tailed deer spent hot summer afternoons in thick spruce plantings where low-hanging branches offered protection as well as handy brushes against flies (Smith, 1959). Ducks congregate on open mud bars jutting out into the water. And sulphur butterflies gather about little pools of water along the summer roadside.

Basic to shelter-seeking behavior is habitat selection. The underlying question here is how do the various species of animals select the environment they inhabit. There is some evidence, among birds at least, that imprinting is involved; yet other evidence suggests that habitat selection among birds and mice is innate and is independent of early experience. The whole question of habitat selection cannot be dissociated from competition and natural selection, the forces which "fit" the organism to the environmental niche it occupies (see Chap. 24).

Animals differ widely in their powers of locomotion and in their capacity to learn. Animals restricted in their ability to move any great distance or dispersed by wind and water survive only if the environment in which they arrive is favorable. Others with greater powers of locomotion move about until they locate a suitable area. This is particularly true of birds, flying insects, and mammals. Between these two extremes are many intermediates.

Habitat selection is partly a psychological process (Lack and Venerables, 1939; Miller, 1942). The lack of singing perches and nesting sites may prevent birds from colonizing an area. On the other hand species tend to select their ancestral habitat instinctively, recognizing it by conspicuous though not necessarily essential features. Salmon recognize their home stream from olfactory experiences gained as fry (Hasler, 1954). The Nashville warbler, a typical inhabitant of the open heath edges of the northern bogs, selects further south in its range young open stands of aspen and balsam fir. In reforestation areas of New York State, the Nashville warbler is a typical inhabitant of blackberry and sweet-fern openings in spruce and mixed conifer plantations, a habitat visually suggestive of bog openings (Smith, 1956). MacArthur and MacArthur (1961) suggest that the foliage-density profile is an essential cue to habitat selection by birds.

Peter Klopfer (1962, 1963) has been able to demonstrate by the use of a test chamber containing oak and pine foliage that adult chipping sparrows of the North Carolina Piedmont preferred pine foliage to oak. All environmental effects except foliage and light had been eliminated, including variations in perch space. In another experiment, chipping sparrows hand reared in isolation from either foliage type chose pine when given a choice. Conversely, isolates reared in the presence of oak foliage chose oak more often than pine.

Somewhat similar work has been done with the two subspecies of deer mice, *Peromyscus maniculatus bairdi,* restricted to open-field habitats, and *P. m. gracilis,* restricted to hardwood forests and brushy habitats. By presenting artificial habitats, one of forest, the other of grassland, to the two subspecies, Harris (1952) demonstrated that the two subspecies selected the appropriate artificial habitat. Since the physical conditions were essentially uniform throughout the experimental room, he concluded that the mice were reacting to the form of artificial vegetation. And since laboratory bred *Peromyscus,* who had no previous experience with either habitat, artificial or natural, exhibited a preference for the type of habitat they normally occupied in the wild state, he concluded that habitat selection was basically genetic.

This problem was probed more deeply by Wecker (1963), who investigated the role of early experience in determining the habitat preference of prairie deer mice under natural conditions. Two strains of mice were used, live-trapped wild stock and laboratory-reared stock. The latter were descendents of 10 pairs of mice live trapped by Harris and were 12 to 20 generations removed from any experience in the natural environment. In separate experiments they were released in a 1600-square-foot rectangular enclosure, constructed with its long axis lying halfway across a woods-field habitat boundary. This provided the introduced animals an opportunity to select one of the two distinct habitats. Movements of the mice were recorded by a sensitized treadle located in runways at various positions in the pen. Six groups of mice were tested in the enclosure: field-caught animals, laboratory animals, offspring of field-caught animals reared in the laboratory, offspring of laboratory animals reared in the field, offspring of field-caught animals reared in the woods, and offspring of laboratory animals reared in the woods. Without elaborating on details, the results of these experiments justified the conclusion that the choice of the grassland environment by the prairie deer mouse is normally predetermined by heredity. Early field experience can reinforce this innate preference, but it is not necessary for subsequent habitat selection. Early experience in other environments, i.e., woods and laboratory, was not sufficient to reverse the normal selection of grassland by the experimental mice.

Confinement of prairie deer mice in the laboratory for 12 to 20 generations resulted in an apparent reduction of hereditary control over habitat selection and led to an increased variability in the behavior of these animals when tested in the enclosure. Although these mice lost their innate preference for the grassland habitat, they still retained an ability to learn from early field experience to respond to the stimuli associated with that environment. When these young, laboratory-strain mice were reared in field, woods, and laboratory environment, only those with early experience in the field habitat chose the appropriate environment when released in the enclosure. Those mice with previous experience in woods and laboratory showed no preference for either the woods or the field habitat.

Habitat selection, however, is not extremely rigid. Most species exhibit some plasticity; otherwise these animals would not spread into "abnormal" habitats. This ability or trait of some members of a particular species to select habitats that deviate from that of their companions must exist on both a phenotypic and genetic level. Hinde (1959) suggests that some animals may accept a normally inadequate habitat if some supernormal releaser, such as nest boxes, exists in the local environment. Plasticity in habitat selection is well illustrated by such birds as the chimney swift, which accepted chimneys over hollow trees as nest sites, and duck hawks, which find themselves as much at home in the manmade cliffs and canyons of our large cities as they do in natural cliff country. Pigeons become an adequate substitute for duck. And the magnolia warbler, partial to spruce and hemlock forests, is a typical inhabitant of the drier oak forests of West Virginia (Brooks, 1940; personal observations).

Feeding behavior

Feeding behavior of any animal is closely bound to its structural adaptation for acquiring food and to its niche in the community, both results of evolution. Moths and butterflies have extendible tongues that enable them to sip nectar. Mergansers have serrated margins on the bill that help them to hold onto fish. Herons have long legs, long necks, and long sharp bills, which permit them to spear fish in deep water. Cats have carnassial teeth, which allow them to shear flesh like scissors. Microtine rodents have teeth well adapted to a vegetable diet. There are nearly as many feeding adaptations as there are species of animals. This great variety has been discussed in one way or another throughout the pages of this book.

The diet of animals is also partly controlled by behavior patterns possessed by the animal. The possession of one or a series of behavior "programs" increases the possibility that the animal will take food that switches on this "program," rather than an item that does not. Among some animals these behavioral patterns are similar and suggest a common ancestry; among others, the "programs" from appetitive behavior to the consummatory act are as individualistic as the morphological structure of the species.

Feeding behavior is triggered by the internal state of the animal. Included are the general sensations of the body, such as hunger pangs and stomach contractions. The depletion of food material in the blood results in changes in blood glucose, which in turn may stimulate sensory nerves that affect centers in the brain. These functions are very closely related to the automatically self-stimulating physiological processes of the body. This, of course, is not the whole story, for food-seeking behavior can be triggered in the absence of any metabolic condition. A well-fed cat does not hesitate to chase a mouse immediately after consuming a meal. So other drives too may be involved in the release of the hunting behavior.

Once initiated, food-seeking behavior among many animals is relatively stereotyped and involves a series or chain of behavior patterns. Each pattern is dependent upon some stimulus different for each step or link and each is necessary for the behavior to proceed from one action to the other.

The solitary digger wasps (Sphecidae) offer a good example of stereotyped food-seeking behavior. Each species tends to be a specialist and hunts a particular prey, disregarding others similar in size and just as abundant, if not more so. Some hunting wasps prey only on a single genus or a single species. Very few find their prey among more than one order of arthropods. Among this interesting family of wasps, the affinity of the predator to the prey is as characteristic of each species as its anatomy. Thus there are such hunting wasps as the grasshopper and cricket killers, the cicada killers, the spider killers, and the like. This is a purely arbitrary classification, since grasshopper and cricket killers, for example, may be found among several subfamilies and tribes.

The unique fact about the predatory wasps is that they do not kill to feed themselves. The adults, male and female, feed on sugar in solution, supplied by nectar, ripe fruit, and the honeydew of aphids. Males are nonpredatory. The females hunt to provide food for the larvae, which are reared in galleries, chambers, or nests in the ground or in rotted wood or in nests built of mud above the ground.

To begin, the hunting behavior of the female predatory wasp is released by the completion of a burrow or nest that needs to be provisioned with food for the larvae before the eggs can be laid (Baerends, 1941). After the nest is completed, the digger wasp flies to the appropriate habitat to search for her prey. If the wasp sights a moving object, she moves in closer and hovers downwind. From this position, the wasp can scent the odor of the potential victim. If correct, the wasp moves in for the kill; but only if the victim has the feel of a bee, cicada, or whatever the specific prey must be, does the female immobilize the victim with a sting. Among the many different species of hunting wasps, this combination of visual, olfactory, and tactile cues guides them to their proper victims. The tendency to respond to the appropriate cue in each of these sensory areas is a part of their innate behavior. So accurate are the responses to these releasers or cues that the wasps rarely make a mistake.

The stinging behavior that follows a capture is also stereotyped. The motions differ from one major group to another. Each species is adapted to the anatomy and physiology of the prey it seeks. Caterpiller hunters sting their prey not only on the thorax but also along the underside of the abdomen, where a well-developed nervous system controls the prolegs, important in the caterpiller's locomotion. The bee killers sting the honeybee around the coxae or anchor segments of the front leg; from there the venom diffuses to the muscles controlling flight and movement of the legs.

Once the prey has been immobilized, the wasp has to carry it back to her nest. Here again clear-cut behavioral patterns have evolved, involving the size of prey, the methods of carrying it, and the distance from the nest that hunting takes place. The most primitive method is found among those wasps who install only a single victim in the brood nest (Evans, 1962). These wasps require a victim as large or larger than themselves to meet the food demands of the larvae, and they must by necessity drag the victim over the ground back to the nest. Even the method of dragging the prey across the ground varies. One group, regarded as the most primitive, seizes the prey with the mandibles, often in some specific place as the base of the hind legs or the mouth parts, and drags it backwards to the nest. Others, somewhat more advanced and exhibiting structural or behavioral modifications that enable them to straddle their prey, move the victims forward over the ground. A few may make a short hopping flight.

Most of the digger wasps and a few vespid wasps use more than one para-

501

lyzed victim per cell (Evans, 1957, 1963). Thus the size of the prey is some-what smaller. This allows the wasp to carry the prey in flight, holding onto the victim with the mandibles and often also with the legs. This ability enables such wasps as the grasshopper killer (*Sphex*) to search the grassy meadows some distance from their nests for suitable prey. Since all of these carry their prey with their mandibles, they cannot dig while holding their load; so they must lay the victim down at some obvious risk of loss while they scrape open the nest. Another group of digger wasps gets around this by carrying its prey by the middle or hind legs alone, without the use of the mandibles. This is the method used by the well-known cicada killer, which carries its prey with the middle legs, although the great weight of the cicada often forces the wasp to drag the victim some of the distance across the ground. These wasps can clear away the nest entrance and perform other tasks without releasing the prey. The most advanced of the sphecid hunting wasps, the Crabroninae and Philan-thinae, carry their prey on their stings, which in some species is barbed. One genus, *Aphilanthops*, has its last abdominal segment modified for clamping the prey.

The stereotyped, highly specialized methods of the hunting wasps for seeking and handling prey represent a type of behavior that is adapted to specific prey. Feeding behavior, too, reduces competition among similar sympatric species less specific in food requirements. Such diversity in feeding behavior may be found among the herons, nine species of which may haunt common feeding grounds. The herons are somewhat separated in their feeding niches by the length of legs and the length of the neck, which limits the depth of the water in which each can feed. The great blue heron can seek fish in deeper water than the green heron; but they differ too in the method they use to capture their meal.

All herons have one basic method of hunting: they stand and wait, usually hunched, with the head retracted (Meyerriecks, 1960). As the prey draws near, the heron flicks its tail up and down slightly, then strikes, darting its head forward and downward. The fish or frog, once seized, is held momentarily be-tween the bill tips, then tossed head first into the mouth by a sharp backward motion of the head. Once the fish is swallowed, the heron dips its bill in the water and quickly shakes its head. This behavior the heron will perform, even if it misses its prey, seemingly a necessary follow through of the strike. A method common to all herons, except the common egret, is to walk or wade slowly while holding the body erect and the head forward at a 45° angle. But there are variations. On sunny days when the surface glare is great, the little blue heron will tilt its extended head and neck sharply to one side and then the other as it peers into the water; and it will stop and quickly extend and withdraw its wings in barely perceptible flicks, which may startle the prey into activity. The Louisiana heron, improving on this, will extend one wing fully, whirl about, fold the wing, whirl again, extend the other, then rapidly pursue the startled prey that respond to the rapid shadow over the water. This same heron possesses an interesting variation in which it extends both wings, turns about, raises one wing higher than the other, then slowly tucks its head beneath the higher wing while peering into the water. As it turns again, the heron shifts the head beneath the other wing. Such action apparently shades the water, and by reducing surface glare, enables the heron to see down into the water. The reddish egret goes one step further. It extends both wings

Figure 26-2 *(left) Hunting behavior of the reddish egret, in which the wings are fully extended; (right) Foot-stirring behavior of the snowy egret.* (After Meyerriecks, 1959.)

fully and while holding this pose stabs rapidly at the prey beneath (Fig. 26-2). This heron exhibits a variation which is most fully evolved in the black heron of Africa. The black heron brings both of its extended wings forward to form a canopy over the bird's body. The heron then tucks its head beneath this feathery umbrella. But the canopy formed by the reddish egret is not quite so complete. Prior to assuming the canopy pose, the reddish egret dashes about in the water, startling and dispersing the fish. Then the egret stops, spreads its wings, and waits for the frightened fish to take up cover beneath a false refuge. Another species, the snowy egret, chases fish out of cover by stirring the water with its feet either as it wades across the shallows or hovers above the surface (Fig. 26-2) (Meyerriecks, 1959).

These examples point out how fixed the food-seeking behavior of animals can be. They also illustrate how behavior, like structure, can evolve through natural selection, further adapting the animal to its niche in the community.

The preponderance of innate behavior patterns in food seeking does not eliminate learning. Like nest-building movements in birds, food seeking undoubtedly improves with experience. The young of precocial birds learn what to pick up and what to leave behind. Learning probably is most highly expressed in the food-seeking behavior of mammals, which often develops into something of an art, especially among the carnivores; undoubtedly some individuals become more proficient than others. Even among mammals, however, one still can see some basic patterns that some groups possess in common (Fig. 26-3). Whatever the organisms, those animals whose feeding behavior involves learning are much more flexible in their choice of food compared to those limited to stereotyped feeding, such as the hunting wasps.

Several diverse groups of animals, notably the bats and the dolphins, seek their food by echolocation. When hunting insects and flying about in the darkness of the night, bats are able to locate food and avoid objects by emitting through the mouth bursts of ultra-high-frequency pulses, which bounce off flying

Figure 26-3 *Hunting behavior of a canid, as exemplified by the red fox. Note the pouncing movement on the prey.* (Drawn from life.)

and still objects about them. The returning echo is picked up by their large ears. The time required for the return of the echo indicates the distance of the objects. When hunting insects, the bat engages in a fairly straight flight, during which it emits repetitive pulses at a relatively long interval of 50 to 100 milliseconds (Griffin et al., 1960). If an insect is picked up by echolocation, the bat turns in that direction and increases the pulse rate to 10 to 50 milliseconds. As the bat closes in, it increases the pulse rate to a very rapid 4 to 7 milliseconds, a buzz. All this requires very little time. Bats have detected, located, and intercepted insects in flight within half a second.

Among animals whose young are highly dependent on parental care, food-seeking behavior is, in the young, care-soliciting behavior. This is reciprocal with the care-giving behavior of the parent. A newly born mammal instinctively seeks the nipple of the mother, yet unless the female is in proper psychological condition, the young animal may be rejected. Normally, however, when the young seeks to nurse the mother, the mother also seeks the young. Among altricial birds, the instinct of the young to seek food and the stimuli that cause the adults to feed them involve a series of highly developed releasers. At the time the young birds hatch, the adults already exhibit a tendency to feed. In fact some birds, such as the starling, some warblers, and tanagers, may bring food to the nest before the eggs have hatched. At the other extreme, some late-nesting swallows may migrate south and leave the young in the nest to starve.

Young birds are fed only if they, to put it anthropomorphically, demand to be fed. The stimuli that elicit the feeding behavior of the adults to a certain extent depend upon the release of food-seeking or demanding behavior in the young. The typical response of the newly hatched young bird is to gape for food. Some newly hatched birds gape without any apparent external stimulus; others require some stimulus to elicit gaping. Since altricial birds usually are born blind, visual stimuli are not effective, but a slight jarring of the nest is. Later, after the eyes are open, the jarring of the nest may result in fear responses instead (Tinbergen and Kuenen, 1939). At this time visual and tactile releasers become important. Young thrushes, after their eyes have opened, gape at any object, provided it is not too small and is located above the horizontal of the nestlings' eyes (Tinbergen and Kuenen, 1939). Later, gaping is directed toward the head of the parent, suggesting that some learning is involved. Experiments show that food-begging responses of both the herring gull (Tinbergen and Perdeck, 1951) and the Franklin gull (Collias and Collias, 1957) are released by the sight of the parents' red-spotted beak and red bill, respectively. To be most effective the bill had to be held low, had to point downward, and had to have something (food) protruding from it. For the procedure involved in these experiments, which included the use of cardboard heads, variously colored bills, and in the case of the Franklin gull, variously colored flashing lights, the reader is referred to the original papers.

Just as the young require releasers to stimulate gaping or food begging, so do the adults require some sign stimuli to release the feeding response. Gaping is one releaser. Some species have evolved color patches, or "targets," at which the parents direct the food. Linings of the mouth, brightly colored in yellow, red, or orange, are one type of releaser, the bright yellow flanges on the margin of the beak another. Other species have bizarre color patterns in the mouth, such as the jet black spots and bars on the tongue in the desert horned lark. Wing fluttering either horizontally or vertically, is another stimulus for the parent bird to feed, as is the food call of the young. Once fed, the young bird ceases to gape; and without gaping the young bird is not fed. Apparently when the young bird has swallowed food, the swallowing reflex becomes inoperative for a short while. Even if the bird should gape when the parent returns, it will refuse to swallow. The parent bird then removes the food and presents it to another. In such a manner food is rather equally distributed among all the young.

Escape and defense behavior

Of all the behavior patterns of animals, the most generalized and the least species-specific are those involving escape and defense. The responses—the escape movements, the distress calls and alarms—may release similar alarm or escape reactions in many different species. This behavior lacks specificity because no selective advantage is gained by having a behavior that emphasizes differences in alarm reactions between species. The importance is individual survival, and a whole effect is necessary.

Enemy recognition

Recognition of some enemies is innate. A combination of visual characters elicit fear or alarm reactions from many birds. The classical experiments of Nice and Ter Pelwyk (1941) and of Hartley (1950) point out the importance of visual recognition. When small birds were presented with models of owls, they showed strong alarm or fright, but only if the models possessed one or a combination of four visual characters: (1) a large head, owllike in outline—short head, short neck, short tail; (2) an owllike pattern—barred, streaked, or spotted; (3) an owllike color—brown, gray, or tone contrasts of these colors; (4) an even contour. The escape reaction of many birds to avian predators flying overhead is a response not only to movement but also to a definite outline involving a short neck. Lorenz and Tinbergen (1938) demonstrated that when a card-

505

board dummy with a characteristic outline of a short head was passed overhead, it released escape behavior in waterfowl and gallinaceous birds, regardless of the shape of wings and tail and regardless of color. When a generalized silhouette, which appears as a bird with a short neck and long tail when pulled in one direction, and as a bird with a long neck and short tail when pulled in the other, was presented, the birds reacted only when the dummy was moved in the direction of the short neck. As a result many birds react to swifts and doves as they do to hawks and owls. Movement, too, is involved. A swiftly moving object releases escape behavior even though an error in recognition is involved. Swiftly moving pigeons and swifts, for example, often release escape behavior in birds. In such situations, it is undoubtedly better for the animal to react swiftly and flee, even though in error, than to hesitate and perhaps die. More slowly moving predators permit distant recognition and allow more time for the release of appropriate behavior patterns, so that energy is not wasted on unnecessary flight or display of hostility.

Although enemy recognition is in many ways innate, the ability to distinguish between what to fear and what not to fear is learned. If an animal is faced with a possible enemy and nothing happens, its fear and alarm reactions decrease until the object no longer elicits a reaction. This is particularly true when an animal (especially a higher vertebrate) is exposed to something new and strange, yet harmless. Fear is the first reaction, but it gradually wanes until the animal accepts the object or other animal.

Reaction to enemies

How an animal reacts to an enemy depends upon the enemy, the behavior of the enemy, the circumstances under which the meeting takes place, and often the stage of the reproductive cycle.

When an animal faces the threat of an enemy or danger, it has five courses of action open to it. The animal may cry out a warning, if vocal; it may lead the enemy away from the nest or young; it may threaten, mob, or attack its adversary; it may hide; or it may flee.

Flight. If the enemy is formidable and resistance is useless or if the animal is unduly startled by swift approach, the animal flees. Often the animal needs no visual cues; scent, sound, or chemical stimuli are sufficient to produce an immediate response. At the sound of a man or dog moving through the woods, a deer will race to some safer spot. In response to the scent of the predatory starfish, sand dollars bury themselves in the sand. The rabbit runs a zigzag course ahead of pursuing hounds. In fact the rabbit's course may be so swift and erratic that a fast dog will turn an accidental somersault as it attempts to cut corners as sharply as the rabbit.

Flight reaction is contagious. If one animal flees, others may be startled into doing the same. This results in stampedes among the ungulates, and in waterfowl massed flight out of the area. If danger is from above, such as from a hawk, bird flocks tend to draw close together to form a dense flock and perform sharp, swift turns with coordination and precision. Such behavior makes picking off an individual much more difficult, an accomplishment achieved only by considerable maneuvering by the hawk.

Warning. Warning calls—a cry, a snort, a yelp—are not, in spite of our story books and our imaginations, given as a conscious alarm to other animals, although the effect may be the same. It is a cry of fear, and the intensity or nature of the call may vary with the intensity of fear. Among birds in particular, perhaps since they are as a group the most vocal of the vertebrates (other than man), the warning or alarm notes vary either in intensity or in kind according to the situation. They may vary with the type of predator or trespasser, with distance or nearness, or with the stage in the reproductive cycle. A hawk flying overhead may induce an animal to crouch or freeze and remain completely silent. A cat entering the territory of almost any bird elicits high-intensity alarm notes that spread rapidly to other birds in the area, yet man and dog may be ignored or be met with only mild alarm.

In her classic study on the song sparrow, Mrs. M. M. Nice (1943) listed three stages of behavior in this species when alarmed. Although all three stages intergrade, each is characterized by a particular note. When alarmed, the bird utters a note *tchunk,* raises its crest, flips its wings, and raises and flips its tail. In the second, or fear, stage the bird utters *tik,* it compresses its body feathers, stretches its neck, and crouches on its perch. When frightened, the bird utters a rapid *tik-tik-tik* and flies and hides, and if unable to escape, pants with its bill open. The rate at which these notes are given indicates to some extent the intensity of the alarm, fear, or fright.

The tendency of birds to give a warning call increases as the reproductive cycle passes through the stages of nest building, incubation, and brooding the young. Just as the defense reaction of mammals is highest when the female is caring for the young, so the intensity of alarm is greatest among birds when the young are about to leave the nest or are under the care of the parents. The intensity of the response increases as the enemy comes nearer and nearer the young. During nest building and incubation, many birds are relatively unconcerned about most trespassing animals unless it is a cat or some other strong enemy. But later when young are in the nest, even human intrusion is met with alarm. The grasshopper sparrow, for example, utters only a sharp monosyllabic *tik* when humans or dogs enter its territory early in the nesting period (Smith, 1963). But if one closely approaches a nest containing young or if a cat enters the territory at any time, the bird raises its crest feathers, flicks its wings and tail, bobs up and down on its legs, and utters a sharp double note *chi-ip.* At high intensity the grasshopper sparrow gives this double note so rapidly, that it runs into a trill. To dogs these birds react differently. They drop into the grass, crouch, and remain silent until the animal passes.

This emphasis on birds may overshadow the fact that mammals too have alarm notes. When a human approaches a fawn, the doe white-tailed deer, if nearby, reacts with a loud snort, the intent of which is unmistakable even to human ears. Squirrels are quite vocal and have a considerable repertoire of sound signals, including alarm. Six alarm signals have been recorded for the gray squirrel, each associated with a particular situation (Table 26-2).

Alarm substances. Some species of fish (confined to the order Ostariophysi) release alarm substances from the skin into the water and induce a fright reaction in other members of the same or related species (Pfeiffer, 1962). This substance is produced in specialized epidermal cells, which do not open on the

TABLE 26-2. CALLS OF THE GRAY SQUIRREL

CALLS	SEX	AGE	DESCRIPTION	ASSOCIATED WITH
ASSOCIATED WITH MATING CHASES				
Buzzing	Male	Yearling and adult	Stridulating insect or partly stifled sneeze	Hunting for or chasing the female during mating chase
ASSOCIATED WITH WARNING OR ALARM				
Intense alarm chuck	Both	All	Rapid kuk, kuk, kuk	Imminent danger
General alarm chuck	Both	All	Drawn out ku-u-uk ca, one per two seconds	Danger
Warning chuck	Both	All	Slower, short kuk, kuk, kuk, kuk; or kuk, kuk, kuk, qua-a-a-a	Immediate past danger; usually follows general alarm call
Attention chuck	Female	Adult	Low chucking barely audible at 30 feet	Given to young as a warning (?) call
Juvenile scream	Both	Juvenile	Soprano scream; mouth at maximum gape	Handling in cone or removal from nest; probably signifies fear
Female scream	Female	Yearling and adult	Lower harsh scream, like combined scream and snarl	At males around her while cornered in mating chase (warning?)
ASSOCIATED WITH GROUPS				
Mew	Both	Adult and ?	Resembles meow of cat	?
Rapid clucking	Both	All ?	Kuk, kuk rolled together	Sometimes given before entering nest
Whistling	?	?	Resembles ground squirrel whistling	Sometimes given by occupants after nest is entered
Purr	Both	Young	Low purring like a cat	Play

From Bakken, 1959.

surface; they can release their contents only when the skin is broken. Fish in the vicinity receive the stimulus through the olfactory organs. Only minute quantities are needed to drive a school of minnows from a feeding area (0.002 milligrams in a 14-liter aquarium). The fright reaction is innate. Regardless of prior experience, fish exhibit this reaction only at a certain age—some time after the alarm substances are produced in the skin. Fright reaction, which may be transferred visually to individuals not exposed to the substance, affords a two-fold protection. It protects schools of young from cannibalistic attacks of adults, since once they break the skin of the young, the would-be cannibals are frightened away by the alarm substance, and it shields older fish from general predation. Fish possessing this alarm substance are mostly social, lack defensive structures such as spines, and generally are nonpredaceous.

Detection by echolocation. Bats, as it has already been pointed out, detect obstacles and prey in complete darkness by echolocation. Several families of moths, a chief prey item of the bat, have evolved countermeasures enabling them to detect the bats. The Noctuidae, or owlet moths, in particular have a pair of ultrasonic ears located near the "waist" between the thorax and the abdomen (Roeder and Treat, 1961). Internal to the eardrum—a tympanum membrane directed obliquely backward and outward in a cavity of the body—is an air-filled cavity spanned by a thin strand of tissue. This contains a sound-detection apparatus of two acoustic sensory cells that eventually connect to the central nervous system by the way of the tympanic nerve. These ears respond to tones from 3 to 100 kilocycles, but they are most sensitive near the middle range, the frequencies contained in the bat chirps. Acoustic stimulation of the moth ear by bat chirps releases erratic flight patterns in the moth, which appear to be highly effective in saving the moth. For every 100 moths that survived because they reacted to the bat chirps, only 60 nonreacting moths survived. This gives the reactors a very high survival rate over the nonreactors, which certainly must influence natural selection in favor of bat detection.

Distraction displays. When danger threatens the nest or young of birds, the adult may attempt to draw the attention of the intruder to itself. To do this some simulate injury. For this reason, such behavior has been termed injury feigning, although the pretense of being crippled is hardly a conscious one.

A predator near a nest releases in many birds, particularly the ground nesters, a distraction display in which the parent flutters along the ground, always keeping just one jump ahead of the enemy. If the predator follows, the bird continues the act until the predator is no longer near the nest. If the enemy remains, the stimulus is increased, and the bird returns to repeat the display until the response tires. When disturbed at the nest, the female grasshopper sparrow, for example, may dart off the nest, run for a short distance, arise in a short fluttering flight, then drop to the ground again where she spreads her tail and trails her wings, as if injured. At other times she may flutter off the nest as if crippled; or she may fly from the nest to a point 25 or 30 feet away, hide in the grass, and scold (Smith, 1963).

Distraction displays, like other behavior, vary from low to **high intensity**. Low-intensity distraction display is elicited in the golden plover when an enemy approaches. The bird holds the head high in alarm and may engage in displacement feeding (Drury, 1961). As the predator or man moves closer, the bird may run with head up, back ruffled, tail barely fanned and tilted, and cry an alarm. Occasionally it stops, stands up, and perhaps goes through displacement feeding again; or the bird may move diagonally to the side, crouched with both wings and tail partly spread. When near the intruder, the plover may stop, stand, and call. At high intensity the bird is hunched with its breast on the ground and it stamps its feet. The tail is often fanned, the head pulled in, the wings partly open and spread to resemble a threatening owl. If pursued, the plover runs off, crouching, with its wings open and down at the sides, with the tail partly fanned and held down, and beating and shuffling as if on four legs, creating an illusion of a four-footed animal. As the bird flees, it looks over its shoulder to watch the intruder.

The basic pattern of distraction displays among birds is similar, but there are some species-specific or at least generic-specific differences (Drury, 1961). The display of the black-bellied plover, closely related to the golden, differs in that at low intensity the bird frequently settles down with a fast squirming into a depression, as if settling on eggs, and it does not engage in a "rodent run" when pursued. Instead the black-bellied plover runs low, rolling from side to side, with tail spread and wings slightly lowered but folded. At high intensity the black-bellied plover is prostrate, with its breast on the ground in a hollow, its tail cocked and fanned, its wings almost fully spread and beaten spasmodically. In contrast the distraction displays of the *Charadrius* plovers, including the ringed plover, little ringed plover, killdeer, and piping plover, involve wiggling along the ground, leaning on one side, and waving one or both wings in an uncoordinated manner. Distraction displays are not as highly developed among sandpipers, and the parent bird sits closer on the nest.

Distraction displays are quite interesting, for they do not appear as an expression of thwarted drives (Simmons, 1955; Drury, 1961). The postures are not solely an expression of conflict between attack and escape; aggression is a strong motivation. Distraction displays, like those of courtship, have become highly ritualized. Although there are variations in intensity, each stage grades uniformly into the other. As the drives of aggression, flight, brooding, fear, and concealment increase and decrease, the bird's behavior changes. Movement elicits fleeing, but it is a deliberate, slow, shuffling, flopping movement, which keeps the bird just ahead of the pursuer. All movements attract attention to the parent, who leads the intruder away. The movements have become ritualized and removed from their original context, including perhaps even the motivation. Compared with courtship, distraction displays are highly generalized, since here the "object" is to attract the attention of the predator. Strong interspecific differences would have no selective advantage and bear no relationship to the isolation of one species from another.

Threat. Threat rather than flight is used against some intruders and is probably more widely used among mammals than birds. Birds may use against their enemy the same or similar aggressive threats that they use against members of their own species (see Chap. 27). Distraction displays may grade into aggressive displays. The killdeer, for example, may run toward such intruders as a cow or a horse, fluff its feathers, trail its wings, then fly up and strike the animal in the face. Other birds, such as the owls, may remain on the nest, raise or spread the wings, and snap the bill. Some reptiles snap and hiss at intruders. Mammals become highly aggressive and lower the head, utter snorts or growls, snarl, bare the fangs, and so on. Other animals may change color, as do some fish, or increase in size, as do some frogs, toads, and snakes, in an attempt to intimidate the enemy.

Attack. When threat fails, attack may do the job. Active defense, especially of the young, is most highly developed among the mammals. Usually it is the function of the female, but in some species, such as the buffalo, the musk-ox, and wolves, defensive attack is also highly developed among the males. Crocodiles vigorously protect eggs and young. Owls and hawks may directly attack intruders at the nest, and kingbirds are highly successful at routing cats from their territory. Small birds have a tendency to gang up on or mob an owl, hawk, snake, or even a cat. A warning call from a bird who has discovered some common enemy is sufficient to bring many birds to the scene, to fly about and scold the animal. Gulls, terns, and some shore birds will in the manner of small birds heckle the intruder, dive at it, and spray it with excrement.

Other means. Some animals assume a passive defense against predators and feign death. Such behavior is well known in the opossum and some species of snakes. Birds may crouch and hide at the approach of an enemy, small mammals may quickly take shelter. Squirrels are particularly adept at keeping a tree trunk between themselves and a hunter.

SUMMARY

Survival is a chief preoccupation of an animal. To escape or defend itself from its enemies may be one of the more dramatic situations associated with the word survival. But the animal's ordinary day by day quest for food and shelter and its care for bodily comfort are just as important for the survival of an animal as escaping its enemies. Thus a good share of an animal's behavioral activities are directed toward its own welfare. Many of the egocentric behavior patterns are simple and relatively stereotyped. But with experience some individuals become more skilled than others at certain activities, such as hunting. Habitat selection too is fairly stereotyped, but animals recognize suitable areas for colonization more by general features than by plant composition. Although feeding, shelter-seeking, and maintenance behavior may in some ways be species-specific, escape reactions—the alarms, the threat postures, defensive attitudes, and flight—are so generalized that the behavior patterns of one species are recognized by many others. While escape and defense behavior of an individual may be largely directed toward its own survival, it also spreads the alarm to others. Involved is sort of a communication and relationship with other individuals that places escape and defense behavior one step beyond the egocentric and into the realm of social behavior. In fact, certain social behavior patterns of some species may be adaptations to reduce their vulnerability to predations.

CHAPTER **27**

Social behavior

Animals are social beings. The bird flocks of fall and winter, schools of fish, and herds of grazing animals, all are evidence of this. Yet an aggregation is not the only expression of sociality in animals. In fact some groups, such as insects attracted to a light, are not social gatherings at all. For most of our animals, aggregations at the best are seasonal. In most species, individuals spend much of their lives apart from the rest of their own kind. But at some time or another, especially during the breeding season, even the most solitary animals seek out and, if possible, come in contact with others of the same species. The meeting is formalized; there is some sort of interaction among individuals. It may be the relationship between two rival males at a territorial boundary, between members of a breeding pair, or between parents and offspring. The interactions or joint activities among individuals of a species make up social behavior.

Agonistic behavior

Socialization, the development of social bonds between and among members of the same species, begins largely in the nest or den, first as a bond between young and parent, then between litter and brood mates. Later the bond between parent and young weakens, and the young show increased ability to recognize and distinguish among individuals of the species. At this stage, the animal begins to exhibit the most commonly observed social behavior patterns—agonistic or aggressive behavior. This is an important form of social behavior, for it regulates population density and is involved in courtship and reproductive behavior.

Agonistic behavior involves the motivations of attack and escape (Moynihan, 1955b). These are usually associated with territoriality and social hierarchy or dominance; and in these situations, hostile displays are most highly developed.

Agonistic behavior involves displays of threat, which seem to have evolved because they conferred upon the animal the ability to achieve certain advantages without having to fight for them or risk physical injury. As a result, a wide variety of hostile displays have developed, as well as associated morphological structures. The displays have become ritualized, that is, the movements or components of the display have become exaggerated to increase their efficiency as a signal.

The most common of all ritualized forms of hostility is the intimidation, or threat display, of which most higher animals possess more than one kind. The primary function of the intimidation display is to force the opponent to retreat or flee—in other words, to increase the actual and relative strengths of the opponent's escape drive. Such threat displays are not always successful, especially among territorial species. An outsider may threaten the owner of a territory—an aggressive opponent at any time—but seldom will cause him to flee. The threat display, however, may tend to cause the owner to hesitate before attacking or threatening back.

The reason is that threat display involves two drives activated simultaneously, attack and escape; and the elements of escape are present in many threat displays. The display itself may vary in intensity or exaggeration in the form of movement with the relative strengths of the two drives. The attack definitely is the stronger in most threat displays; in a few the escape drive may be the stronger, and in others the drives may be equal. In some instances, the latter condition may trigger redirection or displacement activities, such as grass pulling by the herring gull.

Threat displays have been derived from a number of sources, both hostile and nonhostile (Moynihan, 1955c). Of the hostile sources perhaps the most important are a whole series of unritualized intention movements indicating locomotion, retreat, or avoidance (Fig. 27-1). Others undoubtedly were attack

Figure 27-1 Unritualized intention movement of flight in the hermit thrush. (After Dilger, 1956.)

movements, such as pecking at the opponent, flying or charging at another, or actual fighting. Out of this has evolved those attack components—the color of bill or head, feather patterns, feather puffing, horns, bristling of body hair, and other morphological structures that emphasize the visual conspicuousness of threat displays.

It is not uncommon for one threat display to provoke a threat display in return, often the same one (Fig. 27-2). And among birds in particular some threat displays are "designed" to do just that. These are the so-called exemplary displays, as yet little studied. An example is the choking display of gulls, in which the bird or pair of birds lower the breast, bend the legs, point the head downward, and perform rhythmic jerking movements with the head as if they were going to peck at the ground (Moynihan, 1955a). During all this the bird may utter a deep call repeated almost in time with the jerking movement. This threat display usually induces a return choking display. A characteristic of this type of threat display is its infectiousness, for the display invariably causes all birds in the area to undertake identical performances and thus releases a communal suppression of attack of one bird upon another.

Some examples of agonistic display

Agonistic displays vary from species to species, but among families and genera of animals, a number of basic hostile displays appear, interspecific differences being a sort of "variations on a theme." Among passerine birds, in fact among most groups of birds, a common and perhaps universal aggressive posture is the head-forward threat (Fig. 27-3). The body is lowered to the horizontal, head and body are in line, and at the highest intensity, the bill is held open in a gape. Some species, such as the green finch (Andrew, 1961), the grasshopper sparrow (Smith, 1959), and the redpoll (Dilger, 1960), also vibrate their wings. Another display commonly given is bill raising (Fig. 27-3), in which the bill is raised and held well above the horizontal. It is probably derived from an upward flight intention movement and apparently serves as a distance-increasing display (Tinbergen, 1959).

Figure 27-2 *Threat display in underyearling Kamloops trout.* (Redrawn from Stringer and Hoar, 1955.)

Pectoral
sandpiper

Herring
gull

Hermit
thrush

Redpoll

Aggression
displays

Ring-necked
pheasant

Figure 27-3 Agonistic displays among birds. Note the general similarity. Pectoral sandpiper (after Hamilton, 1959); herring gull (based on photos in Tinbergen, 1953); hermit thrush (after Dilger, 1956); redpoll (after Dilger, 1960); ring-necked pheasant (after Collias and Taber, 1951).

Even mammals possess certain aggressive displays the features of which are possessed in common. The facial expressions of canids—the baring of fangs, the curling of the lips, the erection of the ears, and the movement of the tail—all indicate degrees of aggressiveness in dogs, foxes, and wolves (Fig. 27-4). The aggressive behavior of the black-tailed deer consists of three components (Cowan and Geist, 1961). One is the crouch, which involves hunching, partial flexing of the hind legs, shoulders, and elbow joints, all tending to lower the animal. The walk is slow, stiff, and stilted, with the head held in line with the body, the ears laid back. Other features are nose licking, circling, and the snort

515

Figure 27-4 *Aggressive expression and submissive expression in the American wolf, typical of canids.* (Suggested by illustration in Schenkel, 1948.)

(Fig. 27-5), and finally the rush. The most extreme display consists of lowering the head to bring the antlers into contact with the object of aggression. Similar threat displays are found in the moose (Geist, 1963) and the barren-ground caribou (Pruitt, 1960). In the head-low threat of the moose, the head and neck are in line, the head is lowered toward the ground, the hair on the neck, withers, and rump is raised, the ears are down. From this position, the moose will attack in a short, fast rush. In the agonistic display of the caribou, the muzzle is extended, the nose is curled, the ears are laid back, and the animal advances rapidly toward the antagonist.

Appeasement display

Appeasement displays, as one might expect, are almost as common as aggressive displays and are especially characteristic of encounters during the reproductive period. They serve to prevent attack without provoking escape, to reduce the strength of the opponent's attack drive, and to release other specific non-aggressive behavior (Moynihan, 1955b). Appeasement results when the escape drive is much stronger than the attack. Like aggressive patterns, appeasement displays have been derived from hostile sources, but patterns involve most strongly the intention movements of escape. Usually appeasement behavior consists of

Figure 27-5 *Details of the head of the black-tailed deer* (Odocoileus hemionus sitkensis) *during the "snort" that occurs when the buck is circling in the aggressive crouch position. Note the widely opened preorbital gland, curled upper lip, and bulged neck muscles. The snort is a sibilant expulsion of air through closed nostrils, causing them to vibrate.* (Redrawn from Cowan and Geist, 1961.)

withdrawal or avoidance movements, often specialized to hide offensive weapons, such as beaks, fangs, and any threat releasers. Appeasement displays, unlike intimidation, seldom have colors or structures evolved for this use alone.

A common appeasement display is the submissive pose, varying in appearance but still possessing some basic features in common (Fig. 27-6): among birds,

Appeasement displays

Herring gull

Figure 27-6 Appeasement display in some birds. Herring gull (based on photos and drawings in Tinbergen, 1953; Moynihan, 1955); redpoll (after Dilger, 1960); hermit thrush (after Dilger, 1956); ringnecked pheasant (after Collias and Taber, 1951).

Redpoll

Hermit thrush

Ring-necked pheasant

the lowered or indrawn head, the crouched position, the fluffing or ruffling of feathers; among canids, the ears laid back, the eyes looking down, the tail curled between the hind legs (Fig. 27-4); among rabbits, a crouched position with ears laid back, the head pulled in toward the body, and the tail depressed (Marsden and Holler, 1964). Some gulls, such as the black-headed gull, turn their heads away from the opponent (head flagging) to hide the threat stimulus

517

of the red bill and black face (Tinbergen and Moynihan, 1952). Occasionally appeasement displays may be superimposed on threat, and at times attack and escape may integrate, as they do in the "anxiety upright" of the gull (Fig. 27-6). Although basically a threat display, it seldom elicits more than a low escape drive in the opponent.

Sound and scent

Display also involves sound and scent. Song or other auditory effort is aggressive among many species of birds. It serves among territorial species as an announcement that a piece of ground has been claimed and warns males of the same species not to trespass. Territorial song is somewhat infectious, for when one male begins to sing, others in the area follow suit. The same song usually serves a dual role of attracting a potential mate and repelling rival males, but this is not always true. The grasshopper sparrow possesses two songs, a territorial, or grasshopper song, the familiar insectlike buzzing song of the species, and a more musical, sustained song, which serves to attract the female. The latter in its entire form consists of two parts, the grasshopper song, followed by a series of sustained trills. The first phase of the song is hostile, necessary in the early period of courtship when the warning function still is of prime importance, but the second phase—often sung alone—is not (Smith, 1959).

A similar situation possibly exists with the grasshopper sparrow's meadow associate, the meadow grasshopper, who possesses a two-phase song consisting of a series of ticks followed by a buzz. The ticking part of the song seems to be associated with the function of spacing individual males, and the buzzing phase attracts females (Alexander, 1960).

The chirps and songs of the crickets, cicadas, and grasshoppers, like the songs of birds, are associated either with attraction or repulsion. When sexually responsive male crickets are in close proximity, they frequently spar or fight with each other, using their antennas, forelegs, and mandibles, and kicking with their hind legs (Alexander, 1961). At the same time distinctive sounds are produced by the individuals, which affect the outcome of the encounter. Dominant males usually chirp more frequently after an encounter, while the loser rarely chirps after an encounter. After an encounter the dominant male may continue to chirp, the chirps merging into the calling song.

Mammals, too, have some vocalists whose calls are aggressive in function. The choral performances of the howler monkeys of the South American rain forest apparently are important in regulating territorial ranges (Carpenter, 1934). The ability to roar and bellow is a common secondary sexual characteristic among ungulates, seals, and walruses. The sounds, usually confined to the rutting season, are aggressive, a challenge to other males.

Scent too serves to mark territorial holdings and to warn other males to stay away. A number of mammals—the mustelids, the shrews, the deer—have well-developed scent glands. During aggressive posturing, the black-tailed deer opens fully the oriface of the postorbital scent gland (Fig. 27-5). Dogs and other canids have various scent posts (the familiar lamp post or fire hydrant) on which they advertise their presence. The short-tailed shrew may rub its abdominal scent gland along the wall of its tunnel to proclaim that the burrow is occupied (Pearson, 1946).

Aggressive behavior is most conspicuous among males during the breeding season, although it is not exclusively a male function. The female gray squirrel, for example, becomes highly aggressive during the nesting season and establishes a territory about the den tree, which she defends against all ages and both sexes (Bakken, 1959). The seasonal development of aggressive display is closely associated with hormonal secretions. Secretions of gonadotropins by the pituitary stimulates the growth of the gonads and the subsequent output of sex hormones. This, plus external stimuli, stimulates aggressive behavior. As the output of sex hormones declines, aggressive behavior too declines, although here also it is difficult to generalize. The decline of song among many birds, for example, is not related to hormones. Song may decline or even cease when a mate has been acquired (Nice, 1943).

Expression of aggressive behavior

Aggressive behavior is expressed most commonly as territoriality and social dominance (see also Chap. 21). Some species are exclusively territorial; some operate within a framework of social hierarchy; others are territorial during the reproductive season only and may exhibit social dominance during the remainder of the year.

Territoriality. Territories, of which there are a number of types, usually are defended by the males, occasionally by the females, by means of song, aggressive displays, and fighting.

Territoriality exists in many forms. Nice (1941) classified bird territories into six groups, useful for all vertebrates. Most common among songbirds is the mating, nesting, and feeding territory (Fig. 20-13). The males arrive a few days before the females, claim a territory, and defend it by song, display, and occasional fighting. After mating, the female may aid the male in the defense of the territory. The territorial defender usually is invincible on his own area. Late in the breeding season and after it, territorial defense breaks down. A second type is a mating and nesting territory with feeding done elsewhere. This is common among hawks and black-capped chickadees. Others utilize their territory for mating only. This is true of the woodcock and the ruffed grouse. The male woodcock maintains an open-country singing and mating territory separate from the feeding area, which is not defended. The male ruffed grouse defends only his drumming and display areas from other males. A few gallinaceous birds, as the prairie grouse, have elaborate display grounds, or leks, where they mate promiscuously with females that come to them. Some species defend a nesting site only. Colonial birds, such as the puffins, gannets, murres, and swallows, defend territories that are barely large enough to embrace the nest. Their size is determined by the distance the sitting bird can strike with its beak. In fact among cliff swallows, threat displays, song, and territorial fighting influence the form of the nest and the position of the opening (Emlen, 1952). Finally there are feeding (Fig. 27-7) and roosting territories commonly defended during the winter. A pair of coots defend a winter territory, which they enlarge into a breeding territory (Gullion, 1953). The plain titmouse, which remains paired for life, defends its territory throughout the year with no reduction in size during the winter (Dixon, 1949). There

519

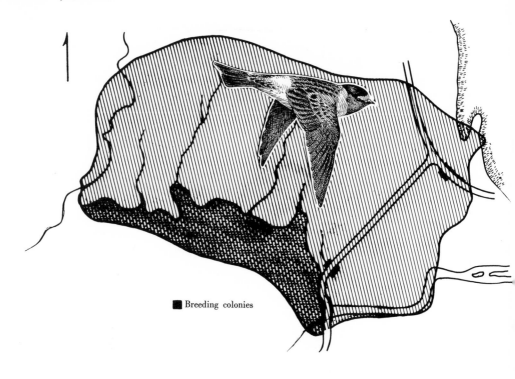

■ Breeding colonies

Figure 27-7   *The territory of such colonial nesters as the cliff swallow embraces only a small area about the nest. Several colonies use a common feeding area.* (After Emlen, 1952.)

are so many variations of territory that it is often difficult to classify them according to the types described. But they all have one feature in common, defense against competitors of the same species.

Defended areas may not be stationary. Canada and other geese maintain moving territories (Jenkins, 1944). These are definite defended areas, which move when the family groups move and are maintained in all types of activities throughout the year, except during the reproductive period. A similar type of territory is maintained by the male goose around the female.

Next to birds, territoriality is most highly developed among fish (Greenberg, 1947; Kallenberg, 1958; Winn, 1958; Gerking, 1959). The males of many species of darters defend a territory that includes reproductive and escape areas, but leave the territory to feed. The territories may be stationary or moving. Salmon maintain within their territories one strongly dominated local station, constant in position, to which the fish returns after a foray (Kallenberg, 1958). From this station the fish defends an irregular area, a poorly defined boundary. Territoriality among mammals is not so well defined. An outstanding example is the vicuna, a near relative of the llama, which lives in the high, treeless pastoral zone of the Andes. The male vicuna is the head of a band of females and young. He defends the area they occupy (Fig. 20-17) against other family males and is intolerant of all other males except the young of his own band (Koford, 1958). Muskrats also appear to defend a territory (Errington, 1937). The

Alaskan fur seal establishes territories on rocky shores prior to the arrival of the females. To hold and maintain these territories, males may have to go without food and water for days and live on accumulated body fat. After the bulls acquire harems, territorial defense wanes. The Uganda kob, one of the antelopes of the African savanna, defends a small, fixed territory of 20 to 60 yards in diameter within a central territorial area approximately 200 yards in diameter (Buechner, 1961). Within this central area are 12 to 15 territories; and this area is surrounded by a zone of more widely spaced territories. The territorial ground is situated on a ridge, knoll, or slightly raised area characterized by short grass, good visibility, and proximity to a permanent stream. Females enter the territorial ground through the year for the purpose of breeding. When disturbed by a lion, elephant, or something else, the kob deserts the territorial ground along an established route. Shortly after the disturbance is gone, the kob returns to its own territory.

Social dominance. Social dominance, which necessarily involves individual recognition of members of the group, usually is firmly fixed in some form of hierarchial arrangement. The simplest of these, first described by Schjelderup-Ebbe (1922) for the domestic chicken, is the straight-line peck order, so named because dominance was indicated by dominant birds pecking the subordinates. There is an alpha bird, which can peck all others, a beta individual, which can peck all but alpha, and finally an omega, which can peck no other (Fig. 27-8). Even within this scheme there are some complexities, common to most flocks, such as triangular hierarchies. These are triplets of individuals whose pair relations are such that the first individual is dominate to the second, the second is dominant over the third, and the third dominates the first. In such a situation an individual of a lower rank can "peck" an individual of higher rank. In some groups peck order is replaced by peck dominance, in which social rank is not absolutely fixed. Threats and pecks are dealt by both members during encounters, and the individual that pecks the most is regarded as the dominant. The position of the individual in the social hierarchy may be influenced by levels of male hormone, strength, size, weight, maturity, previous fighting experience,

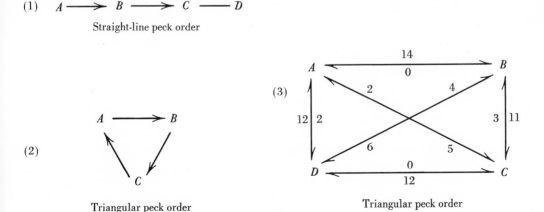

Figure 27-8   Some examples of peck orders.

previous social rank, injury and fatigue, close associates, and environmental conditions.

In flocks made up of both sexes, separate hierarchies may exist—a peck order of males, a peck order of females, and dominance of males over females. Such peck orders are characteristic of flocks of red crossbills (Tordoff, 1954) and ring-necked pheasants (Collias and Taber, 1951). The top-ranking male in a crossbill flock was the most aggressive male (Tables 27-1 and 27-2), yet the low-ranking male was most active in dominating the females, followed closely

TABLE 27-1.   PECK ORDER IN MALE RED CROSSBILLS, BASED ON 404 ENCOUNTERS

	DECEMBER 31–JANUARY 12 DOMINATES					JANUARY 14–MARCH 25 DOMINATES			
W	–	B	A	G	O	–	B	A	G	O
B		–	A	G	O		–	A	G	O
A			–	G	O			–	G	O
G	W			–	O				–	O
O					–					–

From Tordoff, 1954.

NOTE: Each table represents a different method of summarizing dominance in social groups. Table 27-1 is a qualitative summary. Table 27-2 is a quantitative summary showing the number of wins by one individual bird over others in the group.

TABLE 27-2.   SOCIAL HIERARCHY OF A MIXED GROUP OF CAGED MALE AND FEMALE HOUSE FINCHES IN WINTER

(Read from left to right in horizontal rows. The number indicates the number of wins by the bird in question.)

	R	L	GB	WG	GR	WP	Y	O
R♀		1	2	0	4	2	3	2
L♀			2	1	2	1	1	1
GB♀				7	7	4	6	10
WG♀	2				6	8	8	5
GR♀				1		3	2	-5
WP♂							8	1
Y♂								3
O♂						9		

From Thompson, 1960.

by the top-ranking male. A similar situation existed in a flock of ring-necked pheasants in which the males dominated the females, who had their own peck order. But at the onset of the breeding season, the dominance of cock over hen declined. Dominance among white-tailed deer in a wintering yard in Wisconsin (Kabat et al., 1953) was one in which the adult bucks dominated other deer, and the does dominated the fawns. Within this scheme, the larger animals, whether buck, doe, or fawn, dominated the smaller animals. Wintering flocks of juncos exhibit no such dominance based on sex (Sabin, 1959). Females dominate the males in some species, such as the redstart (Ficken, 1963), while in other species, such as the snow goose (Jenkins, 1944) and jackdaws (Lorenz, 1931), the females appear to be equal to the male, especially where family ties are strong.

Once social hierarchies are well established within a group, newcomers and subdominant individuals rise in rank with great difficulty. Strangers attempting to join the group either are rejected or, as in the valley quail, are relegated to the bottom of the social order (Guhl and Allee, 1944). New birds in a wild covey remain a few yards behind the main group and do not mingle until after a period of acquaintanceship. Some individuals newly entering the flock then may rise rather rapidly up the hierarchy, while others remain unassimilated into the group. Several such individuals then may associate together and by coordinating their behavior maintain a mutual social rank against other members, as do some individuals in howler monkey society (Carpenter, 1934). Removal of the dominant individual or its injury causes a scramble for the alpha position. W. L. Thompson (1960) relates that an injured female house finch lost her alpha position because of her inability to move about and attack as readily as she was attacked, and thus she sank to the bottom of the hierarchy.

Rise in the hierarchy often is related to breeding and sexual activity and hormones. This is particularly true among those species that remain in flocks throughout the year. Breeding condition is important in determining social rank. Male house finches that occupied the bottom rung of the social ladder during the winter but came into breeding condition first rose near to the top of the hierarchy during the reproductive season (Thompson, 1960). The top male, however, was still dominated by his mate. Ring-necked pheasant cocks that occupied the dominant position in winter flocks usually were the first to crow and to establish individual territories in the spring. But subdominant males that came into breeding condition earlier rose higher in the hierarchy (Collias and Taber, 1951). Rise in hierarchy, then, appears to be related to a rise in male hormones.

Mating, too, improves the rank of lower individuals. Both members of a pair of house finches rise in hierarchy, but not always to the same level (Thompson, 1960). In the jackdaw, however, one member of the mated pair rises at the time of pair formation to the same level as the other member (Lorenz, 1931).

A rise in male hormone levels is not the only cause of increased aggressiveness. Shortages of food, space, and mates, among other things, will increase competition and hostility between individuals. The dominant individual has first choice of food, shelter, and space, and subdominant individuals may obtain less than the despots. When shortages are severe, the low-ranking individual may be forced to wait until all others have fed, to take the leavings, if any, to face starvation, or be forced to leave the area. The implications of the social hierarchy to population density are discussed in Chap. 20.

Intolerance and social dominance in the flock act as a spacing device, which affords each animal some measure of privacy, a situation somewhat akin to territoriality. This can best be observed, perhaps, by watching a flock of swallows settling on a telephone wire. Cliff swallows, for example, will so disperse themselves that one bird is approximately four inches away from its neighbor; any attempt by another bird to reduce this distance is met with a threat display (Emlen, 1952).

In fact social dominance intergrades with territoriality when distance between territorial centers of individuals influences the order of social dominance. This is nicely illustrated by the Stellar jay, in whose communities hierarchies exist throughout the year (Brown, 1963). A local population of color-banded Stellar jays that foraged in a public park was attracted to feeding stations on picnic tables. At a linear series of feeding stations the rank of a given individual decreased with an increasing distance from the nest area. Thus the dominance relationships of an individual jay can be visualized as a series of concentric zones of diminishing dominance from the center of its nesting area outward. Consequently, the dominance relationships with a population consist of many series of such concentric zones, each overlapping with others, rather than of discrete territories.

Cooperative social groups

Not all aggregations are based on social dominance. Some groups contrast sharply with those in which considerable intragroup conflict exists, and show no evidence of social rank among individuals. There exists a relatively strong group cooperation in intergroup aggressive situations.

The social structure in two animals, the harvester ant and the prairie dog, are excellent examples. Individual ants, possibly by imprinting, soon learn the odor of their own colony. Foraging ants returning to their own colony may stimulate some aggression on the part of their nest mates, but once the identity is clear, the ants are unmolested. But if an ant enters an alien colony, it is threatened, seized, dragged, and killed, for a strange taste or smell stimulates attack among ants in the colony. The colony acts as a unit; and conflicts between colonies may continue for days, leaving the ground littered with corpses.

Among vertebrates few social organizations are more fascinating than that of the prairie dog, aggregrations of which are known as prairie dog towns. Some towns are subdivided by topography or vegetation into wards, while further subdivisions reflect prairie dog behavior. Within each ward a group of prairie dogs is united into a cohesive, cooperative unit, known as a coterie, which defends a particular section of the ward against all trespassers (King, 1955). Territories of coteries, which cover less than an acre, may contain from two to some thirty members. Breeding coteries usually contain one male and three or four females; nonbreeding coteries may have all males, more males than females, or an equal number of both sexes. No social hierarchy exists, although one male, usually the most aggressive and the strongest defender of the territory, may dominate the rest. All coterie members use the same territory without conflict or the threat of it; and social relations among most members are friendly and intimate, involving grooming, play activities, vocalizations, and the identification kiss—a recognition display in which each individual turns its head and opens its mouth to permit contact with the other. A coterie emphasizes its social unity by the defensive action of its members against invasion, and by the inability of any member of the group to wander beyond the coterie territory without becoming involved in conflict (although members are ready to invade other coteries if the opportunity is present). The members of the coterie do not drive away the young; instead the young are protected against the antagonism of neighboring coteries. Overpopulation in a coterie may force territorial expansion, in which the defending male of the adjacent coterie is vanquished and driven out; or it may result in social unrest and the eventual emigration of yearlings. Adults may leave perhaps to escape the demands of the pup or to seek more abundant food. Advantages of living in such a group are many, including a limited control over an area of the habitat, increased defense against predators, the prevention of overcrowding, results that can be achieved only by the combined activity of all individuals.

Prairie dogs exhibit little division of labor; but the most highly organized natural societies—those of ants, termites, and some bees and wasps—do. Insect societies can be regarded as families, for they arise from a family unit of parents— the males and the queens—and their offspring. The latter remain with the female and take over the task of nourishing additional young as well as caring for the mother, the queen. In such societies three basic roles exist, the males, the queens, and the workers, each characterized by differences in structure, appearance, and behavior. The male's sole role is the fertilization of the reproductive female, or queen. Having accomplished this the male either dies or leaves the group. The queen, usually large in size, lays eggs, from which other members of the group develop. The workers among the ants, bees, and wasps are sterile females; among the termites, workers may include males and females, both sterile. The workers, as the name implies, perform the duties of their complicated society. Ants and termites have additional castes, the soldiers, large and equipped with formidable mandibles, who defend the colony. These are males and females in the termites, males in the ants. Defense in bees and wasps, who lack a soldier caste, is a function of the worker. The individuals of these societies have no choice of their roles, and their basic behavior is innate. Individuals have no chance of survival if separated from the social group. Although organically separate, the individuals are inseparably bound to the colony by behavior and psysiology.

Social dominance and leadership

A wedge of geese flying across the blue sky of spring invariably raises the question of leadership in the mind of the observer. Common belief has it that the wedge is led by an old and experienced bird. This may not be quite true, but evidence seems to indicate that adult geese do lead the migratory flights with others following, although the leadership changes throughout the flight. Where leadership is expressed in groups, this probably is the most common type.

The problem of group leadership in the wild has hardly been investigated. True leadership, as the few studies on sheep, goats, and deer show, implies the ability of an animal to move out ahead of the group, which then follows without the use of force. Dominance is not involved; in most cases only by chance do dominant individuals also become the leaders. Among family groups of geese, the male is the guard and leader of the group, and intragroup despotism is rather weak. Only among certain ungulates, particularly the red deer of Europe (Darling, 1937) and the elk of North America (Altmann, 1956a,b) does true leadership appear to be vested in one individual; and in these species it is an old and experienced female. Each female has two or three followers, usually her own offspring of past years, their young, and her own young of the year. Her supremacy is never challenged and she is succeeded only after death or after she ceases to drop a fawn each year. Below the leader is a well-defined peck order, in which the next in rank usually brings up and guards the rear of the herd.

525

This is a matriarchal society, extremely cohesive and gregarious. It probably arises from maternal care and the dependence of the young upon the mother for several years. The young run to the mother and are rewarded by being allowed to nurse; they also rush to her side when danger threatens. The young then are habituated to follow the mother; since the older females have the greatest number of young, they are the natural leaders behind which the rest of the herd moves. During the season of rut, the stag of the red deer and the bull of the elk break into the matriarchal herd and establish a harem. The real leadership still rests with the female, especially in the time of danger, when the stag of the red deer may just as often as not retreat until danger is past (Darling, 1937). The male's interest in the herd is strictly egocentric.

Courtship and reproductive behavior

In the bright cold sunlight of a late winter day a flock of mallards is active on the open water of a pond. Suddenly some rear up out of the water, and some appear to be charging at others. Closer observation reveals a pattern to the activity. A number of green-headed males are swimming with their heads drawn in, the feathers ruffled, the body shaking repeatedly (Fig. 27-9). As the tension increases, a few of the drakes rear up out of the water and flick their heads forward. On occasions a drake rears up, arches his head forward, and rakes his bill across the water (Fig. 27-9). Then with his bill pressed to his breast, he slowly sinks back to the water. At times this display may be accompanied by a low courtship call or followed by still another display, in which the male throws his head back in an arched position and jerks it abruptly upward. As the drake turns toward the female, he erects and spreads the tail feathers vertically and lifts the wing coverts to exposé the irridescent metallic purple speculum (Fig. 27-9). Then the drake lowers his head, stretches the head and neck forward just above the surface of the water (Fig. 27-9), and swims in rapid circles about the female. The female in turn is completely passive. The brown-feathered hens follow a mate or an intended one. With neck arched and head pointed toward the water, the hen moves her head back and forth from front to side away from the drake and toward the females (Fig. 27-9). Often this display is accompanied by short dashes of attack. This courtship display is typical of the mallard. Other surface ducks have similar behavior patterns, but with a number of variations, omissions, or additions to the repertoire.

The ducks represent the courtship behavior of a sexually dimorphic and polygamous group of animals. A somewhat different pattern is common to animals holding territories and to those in which sexual dimorphism is lacking. The female is attracted to the male by song or some other type of sound production, as in birds, frogs, and some insects, or by appearance, as in the case of the three-spined stickleback. The male, in turn, sees an animal of the same species and reacts aggressively. If the intruder happens to be a male or an unreceptive female, the animal flees or threatens back. In the latter situation, a fight, even if a mock one, develops. If the intruder happens to be a receptive female, she remains. She may exhibit some hostility, but eventually she adopts a submissive pose, which tends to reduce or inhibit the male's aggressiveness. When the male's behavior becomes less aggressive, pair formation is accom-

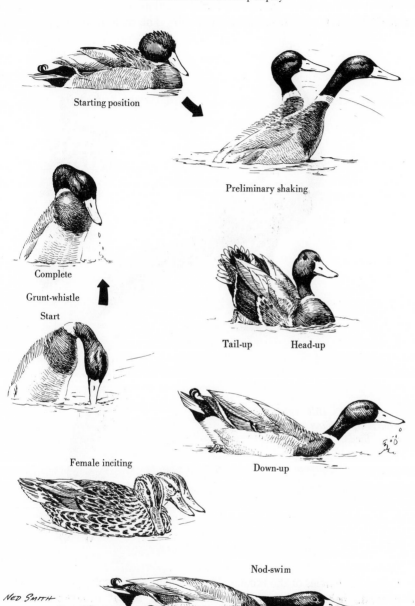

The Mallard duck courtship display

Starting position

Preliminary shaking

Complete

Grunt-whistle

Start

Tail-up   Head-up

Female inciting

Down-up

Nod-swim

NED SMITH

Figure 27-9   *Courtship display of the mallard. Some of these displays are common to many of the river ducks.*

plished. As time goes on, more generalized sexual elements enter courtship behavior. In contrast, the females of some species become more aggressive after pair formation and may dominate the male. The male's first reaction in courtship behavior then is to attack; the initial reaction of the female is to appease (escape) the male and elicit further courtship. The male in turn must suppress

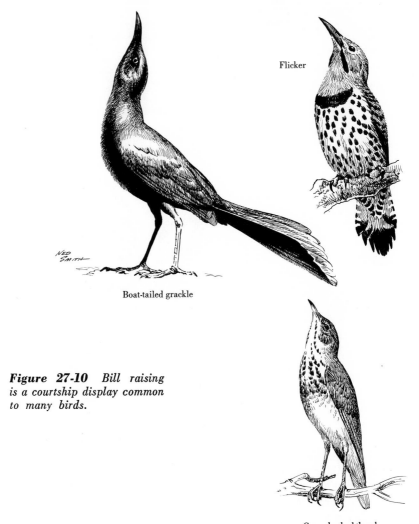

Flicker

Boat-tailed grackle

Figure 27-10 Bill raising is a courtship display common to many birds.

Gray-cheeked thrush

the escape tendencies of the female. Thus all courtship display contains elements of agonistic behavior (attack and escape) and sexual behavior. Progressive changes in the behavior of male and female toward each other depend in part on the stimulus situations presented by the partner: morphological, behavioral, vocal.

The function of courtship display is to attract the female to the male or vice versa. Once oriented to each other, neither may react to the partner's courtship until certain aggressive tendencies have been appeased or the reluctance of the male or female has been overcome. Later in courtship the behavior patterns are involved in the proper synchronization of the mating act, as exemplified by the courtship behavior of the queen butterfly (Fig. 25-2). Finally courtship displays serve to assure that males mate with the females of their own species and tend to reduce the error of mating with the wrong species. Thus the displays act as isolating mechanisms (see Chap. 24).

TABLE 27-3. COMPARISON OF PRESUMABLY HOMOLOGOUS BEHAVIOR PATTERNS IN THE MERGANSERS (*Mergus*) AND GOLDENEYES (*Bucephala*)

	BUFFLE HEAD	COMMON GOLDEN-EYE	BARROW'S GOLDEN-EYE	HOODED MER-GANSER	SMEW	RED-BREASTED MER-GANSER	COMMON MER-GANSER
MALE COURTSHIP							
Upward stretch	X	X	X	X	X	X	X
Wing flapping	**X**	X	X	X	X	X	X
Crest raising	**X**	X	X	**X**	X	X	X
Head throw	—	**X**	X	X	X	—	—
Tail cocking	—	—	—	X	X	X	X
FEMALE COURTSHIP							
Inciting	X	X	X	X	X	X	X
COPULATORY BEHAVIOR							
Drinking by ♂	?	X	X	X	X	X	X
Drinking by ♀	?	X	X	X	X	X	X
Female prone	X	X	X	X	X	X	X
Upward stretch (♂)	—	—	—	X	X	X	X
Preen dorsally (♂)	X	—	—	—	X	X	X
Water twitch (♂)	X	**X**	**X**	X	—	—	?
Preen behind wing (♂)	—	**X**	**X**	**X**	?	—	—
Steaming to ♀	—	**X**	**X**	X	—	—	—
Flick of wings (♂)	X	**X**	**X**	X	X	?	—
Steaming from ♀	—	X	X	X	—	—	—

X the behavior pattern was observed.
X the behavior pattern was exceptionally well developed.

From Johnsgard, 1961.

These functions, orientation, synchronization, persuasion, and appeasement, and reproductive isolation are achieved by species-specific signals or releasers. In fact the most highly developed specific signals and behavior have evolved around courtship, where errors would be most disadvantageous to the species.

Some basic patterns may be common or homologous to a group of animals (see Table 27-3). Among nine species of surface ducks (*Anas*) sympatric to western North America, eight possess many homologous displays (see Fig. 27-9), but there is a striking difference in male plumages. Some displays are almost universal among passerine birds: bill raising (Fig. 27-10), feather sleeking, feather raising, lowering the bill, vibrating the wing or wings (Andrew, 1961). Interspecific differences, so necessary to reduce the chance of interspecific pairings, set one species apart from the other. These include (1) differences in the color of the plumage, skin, or other body structures, (2) variations in display movements involving differences in relative strengths of the tendencies to attack, to flee from, or to behave sexually toward mates, (3) frequency in occurrence of the several behavior patterns and their intensity, and (4) the production of sound (Hinde, 1959).

In spite of this mistakes do occur and some groups, such as the ducks, are notorious hybridizers (Sibley, 1957; Johnsgard, 1960). This may be the result of two situations. One, common to the periphery of overlapping ranges, is the presence of a female in an area where males of her own species are relatively rare and males of a closely related species similar in appearance or voice are common (see Fig. 24-4). The female will seek a mate; but the longer she searches in vain, the lower becomes her threshold to respond, until eventually she reacts to suboptimum releasers, usually exhibited by a male of the next most closely related species. In the other situation, a female, because of a mutation or abnormal genetic recombination, reacts unspecifically to male signals.

In either circumstance the resultant hybrids are selected against. In the former situation, either the species is further restricted to ranges where conflicting stimuli do not exist or else male signal characters and the female responses to them are further refined away from the related species. In the latter situation the abnormal birds either would have offspring selected against or the male would be unable to attract a mate. Hybrids between prairie chickens and sharptailed grouse, for example, carry on mating displays that are a combination or blending of those of both species (Fig. 27-11) with curious results (see Ammann, 1957). The success that these hybrids have in attracting mates is unknown, but it is probably nil. In some areas of Ontario a high percentage, possibly 80 per cent, of the prairie chickens show varying degrees of sharptail characteristics. Some biologists suggest that perhaps such hybridization may be one reason for the rapid reduction of prairie chickens in areas where sharptails have become successfully established. If a prairie chicken hen mated with a sharptail cock and produced a brood of hybrids, the reproductive rate of the sharptails would not be reduced but the prairie chicken would suffer the loss of an entire brood.

In closely related sympatric species, strong sexual dimorphism is due in part to the female's choice of her own species, based on innate and learned responses. The males among ducks and prairie grouse, for example, will court the females of any species. Females, on the other hand, unless in some situation as discussed above, will mate only with males of their own species, distinguished by color pattern and display movements. Competition for mates also increases the development of signal characters, particularly among polygamous species in which the males with the most pronounced or effective releasers are the most successful in attracting a mate. In such instances the females choose the males for the development of secondary sexual characteristics. The same selective pressures that refined the signal characters of the male also influence the innate responses of the female. Thus the females may exhibit as much sexual dimorphism as the males, only it is invisible (Dilger and Johnsgard, 1959).

Source of courtship displays

Since many elements of agonistic behavior enter into courtship and since courtship is so closely related to other aspects of the animal's life, the fact that courtship displays have evolved from other behavior patterns is not surprising. Involved are intention movements, elements of aggressive behavior, ritualized

A

Figure 27-11 (A) *Prairie chicken in display.* (B) *Prairie chicken-sharptailed grouse hybrid displaying. Note the blending of the traits of the two parents in the hybrid.* (C) *Sharptail in courtship display.* (Photos courtesy Michigan Conservation Department.)

B

C

Figure 27-12 *Courtship display of the male red-winged blackbird and invitational display of the female.* (Drawn from photos in Nero, 1956.)

displacement or redirection activities, infantile behavior, and nest building. In fact among some species of birds, such as the wood thrush (Dilger, 1956) and the redstart (Ficken, 1963) there are no special displays associated solely with pair formation. All displays involved are agonistic and appear in other situations. The same is true in many mammals. The courtship display of the male caribou is simply a modified threat pose (Pruitt, 1960). The extended muzzle, the grunts and swift advance express to the does the vigor of the sexual drive in the buck. If the doe is not physiologically receptive, the buck's actions are "interpreted" as antagonistic, and the doe flees; if the doe is sexually receptive, the display fails to release flight.

Once pair formation—that period from the initial meeting of the male until a bond is formed—has been accomplished, other behavioral elements more sexual in nature appear. Male birds may fluff the feathers of the scapulars, rump, and head, spread the tail, drop and wave the wings, and bow (Figs. 27-12 and 27-13). These latter displays, so common among passerine birds in one form or another, probably are ritualized intention movements of flight, indicating either strong sexual tendencies to fly up and mount the female or tendencies to flee from the female. Common among paired gulls is headbobbing, regarded as solicitation, or precopulatory displays (Tinbergen, 1960).

Symbolic nesting and symbolic nest-site selection are common in courtship behavior of birds, from grebes and cormorants to songbirds. Symbolic nesting in-

Figure 27-13 *Invitational display of the king rail. This posture is assumed by a mated male upon the close approach of the female. The bird displays the tail and points the bill downward and slowly swings it from side to side.* (After Meanley, 1957.)

volves either the manipulation of nesting material by that member of the pair, usually the male, who does not ordinarily help in nest construction, or the unnecessary handling of nesting material by the other member (or both, if male and female together build the nest) prior to actual building.

Among some species, symbolic nest-site selection precedes symbolic building. The male red-winged blackbird crouches near the female, spreads his wings and sings, and then flies to a clump of cattails, to which he clings while holding the wings over his back (Nero, 1956a). If the female follows, he may slowly crawl through the cattails with his wings still partly spread. Then he stops, bows with his beak at his feet, breaks off bits of cattail blades and manipulates them as the female would in building a nest. Symbolic nest building probably represents the vestiges of a true nest-building behavior in a time when the male did assist in nest building. Its possible function is reassurance to the female, for it reappears at times when the female is disturbed during nest building or when the female sits on the nest only irregularly during the egg-laying period.

Begging food by the female and reciprocal feeding of the female by the male are part of the sexual behavior patterns of many species of birds. Begging on the part of the female is regarded as a kind of infantilism, the reappearance of her behavior as a chick. Herring gulls feed the female in response to the head toss, in appearance similar to the food begging of the young (Tinbergen, 1960). Terns present a fish to the female, an act that apparently serves in sex recognition. The female may beg several times before the male hands the fish to her, and she may then return it (Palmer, 1941). Only while incubating does the female accept the fish (Tinbergen, 1951). Marsh hawks toss prey to their mates in mid-air prior to incubation. Courtship feeding may serve to reduce or inhibit the aggressive behavior of the male and release sexual behavior, for courtship feeding often precedes or accompanies coition. It also may stimulate and maintain the pair bond. Ethologists still speculate on the origin of this ritualized feeding, but it appears most likely to have arisen in part from anticipatory feeding (described below under Parental Behavior), in which the male prematurely brings to the nest food intended for nestlings not yet hatched. Feeding on part of the male belongs to the parental behavior, which normally appears long after sexual behavior wanes.

Closely related to courtship feeding is the tidbitting behavior of male gallinaceous birds, among them the domestic chicken (Wood-Gush, 1955) and the chukar partridge (Stokes, 1961). The male makes incipient pecks toward the ground, especially at conspicuous objects, such as stones, food particles, and feathers, followed by the actual picking up of the objects. At the same time the male gives a tidbitting call to the female, which is similar to the food-finding call of both sexes to the young. During tidbitting the male holds his legs half bent, his body sloped downward from head to tail, his wings held tightly against the body. Early in the season the female may ignore his calls, but later she breaks off her own activity, runs to the male, and begins to peck at or to pick up the same objects. In a few seconds the male suddenly stands erect, moves off in a stiff-legged step to the rear of the female, and again tidbits. A series of such displays may be followed by coition. This irrelevant activity apparently has an appeasing effect on the hens, who avoid aggressively displaying males. The behavior apparently is ritualized from normal feeding behavior and may be derived from a displacement reaction performed while the cock is undergoing a conflict between sex, attack, or escape or when the sexual drive has been thwarted.

Thwarting of the sex impulse results in irrelevant activities in courtship in animals other than birds. Sexually activated males of the three-spined stickleback and the river bullhead fan their pectoral and caudal fins, movements used in the ventilation of eggs in the nest. These movements appear frequently while the male fish is courting the female that has entered his territory. Over and over the male may swim away from her to the nest he has prepared and do a series of fanning movements even though no eggs are present (van Iersel, 1953; Morris, 1954).

One of the functions of courtship is to release the sexual response in the partner through specific signals. The male stimulates the female and in turn the female stimulates the male. The courtship is mutual. When an animal, especially the male, is under strong sexual impulses yet cannot mate because the partner has not given the final signal to release the mating act, a conflict situation arises, which finds its outlet in irrelevant activities.

Some irrelevant activities act as releasers in courtship just as they do in aggressive behavior. The thwarting of the sexual drive in some birds results in preening, which in ducks has become ritualized. The movements or components have become exaggerated to increase their efficiency as a signal. Brightly colored structures, such as the blue wing speculum of the mallard duck, are so located that they are conspicuous during the ritualized displacement activity. The mandarin duck, related to the North American wood duck, strokes a specialized secondary feather, which is extremely broad and bright orange in color, in contrast to the normal, narrow, dark-green secondary feathers. By such ritualized preening the males call attention to the colored feather or feathers, thus making the movement more conspicuous and more species-specific. Ritualization of movements removes them further away from the original source; they become increasingly independent, which obscures the source or instinct from which they were borrowed.

Solicitation display

Once the pair bond has been established, the need for rather specific displays diminishes. As a result, the precopulatory or solicitation displays are rather generalized and highly stereotyped, the final signals prior to actual mating. Failure of either male or female to respond to solicitation results in thwarted courtship and often irrelevant activities.

Solicitation displays of female passerine birds (Fig. 27-12) include a horizontally crouched body, wing shivering, and elevation of the tail, often accompanied by a note or series of notes. Somewhat similar displays, particularly the crouched or squatting position, are also characteristic of other birds. These solicitation displays may vary in intensity. In the low-intensity, generalized display of female passerines—but among the blackbirds in particular—the wings are held out but not quivered and the tail is not elevated. This low-intensity display may be given upon the approach of a soliciting male or be given independently, in absence of the male. Such displays in the redstart often follow periods or bouts of nest building or after the male departs (Ficken, 1963). At high-intensity solicitation display, the tail is cocked at a greater angle, the body is tipped forward, and the display is often accompanied by solicitation notes. Solicitation usually does not appear in the female until the nest-building period, although this varies among species. Most displays prior to this time indicate weak sexual tendencies and are not accompanied by copulation. Actual mating cannot take place unless the drive of both male and female are approximately at the same level, and the responses of both rely closely on the interplay of internal drive and external stimuli.

Recognition of the mate is important to those animals which maintain a long pair bond, since it is toward the mate that aggression and timidity are reduced. Some birds, such as the gannet and penguin, the heron and pelican, have rather elaborate nest-relief ceremonies, which are given when one bird returns to relieve the other at the nest. These displays probably have an appeasement value as well as recognition.

Figure 27-14
*Courtship behavior
of the common newt.*

Among animals, such as the amphibians, which form no lasting pairs and which lack a long-term courtship, the precoital displays are rather intense and serve more to stimulate each member of the pair rather than to attract a mate (Fig. 27-14). Some species of mole salamanders (Ambystomidae) participate in a sort of nuptial dance involving large numbers of individuals, the purpose of which seems to be to stimulate the sexes for the mating activities that follow. The males deposit stump-shaped structures of jelly surmounted by a cap of sperm, the spermatophores, which are picked up by the female with the lips of her cloaca. In some species the male may grasp the female, holding her in firm embrace for a while, after which the two separate, the male to deposit the spermatophore and the female to retrieve it (Fig. 27-14). The behavior of the woodland salamanders (Plethodontidae) includes a series of preliminary movements during which the male rubs his lips, cheeks, mental gland, or side of body on the snout of the female to arouse her (Noble and Brady, 1930). Later the female in a "tail walk" follows the male, keeping her chin closely pressed against the base of his tail until she picks up the spermatophore.

The role of voice in courtship

Courtship among animals is often characterized by a vocal performance, which may or may not accompany display. Birds and frogs make the most conspicuous use of voice in courtship, although voice is widespread through the animal kingdom. Songs, calls, and other notes may serve to attract females to males or vice versa, to maintain the pair bond, and to stimulate each member of the pair.

Most familiar of all are the songs of birds. These are any vocalizations that when given by one bird repel rivals and attract the opposite sex of the same species, or both (Smith, 1959; Moynihan, 1962). Song in many species serves a dual function and is essentially hostile in nature. When a female invades the territory of a male, she is greeted in a hostile manner. Some species, such as the chickadee (Odum, 1941) and the grasshopper sparrow (Smith, 1959), have songs that serve primarily to attract the female. Females of some species also possess a song or call that attracts the male. The female grasshopper sparrow possesses a trill, which she sings independently of any vocalization of the male but which is answered by the male either by his own sustained mating song or by flying to her. Recent studies in sound production by fish reveal that even these animals possess some form of vocalization used in courtship. Male satinfin shiners "knock" aggressively when a female enters their territory (Winn and Stout, 1960). If the female remains, the male swims quickly to the potential egg site and vibrates his body. If the female is ready to spawn, she will follow him to the nesting site. Frogs and toads are the most vocal of amphibians, and the pools and roadside ditches of spring resound with their calls. Calling in anurans is restricted largely to males and indicates that they are sexually receptive. The calls play a significant role in the formation of breeding aggregations and in the attraction of receptive females and sexually aroused males to breeding pools. Once on the spawning site, the frogs respond to a complex of auditory, visual, and tactile stimuli, depending upon the species. Calls in the singing insects, the grasshoppers, crickets, and cicadas, attract sexually responsive females and in some species stimulate the congregation of males and females. Thus vocalization plays an important role in bringing male and female of the same species together.

Once male and female are near each other, vocalizations serve as sexual recognition. Birds, frogs, and singing insects are able to discriminate between the calls of males of their own species and those of others. That both wide and subtle differences exist between songs is readily apparent from spectrographs of the songs. These differences are important in maintaining reproductive isolation and in enabling close-range orientation of male to female, especially where a number of similar species assemble on a common breeding site, as do the frogs and toads. This discrimination is reinforced by other isolating mechanisms involving visual and tactile cues, as well as the animals' spatial distribution on the breeding area. Depending upon the species, male frogs call from perches at various elevations above ground, on the ground, in exposed or sheltered situations, away from the water, or floating in the water.

Vocalizations play an important role in the stimulation of the sexes during mating activities. Females of many species of birds give a solicitation call or note that releases copulatory behavior in the male. Males of some species, notably the blackbirds, likewise possess solicitation notes that indicate their readiness to mate (Nero, 1960). These calls are almost always given by grackles during the solicitation display (Selander and Giller, 1961). When sexually responsive male and female crickets and cicadas are at close range, the male produces specialized courtship sounds, which stimulate the female to move forward and walk up the back of the male into position to receive the spermatophore (Alexander, 1960, 1961). During courtship display the male cod grunts to stimulate the female to display and to swim upward and spawn (Brawn, 1961); and the male satinfin shiner emits a purring sound while he courts the female prior to spawning (Winn and Stout, 1960).

Proper orientation of male to female often is a necessary stimulus to release mating behavior. Under ordinary conditions the stimulus necessary to release copulatory behavior in the male chukar partridge is the sight of a fully crouched female facing away from him. The female may initiate proper orientation by turning away from the male, or the male may move around until he is behind the female. And the female by turning so that the male is no longer behind her can disrupt the male's intentions (Stokes, 1961). A male field cricket, encountering a female face to face, quickly reverses his position and changes his stridulation to courtship sounds, accompanied by a rocking and swaying of his body (Alexander, 1961). This behavior is necessary to induce the female to mount the back of the male, from which position the female picks up the spermatophore released by the male. If the female withdraws upon contact, the male again gives the courtship sounds and initiates distinctive movements with his posterior end directed toward the female's head. If her withdrawal is more pronounced, the male may stop courting, turn around to face the female, and start the preliminaries all over again. If the female leaves, the males of some species will give calls or chirps similar to those produced in aggressive encounters with males.

Communal courtship and harems

Most courtship involves sequences of behavior patterns between single males and single females. But there are species in which courtship is a communal affair. The animals congregate in a special courting area, sexual relations are promiscuous and usually dominated by only a few of the many males present; and the courtship activity tends to have stimulatory effect upon the whole group. The latter effect is not confined to this type of situation alone, since courtship and other social activities of such colonial animals as herring gulls, terns, and herons have a stimulatory effect on the whole colony. Even in the congregations of frogs and insects, the singing of one male stimulates the others to vocalize.

Communal display is especially well developed in some species of grouse, notably the black grouse of the Scottish Highlands and the prairie and sage grouse of North America. Early in spring the prairie and sage grouse congregate on their strutting grounds, or leks—called booming grounds for prairie chickens, dancing or parade grounds for the sharptail grouse, and strutting grounds for the sage grouse. The leks are located on areas of open ground, somewhat elevated and so situated that they are visible to the surrounding area. The cocks gather early in the morning and at daybreak the performances begin (for detailed descriptions of the actual performances of each of the three species see Schwartz, 1944; Hamerstrom, 1939; Scott, 1942, 1950). Early in the season there is much strutting and challenging with accompanying display, inflation and expellation of air from the air sacs to produce the hooting and booming sound so characteristic of each species, and fighting. Out of this the males acquire locations on the leks and determine dominance. Each dominant bird—the master cock and the most active, aggressive, and vigorous males—has his own accustomed place on the lek, which he must continue to defend from rivals. When the hens arrive, strutting and display by the cocks is most intense, as each endeavors to attract the females to his mating area. Receptive hens wander into the area held by the master cock of their choice.

The master cock of the prairie grouse has two or three subdominant cocks associated with him on the mating area. Except for this master cock, no hierarchy exists and the master cock must ward off his rivals alone. The subcocks and others may gang up on the master cock and steal matings with the hens, especially in the latter part of the mating period when the number of females visiting the leks decreases. The sage grouse master cock, on the other hand, is accompanied by a subcock and several guard cocks who ward off outsiders attempting to break into the mating circle. Nearly 74 per cent of all sage grouse matings are accomplished by the master cock, and he may mate with up to 21 birds per morning. When the master cock is satiated, the subcock and later the guard cock may steal some matings. Other males leave the general area to strut and display before the departing females. Among the prairie and sage grouse, the unsuccessful males are for all practical purposes psychological castrates.

A somewhat similar behavior exists among some mammals, in particular the fur, gray, and elephant seals. Dominant males establish territories, which they must constantly defend. Within these territories they rule over harems of females. In the harem of the elephant seal there is a hierarchy of dominance among the females; females of low dominance often are forced to move by females of higher dominance (Bartholomew and Collias, 1962). Elk too have harems, but the bull does not collect a group of females, instead he joins an existing group of cows, a group that also includes calves, yearlings, and extra juvenile males, whom he tolerates to some extent (Altmann, 1956).

Parental behavior

Courtship and mating in animals inevitably result in the production of young; and in anticipation of the arrival of offspring, behavior gradually becomes orientated toward the care and protection of young. Nest, den, or lodge building among many animals precedes the laying of eggs or the birth of young. The hatching of eggs and birth of young induce behavioral changes appropriate to the care of young, basically those of defense and nourishment.

The degree of parental care given to the young varies widely in the animal kingdom. In a general way the greater the degree of care given to the offspring, the lower is the fecundity of the species. Those invertebrates in which brood protection is highly developed lay relatively few eggs; and those that give the eggs no protection whatsoever produce eggs in the millions (see Thorson, 1950, for example). Parental care is not highly developed among most invertebrates. Some retain eggs within the body until they hatch; others carry the eggs externally. Invertebrate parental care is most highly developed in social ants, bees, and the hunting wasps. The social insects provide all five functions of parental care: defense, food, sanitation, heat, and guidance. Fish and amphibians either lay a few eggs and actively protect both these and the young; or they may lay many eggs and give them no care at all. Parental care is usually poorly developed among the amphibians, although a few salamanders remain with the eggs. Some frogs, notably the male midwife toad, carry the eggs and the subsequent young on their bodies and eventually place them in a suitable environment for further growth. Fish, likewise, may or may not care for the eggs. The cod lays its eggs in the open sea; the trout constructs a gravel nest to ensure proper protection and ventilation of the eggs, but gives no care to the young. Other species, especially those that have highly developed courtship and mating patterns, build a nest, defend and aerate the eggs, and protect the young. This behavior is typical in the sticklebacks and catfish. Internal fertilization and terrestrial reproduction is fully developed among the reptiles. Relatively few eggs well supplied with yolk may be carried inside the mother's body until they hatch; or they may be placed in nests buried in the ground and given little subsequent care. Crocodiles, however, actively defend the nest and later the young for a considerable period of time.

It is among the homotherms that parental care reaches its highest development and becomes universal. Parental care is most complex among birds, since the young are hatched outside the body. Care must start with the nest, carry through the incubation of eggs and brooding and feeding the young until they become independent. The female plays the major role in the care of eggs and young, but among some animals the males perform this function, while in others both sexes participate. All species defend the eggs, directly or indirectly, and many actively defend the young. Among the mammals, the mother plays the most significant role by carrying the young in the uterus until birth, by nourishing the young with milk, and providing them with heat, sanitation, and guidance after birth. The male may play no part in the care of the young, as in the seals and deer; he may defend them, as does the musk-ox; or he may share in other parental duties by supplying food, for example, as do the wolf and the fox.

Incubation behavior

Brooding or incubation behavior is that phase of parental activity that provides warmth and shelter for the eggs and young. As one would expect, it is best developed in birds. From the time of the laying of the last eggs, and in some species from the laying of the first, through to the independence of the young, incubation and brooding dominate all other behavior. Sexual behavior is suspended and even self-feeding, after the young have hatched, is reduced. The duration of the incubation period is influenced by a genetically fixed period of embryonic development and the length of time the young remain in the nest.

The start and continuation of incubation in birds and in those fish that tend the eggs are highly dependent upon nest and eggs, the sign stimuli that induce these animals to settle on the eggs. Effective incubation continues only when there is a proper feedback of the tactile and visual stimuli of the eggs and in some species (perhaps in the females of all) the thermoreceptors of the brood patch (Baerends, 1959). Fanning of eggs by the three-spined stickleback is released by the appearance and fertilization of the eggs. If the eggs are removed, the cycle is broken; at the same time the fanning drive inhibits sexual behavior (van Iersel, 1953).

Interruptions, disturbances, and the lack of proper "releasers" during incubation result in conflict situations and subsequent displacement activities. Building and preening behavior among gulls and terns appear when the number of eggs in the nest is insufficient, when the eggs are abnormal in size and shape, when

539

the temperature is too high or too low, or when the position of the eggs is incompatible with the favorite direction for sitting in the nest (Baerends, 1959). Displacement building and preening are most frequent when resettling or reshifting on the eggs fails to improve the situation, or some disturbance takes place. Building and preening often appear at the same time, but one usually is predominant over the other. Preening is the dominant activity if the bird is reluctant to return to the nest and shows a tendency to escape. If building is dominant, the bird usually returns quickly to the nest. Both patterns appear when the bird, because of the opposing influences of the presence and disturbance of the clutch, is influenced at once to flee and to stay. The ratio of these two drives then determines which of the two, building or preening, appears.

Care and concern for the eggs increase as the incubation period progresses. Birds tend to desert nests less frequently after a disturbance as the time for hatching approaches. Ground-nesting birds, especially geese, gulls, and terns, tend to retrieve any eggs accidently kicked from the nest, although it may take some time for the bird to respond to the egg-out-of-nest stimulus (Tinbergen, 1960). Then the bird rolls or attempts to roll the egg with its bill back into the nest. A broken or pecked egg does not release retrieval; rather the bird may eat the egg. No longer a normal shape, the egg has become instead a bit of food. The three-spined stickleback, too, will retrieve eggs that happen to lie outside the nest (van Iersel, 1953). These the male sucks up and inserts back into the nest, but only if the clump of eggs is large enough, at least five or six. Single eggs are eaten. The male also removes or attempts to remove eggs that have become moldy.

The eggs are seldom left unattended among those birds in which both sexes incubate. As one bird arrives to relieve the other at the nest, one of several actions may happen. The signs or signals of broodiness in the mate may stimulate the sitting bird to rise from the nest and allow the other to take over. On the other hand, nest relief may arrive before the sitter is prepared to go. In this case the relief bird, unable to satisfy its brooding urge, may perform some irrelevant activity such as nest building. This activity seems to stimulate the sitting bird to rise. But if all else fails, the relief bird may force the sitter off the nest. Some birds, the herons for example, have a ritualized nest-relief ceremony; others may announce their approach with a call.

Care of young

The hatching or birth of young ushers in another phase of parental behavior, the care of young. The extent and kind of care given to the young is influenced by the maturity of the young at the time of birth. Basically, birds and mammals are either precocial or altricial at birth. Precocial animals are able to move about at or shortly after birth, although some time may elapse before they can fly or move about as adults. Altricial animals are born helpless, naked or nearly so, often blind and deaf. Between the two extremes there is a rather wide variation in the stage and nature of maturity at birth.

Mrs. M. M. Nice (1962) has classified the maturity at hatching in birds (Table 27-4). Precocial and semiprecocial birds, hatched with eyes open and completely covered with down, are mobile to some degree and leave the nest in a day or so. Most precocial birds are capable of feeding themselves on small invertebrates and seeds; others follow the parents and respond to their food calls; still others are fed by the parents. Semiprecocial birds are able to walk, but because of feeding habits of the parents, they are forced to remain in the nest. Semialtricial birds are hatched with a substantial covering of down and with eyes open or closed, but are unable to leave the nest. Altricial birds are completely helpless; their eyes are closed and they have little or no down.

TABLE 27-4. CLASSIFICATION OF MATURITY AT HATCHING IN BIRDS

FEED SELVES

PRECOCIALS—eyes open, down-covered, leave nest first day or two

Precocials 1. Independent of parents—e.g., megapodes

Precocials 2. Follow parents but find own food—e.g., ducks, shorebirds

Precocials 3. Follow parents and are shown food—e.g., quail, chickens

FED BY PARENTS

Precocials 4. Follow parents and are fed by them—e.g., grebes, rails

SEMIPRECOCIALS—eyes open, down-covered, stay at nest though able to walk—e.g., gulls, terns

SEMIALTRICIALS—down-covered, unable to leave nest

Semialtricials 1. Eyes open—e.g., herons, hawks

Semialtricials 2. Eyes closed—e.g., owls

ALTRICIALS—eyes closed, little or no down, unable to leave nest—e.g., passerines

---

From Nice, 1962.

A somewhat similar classification could be devised for mammals. Young mice, bats, and rabbits are born blind and naked and thus are altricial. The young of wolves, foxes, dogs, and cats are born with hair and are soon able to crawl about the nest or den, but are blind for several days. These might be called semialtricial. Deer, moose, and other ungulates, as well as horses and pigs, would fall into the semiprecocial category. They are very ungainly on their legs for several days after birth, and during this time they establish a nursing routine. They may be hidden alone by the mother or held in a "pool," characteristic of the elk (Altmann, 1960). The young wait for the dam to return to the hiding place to nurse and to be licked. The most precocial of all mammals are the seals, which might well be a "precocial 4" according to the classification in Table 27-4. Not only is delivery extremely rapid, approximately 45 seconds in the gray seal (Bartholomew, 1959), but movements and vocalization appear very shortly after birth. Newly born fur seals are able to stand up and call from 15 to 45 seconds after birth and are capable of shaky but effective locomotion a few minutes after birth (Bartholomew, 1959). Even while the umbilical cord is still attached, the pups are able to shake off water, bite and nip at each other, and scratch dog-fashion with the hind flippers. They attempt to nurse within five minutes after birth. Although the pups continue to nurse the cows for some time, the cows are protective and attentive toward their young only between parturition and oestrus. Thus this behavior is conspicuous only for a few hours to a day after the cow has given birth to the pup.

As a rule parental behavior is not well developed in the poikilotherms, but care for young by the sticklebacks and chiclid fish deserves some comment. At hatching, the young sticklebacks have rather large yolk sacs from which they draw nourishment, and so they tend to remain embedded in or lying on the nest material. After a while the young, moving in a series of jumps, attempt to swim out of the nest. The male tries to catch the jumping and swimming young, chasing them, sucking them into his mouth, and spitting them back into the nest pit. But in most instances the male is unsuccessful (van Iersel, 1953). Young chiclid fish remain near their mother and for about six days return to the mouth of their mother for protection (Tinbergen, 1952).

Nourishment of the young is chiefly a function of the female among the mammals, for only she can provide milk. The males defend the young or ignore them. Among the canids, however, the males hunt and bring the prey to the den for the female and later for the female and young when the young have started on solid food. No such behavior exists among the cats.

Among those birds who must feed their young, both male and female participate whether the male assisted in the brooding or not. (There are exceptions, however, such as the hummingbirds.) Exactly how the male knows that the young have hatched when the female alone incubates the eggs is not really known, although changes in the female's behavior probably give the cue. In some species, such as the starling and the prairie warbler, the male may start bringing food to the nest several days to a week prior to the hatching of the young (Nolan, 1958). This is known as anticipatory feeding.

Providing sanitation, guidance, and heat are other parental functions. Brooding provides the necessary warmth for the young while altricial and semi-precocial mammals are sheltered in nests or dens; such precocials as the ungulates have temperature controls of their own from birth. Sanitation is no problem among precocial birds. Altricial birds usually deposit their wastes in fecal sacs, which are carried away by the parents. Mothers of some altricial mammals stimulate excretion in the young by licking their genital and anal regions and then swallowing the excreta.

Guidance by the parents of young who have left the nest and are beginning to acquire some independence occurs among few species of invertebrates other than the social insects, and among only a few species of amphibians, reptiles, or fish. The female caiman of Guiana keeps the young with her until the spring following their birth. Guidance, again, is best developed among birds and mammals. The female ducks, especially the river ducks, stay with the young until they can fly and set the rhythm for such activities as feeding, preening, and resting. The young of diving ducks do not fare so well, since the hen abandons them much earlier. The two- to three-week-old ducklings then band together and follow after the five- to six-week-old ducklings. Gallinaceous birds are highly dependent on parental guidance for food as well as warmth. Altricial birds also follow the parents for several weeks after they leave the nest (see Nice, 1943). Parental guidance is highly important among the ungulates. The young of moose and elk, for example, may follow the dam until they are yearlings (Altmann, 1960). A close bond exists between dam and calf and there is considerable vocal communication. The moose cow makes the calf stay within her sight and will retrieve it if it strays. If the dam is killed during the first year, the calf rarely survives the winter. In fact during the rut season a moose cow will leave with her calf at once if the bull intimidates the young animal. Young raccoons and skunks follow the mother on nightly forays, and young wolves join their parents in the hunt. Young gray squirrels follow the female for a while after they have left the nest, respond to her calls, and may even be groomed by her (Bakken, 1959).

A rather strong bond exists between the young of the same brood or litter. Ducklings seemingly need the companionship of their fellows and may do poorly without it. The attachment between members of a brood often outlasts their bond with the parent. A strong bond also exists in broods of gallinaceous birds, but among some shore birds the bond between siblings is not especially strong (Nice, 1962).

As the young mature into adults, the bond between parent and offspring breaks and agonistic behavior replaces it. This split between the young and the parents, more often than not, is initiated by the parents themselves. The moose cow becomes hostile to the yearling, especially the female offspring, whom the old cow regards as a rival. The yearling bull is tolerated, but if near his mother he becomes a target for the courting bull (Altmann, 1960).

SUMMARY

Sociality in animals implies more than the fact that animals stay together. The outstanding characteristic of social behavior is that animals do something together. Their activities are jointly timed and oriented, whether it be fighting between males, relationships between the breeding pair, or flocking. The accomplishment of such joint action requires a means of communication, a "language" between animals. This language may be visual, vocal, or chemical signals; but whatever the displays, the animals understand each other. These behavior patterns are associated with such activities as territoriality, social dominance, pair formation, suppression of agonistic responses between individuals, and the maintenance of reproductive isolation. It is to increase the latter that many of the major differences in display are believed to have evolved. But the distinctive social behavior of a species also may be influenced by the ecology of the animal—its food habits, its habitat, its avoidance of enemies. Whatever the species of animal, the full significance of its social behavior can be understood only by a thorough study of its ecology.

Bibliography

Abbot, B. C., and D. Ballantine
1957 The toxin from *Gymnodinium veneficum* Ballantine, *J. Marine Biol. Assoc. U. K.*, **36**: 169–189.

Adams, L.
1959 An analysis of a population of snowshoe hares in northwestern Montana, *Ecol. Monographs*, **29**:141–170.

Adkisson, P. L.
1964 Action of the photoperiod in controlling insect diapause, *Am. Naturalist*, **98**:357–374.

Ahlgren, I. F., and C. E. Ahlgren
1960 Ecological effects of forest fires, *Botan. Rev.*, **26**:483–533.

Alexander, R. D.
1960 Sound communication in Orthoptera and Cicadidae, in Lanyon and Tavolga (eds.), 1960, "Animal Sounds and Communication," pp. 38–96.
1961 Aggressiveness, territoriality and sexual behaviour in field crickets (Orthroptera Gryllidae), *Behaviour*, **17**:130–223.
1962 The role of behavioral study in cricket classification, *Systematic Zool.*, **11**:53–72.

Alexander, R. D., and T. E. Moore
1962 The evolutionary relationships of 17-year and 13-year Cicadas, and three new species (Homoptera, Cicadidae, Magicicada), *Museum Zool. Misc. Publ. Univ. Mich.*, **121**:1–59.

Allee, W. C.
1926 Measurements of environmental factors in the tropical rain forest of Panama, *Ecology*, **7**: 273–302.

Allee, W. C., A. E. Emerson, O. Park, T. Park, and K. P. Schmidt
1949 "Principles of Animal Ecology," Saunders, Philadelphia.

Allee, W. C., B. Greenberg, G. M. Rosenthal, and P. Frank
1948 Some effects of social organization on growth in the green sunfish *Lepomis cyanellas*, *J. Exp. Zool.*, **108**:1–19.

Allen, D. L.
1943 Michigan fox squirrel management, *Mich. Dept. Conserv. Game Div. Publ.* 100 (Lansing, Mich.), p. 404.

Allen, K. R.
1960 Effect of land development on stream bottom faunas, *Proc. New Zealand Ecol. Soc.*, **7**:20–31.

Altmann, Margaret
1952 Social behaviour of elk, *Cervus canadensis nelsoni*, in the Jackson Hole area of Wyoming, *Behaviour*, **4**:116–143.
1956a Patterns of social behavior in big game of the United States and Europe, *Trans. North Am. Wildlife Conf.*, **21**:538–545.

1956b Patterns of herd behavior in free-ranging elk of Wyoming, *Cervus canadensis nelsoni*, *Zoologica*, **41**:65–71.
1960 The role of juvenile elk and moose in the social dynamics of their species, *Zoologica*, **45**:35–40.

Amadon, D.
1947 Ecology and evolution of some Hawaiian birds, *Evolution*, **1**:63–68.
1950 The Hawaiian honey creepers (Aves, Drepanididae), *Bull. Am. Mus. Nat. Hist.*, **100**:397–451.
1959 Behavior and classification: some reflections, *Naturforschenden Gesellschaft* (Zurich), **104**:73–78.

Ammann, G. A.
1957 "The Prairie Grouse of Michigan," *Mich. Dept. Conserv.*, Lansing, Mich.

Anderson, C. C.
1958 The elk of Jackson Hole, *Wyoming Fish and Game Comm. Bull. No. 10* (Cheyenne, Wisc.).

Andrew, R. J.
1956 Normal and irrelevant toilet behaviour in *Emberiza*, *Supp. Brit. J. Animal Behaviour*, **4**: 85–91.
1961 The displays given by passerines in courtship and reproductive fighting: a review, *Ibis*, **103a**:315–348.

Andrewartha, H. G.
1961 "Introduction to the Study of Animal Populations," University of Chicago Press, Chicago.

Andrewartha, H. G., and L. C. Birch
1954 "The Distribution and Abundance of Animals," University of Chicago Press, Chicago.

Aschoff, J.
1958 Tierische Periodik unter dem Einfluss von Zeitgebern, *Z. F. Tierpsychol.*, **15**:1–30.
1962 Comparative physiology—Diurnal rhythms, *Ann. Rev. Physiol.*, **25**:581–601.
1965 Circadian rhythms in man, *Science*, **148**: 1427–1432.

Aschoff, J., and J. Meyer-Lohmann
1954 Angeborene 24-Stunden-Periodik beim Kucken, *Pfluegers Arch. Ges. Physiol.*, **260**: 170–176.

Aschoff, J., and R. Wever
1962 Spontanperiodik des Menschen bei Ausschluss aller Zeitgeber, *Naturwissenschaften*, **49**:337 ff.

Atkins, E. S.
1957 Light measurement in a study of white pine reproduction, *Can. Dept. Northern Affairs Nat. Resources, Forestry Branch, For. Res. Div. Tech. Note No.* 60.

Baer, Jean G.
1951 "Ecology of Animal Parasites," pp. 1–224, University of Illinois Press, Urbana, Ill.

Baerends, G. P.
1941 Fortpflanzungsverbalten und Orientierung der Grabwespe *Ammophila campestris, Jur. Tijd voor Entom.,* **84**:71–275.
1959 The ethological analysis of incubation behaviour, *Ibis,* **101**:357–368.

Baerends, G. P., and J. M. Baerends-van Roon
1950 An introduction to the study of the ethology of cichlid fishes, *Behaviour Suppl.,* **1**:7–242.

Bailey, R. E.
1952 The incubation patch of passerine birds, *Condor,* **54**:121–136.

Bakken, A.
1959 Behavior of gray squirrels, *Symp. Gray Squirrel Cont. 162, Maryland Dept. Res. Ed.,* pp. 393–407.

Ball, R. C., and F. F. Hooper
1963 Translocation of phosphorus in a trout stream ecosystem, in Schultz and Klement (eds.), 1963, "Radioecology," pp. 217–228.

Banfield, A. W. F.
1961 Migrating caribou, *Nat. Hist.,* **70**(5):57–62.

Bank, T. P. II
1953 Ecology of prehistoric Aleutian village sites, *Ecology,* **34**:246–264.

Barber, H. S.
1951 North American fireflies of the genus *Photuris, Smithsonian Inst. Misc. Collections,* **117**:1–58.

Barlow, J. P.
1955 Physical and biological processes determining the distribution of zooplankton in a tidal estuary, *Biol. Bull.,* **109**:211–225.
1956 Effect of wind on salinity distribution in an estuary, *J. Marine Res.,* **15**:193–203.

Bartholomew, G. A.
1959 Mother-young relations and the maturation of pup behaviour in the Alaskan fur seal, *Animal Behaviour,* **7**:163–171.

Bartholomew, G. A., and T. J. Cade
1957 Temperature regulation, hibernation and aestivation in the little pocket mouse *Perognathus longimembris, J. Mammal.,* **38**:60–72.

Bartholomew, G. A., and N. E. Collias
1962 The role of vocalization in the social behaviour of the northern elephant seal, *Animal Behaviour,* **10**:7–14.

Bartholomew, G. A., T. R. Howell, and T. J. Cade
1959 Torpidity in the white-throated swift, Anna humming-bird, and poor-will, *Condor,* **59**:145–155.

Bartholomew, G. A., and F. Wilke
1956 Body temperature in the northern fur seal *Callorhinus ursinus, J. Mammal.,* **37**:327–337.

Bastock, M., D. Morris, and M. Moynihan
1953 Some comments on conflict and thwarting in animals, *Behaviour,* **6**:66–84.

Bates, H. W.
1863 "The Naturalist on the River Amazon," J. Murray, London.

Bateson, G.
1963 The role of somatic change in evolution, *Evolution,* **17**:529–539.

Beal, H. W.
1934 The penetration of rainfall through hardwood and softwood forest canopy, *Ecology,* **15**:412–415.

Beall, G.
1941a The monarch butterfly *Danaus archippus* Fab.: I, General observations in southern Ontario, *Can. Field Naturalist,* **55**:123–129.
1941b The monarch butterfly *Danaus archippus* Fab.: II, The movement in southern Ontario, *Can. Field Naturalist,* **55**:133–137.
1946 Seasonal variation in sex proportion and wing length in the migrant butterfly *Danaus plexippus* L. (Lep. Danaidae), *Trans. Royal Entomol. Soc.* (London), **97**:337–353.

Beckwith, S. L.
1954 Ecological succession on abandoned farm lands and its relationship to wildlife management, *Ecol. Monographs,* **24**:349–376.

Beebe, F. L.
1960 The marine peregrines of the northwest Pacific coast, *Condor,* **62**:145–189.

Beer, J. R., and W. Traux
1950 Sex and age ratios in Wisconsin muskrats, *J. Wildlife Management,* **14**:323–331.

Behle, W. H.
1956 A systematic review of the mountain chickadee, *Condor,* **58**:51–70.

Bellinger, P. F.
1954 Studies of soil fauna with special reference to the Collembola, *Conn. Agr. Exp. Sta. Bull. No. 583.*

Bellrose, F. C., T. G. Scott, A. S. Hawkins, and J. B. Low
1961 Sex ratios and age ratios in North American ducks, *Illinois Nat. Hist. Surv. Bull.,* **27**:391–474.

Bennett, R.
1951 Some aspects of Missouri quail and quail hunting, 1938–1948, *Missouri Conserv. Comm. Tech. Bull. No. 2* (Jefferson City, Mo.).

Benninghoff, W. S.
1952 Interaction of vegetation and soil frost phenomena, *Arctic,* **5**:34–44.

Benson, L.
1962 "Plant Taxonomy, Methods and Principles," Ronald, New York.

Bernier, B.
1961 Forest humus, a consequence and cause of the local ecological conditions, mimeo., 1961, Northeast Forest Soils Conference.

Biel, E. R.
1961 Microclimate, bioclimatology and notes on

comparative dynamic climatology, *Am. Scientist,* **49**:326–357.

Billings, W. D., and L. C. Bliss
1959 An alpine snowbank and its effects on vegetation, plant development, and productivity, *Ecology,* **40**:388–397.

Birch, L. C.
1948 The intrinsic rate of natural increase of an insect population, *J. Animal Ecology,* **17**:15–26.

Birch, L. C., and D. P. Clark
1953 Forest soil as an ecological community with special reference to the fauna, *Quart. Rev. Biol.,* **28**(1):13–36.

Black, R. F.
1954 Permafrost—a review, *Geol. Soc. Am. Bull.,* **65**:839–856.

Blair, A. P.
1942 Isolating mechanisms in a complex of four species of toad, *Biol. Symp.,* **6**:235–249.

Blair, W. F.
1943 Populations of the deer mouse and associated small mammals in southern New Mexico, *Contrib. Lab. Vert. Biol.* (University of Michigan), **21**:1–40.
1955 Mating call and stage of speciation in the *Microhyla olivacea—M. carolinensis* complex, *Evolution,* **9**:469–480.
1958 Mating call in the speciation of Anuran amphibians, *Am. Naturalist,* **92**:27–51.
1960 "The Rusty Lizard: A Population Study," University of Texas Press, Austin, Tex.
1961 Calling and spawning seasons in a mixed population of Anurans, *Ecology,* **42**:99–110.

Blest, A. D.
1957 The function of eyespot patterns in the Lepidoptera, *Behaviour,* **11**:209–256.

Bliss, L. C.
1956 A comparison of plant development in microenvironments of arctic and alpine tundras, *Ecol. Monographs,* **26**:303–337.
1963 Alpine plant communities of the Presidential Range, New Hampshire, *Ecology,* **44**:678–697.

Blum, J. L.
1960 Algae populations in flowing waters, in "The Ecology of Algae," *Spec. Publ. No. 2, Pymatuning Lab. of Field Biology,* pp. 11–21.

Bobvjerg, R. V., and P. W. Glynn
1960 A class exercise on a marine microcosm, *Ecology,* **41**:229–232.

Bogert, C. M.
1960 The influence of sound on the behavior of amphibians and reptiles, in Lanyon and Tavolga (eds.), 1960, "Animal Sounds and Communication," pp. 137–320.

Bond, R. R.
1957 Ecological distribution of breeding birds in the upland forests of Southern Wisconsin, *Ecol. Monographs,* **27**:351–384.

Bonner, J.
1962 The upper limit of crop yield, *Science,* **137**:11–15.

Bornebusch, C. H.
1930 "The Fauna of Forest Soils," Nielsen and Lydiche, Copenhagen.

Borror, D. J.
1961 Intraspecific variation in passerine bird songs, *Wilson Bull.,* **73**:57–78.

Braemer, W.
1959 Versuche zu der im Richlungsfinder der Fische enthaltenen Zeitschatzung, *Verh. d. deutschen Zool Ges. Zool. Anz 23, Supplementband* 276, pp. 288.
1960 A critical review of the sun-azimuth hypothesis, *Cold Spring Harbor Symp. Quant. Biol.,* **25**:413–427.

Bragg, A. N.
1950 Observations on *Microhyla* (Salientia: Microhylidae), *Wasmann J. Biol.,* **8**:113–118.

Bramble, W. C., and R. H. Ashley
1955 Natural revegetation of spoil banks in central Pennsylvania, *Ecology,* **36**:417–423.

Braun, E. Lucy
1950 "Deciduous Forests of Eastern North America," McGraw-Hill–Blakiston, New York.

Brawn, V. M.
1961 Reproductive behaviour of the cod (*Gadus callarias* L.), *Behaviour,* **18**:177–198.

Bray, J. R.
1961 Measurement of leaf utilization as an index of minimum level of primary consumption, *Oikos,* **12**:70–74.

Breder, C. M. Jr.
1951 Studies on the structure of the fish school, *Bull. Am. Mus. Nat. Hist.,* **98**:1–28.

Brett, J. R., and D. MacKinnon
1954 Some aspects of olfactory perception in migrating adult coho and spring salmon, *J. Fisheries Res. Board Can.,* **11**:310–318.

Brock, V. E., and R. H. Riffenburgh
1960 Fish schooling, a possible factor in reducing predation. *J. Du Conseil,* **25**:307–317.

Brooks, J. L., and G. E. Hutchinson
1950 On the rate of passive sinking of Daphnia, *Proc. Nat. Acad. Sci. U.S.,* **36**:272–277.

Brooks, M. B.
1940 The breeding warblers of the central Allegheny Mountain region, *Wilson Bull.,* **52**:249–266.

Brower, Jane van Zandt
1958 Experimental studies of mimicry in some North American butterflies: part I, The monarch, *Danaus plexippus* and Viceroy, *Limenitis archippus archippus;* part II, *Battus philenor* and *Papilio troilus,* P. *polyxenes* and P. *glaucus;* part III, *Danaus gilippus berenice* and *Limenitis archippus Floridensis, Evolution,* **12**:32–47, 123–136, 273–285.

Brower, Jane Van Z., and L. P. Brower

1962 Experimental studies of mimicry: 6, The reaction of toads (*Bufo terrestris*) to honeybees (*Apis mellifera*) and their dronefly mimics (*Eristalis vinetorum*), *Am. Naturalist*, **97**:297–307.

Brower, L. P.

1961 Studies on the migration of the monarch butterfly: I, Breeding populations of *Danaus plexippus* and *D. gilippus berenice* in south central Florida, *Ecology*, **42**:76–83.

Brower, L. P., Jane Van Z. Brower, and F. P. Cranston

1965 Courtship behavior of the Queen butterfly, *Danaus gilippus berenice* (Cramer), *Zoologica*, **50**:1–39.

Brower, L. P., Jane Van Z. Brower, and P. W. Westcott

1960 Experimental studies of mimicry: 5, The reactions of toads (*Bufo terrestris*) to bumblebees (*Bombus americanorum*) and their robberfly mimics (*Mallophora bomboides*) with a discussion of aggressive mimicry, *Am. Naturalist*, **94**:343–355.

Brown, E. R.

1961 The black-tailed deer of western Washington, *Washington State Game Dept. Biol. Bull. No. 13* (Olympia).

Brown, F. A., Jr.

1959 Living clocks, *Science*, **130**:1535–1544.

Brown, J. H., and E. H. Tryon

1960 Establishment of seeded black locust on spoil banks, *West Va. Univ. Agr. Exp. Sta. Bull. 440.*

Brown, J. L.

1963 Aggressiveness, dominance and social organization in the Stellar jay, *Condor*, **65**:460–484.

Bruce, V. G.

1960 Environmental entertainment of circadian rhythms, *Cold Spring Harbor Symp. Quant. Biol.*, **25**:29–47.

Bryson, R. A., and R. A. Ragotzkie

1960 On internal waves in lakes, *Limnol. Oceanog.*, **5**:397–408.

Buckner, C. H., and W. J. Turnock

1965 Avian predation on the larch sawfly, *Pristiphora erichsonii* (Htg) (Hymenoptera: Tenthredinidae), *Ecology*, **46**:223–236.

Buechner, H. K.

1961 Territorial behavior in the Uganda kob, *Science*, **133**:698.

Buell, M. F., and R. E. Wilbur

1948 Life form spectra of the hardwood forests of the Itasca Park region, Minnesota, *Ecology*, **29**:352–359.

Bünning, E.

1935a Zur kenntnis der erblichen Tagesperiodizität bei den Primärblättern von *Phaseolus multifloris*, *Jb. Wiss. Botany*, **81**:411 ff.

1935b Zur Kenntnis der endogenen Tagesrhythmik bei Insekten und bei Pflanzen, *Ber. Deut. Botan. Ges.*, **53**:594–623.

1959 Physiological mechanism and biological importance of the endogenous diurnal periodicity in plants and animals, in R. B. Withrow, 1959, "Photoperiodism and Related Phenomena," pp. 507–530.

1964 "The Physiological Clock," 2nd ed., Academic, New York.

Bünning, E., and G. Joerrens

1960 Tagesperiodische antagonistische Schwankungen der Blauviolett- und Gelbrot-Empfindlichkeit als Grundlage der photoperiodischen Diapause-Induktion bei *Pieris brassicae*, *Z. Naturforsch.*, **15b**:205–223.

Bünning, E., and D. Müller

1961 Wie messen Organismen lunare Zyklen?, *Z. Naturforsch.* **16b**:391–395.

Bünsow, R.

1953 Endogene Tagesrhythmik und Photoperiodismus bei *Kalanchoe blossfeldiana*, *Planta*, **42**:220–252.

Burdick, G. E., E. J. Harris, H. J. Dean, T. M. Walker, J. Skea, and D. Colby

1964 The accumulation of DDT in lake trout and the effect on reproduction, *Trans. Am. Fisheries Soc.*, **93**:127–136.

Burt, W. H.

1940 Territorial behavior and populations of some small mammals in southern Michigan, *Museum Zool. Misc. Publ. Univ. Mich.*, **45**:1–58.

Burt, W. V., and J. Queen

1957 Tidal overmixing in estuaries, *Science*, **126**(3280):973–974.

Cain, A. J., and P. M. Sheppard

1950 Selection in the polymorphic land snail *Cepaea nemoralis*, *Heredity*, **4**:275–294.

1954 Natural selection in *Cepaea*, *Genetics*, **39**:89–116.

Cain, S. A., and G. M. Castro

1959 "Manual of Vegetation Analysis," Harper & Row, New York.

Cantlon, J. E.

1953 Vegetation and microclimates on north and south slopes of Cushetunk Mountain, New Jersey, *Ecol. Monographs*, **23**:241–270.

Carpenter, C. R.

1934 A field study of the behavior and social relations of howling monkeys (Aloatta palliata), *Comp. Psychol. Monographs*, No. 2.

Carr, A.

1962 Orientation problems in the high seas travel and terrestrial movements of marine turtles, *Am. Scientist*, **50**:359–374.

Chambers, R. E., and W. M. Sharp

1958 Movement and dispersal within a population of ruffed grouse, *J. Wildlife Management,* **22**:231–239.

Chapman, V. J.
1960 "Salt Marshes and Salt Deserts of the World," Interscience, New York.

Chappel, H. G.
1963 The effect of ionizing radiation on *Smilax* with special reference to the protection afforded by their production of underground vegetative structures, in Schultz and Klement (eds.), 1963, "Radioecology," pp. 289–294.

Cheatum, E. L., and C. W. Severinghaus
1950 Variations in fertility of white-tailed deer related to range conditions, *Trans. North Am. Wildlife Conf.,* **15**:170–189.

Chitty, D.
1952 Mortality among voles (*Microtus agrestus*) at Lake Vyrnwy, Montgomeryshire in 1936–9, *Phil. Trans. Roy. Soc. London, Ser. B,* **236**:505–552.
1960 Population processes in the vole and their reference to general theory, *Can. J. Zool.,* **38**:99–113.

Christensen, A. M., and J. J. McDermott
1958 Life history and biology of the oyster crab *Pinnotheres ostreum* Say, *Biol. Bull.,* **114**:146–179.

Christian, J. J.
1963 Endocrine adaptive mechanisms and the physiologic regulation of population growth, in Mayer and van Gelder (eds.), 1963, "Physiological Mammalogy," vol. 1, "Mammalian Populations," pp. 189–353, Academic, New York.

Christian, J. J., and D. E. Davis
1964 Endocrines, behavior and population, *Science,* **146**:1550–1560.

Christian, J. J., V. Flyger, and D. E. Davis
1960 Factors in the mass mortality of a herd of Sika deer, *Cervus nippon, Chesapeake Science,* **1**:79–95.

Christy, H. R.
1952 Vertical temperature gradients in a beech forest in central Ohio, *Ohio J. Sci.,* **52**:199–209.

Churchill, E. D., and H. C. Hanson
1958 The concept of climax in arctic and alpine vegetation, *Botan. Rev.,* **24**:127–191.

Clark, L. B.
1938 Observations on the Atlantic palolo, *Yearbook Carnegie Inst. Wash.,* 37.

Clausen, J.
1965 Population studies of alpine and sub-alpine races of conifers and willows in the California High Sierra Nevada, *Evolution,* **19**:56–68.

Clausen, J., D. D. Keck, and W. M. Hiesey
1948 Experimental studies on the nature of species: III, Environmental responses of climatic races of Achillea, *Carnegie Inst. Wash. Publ.* 581.

Clawson, S. G.
1958–59 Fire ant eradication and quail, *Alabama Conserv.,* **30**(4):14–15, 25.

Clay, W. M.
1953 Protective coloration in the American sparrow hawk, *Wilson Bull.,* **65**:129–134.

Clements, F. C.
1916 "Plant Succession," *Carnegie Inst. Wash. Publ.* 242, Washington, D.C.

Clements, F. E., and V. E. Shelford
1939 "Bio-ecology," Wiley, New York.

Cloudsley-Thompson, J. L.
1956 Studies in diurnal rhythms: VII, Humidity responses and nocturnal activity in woodlice (Isopoda), *J. Exp. Biol.,* **33**:576–582.
1960 Adaptive functions of circadian rhythms, *Cold Spring Harbor Symp. Quant. Biol.* **25**:345–355.

Clough, G. C.
1965a Lemmings and population problems, *Am. Scientist,* **53**:199–212.
1965b Viability of wild voles, *Ecology,* **46**:119–134.

Cold Spring Harbor Symposia on Quantitative Biology
1957 Population studies—animal ecology and demography, vol. XXII, Biological Lab., Cold Spring Harbor, New York.

Cold Spring Harbor Symposia on Quantitative Biology
1960 Biological clocks, vol. XXV, Biological Lab., Cold Spring Harbor, New York.

Cole, L. C.
1946 A study of the crypotozoa of an Illinois woodland, *Ecol. Monographs,* **16**:49–86.
1951 Population cycles and random oscillations, *J. Wildlife Management,* **15**:233–252.
1954a The population consequences of life history phenomena, *Quart. Rev. Biol.,* **29**:103–137.
1954b Some features of random cycles, *J. Wildlife Management,* **18**:107–109.
1957 Sketches of general and comparative demography, *Cold Spring Harbor Symp. Quant. Biol.,* **22**:1–15.

Collias, Elsie R., and N. E. Collias
1957 The response of chicks of the Franklin's gull to parental bill color, *Auk,* **74**:371–375.

Collias, N. E.
1956 Analysis of socialization in sheep and goats, *Ecology,* **37**:228–239.

Collias, N. E., and R. D. Taber
1951 A field study of some grouping and dominance relations in ring-necked pheasants, *Condor,* **53**:265–275.

Connell, J. H.
1961 The influence of interspecific competition and other factors on the distribution of the

barnacle *Chthamalus stellatus, Ecology,* **42:** 710–723.

Connell, J. H., and E. Orias
1964 The ecological regulation of species diversity, *Am. Naturalist,* **98:**399–414.

Cooper, C. F.
1960 Changes in vegetation, structure and growth of southwestern pine forests since white settlement, *Ecol. Monographs,* **30:**129–164.

Cooper, E. L.
1959 Trout stocking as an aid to fish management, *Penn. State Univ. Agr. Exp. Sta. Bull. No. 663.*

Cordone, A. L., and W. Kelly
1961 The influences of inorganic sediment on the aquatic life of streams, *Calif. Fish Game,* **47:**189–228.

Core, E. A.
1955 "Plant Taxonomy," Prentice-Hall, Englewood Cliffs, New Jersey.

Cott, H. B.
1940 "Adaptative Coloration in Animals," Methuen, London.

Cottam, G., and J. T. Curtis
1956 The use of distance measures in phytosociological sampling, *Ecology,* **37:**451–460.

Coupland, R. T.
1950 Ecology of mixed prairie in Canada, *Ecol. Monographs,* **20:**217–315.
1958 The effects of fluctuations in weather upon the grasslands of the Great Plains, *Botan. Rev.,* **24:**273–317.
1959 Effect of changes in weather conditions upon grasslands in the northern Great Plains, in Sprague (ed.), 1959, "Grassland," pp. 291–306.

Cowan, I., and V. Geist
1961 Aggressive behavior in deer of the genus *Odocoileus, J. Mammal.,* **42:**522–526.

Cowan, R. L.
1962 Physiology of nutrition as related to deer, *Proc. 1st. Natl. White-tailed Deer Disease Symp.,* pp. 1–8.

Cowles, H. C.
1899 The ecological relations of the vegetation on the sand dunes of Lake Michigan, *Botan. Gaz.* **27:**95–117, 167–202, 281–308, 361–391.

Cragg, J. B. (ed.)
1962 "Advances in Ecological Research," vol. I, Academic, New York.

Craig, W.
1918 Appetites and aversions as constituents of insects, *Biol. Bull.* (Woods Hole, Massachusetts), **34:**91–107.

Craighead, F., and J. Craighead
1956 "Hawks, Owls and Wildlife," Stackpole, Harrisburg, Pa.

Crombie, A. C.
1947 Interspecific competition, *J. Animal Ecol.,* **16:**44–73.

Crossley, D. A. Jr., and K. K. Bohnsack
1960 Long-term ecological study in the Oak Ridge area: III, Oribatid mite fauna in pine litter, *Ecology,* **41:**628–638.

Crossman, E. J.
1959*a* Distribution and movements of a predator, the rainbow trout, and its prey, the redside shiner, in Paul Lake, British Columbia, *J. Fisheries Res. Board Can.,* **16:**247–267.
1959*b* A predator-prey interaction in freshwater fish, *J. Fisheries Res. Board Can.,* **16:** 269–281.

Curry-Lindahl, K.
1962 The irruption of Norway lemming in Sweden during 1960, *J. Mammal.,* **43:**171–184.

Curtis, J. T.
1959 "The Vegetation of Wisconsin," p. 657, University of Wisconsin Press, Madison, Wisc.

Curtis, J. T., and R. P. McIntosh
1951 An upland forest continuum in the prairie-forest border region of Wisconsin, *Ecology,* **32:**476–496.

Dahl, E.
1953 Some aspects of the ecology and zonation of the fauna of sandy beaches, *Oikos,* **4:**1–27.

Dahlberg, B. L., and R. C. Guettinger
1956 The white-tailed deer in Wisconsin, *Tech. Wildlife Bull. No. 14, Wisconsin Conserv. Dept.* (Madison, Wisc.).

Dale, T., and V. G. Carter
1955 "Topsoil and Civilization," p. 270, University of Oklahoma Press, Norman, Okla.

Damback, C. A., and E. Good
1943 Life history and habits of the cicada killer in Ohio, *Ohio J. Sci.,* **43:**32–41.

Daniel, C. P.
1963 Study of succession in fields irradiated with fast neutron and gamma radiation, in Schultz and Klement (eds.), 1963, "Radioecology," pp. 277–282.

Dansereau, P.
1945 Essae de correlation sociologique entre les plantes superieures et les poissons de la Beine du Lac Saint-Louis, *Rev. Can. Biol.,* **4:**369–417.
1959 Vascular aquatic plant communities of southern Quebec: A preliminary analysis, *Trans. 10th Northeast Wildlife Conf.,* 27–54.
1959 "Biogeography: An Ecological Perspective," Ronald, New York.

Dansereau, P., and F. Segadas-Vianna
1952 Ecological study of the peat bogs of eastern North America, *Can. J. Botany,* **30:** 490–520.

Darling, F. F.
1937 "A Herd of Red Deer," Oxford, London.
1960 "Wildlife in an African Territory," Oxford, London.

Darlington, P. J. Jr.
1957 "Zoogeography: the Geographical Distribution of Animals," Wiley, New York.

Darnell, R. M.
1961 Trophic spectrum of an estuarine community based on studies of Lake Pontchartrain, Louisiana, *Ecology,* **42**:553–568.

Darwin, C.
1881 "The Formation of Vegetable Mould Through the Action of Worms, with Observations on Their Habits," J. Murray, London.

Davidson, J., and H. G. Andrewartha
1948*a* Annual trends in a natural population of *Thrips imaginis* (Thysanoptera), *J. Anim. Ecology,* **17**:193–199.
1948*b* The influence of rainfall, evaporation and atmospheric temperature on fluctuations in size of a natural population of *Thrips imaginis* (Thysanoptera), *J. Anim. Ecology,* **17**:200–202.

Davis, D. E.
1960 A chart for estimation of life expectancy, *J. Wildlife Management,* **24**:344–348.

Davis, J. H.
1940 The ecology and geologic role of mangroves in Florida, *Papers Tortugas Lab.,* **32**:302–412.

Davis, T. A. W., and P. W. Richards
1933 The vegetation of Moraballi Creek, British Guiana; an ecological study of a limited area of tropical rain forest, *Ecology,* **19**:503–514.

Day, R. K., and D. DenUyl
1932 The natural regeneration of farm woods following the exclusion of livestock, *Purdue Univ. Agr. Exp. Sta., Res. Bull.,* 368.

DeCoursey, Patricia J.
1960*a* Phase control of activity in a rodent, *Cold Spring Harbor Symp. Quant. Biol.,* **25**:49–54.
1960*b* Daily light sensitivity rhythm in a rodent, *Science,* **131**:33–35.
1961 Effect of light on the circadian activity rhythm of the flying squirrel, *Glaucomys volans, Z. Vergleich. Physiol.,* **44**:331–354.

Deevey, E. S.
1947 Life tables for natural populations of animals, *Quart. Rev. Biol.,* **22**:283–314.

Delacour, J., and C. Vaurie
1950 Les mesanges charbonnieres (revision de l'espece *Parus major*), *L' Oiseau,* **20**:91–121.

Denyes, H. Arliss, and Jeanne M. Joseph
1956 Relationships between temperature and blood oxygen in the large-mouth bass, *J. Wildlife Management,* **20**(1):56–64.

Dice, L. R.
1943 "The Biotic Provinces of North America," University of Michigan Press, Ann Arbor, Mich.

1947 Effectiveness of selection by owls on deermice (*Peromyscus maniculatus*) which contrast in color with their background, *Contrib. Lab. Vert. Biol.* (University of Michigan), **34**:1–20.

Dilger, W. C.
1956 Adaptive modifications and ecological isolating mechanisms in the thrush genera *Catharus* and *Hylocichla, Wilson Bull.,* **68**:171–199.
1956 Hostile behavior and reproductive isolating mechanisms in the avian genera *Catharus* and *Hylocichla, Auk,* **73**:313–353.
1960 Agonistic and social behavior of captive redpolls, *Wilson Bull.,* **72**:115–132.

Dilger, W., and P. Johnsgard
1959 Comments on species recognition with special reference to the wood duck and mandarin duck, *Wilson Bull.,* **71**:46–53.

Dix, R. L.
1960 The effects of burning on the mulch structure and species composition of grassland in western North Dakota, *Ecology,* **41**:49–56.

Dixon, K. L.
1949 Behavior of the plain titmouse, *Condor,* **51**:110–136.

Dobzhansky, T.
1947 Effectiveness of intraspecific and interspecific matings in *Drosophila pseudoobscura* and *D. persimilis, Am. Naturalist,* **81**:66–72.
1951 "Genetics and the Origin of Species," 3d ed., Columbia Univ. Press, New York.

Dodd, A. P.
1940 The biological campaign against prickly pear, *Comm. Prickly Pear Board,* Brisbane, Queensland, Australia.
1959 The biological control of prickly pear in Australia, *Biogeography and Ecology in Australia, Monog. Biologicae,* **8**:565–577.

Dodds, D. G.
1960 Food competition and range relationships of moose and snowshoe hare in Newfoundland, *J. Wildlife Management,* **24**:52–60.

Doty, M. S.
1957 Rocky intertidal surfaces, in Hedgpeth, 1957, "Treatise on marine ecology and paleoecology I, Ecology," pp. 535–585.

Dowdy, W. W.
1944 The influence of temperature on vertical migration of invertebrates inhabiting different soil types, *Ecology,* **25**:449–460.
1951 Further ecological studies on stratification of the arthropods, *Ecology,* **32**:37–52.

Drew, J. V., J. C. Tedrow, R. E. Shanks, and J. J. Koranda
1958 Rate and depth of thaw in Arctic soils, *Trans. Am. Geophys. Union,* **39**:697–701.

Drift, J. van der
1951 Analysis of the animal community in a

bech forest floor, *Tijdschrift voor Entomologie,* **94**:1–168.

Drury, W. H. Jr.
1961 The breeding biology of shorebirds on Bylot Island, Northwest Territories, Canada, *Auk,* **78**:176–219.

Drury, W. H. Jr., I. C. T. Nisbet, and R. E. Richardson
1961 The migration of "angels," *Nat. Hist.,* **70**(8):11–16.

Duddington, C. L.
1955 Inter-relations between soil microflora and soil nematodes, in Kevan, 1955, "Soil Zoology," pp. 284–301, Butterworth, Washington, D.C.

Dybas, H. S., and M. Lloyd
1962 Isolation by habitat in two synchronized species of periodical cicadas (Homoptera, Cicadidae, Magicada), *Ecology,* **43**:444–459.

Dyksterhuis, E. J., and E. M. Schmutz
1947 Natural mulches or "litter of grasslands"; with kinds and amounts on a southern prairie, *Ecology,* **28**:163–179.

Eaton, T. H. Jr., and R. F. Chandler, Jr.
1942 The fauna of the forest humus layers in New York, *Cornell Univ. Agr. Exp. Sta. Mem. No. 247.*

Edeburn, R.
1947 A study of the breeding distribution of birds in a typical upland area, *Proc. W. Va. Acad. Sci. V 18, W. Va. Univ. Bull. Ser. 47,* no. 9–I pp. 34–47.

Edmondson, W. T.
1956 The relation of photosynthesis by phyloplankton to light in lakes, *Ecology,* **37**:161–174.

Egler, F. E.
1953 Vegetation management for rights-of-way and roadsides, *Smithsonian Inst. Ann. Rep. 1953,* pp. 299–322.

Eisner, E.
1960 The relationship of hormones to the reproductive behavior of birds, referring especially to parental behavior; a review, *Animal Behaviour,* **8**:155–179.

Ellis, M. M.
1936 Erosion silt as a factor in aquatic environments, *Ecology,* **17**:29–42.

Ellison, L.
1954 Subalpine vegetation of the Wasatch Plateau, Utah, *Ecol. Monographs,* **24**:89–184.
1960 Influence of grazing on plant succession on rangelands, *Botan. Rev.* **26**:1–78.

Elton, C. S.
1927 "Animal Ecology," Sidgwick & Jackson, London.
1958 "The Ecology of Invasions by Animals and Plants," Methuen, London.

Emanuelsson, A., E. Eriksson, and H. Egner
1954 Composition of atmospheric precipitation in Sweden, *Tellus,* **3**:261–267.

Emlen, J. T., Jr.
1940 Sex and age ratios in the survival of California Quail, *J. Wildlife Management,* **4**: 92–99.
1952 Social behavior in nesting cliff swallows, *Condor,* **54**:177–199.

Engelmann, M. D.
1961 The role of soil arthropods in the energetics of an old field community, *Ecol. Monographs,* **31**:221–238.

Enright, J. T.
1963a The tidal rhythm of activity of a sand beach amphipod, *Z. Vergleich Physiol.,* **46**: 276–313.
1963b Endogenous tidal and lunar rhythms, *Proc. XVI Inter. Congress Zool.,* pp. 355–359.
1965 Entrainment of a tidal rhythm, *Science,* **147**:864–867.

Errington, P. L.
1937a Habitat requirements of stream-dwelling muskrats, *Trans. North Am. Wildlife Conf.,* **2**: 411–416.
1937b Drowning as a cause of mortality in muskrats, *J. Mammal.,* **18**:497–500.
1939 Reactions of muskrat populations to drought, *Ecology,* **20**:168–186.
1940 Natural restocking of muskrat-vacant habitats, *J. Wildlife Management,* **4**:173–185.
1943 An analysis of mink predation upon muskrats in north-central United States, *Iowa Agr. Exp. Sta. Res. Bull.,* **320**:797–924.
1946 Predation and vertebrate populations, *Quart. Rev. Biol.,* **21**:144–177, 221–245.
1951 Concerning fluctuations in populations of the prolific and widely distributed muskrat, *Am. Naturalist,* **85**:273–292.
1957 Of population cycles and unknowns, *Cold Spring Harbor Symp. Quant. Biol.,* **22**:287–300.
1963 "Muskrat Populations," Iowa State University Press, Ames, Iowa.

Eschmeyer, P. H., and W. R. Crowe
1955 The movement and recovery of tagged walleyes in Michigan, 1929–53, *Misc. Publ. Inst. Fishery Research* (University of Michigan), **3**:1–32.

Eustis, A. B., and R. H. Hiller
1954 Stream sediment removal by controlled reservoir releases, *Progressive Fish Culturalist,* **16**:30–35.

Evans, A. C.
1948 Studies on the relationships between earthworms and soil fertility: II, Some effects

of earthworms on soil structure, *Ann. Appl. Biol.,* **35**:1–13.

Evans, A. C., and W. J. McLaren Guild
1948 Studies on the relationships between earthworms and soil fertility: V, Field populations, *Ann. Appl. Biol.,* **35**:485–493.

Evans, F. C., and S. A. Cain
1952 Preliminary studies on the vegetation of an old-field community in southeastern Michigan, *Contrib. Lab. Vert. Biol.* (University of Michigan), **51**:1–17.

Evans, H. E.
1957 "Studies on the Comparative Ethology of Digger Wasps of the Genus *Bembex*," Comstock, Ithaca, N.Y.
1962 A review of the nesting behavior of the digger wasps of the genus *Aphilanthops,* with special attention to the mechanics of prey carriage, *Behaviour,* **19**:239–260.
1963 Predatory wasps, *Sci. Am.,* **208**(4):144–154.

Farner, D. S.
1955 The annual stimulus for migration: experimental and physiologic aspects, in A. Wolfson (ed.), 1959, "Recent Studies in Avian Biology," pp. 198–237.
1959 Photoperiodic control of animal gonodal cycles in birds, in Withrow (ed.), 1959, "Photoperiodism and Related Phenomena," pp. 717–758.
1964*a* The photoperiodic control of reproductive cycles in birds, *Am. Scientist,* **52**:137–156.
1964*b* Time measurement in vertebrate photoperiodism, *Am. Naturalist,* **98**:375–386.

Fenner, F.
1953 Host-parasite relationships in myxomatosis of the Australian wild rabbit, *Cold Spring Harbor Symp. Quant. Biol.,* **18**:291–294.

Fichter, E.
1954 An ecological study of invertebrates of grassland and deciduous shrub savanna in eastern Nebraska, *Am. Midland Naturalist,* **51**:321–439.

Ficken, Millicent S.
1963 Courtship of the American redstart, *Auk,* **80**:307–317.

Ficken, Millicent S., and R. W. Ficken
1962 The comparative ethology of the wood warblers, a review, *Living Bird,* **1**:103–122.

Ficken, R. W.
1963 Courtship and behavior of the common grackle *Quiscalus quiscula, Auk,* **80**:52–72.

Fischer, A. G.
1960 Latitudinal variation in organic diversity, *Evolution,* **14**:64–81.

Fischer, K.
1960 Experimentelle Beeinflussung der inneren Uhr bei der Sonnen-kompassorientierung und der Laufaktivitat von *Lacerta viridis* (Laur.), *Naturwissenschaften,* **47**:287–288.

Fischer, R. A.
1929 "The Genetical Theory of Natural Selection," 2d rev. ed., Dover, New York.

Fisher, K. C.
1958 An approach to organ and cellular physiology of adaptation to adaptation to temperature in fish and small mammals, in Prosser, (ed.), 1958, "Physiological Adaptations."

Fitch, H. S., and J. R. Bentley
1949 Use of California, annual plant forage by range rodents, *Ecology,* **30**:306–321.

Fons, W. L.
1940 Influence of forest cover on wind velocity, *J. Forestry,* **38**:481–486.

Forsslund, K. H.
1947 Nagot om insamlingsmetodiken vid markfaunaundersokingar, *Medd Skogsforsoksanst* (Stockholm), **37**:1–22.

Fowells, H. A.
1948 The temperature profile in a forest, *J. Forestry,* **46**:897–899.

Frank, F.
1957 The causality of microtine cycles in Germany, *J. Wildlife Management,* **21**:113–121.

Frank, P. W.
1952 A laboratory study of intraspecies and interspecies competition in *Daphnia puliceria* and *Simocephalus vetulus, Physiol. Zool.,* **25**:178–204.

Franz, H.
1950 Bodenzoologie als Grundlage der Bodenpflege, *Akademie-Verlag* (Berlin), pp. 316 ff.

French, C. E., L. C. McEwen, N. D. Magruder, R. H. Ingram, and R. W. Swift
1955 Nutritional requirements of white-tailed deer for growth and antler development, *Penn. State Univ. Agr. Exp. Sta. Bull. No. 600.*

Frenzel, G.
1936 "Untersuchungen uber die Tierwelt des Wiesenbodens," Gustav Fischer, Jena.

Frisch, K. von
1954 "The Dancing Bees," Methuen, London.

Gaufin, A. R.
1957 The use and value of aquatic insects as indicators of organic enrichment, *Biol. Problems in Water Pollution* (Robert A. Taft Sanitary Eng. Center, Cincinnati, Ohio), pp. 136–143.

Gause, G. F.
1934 "The Struggle for Existence," Williams & Wilkins, Baltimore.

Geist, V.
1963 On the behaviour of the North American moose (*Alces alces andersoni* Peterson, 1950) in British Columbia, *Behaviour,* **20**:377–416.

Gerking, S. D.
1959 The restricted movement of fish populations, *Biol. Rev.* **34**:221–242.

Gibson, J. B., and J. M. Thoday
1962 Effects of disruptive selection: VI, A second chromosome polymorphism, *Heredity*, **17**:1–26.

Gilmour, J. S. L.
1951 The development of taxonomic theory since 1851, *Nature*, **168**:400–402.

Gisborne, H. T.
1941 How the wind blows in the forest of northern Idaho, *Northern Rocky Mt. Forest Range Expt. Sta.*

Gleason, H. A.
1926 The individualistic concept of the plant association, *Bull. Torrey Botan. Club*, **53**:7–26.

Golley, F. B.
1960 Energy dynamics of a food chain of an old-field community, *Ecol. Monographs*, **30**:187–206.

Good, E. E., and C. A. Dambach
1943 Effect of land use practices on breeding bird populations in Ohio, *J. Wildlife Management*, **7**:291–297.

Goodhart, C. B.
1962 Variation in a colony of the snail *Cepaea nemoralis* (L), *J. Animal Ecology*, **31**:207–237.

Gottlieb, G.
1963 "Imprinting" in nature, *Science*, **139**:497–498.

Graham, S. A.
1958 Results of deer exclosure experiments in the Ottawa National Forest, *Trans. North Am. Wildlife Conf.*, **23**:478–490.

Grant, V.
1963 "The Origins of Adaptations," Columbia University Press, New York.

Greenbank, D. O.
1956 The role of climate and dispersal in the initiation of outbreaks of the spruce budworm in New Brunswick: I, The role of climate, *Can. J. Zool.*, **34**:453–476.

Greenberg, B.
1947 Some relations between territory, social hierarchy and leadership in the green sunfish (*Lepomis cyanellus*), *Physiol. Zool.*, **20**:267–299.

1963 Parental behaviour and imprinting in cichlid fishes, *Behaviour*, **21**:127–144.

Greig-Smith, P.
1964 "Quantitative Plant Ecology," 2d ed., Butterworth, Washington, D.C.

Gretschy, G.
1952 Die Suksession der Bodentiere auf Fitchlenschlagen, *Veroffent lichungen der Bundes anstalt fur Alpine Landwirtsclaft in Admont.*, **6**:25–85.

Griffin, D. R., F. A. Webster, and C. R. Michael
1960 The echolocation of flying insects by bats, *Animal Behaviour*, **8**:141–154.

Griggs, R. F.
1946 The timberlines of northern America and their interpretation, *Ecology*, **27**:275–289.

Guhl, A. M., and W. C. Allee
1944 Some measurable effects of social organization in flocks of hens, *Physiol. Zool.*, **17**:320–347.

Gullion, G. W.
1953 Territorial behavior of the American coot, *Condor*, **55**:169–186.

Gunter, G.
1961 Some relations of estuarine organisms to salinity, *Limnol. Oceanog.* **6**:182–190.

Gysel, L. W.
1960 An ecological study of the winter deer range of elk and mule deer in the Rocky Mountain National Park, *J. Forestry*, **58**:696–703.

Haarløv, N.
1960 Microarthropods from Danish soils, *Oikos, Supplement No. 3*, pp. 1–176.

Hadley, E. B., and Barbara J. Kieckhefer
1963 Productivity of two prairie grasses in relation to fire frequency, *Ecology*, **44**:389–395.

Hagan, D. C.
1960 Interrelationships of logging, birds, and timber regeneration in Douglas fir region of northwestern California, *Ecology*, **41**:116–125.

Hahn, H. C., and W. P. Taylor
1950 Deer movements in the Edwards Plateau, *Texas Game and Fish*, **8**:4–9, 31.

Hairston, N. G.
1949 The local distribution and ecology of the plethodontid salamanders of the southern Appalachians, *Ecol. Monographs*, **19**:47–73.

Hairston, N. G., and C. H. Pope
1948 Geographic variation and speciation in Appalachian salamanders (*Plethodon jordani* Group), *Evolution*, **2**:266–278.

Hamerstrom, F. N. Jr.
1939 A study of Wisconsin prairie chicken and sharp-tailed grouse, *Wilson Bull.*, **51**:105–120.

Hamerstrom, F. N. Jr., O. E. Mattson, and Frances Hamerstrom
1957 A Guide to Prairie Chicken Management, *Tech. Wildlife Bull. No. 15*, Wisconsin Conserv. Dept., Madison, Wisc.

Hamilton, W. J., III
1959 Aggressive behavior in migrant pectoral sandpipers, *Condor*, **61**:161–179.

1962 Bobolink migratory pathways and their experimental analysis under night skies, *Auk*, **79**:208–233.

Hammel, H. T.
1956 Infrared emissivities of some arctic fauna, *J. Mammal.,* **37**:375–378.

Hammond, J.
1953 Periodicity in animals; the role of darkness, *Science,* **117**:389–390.

Hamner, W. M.
1963 Diurnal rhythm and photoperiodism in testicular recrudescense of the house finch, *Science,* **142**:1294–1295.

Hanson, H. C.
1953 Vegetation types in northwestern Alaska and comparisons with communities in other arctic regions, *Ecology,* **34**:111–140.
1958 Principles concerned in the formation and classification of communities, *Botan. Rev.,* **24**:65–125.

Hanson, H. C., and E. D. Churchill
1961 "The Plant Community," Reinhold, New York.

Hardin, G.
1960 The competitive exclusion principle, *Science,* **131**:1292–1297.

Harrington, R. W., Jr.
1959 Photoperiodism in fishes in relation to the annual sexual cycle, in Withrow (ed.), 1959, "Photoperiodism and Related Phenomena," pp. 651–667.

Harris, V. T.
1952 An experimental study of habitat selection by prairie and forest races of the deermouse, *Peromyscus maniculatus, Contrib. Lab. Vert. Zool.* (University of Michigan), **56**:1–53.

Harrison, J. L.
1962 The distribution of feeding habits among animals in a tropical rain forest, *J. Animal Ecol.,* **31**:53–63.

Hart, J. S.
1951 Photoperiodicity in female ferret, *J. Expt. Biol.* **28**:1–12.

Hartley, P. H. T.
1950 An experimental analysis of interspecific recognition, *Symp. Soc. Expt. Biol.,* **4**:313–336.

Hartman, R. T., and C. L. Himes
1961 Phytoplankton from Pymatuning Reservoir in downstream areas of the Shenango River, *Ecology,* **42**:180–183.

Hartman, W. C.
1957 Finger Lakes rainbows, Part III, A chronicle of their progress from egg to adult, *N. Y. State Conserv.,* **11**(6): 20–22, 34.

Harvey, H. W.
1950 On the production of living matter in the sea off Plymouth, *J. Marine Biol. Assoc. U.K.,* N.S. **29**:97–137.

Hasler, A. D.
1954 Odour perception and orientation in fishes, *J. Fisheries Res. Board Can.,* **11**:107–129.
1960 Guideposts of migrating fishes, *Science,* **132**:785–792.

Hasting, J. W.
1959 Unicellular clocks, *Ann. Rev. Microbiol.,* **13**:297–312.

Hastings, J. W., and B. M. Sweeney
1958 A persistent diurnal rhythm of luminescence in *Gonyaulax polyedra, Biol. Bull.,* **115**:440–458.

Hauenschild, C.
1960 Lunar periodicity, *Cold Spring Harbor Symp. Quant. Biol.,* **25**:491–497.

Hauser, Doris C.
1957 Some observations on sun-bathing in birds, *Wilson Bull.,* **69**:78–90.

Hayne, D. W., and R. C. Ball
1956 Benthic productivity as influenced by fish predation, *Limnol. Oceanog.,* **1**:162–175.

Hedgpeth, J. W. (ed)
1957 "Treatise in marine ecology and paleoecology," I, Ecology, *Mem,* **67**, Geological Soc. Am.
1957 Sandy beaches, in Hedgpeth (ed.), "Treatise in marine ecology and paleoecology," I, pp. 587–608.

Heinroth, O.
1911 Beitrange zur Biologie, namentlich Ethologie und Psychologie der Anatiden, *Verhl. 5 Int. Orn. Kongr.,* pp. 589–702.

Hellmers, H., and J. Bonner
1959 Photosynthetic limits of forest tree yields, *Proc. Soc. Am. Foresters,* pp. 32–35.

Henderson, Nancy E.
1963 Influence of light and temperature on the reproductive cycle of the eastern brook trout *Salvelinus fontinalis, J. Fisheries Res. Board Can.,* **20**:859–897.

Hensley, M. M., and J. B. Cope
1951 Further data on removal and repopulation of the breeding birds in a spruce-fir forest community, *Auk,* **68**:483–493.

Hess, E. H.
1959 Imprinting, *Science,* **130**:133–141.

Hickey, J. J.
1952 Survival studies of banded birds, *U. S. Fish Wildlife Serv. Spec. Sci. Rep.* 15.

Hinde, R. A.
1954 Factors governing the changes in strength of a partially inborn response as shown by the mobbing behaviour of the chaffinch (*Fringella coelebs*): I. The nature of the response and the examination of its course, *Proc. Roy. Soc.* (London), *Ser. B.* **142**:306–331.
1955–1956 A comparative study of the courtship of certain finches (Fringillidae), *Ibis,* **97**:706–745; **98**:1–23.

1959 Behaviour and speciation in birds and lower vertebrates, *Biol. Rev.,* **34**:85–128.

Hinde, R. A., W. H. Thorpe, and M. A. Vince
1956 The following response of young coots and moorhens, *Behaviour,* **9**:214–242.

Hirth, H. F.
1959 Small mammals in old field succession, *Ecology,* **40**:417–425.

Hochbaum, H. A.
1955 "Travels and Traditions of Waterfowl," University of Minnesota Press, Minneapolis.

Hock, R. J.
1960 Seasonal variations in physiological functions of arctic ground squirrels and black bears, in Lyman and Dawe (eds.), 1960, "Mammalian Hibernation," pp. 155–169.

Hoese, H. D.
1960 Biotic changes in a bay associated with the end of a drought, *Limnol. Oceanog.,* **5**:326–336.

Hoffman, K.
1959 Die aktivitalsperiodik von im 18-und-36 stunden-tag eibruteten eidechsen, *Z. Vergleich. Physiol.,* **42**:422–432.
1960 Versuche zur analyse der tagesperiodik. 1. Der einfluss der licktintensitat, *Z. Vergleich. Physiol.,* **43**:544–566.
1963 Zur Beziehung zwischen Phasenlage und Spontanfrequenz bei der endogenen Tagesperiodik, *Z. Naturforsch.,* **18b**:154–157.

Holling, C. C.
1959 The components of predation as revealed by a study of small mammal predation of the European pine sawfly, *Can. Entomologist,* **91**:293–320.
1961 Principles of insect predation, *Ann. Rev. Entomol.,* **6**:163–182.

Holmgren, R. C.
1956 Competition between annuals and young bitterbrush (*Purshia tridentata*) in Idaho, *Ecology,* **37**:370–377.

Hoover, E. E., and H. E. Hubbard
1937 Modifications of the sexual cycle in trout by control of light, *Copeia,* **4**:206–210.

Hope, J. G.
1943 An investigation of the litter fauna of two types of pine forest, *Bull. Wagner Free Inst. Sci.* (Philadelphia), **18**:1–7.

Hopkins, H. H.
1954 Effects of mulch upon certain factors of the grassland environment, *J. Range Management,* **7**:255–258.

Hopkins, S. H.
1958 The planktonic larvae of *Polydora websteri* Hartman (Annelida, Polychaeta) and their settling on oysters, *Bureau Marine Sci. of Gulf and Carribbean,* **8**:268–277.

Hosley, N. W., and R. K. Ziebarth
1935 Some winter relations of the white-tailed deer to the forests in north-central Massachusetts, *Ecology,* **16**:535–553.

Howard, W. E.
1960 Innate and environmental dispersal of individual vertebrates, *Am. Midland Naturalist,* **63**:152–161.

Howard, E.
1920 "Territory in Bird Life," Dutton, New York.

Huffaker, C. B.
1958 Experimental studies on predation: dispersion factors and predator-prey oscillations, *Hilgardia,* **27**:343–383.

Humphrey, R. R.
1958 The desert grassland, a history of vegetational change and an analysis of causes, *Botan. Rev.,* **24**:193–252.

Hunt, E. G., and A. I. Bischoff
1960 Inimical effects on wildlife of periodic DDD applications to Clear Lake, *Calif. Fish Game,* **46**:91–106.

Hunt, L. B.
1960 Songbird breeding populations in DDT-sprayed Dutch elm disease communities, *J. Wildlife Management,* **24**:139–146.

Hunter, G. W. III, and Wanda S. Hunter
1934 Further studies on fish and bird parasites, *Suppl. 24th Ann. Rep. N. Y. State Dep. Conserv.,* No. 9, *Rept. Biol. Surv. Mohawk-Hudson Watershed,* pp. 267–283.

Hutchinson, G. E.
1957 "A Treatise on Limnology," vol. I, "Geography, Physics, Chemistry," Wiley, New York.

Ide, F. P.
1935 The effect of temperature on the distribution of the mayfly fauna of a stream, *Univ. Toronto Biol. Ser.,* **39**:1–76.

Iersel, J. J. A. van
1953 An analysis of the parental behaviour of the three-spined stickleback, *Behaviour, supplement No. 3.*

Iersel, J. J. A. van, and A. C. A. Bol
1958 Preening of two tern species: A study on displacement activities, *Behaviour,* **13**:1–88.

Irving, L.
1960 Birds of Anaktuviik Pass, Kobuk and Old Crow: A study in Arctic adaptation, *U.S. Natl. Museum Bull.,* 217.

Irving, L., and J. Krogh
1954 Body temperatures of arctic and subarctic birds and mammals, *J. Appl. Physiol.,* **6**:667–680.

Jacot, A. P.
1939 Reduction of spruce and fir litter by minute animals, *J. Forestry,* **37**:858–860.
1940 The fauna of the soil, *Quart. Rev. Biol.,* **15**:38–58.

Jahn, E.
1950 Bodentieruntersuchungen in den Flug-sandgebieten des Marchfeldes, *Z. Angew Entomol.*, **32**:208–274.

Jenkins, D., A. Watson, and G. R. Miller
1963 Population studies on red grouse *Lagopus lagopus scoticus* (Lath) in northeast Scotland, *J. Anim. Ecology*, **32**:317–376.

Jenkins, D. W.
1944 Territory as a result of despotism and social organization in geese, *Auk*, **61**:30–47.

Jepsen, G. L., E. Mayr, and G. G. Simpson (eds.)
1949 "Genetics, Paleontology, and Evolution," Princeton University Press, Princeton, N.J.

Johnsgard, P. A.
1960 Hybridization in the Anatidae and its taxonomic implications, *Condor*, **62**:25–33.
1961 The sexual behavior and systematic position of the hooded merganser, *Wilson Bull.*, **73**:227–236.

Johnson, M. G., and W. H. Charlton
1960 Some effects of temperature on the metabolism and activity of the large mouth bass *Micropterus salmoides* Lacepede, *Progressive Fish Culturist*, **22**:155–163.

Johnson, P. L., and W. O. Billings
1962 The alpine vegetation of the Beartooth Plateau in relation to cryopedogenic processes and patterns, *Ecol. Monographs*, **32**:105–135.

Johnston, D. W., and E. P. Odum
1956 Breeding bird populations in relation to plant succession on the Piedmont of Georgia, *Ecology*, **37**:50–62.

Johnston, J. W.
1936 The macrofauna of soils as affected by certain coniferous and hardwood types in the Harvard Forest, unpublished PhD thesis, Harvard University Library, Cambridge, Mass.

Johnston, R. F.
1956 Predation by short-eared owls in a Salicornia salt marsh, *Wilson Bull.*, **68**:91–102.
1956 Population structure in salt marsh song sparrows: part II, Density, age structure and maintenance, *Condor*, **58**:254–272.

Johnston, Verna R.
1947 Breeding birds of the forest edge in Illinois, *Condor*, **49**:45–53.

Kabat, C., N. E. Collias, and R. C. Guettinger
1953 Some winter habits of white-tailed deer and the development of census methods in the flag yard of northern Wisconsin, *Tech. Wildlife Bull. No. 7, Wisconsin Conserv. Dept.* (Madison, Wisc.).

Kabat, C., and D. R. Thompson
1963 Wisconsin Quail, 1834–1962: Population dynamics and habitat management, *Tech. Bull. No. 30, Wisconsin Conservation Dept.* (Madison, Wisc.).

Kalleberg, H.
1958 Observations in a stream tank of territoriality and competition in juvenile salmon and trout (*Salmo salar* L. and *S. trutta* L.), *Report No. 39, Inst. Freshwater Research* (Sweden), pp. 55–98.

Karplus, M.
1949 Bird activity in continuous day-light of arctic summer, *Bull. Ecol. Soc. Am.* **30**:60.

Keast, A.
1959 Australian birds: their zoogeography and adaptation to an arid continent, *Biogeography and Ecology in Australia*, **8**:89–114.

Keith, L. B.
1963 "Wildlife's Ten-year Cycle," University of Wisconsin Press, Madison, Wisc.

Kellogg, C. E.
1936 Development and significance of the great soil groups of the United States, *U.S. Dept. Agr. Misc. Publ.* 229.

Kelso, L., and Margaret M. Nice
1963 A Russian contribution to anting and feather mites, *Wilson Bull.*, **75**:23–26.

Kendeigh, S. C.
1932 A study of Merrian's temperature laws, *Wilson Bull.*, **44**:129–143.
1945 Community selection by birds on the Helderberg Plateau of New York, *Auk*, **62**:418–436.

Kendeigh, S. C., G. C. West, and G. W. Cox
1960 Annual stimulus for spring migration in birds, *Animal Behaviour*, **8**:180–185.

Kenk, R.
1949 The animal life of temporary and permanent ponds in southern Michigan, *Misc. Publ. Museum Zool.* (University of Michigan), No. 71, pp. 1–66.

Kessel, B.
1953 Distribution and migration of the European starling in North America, *Condor*, **55**:49–67.

Ketchum, B. H.
1951 The exchanges of fresh and salt waters in tidal estuaries, *J. Marine Res.*, **10**:18–38.
1954 Relation between circulation and planktonic populations in estuaries, *Ecology*, **35**:191–200.

Kettlewell, H. B. D.
1961 The phenomenon of industrial melanism in Lepidoptera, *Ann. Rev. Entomol.*, **6**:245–262.
1965 Insect survival and selection for pattern, *Science*, **148**:1290–1296.

Kevan, D. K. McE.
1955 "Soil Zoology," Butterworth, Washington, D.C.
1962 "Soil Animals," Philosophical Library, New York.

Kilham, L.
   1959 Early reproductive behavior of flickers, *Wilson Bull.*, **71**:299–408.

King, J. A.
   1955 Social behavior, social organization and population dynamics in a black-tailed prairie dog town in the Black Hills of South Dakota, *Contrib. Lab. Vert. Biol.* (University of Michigan), No. 67, pp. 1–123.

Kleerekoper, H.
   1953 The mineralization of plankton, *J. Fisheries Res. Board Can.*, **10**:283–291.

Klimstra, W. D., and V. C. Ziccardi
   1963 Night-roosting habitat of bobwhites, *J. Wildlife Management*, **27**:202–214.

Klomp, H.
   1964 Intraspecific competition and the regulation of insect numbers, *Ann. Rev. Entomol.*, **9**:17–40.

Klopfer, P. H.
   1959 An analysis of learning in young Anatidae, *Ecology*, **40**:90–102.
   1962 "Behavioral Aspects of Ecology," Prentice-Hall, Englewood Cliffs, N. J.
   1963 Behavioral aspects of habitat selection: The role of early experience, *Wilson Bull.*, **75**:15–22.
   1964 Parameters of imprinting, *Am. Naturalist*, **98**:175–182.
   1965 Imprinting: a reassessment, *Science*, **147**:302–303.

Klopfer, P. H., and J. P. Hailman
   1964 Perceptual preferences and imprinting in chicks, *Science*, **145**:1333–1334.

Klopfer, P. H., and R. H. MacArthur
   1961 On the causes of tropical species diversity and niche overlap, *Am. Naturalist*, **95**:223–226.

Kluijver, H. N., and L. Tinbergen
   1953 Territory and the regulation of density in titmice, *Arch. Neerl. Zool.*, **10**:265–289.

Knox, E. G.
   1952 Jefferson County (N.Y.) soils and soil map, *N.Y. State College Agr.* (Cornell University, Ithaca, N.Y.).

Koford, C. B.
   1957 The vicuna and the puna, *Ecol. Monographs*, **27**:153–219.
   1958 Prairie dogs, white faces, and blue grama, *Wildlife Monograph*, No. 3, pp. 1–78.

Kolman, W. A.
   1960 The mechanism of natural selection for the sex ratio, *Am. Naturalist*, **94**:373–377.

Korstian, C. F.
   1931 Southern white cedar, *U. S. Dept. Agr. Tech. Bull. No. 251.*

Krebs, C.
   1963 Lemming cycle at Baker Lake, Canada during 1959–62, *Science*, **146**:1559–1560.

   1964 The lemming cycle at Baker Lake, Northwest Territories, during 1959–1962, *Tech. Paper No. 15. Arctic Institute of North America.*

Krog, J.
   1955 Notes on temperature measurements indicative of special organization in arctic and subarctic plants for utilization of radiated heat from the sun, *Physiol. Plantarum*, **8**:836–839.

Kuenzler, E. J.
   1961 Phosphorus budget of a mussel population, *Limnol. Oceanog.*, **6**:400–415.

Kuhnelt, W.
   1950 "Bodenbiologie mit besonderer Berucksichtigung der Tierwelt," Herold, Vienna, pp. 368 ff.

Lack, D.
   1947 The significance of clutch size, *Ibis*, **89**:30–52; **90**:25–45.
   1953 "The Life of the Robin," Penguin, London.
   1954 "The Natural Regulation of Animal Numbers," Clarendon Press, Oxford.

Lack, D., and L. S. V. Venerables
   1939 The habitat distribution of British woodland birds, *J. Animal Ecology*, **8**:39–71.

Lanyon, W. E.
   1958 The motivation of sun-bathing in birds, *Wilson Bull.*, **70**:280.

Lanyon, W. E., and W. N. Tavolga (eds.)
   1960 "Animal Sounds and Communication," *AIBS Symposium Series, Publ. No. 7.*

Larson, F.
   1940 The role of bison in maintaining the short grass plains, *Ecology*, **21**:113–121.

Lawrence, D. B.
   1958 Glaciers and vegetation in southeastern Alaska, *Am. Scientist*, **46**:89–122.

Lay, D. W.
   1958 Fire ant eradication and wildlife, *Proc. 12th Annual Conf. Southeast Assoc. Game Fish Comm.*, pp. 22–24.

Lees, A. D.
   1955 "The Physiology of Diapause in Arthropods," Cambridge, London.
   1960 Some aspects of animal photoperiodism, *Cold Spring Harbor Symp. Quant. Biol.*, **25**:261–268.

Lehrman, D. S.
   1959 Hormonal responses to external stimuli in birds, *Ibis*, **101**:478–496.

Leopold, A.
   1933 "Game Management," Scribner, New York.

Leopold, A., and A. Eynon
   1961 Avian daybreak and evening song in relation to time and light intensity, *Condor*, **63**:269–293.

Libby, W. F.
1961 Radiocarbon dating, *Science*, **133**:621–629.

Lindquist, B.
1942 Experimentelle Untersuchungen uber die Bedeutung einiger Landmollusken fur die Zersetgung der Waldstreu, *Kgl. Fysiograf. Sallskap Lund Forh.*, **11**:144–156.

Linduska, J. P.
1947 Winter den studies of the cottontail in southern Michigan, *Ecology*, **28**:448–454.

Lloyd, M., and H. S. Dybas.
In press The periodical cicada problem: 1, Population ecology. *Evolution*.

Loftus, K.
1958 Studies on river-spawning populations of lake trout in eastern Lake Superior, *Trans. Am. Fishery Soc.*, **87**:259–277.

Lord, R. D. Jr.
1961*a* A population study of the gray fox, *Am. Midland Naturalist*, **66**:87–109.
1961*b* Magnitudes of reproduction in cottontail rabbits, *J. Wildlife Management*, **25**:28–33.
1961*c* Mortality rates of cottontail rabbits, *J. Wildlife Management*, **25**:33–40.

Lorenz, K.
1931 Beitrage zur Ethologie der sozialer corviden, *J. fur Ornith.*, **46**:67–127.
1935 Der Kumpan in der Umwelt des Vogels, *J. fur Ornith.*, **83**:137–213; 289–413.
1937 The companion in the bird's world, *Auk*, **54**:245–273.

Lorenz, K., and N. Tinbergen
1938 Taxis und Instinkthandlung in der Eirollbewegung der Grangans I, *Z. Tierpsychol.*, **2**:1–29.

Lotka, A. J.
1925 "Elements of Physical Biology," Williams and Wilkins, Baltimore.

Lowdermilk, W. C.
1953 Conquest of the land through 7000 years, *U.S. Dept. Agr. Soil Conserv. Serv. Agr. Information Bull.*, 99.

Lunk, W. A.
1952 Notes on variation in the Carolina chickadee, *Wilson Bull.*, **64**:7–21.

Lutz, H. J.
1956 Ecological effects of forest fires in the interior of Alaska, *U.S. Dept. Agr. Tech. Bull.* 1133.

Lutz, H., and R. F. Chandler
1946 "Forest Soils," Wiley, New York.

Lyman, C. P., and A. R. Dawe
1960 "Mammalian Hibernation," *Museum Comp Zool.*, Harvard, Cambridge, Mass.

MacArthur, R. H.
1958 Population ecology of some warblers of northeastern coniferous forests, *Ecology*, **39**:599–619.

1960 On the relative abundance of species, *Am. Naturalist* **94**:25–36.
1961 Population effects of natural selection, *Am. Naturalist,* **95**:195–199

MacArthur, R. H., and J. W. MacArthur
1961 On bird species diversity, *Ecology*, **42**:594–598.

MacLulich, D. A.
1947 Fluctuations in the numbers of varying hare (*Lepus americanus*), *Univ. Toronto Biol. Ser. No. 43*.

Madgwick, H. A. I., and J. D. Ovington
1959 The chemical composition of precipitation in adjacent forest and open plots, *Forestry*, **32**:14–22.

Maio, J. J.
1958 Predatory fungi, *Sci. Am.*, **199**:67–72.

Maisurow, D. K.
1941 The role of fire in the perpetuation of virgin forests of northern Wisconsin, *J. Forestry*, **39**:201–207.

Margalef, R.
1963 On certain unifying principles in ecology, *Am. Naturalist*, **47**:357–374.

Marler, P.
1956 Behaviour of the chaffinch, *Fringilla coelebs, Behaviour Suppl.*, **5**:1–184.

Marsden, H. M., and N. R. Holler
1964 Social behavior in confined populations of the cottontail and swamp rabbit, *Wildlife Monographs No. 13*.

Marshall, J. T. Jr.
1948 Ecological races of song sparrows in the San Francisco Bay region: part II, Geographic variation, *Condor*, **50**:233–256.

Marshall, S. M., and A. P. Orr
1955 On the biology of *Calanus finmarchicus*: 8, Food uptake, assimilation, and excretion in stage V *Calanus, J. Marine Biol. Assoc. U.K.*, **34**:495–529.

Marshall, W. H.
1951 Pine marten as a forest product, *J. Forestry*, **49**:899–905.

Martin, N. D.
1960 An analysis of bird populations in relation to forest succession in Algonquin Provincial Park, Ontario, *Ecology*, **41**:126–140.

Mather, K.
1955 Polymorphism as an outcome of disruptive selection, *Evolution*, **9**:52–61.

Matthews, G. V. T.
1955 Bird navigation, *Cambridge Monogr. Exp. Biology No. 3*, Cambridge, London.

Mayer, W. V.
1960 Histological changes during the hibernating cycle in the arctic ground squirrel, in Lyman and Dawe (eds.), 1960, "Mammalian Hibernation," pp. 131–148.

Mayfield, H. F.
1960 "The Kirtland's warbler," *Cranbrook Inst. Sci. Bull.* No. 40.

Mayr, E.
1942 "Systematics and the Origin of Species," Columbia Univ. Press, New York.
1963 "Animal Species and Evolution," Harvard, Cambridge, Mass.

Mayr, E., E. G. Linsley, and R. L. Usinger
1953 "Methods and Principles of Systematic Zoology," McGraw-Hill, New York.

McAtee, W. L.
1939 Wildlife of the Atlantic Coast salt marshes, *U.S. Dept. Agr. Circ.,* **520**:1–28.

McCalla, T. M.
1943 Microbiological studies of the effect of straw used as a mulch, *Trans. Kansas Acad. Sci.,* **43**:52–56.

McCormick, J.
1959 "The Living Forest," Harper & Row, New York.

McCormick, F.
1963 Changes in a herbaceous plant community during a three-year period following exposure to ionizing radiation gradients, in Schultz and Klements (eds.), 1963, "Radioecology," pp. 271–276.

McIntosh, R. P.
1958 Plant communities, *Science,* **128**:115–120.

McMillan, C.
1959 The role of ecotypic variation in the distribution of the Central Grassland of North America, *Ecol. Monographs,* **29**:285–308.

McNab, B. K.
1963 Bioenergetics and the determination of home range size, *Am. Naturalist,* **97**: 133–140.

Meanley, B.
1957 Notes on the courtship behavior of the king rail, *Auk,* **74**:433–440.

Mendall, H. L.
1958 The Ring-necked Duck in the Northeast, *Univ. Maine Studies, Second Series,* No. 73,

Mentzer, L. W.
1951 Studies on plant succession in true prairie, *Ecol. Monographs,* **21**:255–267.

Mergen, Francois
1963 Ecotypic variation in *Pinus strobus* L, *Ecology,* **44**:716–727.

Merriam, C. H.
1898 Life zones and crop zones of the United States, *Bull., U.S. Bureau Biol. Survey,* **10**:1–79.

Merriam, H. G.
1960 Problems in woodchuck population ecology and a plan for telemetric study, PhD thesis, Cornell University, Ithaca, N.Y.

Meyerriecks, A. J.
1959 Foot stirring behavior in herons, *Wilson*

Bull., **71**:153–158.
1960 "Comparative Breeding Behavior of Four Species of North American Herons," *Publ. Nuttall Ornithological Club,* No. 2.

Miller A. H.
1942 Habitat selection among higher vertebrates and its relation to intraspecific variation, *Am. Naturalist,* **76**:25–35.

Miller, C. A.
1963 The spruce budworm, 1. The bionomics of the spruce budworm, in Morris (ed.), 1963, "The dynamics of epidemic spruce budworm population," pp. 12 ff.

Miller, W. R., and F. E. Egler
1950 Vegetation of the Wequetequock-Pawcatuck tidal marshes, Connecticut, *Ecol. Monographs,* **20**:141–172.

Millicent, E., and J. M. Thoday
1960 Gene flow and divergence under disruptive selection, *Science,* **131**:1311–1312.
1961 Effects of disruptive selection: IV, Gene flow and divergence, *Heredity,* **16**:199–217.

Mobius, K.
1883 The oyster and oyster-culture, *Rept. U.S. Fish Comm. 1880,* **8**:683–824.

Mohler, L. L., J. H. Wampole, and E. Fichter
1951 Mule deer in Nebraska National Forest, *J. Wildlife Management,* **15**:129–157.

Mook, L. J.
1963 Birds and spruce budworm, in Morris, 1963, "The dynamics of epidemic spruce budworm populations," pp. 244–248.

Mooney, H. A., and W. O. Billings
1960 The annual carbohydrate cycle of alpine plants as related to growth, *Am. J. Botany,* **47**:594–598.

Moore, C. W. E.
1959 The competitive effect of *Danthonia* spp. on the establishment of *Bothriochloa ambigua, Ecology,* **40**:141–143.

Moore, H. B.
1934 The relation of shell growth to environment in *Patella vulgata, Proc. Malacological Soc.* (London), **21**:217–222.

Moore, J. A.
1949*a* Geographic variation of adaptive characters in *Rana pipiens* Schreber, *Evolution,* **3**:1–24.
1949*b* Patterns of evolution in the genus *Rana,* in Jepsen, Mayr, and Simpson, 1949, "Genetics Paleontology and Evolution," pp. 315–338.

Morris, D.
1954 The reproductive behaviour of the river bullhead (*Cottus gobio* L.) with special reference to the fauning activity, *Behaviour,* **7**:1–32.

Morris, R. F. (ed.)
1963 The dynamics of epidemic spruce budworm populations, *Mem. Entomol. Soc. Canada,* No. 31.

Morris. R. F., W. F. Cheshire, C. A. Miller, and D. G. Mott.
1958 The numerical response of avian and mammalian predators during a gradation of the spruce budworm, *Ecology,* **39**:487–494.

Morrison, P. R., and F. A. Ryser
1952 Weight and body temperature in mammals, *Science,* **116**:231–232.

Mortimer, C. H.
1952 Water movements in lakes during summer stratification: evidence from the distribution of temperature in Windermere, *Phil. Trans. Roy. Soc.* (London) *Ser. B,* pp. 236–355.

Moynihan, M.
1955a Some aspects of reproductive behaviour in the blackheaded gull (*Larus ridibundus ridibundus* L.) and related species, *Behaviour Suppl.,* **4**:1–201.
1955b Types of hostile display, *Auk,* **72**:247–259.
1955c Remarks on the original sources of displays, *Auk,* **72**:240–246.
1962 Display patterns of tropical American "Nine-primaried" songbirds: I, *Chlorospingus, Auk,* **79**:310–344.

Moynihan, M., and M. F. Hall
1954 Hostile, sexual and other social behaviour patterns of the spice finch (*Lonchura punctulata*) in captivity, *Behaviour,* **7**:3–76.

Muller, C. H.
1953 The association of desert annuals with shrubs, *Am. J. Botany,* **40**:53–59.

Muller, K.
1954 Investigations on the organic drift in north Swedish streams, *Dept. Inst. Freshwater Research* (Drottningholm), **35**:133–148.

Muller, P. E.
1889 Becherches sur les formes naturelles de l'humus, *Ann. Sci. Agron.* (Paris), **6**:85–423.

Murie, A.
1944 The Wolves of Mount McKinley, *U.S. Dept. Interior Natl. Park Serv., Fauna Ser.,* **5**:1–238.

Murphy, P. W.
1952 "Soil Faunal Investigations," in "Report on Forest Research for the year ending March, 1951," *Forestry Comm.* (London), pp. 130–134.
1953 The biology of the forest soils with special reference to the mesofauna or meiofauna, *J. Soil Sci.,* **4**:155–193.

Muscatine, L., and H. M. Lenhoff
1963 Symbiosis on the role of algae symbiotic with hydra, *Science,* **142**:956–958.

Muul, I.
1965 Daylength and food caches, *Nat. Hist.,* **74**(3):22–27.

Nagel, W. V.
1943 How big is a coon? *Missouri Conservation,* **4**(7):6–7.

Naylor, E.
1958 Tidal and diurnal rhythms of locomotory activity in *Carcinus maenus* (L), *J. Exptl. Biol.,* **35**:602–610.

Neave, F.
1944 Racial characteristics and migratory habits in *Salmo gairdneri, J. Fisheries Res. Board Can.,* **6**:245–251.

Neel, J. K.
1951 Interrelations of certain physical and chemical features in headwater limestone streams, *Ecology,* **32**:368–391.

Nelson, D. J., and D. C. Scott
1962 Role of detritus in the productivity of a rock-outcrop community in a Piedmont stream, *Limnol. Oceanog.* **3**:396–413.

Nelson, P. R., and W. T. Edmondson
1955 Limnological effects of fertilizing Bare Lake, Alaska, *U.S. Fish Wildlife Serv. Fishery Bull.,* **56**:415–436.

Nero, R. W.
1956a A behavior study of the red-winged blackbird: I, Mating and nesting activities, *Wilson Bull.,* **68**:5–37.
1956b A behavior study of the redwinged blackbird: II, Territoriality, *Wilson Bull.,* **68**:129–150.

Neuwirth, R.
1957 Some recent investigations into the chemistry of air and of precipitation and their significance for forestry, *Allg. Forst-v. Jagdztg,* **128**:147–150.

Newman, M. A.
1956 Social behavior and interspecific competition in two trout species, *Physiol. Zool.,* **29**:64–81.

Nice, Margaret M.
1941 The role of territory in bird life, *Am. Midland Naturalist,* **26**:441–487.
1943 Studies in the life history of the song sparrow: II, *Trans. Linn. Soc.* (New York), **6**:1–329.
1950 Development of a redwing: *Agelaius phoeniceus, Wilson Bull.,* **62**:87–93.
1962 Development of behavior in precocial birds, *Trans. Linn. Soc.* (New York), vol. 8.

Nice, Margaret M., and W. E. Schantz
1959 Head-scratching in Passerines, *Ibis,* **101**:250–251.

Nice, Margaret M., and J. J. Ter Pelwyk
1941 Enemy recognition by the song sparrow, *Auk,* **58**:195–214.

Nicholson, A. J.
1954 An outline of the dynamics of animal populations, *Australian J. Zool.,* **2**:9–65.
1958 The self-adjustment of populations to change, *Cold Spring Harbor Symp. Quant. Biol.,* **22**:153–173.

Nicholson, A. J., and V. A. Bailey
 1935 The balance of animal populations, Part 1, *Proc. Zool. Soc. London,* pp. 551–598.
Nielsen, A.
 1950 The torrential invertebrate fauna, *Oikos,* 2:176–196.
Nielsen, C. O.
 1961 Respiratory metabolism of some populations of enchytraeid worms and free-living nematodes, *Oikos,* 12:17–35.
 1962 Carbohydrases in soil and litter invertebrates, *Oikos,* 13:200–215.
Niering, W. A., and F. E. Egler
 1955 A shrub community of *Viburnum lentago* stable for twenty-five years, *Ecology,* 36:356–360.
Noble, G. K.
 1936 Courtship and sexual selection of the flicker (*Colaptes auratus luteus*), *Auk,* 53:269–282.
Noble, G. K., and H. T. Bradley
 1933 The mating behavior of lizards: Its bearing on the theory of sexual selection, *Ann. N. Y. Acad. Sci.,* 35:25–100.
Nolan, V. Jr.
 1958 Anticipatory food-bringing in the prairie warbler, *Auk,* 75:263–278.
Norris, K. S.
 1963 The functions of temperature in the ecology of the percoid fish *Girella nigricans* (Ayres), *Ecol. Monographs,* 33:23–62.
Odum, E. P.
 1941 Annual cycle of the black-capped chickadee, *Auk,* 58:314–333, 518–535; 59:499–531.
 1959 "Fundamentals of Ecology," 2d ed., Saunders, Philadelphia.
 1960 Organic production and turnover in old field succession, *Ecology,* 41:34–49.
Odum, E. P., and E. J. Kuenzler
 1963 Experimental isolation of food chains in old-field ecosystem with the use of phosphorus-32, in Schultz and Klement (eds.), 1963, "Radioecology," pp. 113–120.
Odum, H. T.
 1956 Primary production in flowing water, *Limnol. Oceanog.,* 1(2):102–117.
 1957a Trophic structure and productivity of Silver Springs, Florida, *Ecol. Monographs,* 27:55–112.
 1957b Primary production measurements in eleven Florida springs and a marine turtle-grass community, *Limnol. Oceanog.,* 2:85–97.
Odum, H. T., and E. P. Odum
 1955 Trophic structure and productivity of a windward coral reef community on Eniwetok Atoll, *Ecol. Monographs,* 25:291–320.
Ogawa, H., K. Yoda, and T. Kira
 1961 A preliminary survey on the vegetation of Thailand, *Nature and Life in Southeast Asia,* 1:21–157.

Olson, J. S.
 1958 Rates of succession and soil changes on southern Lake Michigan sand dunes, *Botan. Gaz.,* 119:125–170.
Oosting, H. J., and L. E. Anderson
 1937 The vegetation of a bare-faced cliff in western North Carolina, *Ecology,* 18:280–292.
 1939 Plant succession on granite rock in eastern North Carolina, *Botan. Gaz.,* 100:750–768.
Ophel, I. L.
 1959 Investigation of the effects of radioactive material on aquatic life in Canada, *Trans. 2nd Seminar Biol. Problems. Water Pollution* (Robert A. Taft Sanit. Eng. Centre), *Tech Report* W 60, pp. 3–21.
 1963 The fate of radiostrontium in a freshwater community, in Schultz and Klement (eds.), 1963, "Radioecology," pp. 213–216.
Orians, G. H., and G. Collier
 1963 Competition and blackbird social systems, *Evolution,* 17:449–459.
Orians, G. H., and M. F. Willson
 1964 Interspecific territories of birds, *Ecology,* 45:736–745.
Osborn, B., and P. F. Allen
 1949 Vegetation of an abandoned prairie-dog town in tall grass prairie, *Ecology,* 30:322–332.
Overgaard, C.
 1949 Studies on the soil microfauna: II, The soil inhabiting nematodes, *Nat. Jutland,* 2:131ff.
Overland, Lillian
 1960 Endogenous rhythms in opening and odor of flowers of *Cestrum nocturnum, Am. J. Botany,* 47:378–382.
Ovington, J. D.
 1957 Dry matter production by *Pinus sylvestris* L, *Ann. Botany London N.S.,* 21:287–314.
 1959 Mineral content of plantations of *Pinus sylvestris* L, *Ann. Botany London N.S.,* 23:75–88.
 1961 Some aspects of energy flow in plantation of *Pinus sylvestris* L, *Ann. Botany London N.S.,* 25:12–20.
 1962a Quantitative ecology and the woodland ecosystem concept, in Cragg (ed.), 1962, "Advances in Ecological Research I," pp. 103–192.
 1962b The application of ecology to multipurpose use of woodlands, *Proc. Lockwood Conf. on the Suburban Forest and Ecology Bull.* 652, *Conn. Agr. Expt. Sta.* pp. 76–89.
Ovington, J. D., D. Heitkamp, and D. B. Lawrence
 1963 Plant biomass and productivity of prairie, Savanna, oakwood and maize field ecosystems in Central Minnesota, *Ecology,* 44:52–63.
Ovington, J. D., and H. A. I. Madgwick
 1959 The growth and composition of natural stands of birch: 1, Dry matter production, *Plant Soil,* 10:271–283.

Palmer, H. E., W. C. Hanson, B. I. Griffin, and W. C. Roesch
1963 Cesium 137 in Alaskan Eskimos, *Science,* **142**(3588):64–65.

Palmer, R. S.
1941 A behavior study of the common tern (*Sterna hirundo hirundo* L.), *Proc. Boston Soc. Nat. Hist.,* **42**:1–119.

Palmgren, P.
1949 Some remarks on the short-term fluctuations in the numbers of northern birds and mammals, *Oikos,* **1**:114–121.

Papi, F.
1955 Astronomische Orientierung bei der Wolfspinne *Arctosa perita, Z. Vergleich. Physiol.,* **37**:230–233.

Papi, F., L. Serretti, and S. Parrini
1957 Nuove richerche sull'orientamento e il senso del tempo di *Arctosa perita, Z. Vergleich. Physiol.,* **39**:531–561.

Park, T.
1948 Experimental studies of interspecies competition: I, Competition between populations of the flour beetles, *Trilobium confusum* Duval and *Trilobium castaneum* Herbst, *Ecol. Monographs,* **18**:265–308.
1954 Experimental studies of interspecies competition: II, Temperature, humidity, and competition in two species of *Trilobium, Physiol. Zool.,* **27**:177–238.

Pate, V. S. L.
1933 Studies on fish food in selected areas: A Biological survey of Raquette Watershed, N.Y., *State Conserv. Dept. Biol. Survey No. 8,* 136–157.

Patrick, Ruth
1949 A proposed biological measure of stream conditions based on a survey of the Conestoga Basin, Lancaster County, Pennsylvania, *Proc. Acad. Nat. Sci. Phila.,* **101**:277–341.

Pearcy, W.
1962 Ecology of an estuarine population of winter flounder *Pseudopleuronectes americanus* (Walbaum), Parts I–IV, *Bull. Bingham Oceanographic Collection,* Vol. 18, art. 1, pp. 1–78.

Pearl, R., and L. J. Reed
1920 On the rate of growth of the population of the United States since 1790 and its mathematical representation, *Proc. Nat. Acad. Sci., U.S.,* **6**:275–288.

Pearse, A. S., H. J. Humm, and G. W. Wharton
1942 Ecology of sand beaches at Beaufort, North Carolina, *Ecol. Monographs,* **12**:136–190.

Pearson, O. A.
1946 Scent glands of the short-tailed shrew, *Anat. Record,* **94**:615–629.

Pearson, P. G.
1959 Small mammals and old field succession on the Piedmont of New Jersey, *Ecology,* **40**:249–255.

Pennak, R. W.
1942 Ecology of some copepods inhabiting intertidal beaches near Woods Hole, Massachusetts, *Ecology,* **23**:446–456.
1951 Comparative ecology of the interstitial fauna of fresh-water and marine beaches, *Ann. Biologique,* **27**:217–248.

Pennak, R. W., and E. D. VanGerpen
1947 Bottom fauna production and physical nature of a substrate in a northern Colorado trout stream, *Ecology,* **28**:42–48.

Pennak, R. W., and D. J. Zinn
1943 Mystacocarida, a new order of Crustacea from intertidal beaches in Massachusetts and Connecticut, *Smith's Misc. Coll.,* vol. 103, no. 9.

Pequegnat, W. E.
1961 Life in the scuba zone II, *Natural History,* **70**(5):46–54.

Petrov, V. S.
1946 Aktevnaia reaktsiia pochvy pH kah faktor rasprpstraneniia dozhdevykh chorvei (Lumbricidae, Oligochaetae), *Zool. Zh.,* **25**:107–110.

Pfeiffer, W.
1962 The fright reaction of fish, *Biol. Rev.,* **37**:495–511.

Phillips, W. S.
1963 Depth of roots in soil, *Ecology,* **44**:424.

Pike, G. C.
1962 Migration and feeding of the gray whale, *J. Fisheries Res. Board Can.,* **19**:815–838.

Pimentel, D.
1961 Animal population regulation by the genetic feed-back mechanism, *Am. Naturalist,* **95**:65–79.

Pimentel, D., J. E. Dewey, and H. H. Schwardt
1951 An increase in the duration of the life cycle of DDT-resistant strains of the house fly, *J. Econ. Entomol.,* **44**:477–481.

Pimentel, D., E. H. Feinberg, P. W. Wood, and J. T. Hayes
1965 Selection, spacial distribution, and the co-existance of competing fly species, *Am. Naturalist,* **99**:97–109.

Pimentel, D., W. P. Nagel, and J. L. Madden
1963 Space-time structure of the environment and the survival of parasite-host system, *Am. Naturalist,* **97**:141–167.

Pitelka, F. A.
1957a Some aspects of population structure in the short term cycle of the brown lemming in northern Alaska, *Cold Spring Harbor Symp. Quant. Biol.,* **22**:237–251.
1957b Some characteristics of microtine cycles in the Arctic. 18th Biology Coll. Proc., Oregon State College (Corazallis), pp. 73–88.

Pittendrigh, C. S.
1954 On temperature independence in the clock

system controlling emergence time in *Drosophila,* *Proc. Natl. Acad. Sci. U.S.,* **40**:1018–1029.

Platt, R. B.

1963 Ecological effects of ionizing radiation on organisms, communities and ecosystems, in Schultz and Klement (eds.), 1963, "Radioecology," pp. 243–255.

Polt, J. M., and E. H. Hess

1964 Following and imprinting effects of light and social experience, *Science,* **143**:1185–1187.

Polunin, N.

1934–1935 The vegetation of Akpatok Island I-II, *J. Ecology,* **22**:337–395; **23**:161–209.

1948 Botany of the Canadian eastern Arctic, III. Vegetation and ecology, *Nat. Museum Canada Bull.* 104.

1960 "Introduction to Plant Geography," McGraw-Hill, New York.

Pomeroy, L. R.

1959 Algae productivity in salt marshes of Georgia, *Limnol. Oceanog.,* **4**:386–397.

Pomeroy, L. R., H. M. Mathews, and H. Shik Min

1963 Excretion of phosphate and soluble organic phosphorus compounds by zooplankton, *Limnol. Oceanog.,* **8**:50–55.

Poore, M. E. D.

1962 The method of successive approximation in descriptive ecology, in Cragg (ed.), 1962, "Advances in Ecological Research," pp. 35–68.

Potzger, J. E.

1956 Pollen profiles as indicators in the history of lake filling and bog formation, *Ecology,* **37**:476–483.

Prescott, G. W.

1960 Biological disturbances resulting from algal populations in standing water, in "The Ecology of Algae," *Pymatuning Lab. Field Biol. Spec. Publ. No. 2.*

Preston, F. W.

1948 The commonness, and rarity of species, *Ecology,* **29**:254–283.

Pritchard, D. W.

1952 Salinity distribution and circulation in the Chesapeake Bay estuarine system, *J. Marine Res.,* **11**:106–123.

Prosser, C. L., (ed.)

1958 "Physiological Adaptations," American Physiological Society, Washington, D.C.

Pruitt, W. O. Jr.

1960 Behavior of the barren-ground caribou, *Biol. Paper, University of Alaska, No. 3.*

Pschorn-Walcher, H.

1952 Vergleich der Bodenfauna in Mischwaldern und Fichtenmonokulturen der Nordostalpen, *Mitt. forstl. Versanst. Mariabrunn.,* **48**:44–111.

Rainey, R. C., and Z. Waloff

1948 Desert locust migrations and synoptic meteorology in the Gulf of Aden area, *J. Animal Ecology,* **17**:101–112.

1951 Flying locusts and convection currents, *Bull. Anti-locust Research Centre* (London), **9**:51–70.

Rand, A. L.

1961 Some size gradients in North American birds, *Wilson Bull.,* **73**:46–56.

Ransay, A. O.

1956 Seasonal patterns in the epigamic displays of some surface-feeding ducks, *Wilson Bull.,* **68**:275–281.

Rasmussen, D. I.

1941 Biotic communities of Kaibab Plateau, Arizona, *Ecol. Monographs,* **3**:229–275.

Raup, H. M.

1951 Vegetation and cyroplanation, *Ohio J. Sci.,* **51**:105–116.

Read, R. A., and L. C. Walker

1950 Influence of eastern red cedar on soil in Connecticut pine plantations, *J. Forestry,* **48**:337–339.

Redd, B. L., and A. Benson

1962 Utilization of bottom fauna by brook trout in a northern West Virginia stream, *Proc. West Va. Acad. Sci.,* **34**:21–26.

Reitemeier, R. F.

1957 Soil potassium and fertility, in "Soil," Yearbook of Agriculture 1957, *U.S. Dept. Agr.,* Washington, D.C., pp. 101–106.

Renner, M.

1960 The contribution of the honey bee to the study of time-sense and astronomical orientation, *Cold Spring Harbor Symp. Quant. Biol.,* **25**:361–367.

Retzer, J. L.

1956 Alpine soils of the Rocky Mountains, *J. Soil Sci.,* **7**:22–32.

Rice, E. L., W. T. Penfound, and L. M. Rohrbaugh

1960 Seed dispersal and mineral nutrition in succession in abandoned fields in central Oklahoma, *Ecology,* **41**:224–228.

Richards, P. W.

1952 "The Tropical Rain Forest," Cambridge, London.

Ricker, W. E.

1940 On the origin of Kokanee, a freshwater type of sockeye salmon, *Trans. Roy. Soc. Can. Sect. V,* **34**:121–135.

1954 Stock and recruitment, *J. Fisheries Res. Board Can.,* **11**:559–623.

1958a Maximum sustained yields from fluctuating environments and mixed stocks, *J. Fisheries Res. Board Can.,* **15**:991–1006.

1958b Handbook of computations for biological statistics of fish populations, *Bull. 119, J. Fisheries Res. Board Can.,* pp. 1–300.

Rigler, F. H.

1956 A tracer study of the phosphorus cycle in lake water, *Ecology,* **37**:550–567.

Robertson, J. H.
1939 A quantitative study of the true-prairie vegetation after three years of extreme drought, *Ecol. Monographs,* **9**:433–492.

Roe, Anne, and G. G. Simpson
1958 "Behavior and Evolution," Yale, New Haven, Conn.

Roeder, K. D., and A. E. Treat
1961 The detection and evasion of bats by moths, *Am. Scientist,* **49**:135–148.

Ross, H. H.
1944 The caddisflies or Trichoptera, of Illinois, *Bull. Illinois Nat. Hist. Surv.* **23**:1–326.
1962 "A Synthesis of Evolutionary Theory," Prentice-Hall, Englewood Cliffs, N.J.

Rowan, W. R.
1925 Relation of flight to bird migration and developmental changes, *Nature,* **115**:494–495.
1929 Experiments in bird migration: I, Manipulation of the reproductive cycle, seasonal histological changes in the gonads, *Proc. Boston Soc. Nat. Hist.,* **39**:151–208.

Rowe, P. B., and T. M. Hendrix
1951 Interception of rain and snow by second growth ponderosa pine, *Trans. Am. Geophys. Union,* **32**:903–908.

Rowell, C. H. F.
1961 Displacement grooming in the Chaffinch, *Animal Behaviour,* **9**:38–63.

Rudd, R. L.
1964 "Pesticides and the Living Landscape," University of Wisconsin Press, Madison, Wisc.

Rudd, R. L., and R. E. Genelly
1956 Pesticides: their use and toxicity in relation to wildlife, *Calif. Fish and Game Bull.* No. 7.

Ruttner, F.
1953 "Fundamentals of Limnology," University of Toronto Press, Toronto.

Ryther, J. H.
1956 Photosynthesis in the ocean as a function of light intensity, *Limnol. Oceanog.,* **1**:61–70.
1960 Organic production by plankton algae and its environmental control, in "Ecology of Algae," the *Pymatuning Lab. Field Biol. Spec. Publ.* No. 2. University of Pittsburgh Press, Pittsburgh, pp. 72–83.

Ryther, J. H., and C. S. Yentsch
1957 The estimation of phytoplankton production in the ocean from chlorophyll and light data, *Limnol. Oceanog.,* **2**:281–286.

Sabine, W. S.
1959 The winter society of the Oregon junco: intolerance, dominance, and the pecking order, *Condor,* **61**:110–135.

Salt, G., F. S. J. Hollick, F. Raw, and M. V. Brian
1948 The arthropod population of pasture soil, *J. Animal Ecology,* **17**:139–150.

Salt, G. W.
1952 The relation of metabolism to climate and distribution in three finches of the genus *Carpodacus, Ecol. Monographs,* **22**:121–152.
1957 An analysis of avifaunas in the Teton Mountains and Jackson Hole, Wyoming, *Condor,* **59**:373–393.

Sandon, H.
1927 "The Composition and Distribution of the Protozoan Fauna of the Soil," Oliver and Boyd, London.

Sauer, E. G. F., and Elenore Sauer
1955 Zur Frage der nächtlichen Zugorientierung von Grasmüken, *Rev. Suisse Zool.,* **62**:250–259.
1960 Star navigation of nocturnal migrating birds, *Cold Spring Harbor Symp. Quant. Biol.,* **25**:463–473.

Saunders, J. K., Jr.
1963 Movements and activities of the lynx in Newfoundland, *J. Wildlife Management,* **27**:390–400.

Schelderup-Ebbe, T.
1922 Beitrage zur Socialpsychologie des Haushuhns, *Zeitschr. Psychol.,* **88**:225–252.

Schenkel, R.
1948 Ausdruckstudien an Wolfen, *Behaviour,* **1**:81–130.

Schmidt, K. P.
1954 Faunal realms, regions and provinces, *Quart. Rev. Biol.,* **29**:322–331.

Schmidt-Nielsen, K.
1956 Animals and arid conditions: physiological aspects of productivity and management, in White, 1956, "Future of Arid Lands," pp. 368–389.
1959 Physiology of the camel, *Sci. Am.,* **201**:140–151.
1960 The salt secreting gland of marine birds, *Circulation,* **21**:955–967.
1964 "Desert Animals: Physiological Problems of Heat and Water," Oxford, London.

Schmidt-Nielsen, K., and B. Schmidt-Nielsen
1952 Water metabolism of desert mammals, *Physiol. Rev.,* **32**:135–166.

Scholander, P. F.
1955 Evolution of climatic adaptation in homeotherms, *Evolution,* **9**:15–26.

Scholander, P. F., R. Hock, V. Walters, F. Johnson, and L. Irving
1950 Heat regulation in some arctic and tropical birds and mammals, *Biol. Bull.,* **99**:237–258.

Scholander, P. F., V. Walters, R. Hock, L. Irving, and F. Johnson
1950 Body insulation of some arctic and tropical mammals and birds, *Biol. Bull.,* **99**:225–236.

Schuck, H.
1943 Survival, population density, growth and movement of the wild brown trout in Crystal Creek, *Trans. Am. Fisheries Soc.,* **73**:209–230.

Schultz, V., and A. W. Klement (eds.)
1963 "Radioecology," Reinhold, New York.

Schwartz, C. W.
1944 "The Prairie Chicken in Missouri," Missouri Conserv. Comm. (Jefferson City, Mo.).

Schnell, J. H.
1963 The effect of neutron-gamma radiation on free-living small mammals at the Lockheed Reactor Site, in Schultz and Klement (eds.), 1963, "Radioecology," pp. 339–344.

Sclater, P. L.
1858 On the general geographical distribution of the members of the class Aves, *J. Proc. Limn. Soc. (Zool.)*, **2**:130–145.

Scott, J. P.
1958 "Animal Behavior," University Chicago Press, Chicago.
1962 Critical periods in behavioral development, *Science*, **138**:949–958.

Scott, J. W.
1942 Mating behavior of the sage grouse, *Auk*, **59**:472–498.
1950 A study of the phylogenetic or comparative behavior of three species of grouse, *Ann. N.Y. Acad. Sci.*, **51**:1062–1073.

Scott, T. C.
1943 Some food coactions of the northern plains red fox, *Ecol. Monographs*, **13**:427–479.

Segerstråle, S. G.
1947 New observations on the distribution and morphology of the amphipod *Gammarus zaddachi* Sexton with notes on related species, *J. Marine Biol. Assoc. U.K.*, **27**:219–244.

Selander, R. K., and D. R. Giller
1961 Analysis of sympatry of great-tailed and boat-tailed grackles, *Condor*, **63**:29–56.

Selleck, G. W.
1960 The climax concept, *Botan. Rev.*, **26**:534–545.

Sevenster, P.
1961 "A Causal Analysis of Displacement Activity in Fanning in *Gasterosteus aculeatus* L," Brill, Leiden.

Severinghaus, C. W., and Rosalind Gottleib
1959 Big deer vs. little deer, *N.Y. State Conservationist*, **14**(2):30–31.

Shelford, V. E.
1932 Life zones, modern ecology, and the failure of the temperature summing, *Wilson Bull.*, **44**:144–157.

Shelford, V. E., and A. C. Twomey
1941 Tundra animal communities in the vicinity of Churchill, Manitoba, *Ecology*, **22**:47–69.

Sheppard, P. M.
1951 Fluctuations in the selective value of certain phenotypes in the polymorphic land snail *Cepaea nemoralis* (L), *Heredity*, **5**:125–134.
1959 "Natural Selection and Heredity," Hutchinson, London.

Shetter, D. S.
1937 Migration, growth rate, and population density of brook trout in the north branch of the Au Sable, Michigan, *Trans. Am. Fisheries Soc.*, **66**:203–210.

Shreve, F.
1951 Vegetation of the Sonoran Desert, *Carnegie Inst. Wash. Publ.* 591, Washington, D.C.

Sibley, C. G.
1957 The evolutionary and taxonomic significance of sexual dimorphism and hybridization in birds, *Condor*, **59**:166–191.
1960 The electrophoretic patterns of avian egg-white proteins as taxonomic characters, *Ibis*, **102**:215–284.

Sigafoos, R. S.
1951 Soil instability in tundra vegetation, *Ohio J. Sci.*, **51**:281–298.
1952 Frost action as a primary physical factor in tundra plant communities, *Ecology*, **33**:480–487.

Simmons, K. E. L.
1955 The nature of predator-reactions of waders towards humans; with special reference to the role of aggressive-, escape-, and brooding-drives, *Behaviour*, **8**:130–173.
1957a A review of the anting behaviour of passerine birds, *British Birds*, **50**:401–424.

Skinner, W. A., R. D. Mathews, and R. M. Parkhurst
1962 Alarm reaction of the topsmelt *Atherinops affinia* (Ayers), *Science*, **138**:681–682.

Slobodkin, L. B.
1962 "Growth and Regulation of Animal Populations," Holt, New York.

Smalley, A. E.
1960 Energy flow of a salt marsh grasshopper population, *Ecology*, **41**:672–677.

Smith, F. E.
1952 Experimental methods in population dynamics: a critique, *Ecology*, **33**:441–450.
1961 Density dependence in the Australian thrips, *Ecology*, **42**:403–407.

Smith, R. L.
1956 An evaluation of conifer plantations as wildlife habitat, PhD thesis, Cornell University, Ithaca, N.Y.
1959 Conifer plantations as wildlife habitat, *N. Y. Fish Game J.*, **5**:101–132.
1959 The songs of the grasshopper sparrow, *Wilson Bull.*, **71**:141–152.
1962 Acorn consumption by white-footed mice (*Peromyscus leucopus*), *Bull.* 482T, *West Va. Univ. Agr. Expt. Sta.*
1963 Some ecological notes on the grasshopper sparrow, *Wilson Bull.*, **75**:159–165.

Snyder, R. L.
1962 Reproductive performance of a population of woodchucks after a change in sex ratio, *Ecology*, **43**:506–515.

Sollberger, A.
1965 "Biological Rhythm Research," Elsevier, Amsterdam.

Solomon, M. E.
1957 Dynamics of insect populations, *Ann. Rev. Entomol.*, **2**:121–142.
1964 Analysis of processes involved in the natural control of insects, in Cragg (ed.), 1964, "Advances in Ecological Research," vol. 2, pp. 1–58.

Sorensen, T.
1954 Adaptation of small plants to deficient nutrition and a short growing season, *Botan. Tidsskr.*, **51**:339–361.

Sowls, L. K.
1960 Results of a banding study of Gambels quail in southern Arizona, *J. Wildlife Management*, **24**:185–190.

Spaeth, J. N., and C. H. Diebold
1938 Some interrelations between soil characteristics, water tables, soil temperature, and snow cover in the forest and adjacent open areas in south-central New York, *Cornell Univ. Agr. Expt. Sta. Mem.*, 213.

Sparrow, A. H., and G. M. Woodwell
1963 Prediction of the sensitivity of plants to chronic gamma radiation, in Schultz and Klement (eds.), 1963, "Radioecology," pp. 257–270.

Specht, R. L., P. Rayson, and M. E. Jackson
1958 Dark Island Heath (Ninety-mile Plain, South Australia): VI, Pyric succession: Changes in composition, coverage, dry weight, and mineral nutrient status, *Australian J. Botany*, **6**:59–88.

Spooner, G. M.
1947 The distribution of *Gammarus* species in estuaries. Part I, *J. Marine Biol. Assoc. U.K.*, **27**:1–52.

Sprague, H. B.
1959 "Grasslands," American Assoc. Adv. Science, Washington, D.C.

Spurr, S. H.
1952 Origin of the concept of forest succession, *Ecology*, **33**:426–427.
1957 Local climate in the Harvard Forest, *Ecology*, **38**:37–56.

Stamp, L. D.
1961 A history of land use in arid regions, *Arid Zone Research, no. 17.*

Stebbins, G. L. Jr.
1950 "Variation and Evolution in Plants," Columbia, New York.

Stegeman, L. C.
1960 A preliminary survey of earthworms of the Tully Forest in central New York, *Ecology*, **41**:779–782.

Stenger, Judith, and J. B. Falls
1959 The utilized territory of the ovenbird, *Wilson Bull.*, **71**:125–140.

Stephenson, T. A., and Anne Stephenson
1949 The universal features of zonation between tide-marks on rocky coasts, *J. Ecology*, **37**:289–305.
1950 Life between tide-marks in North America: I, The Florida Keys, *J. Ecology*, **38**:354–402.
1952 Life between tide-marks in North America: II, North Florida and the Carolinas, *J. Ecology*, **40**:1–49.
1954 Life between the tide-marks in North America: IIIA, Nova Scotia and Prince Edward Island: Description of the Region; IIIB, Nova Scotia and Prince Edward Island: The geographical features of the region, *J. Ecology*, **42**:14–45, 46–70.
1961 Life between tide-marks in North America: IVA, IVB, Vancouver Island, I, II, *J. Ecology*, **49**:1–29, 229–243.

Stern, W. L., and M. F. Buell
1951 Life-form spectra of New Jersey pine barren forest and Minnesota jack pine forest, *Torrey Botan. Club Bull.*, **78**:61–65.

Stevanovic, D.
1956 (Populations of collembola in forest associations on Mt. Kopaonik), *Zbornik Radov Inst. Ekol. Biogeogr. (Beograd)*, **7**:16 ff.

Stewart, P. A.
1952 Dispersal, breeding behavior and longevity of banded barn owls in North America, *Auk*, **69**:227–245.

Stewart, R. E., and J. W. Aldrich
1952 Ecological studies of breeding bird populations in northern Maine, *Ecology*, **33**:226–238.

Stewart, R. E., A. D. Geis, and C. D. Evans
1958 Distribution of populations and hunting kill of the canvasback, *J. Wildlife Management*, **22**:333–370.

Stoeckeler, J. H.
1962 Shelterbelt influence on Great Plains field environment and crops, *U.S. Dept. Agr. Prod. Res. Rept. No. 62.*

Stokes, A. W.
1955 Population studies of the ring-necked pheasants on Pelee Island, Ontario, *Ontario Dept. Lands Forests, Tech. Bull. Wildlife Ser. No. 4* (Ottawa, Canada).
1961 Voice and social behavior of the chukar partridge, *Condor*, **63**:111–127.

Stout, B. B., and R. J. McMahon
1961 Throughfall variation under tree crowns, *J. Geophys. Res.*, **66**:1839–1843.

Stout, J. F.
1963 The significance of sound production during the reproductive behaviour of *Notropis analostanus* (Family Cyprinidae), *Animal Behaviour*, **11**:83–92.

Stringer, G. E., and W. S. Hoar
1955 Aggressive behavior of underyearling Kamloops trout, *Can. J. Zool.,* **33**:148–160.

Strumwasser, F.
1960 Some physiological principles governing hibernation in *Citellus beecheyi,* in Lyman and Dawe (eds.), 1963, "Mammalian Hibernation," pp. 285–318.

Sullivan, Charlotte M., and K. C. Fisher
1953 Seasonal fluctuations in the selected temperature of speckled trout *Salvelinus fontinalis* (Mitchell), *J. Fisheries Res. Board Can.,* **10**:187–195.

Swank, W. G.
1959 The mule deer in Arizona Chaparral, *Wildlife Bull. No. 3, Arizona Game Fish Dept.* (Phoenix, Ariz.).

Sweeney, B. M., and J. W. Hastings
1957 Characteristics of the diurnal rhythm of luminescence in *Gonyaulax polyedra, J. Cellular Comp. Physiol.* **49**:115.

Taber, R. D.
1949 Observations on the breeding behavior of the ring-necked pheasant, *Condor,* **51**:153–175.
1953 Studies of black-tailed deer reproduction on three chaparral cover types, *Calif. Fish Game,* **39**:177–186.

Taber, R. D., and R. F. Dasmann
1957 The dynamics of three natural populations of the deer *Odocoileus hemionus columbianus, Ecology,* **38**:233–246.
1958 The black-tailed deer of the Chaparral, *Calif. Dept. Fish Game, Game Bull. No. 8.* (Sacramento, Calif.).

Talbot, L. M., and Martha H. Talbot
1963 The wildebeest in western Masailand, East Africa, *Wildl. Monographs,* no. 12.
1963 The high biomass of wild ungulates on East African Savanna, *Trans. N. Amer. Wildl. Conf.,* **28**:465–476.

Tamm, C. O.
1951 Removal of plant nutrients from tree crowns by rain, *Physiol. Plant.,* **4**:184–188.

Taylor, W. P. (ed.)
1956 "The Deer of North America," Stackpole, Harrisburg, Pa.

Teal, J. M.
1957 Community metabolism in a temperate cold spring, *Ecol. Monographs,* **27**:283–302.
1962 Energy flow in the salt marsh ecosystem of Georgia, *Ecology,* **43**:614–624.

Teal, J. M., and J. Kanwisher
1961 Gas exchange in a Georgia salt marsh, *Limnol. Oceanog.,* **6**:388–399.

Tedrow, J. F. C., J. V. Drew, D. E. Hill, and L. A. Douglas
1958 Major genetic soils of the arctic slope of Alaska, *J. Soil Sci.,* **9**:33–45.

Tedrow, J. F. C., and H. Harries
1960 Tundra soil in relation to vegetation, permafrost and glaciation, *Oikos,* **11**:237–249.

Tester, J. R., and W. H. Marshall
1961 A study of certain plant and animal interrelations on a native prairie in northwestern Minnesota, *Minnesota Museum Natural Hist., Occasional Paper No. 8.*

Tevis, L., Sr.
1956 Responses of small mammal populations to logging of Douglas fir, *J. Mammal.,* **37**:189–196.

Thoday, J. M.
1958 Effects of disruptive selection: the experimental production of a polymorphic population, *Nature,* **181**:1124–1125.

Thoday, J. M.
1959 Effects of disruptive selection: I, Genetic flexibility, *Heredity,* **13**:187–203.
1960 Effects of disruptive selection: III, Coupling and repulsion, *Heredity,* **14**:35–49.

Thoday, J. M., and T. B. Boam
1959 Effects of disruptive selection: II, Polymorphism and divergence without isolation, *Heredity,* **13**:205–218.

Thomas, W. L. Jr. (ed.)
1956 "Man's Role in Changing the Face of the Earth," University of Chicago Press, Chicago.

Thompson, H. V.
1954 The rabbit disease, myxamatosis, *Ann. Appl. Biol.,* **41**:358–366.

Thompson, W. L.
1960 Agonistic behavior in the house finch: Part I, Annual cycle and display patterns, *Condor,* **62**:245–271.

Thoreau, H. D.
1860 Succession of Forest Trees: Address Read to the Middlesex Agricultural Society, Sept., 1860, in "Excursion," 1891, Houghton Mifflin, Cambridge, Mass.

Thorpe, J.
1949 Effects of certain animals that live in soils, *Sci. Monthly,* **68**:180–191.

Thorpe, W. H.
1945 The evolutionary significance of habitat selection, *J. Animal Ecol.,* **14**:67–70.
1951 The learning abilities of birds, *Ibis,* **93**:1–52, 252–296.
1958 The learning of song patterns by birds, with special reference to the song of the chaffinch *Fringilla coelebs, Ibis,* **100**:535–570.
1963 "Learning and Instinct in Animals," 2d ed. Methuen, London.

Thorson, G.
1950 Reproductive and larval ecology of marine bottom invertebrates, *Biol. Rev.,* **25**:1–45.

1957 Bottom communities, in Hedgpeth (ed.), 1957, "Treatise on marine ecology and paleoecology," vol. 1, pp. 461–534.

Tinbergen, L.
1960 The natural control of insects in pinewoods: I, Factors influencing the intensity of predation by songbirds, *Arch. Neerl. Zool.*, **13**: 265–343.

Tinbergen, L., and H. Klomp
1960 The natural control of insects in pinewoods: II, Conditions for damping of Nicholson oscillations in parasite-host systems, *Arch. Neerl. Zool.*, **13**:344–379.

Tinbergen, N.
1951 "The Study of Instinct," Oxford, New York.
1952 Derived activities, their causation, biological significance, origin and emancipation during evolution, *Quart. Rev. Biol.*, **27**:1–32.
1953 "The Herring Gull's World," Collins, London.
1960 Comparative studies of the behaviour of gulls (Laridae): A progress report, *Behaviour*, **15**:1–70.

Tinbergen, N., and D. J. Kuenen
1939 Uber die austosenden und die richtunggebenden Reizsituationen der Sperrbewegung von jengen Drosseln (*Turdus m. merula* L und *T. e. ericetorum* Tuxton), *Z. Tierpsychol.*, **5**:182–226.

Tinbergen, N., and M. Moynihan
1952 Head flagging in the black-headed gull: its function and origin, *British Birds*, **45**:19–22.

Tinbergen, N., and A. C. Perdeck
1950 On the stimulus situation releasing the begging response in the newly hatched herring gull chick (*Larus argentatus*), *Behaviour*, **3**: 1–39.

Tompa, F. S.
1962 Territorial behavior: the main controlling factor of a local song sparrow population, *Auk*, **79**:687–697.
1964 Factors determining the numbers of song sparrows *Melospiza melodia* (Wilson), on Mandarte Island, B.C., Canada, *Acta Zool. Fennica*, **109**:73 ff.

Tordoff, H. B.
1954 Social organization and behavior in a flock of captive, non breeding red crossbills, *Condor*, **56**:346–358.

Transeau, E. N.
1926 The accumulation of energy by plants, *Ohio J. Sci.*, **26**:1–10.

Trimble, G. R. Jr., and S. Weitzman
1954 Effect of a hardwood forest canopy on rainfall intensities, *Trans. Amer. Geophys. Union*, **35**:226–234.

True, R. P., H. L. Barnett, C. K. Dorsey, and J. G. Leach
1960 Oak Wilt in West Virginia, *West Va. Univ. Agr. Expt. Sta. Bull.* 448T.

Tsivoglou, E. C., and W. W. Towne
1957 Sources and control of radioactive water pollutants, *Sewage Ind. Wastes*, **29**:143–156.

Turcek, F. J.
1951 On the stratification of the avian population of the Querceto-Carpinetum forest communities in southern slovakia (English summary), *Sylvia*, **13**:71–86.

Udvardy, M. D. F.
1958 Ecological and distributional analysis of North American birds, *Condor*, **60**:50–66.

Uebelmesser, E. R.
1954 Uber den endonomen Rhythmus der Sporan-gientrager-Bildung von *Pilobolus*, *Arch. Mikrobiol.*, **20**:1–33.

Uhlig, H.
1955 The gray squirrel, its life history, ecology, and population characteristics in West Virginia, *Conserv. Comm. W.Va.*, Final Rept. PR Project 31-R.

Ulrich, A. T.
1933 Die Macrofauna der Waldstreu, *Mitt. Forstwirtsch Fortwiss*, **4**:283–323.

Vallentyne, J. R.
1957 The principles of modern limnology, *Am. Scientist*, **45**:218–244.

Veale, P. T., and H. L. Wascher
1956 Henderson county soils, *Illinois Univ. Agr. Expt. Sta., Soil Report No.* 77.

Verduin, J.
1956 Energy fixation and utilization by natural communities in western Lake Erie, *Ecology*, **37**:40–50.

Vezina, P. E.
1961 Variation in total solar radiation in three Norway spruce plantations, *Forest Sci.*, **7**:257–264.

Viro, P. J.
1953 Loss of nutrients and the natural nutrient balance of the soil in Finland, *Comm. Inst. Forest. Fenn.*, **42**:1–50.

Voigt, G. K.
1960 Distribution of rainfall under forest stands, *Forest Sci.*, **6**:2–10.

Voigt, J. W., and J. E. Weaver
1951 Range condition classes of native midwestern pasture: An ecological analysis, *Ecol. Monographs*, **21**:39–60.

Volterra, V.
1926 Variazione e fluttazioni de numero d'individiu in specie animali conviventi, *Mem. Accad. Lincei*, **2**:31–113 (translated in R. N. Chapman, 1931, "Animal Ecology," McGraw-Hill, New York.)

Waddington, C. H.
1957 "The Strategy of the Genes," G. Allen, London.

Waksman, S.
1952 "Soil Microbiology," Wiley, New York.

Walker, P. C., and R. T. Hartman
1960 Forest sequence of the Hartstown bog area in western Pennsylvania, *Ecology*, **41**:461–474.

Walker, T. J., and A. D. Hasler
1949 Detection and discrimination of odors of aquatic plants by the bluntnose minnow (*Hyborhynchus notatus*), *Physiol. Zool.*, **22**:45–63.

Wallace, A. R.
1876 "The Geographical Distribution of Animals," 2 vols., Macmillan, London.

Wallace, L.
1940 Influence of forest cover on wind velocity, *J. Forestry*, **38**:481–486.

Wallace, G. J.
1959 Insecticides and birds, *Audubon Mag.*, **61**:10–12.

Wallraff, H. G.
1960 Does celestial navigation exist in animals? *Cold Spring Harbor Symp. Quant. Biol.*, **25**: 451–460.

Wassink, E. C.
1959 Efficiency of light energy conversion in plant growth, *Plant Physiol.*, **34**:356–361.

Waterhouse, F. L.
1955 Microclimatological profiles in grass cover in relation to biological problems, *Quart. J. Roy. Meteorol. Soc.*, **81**:63–71.

Waters, T. F.
1961 Standing crop and drift of stream bottom organisms, *Ecology*, **42**:532–537.

Watt, A. S.
1947 Pattern and process in the plant community, *J. Ecology*, **35**:1–22.

Watson, G. E.
1962a Three sibling species of *Alectoris* partridge, *Ibis*, **104**:353–367.
1962b Sympatry in Palearctic *Alectoris* partridges, *Evolution*, **16**:11–19.

Weaver, C. R.
1943 Observations of the life cycle of the fairy shrimp, *Eubranchipus vernalis*, *Ecology*, **24**: 500–502.

Weaver, J. E.
1954 "North American Prairie," Johnson, Lincoln, Neb.

Weaver, J. E., and F. W. Albertson
1956 "Grasslands of the Great Plains: Their Nature and Use," Johnson, Lincoln, Neb.

Weaver, J. E., and N. W. Rowland
1952 Effects of excessive natural mulch on development, yield and structure of native grassland, *Botan. Gaz.*, **114**:1–19.

Webster, D. W.
1954 Smallmouth bass *Micropterus dolomieui* in Cayuga Lake: Part I, Life history and environment, *Cornell Univ. Agr. Expt. Sta. Mem.*, **327**:3–39.

Wecker, S. C.
1963 The role of early experience in habitat selection by the prairie deer mouse. *Peromyscus maniculatus bairdi*, *Ecol. Monographs*, **33**:307–325.

Weis-Fogh, T.
1948 Ecological investigations of mites and collembola in the soil, *Nat. Jutland*, **1**:135–270.

Welch, P. S.
1952 "Limnology," McGraw-Hill, New York.

Weller, M. W.
1959 Parasitic egg laying in the redhead (*Aythya americana*) and other North American Anatidae, *Ecol. Monographs*, **29**:333–365.

Wellington, W. G.
1960 Qualitative changes in natural populations during changes in abundance, *Can. J .Zool.*, **38**:289–314.

Wells, H. W.
1961 The fauna of oyster beds, with special reference to the salinity factor, *Ecol. Monographs*, **31**:239–266.

Wells, H. W., and I. E. Gray
1960 Some oceanic subtidal oyster populations, *Nautilus*, **73**:139–146.

Wells, L.
1960 Seasonal abundance and vertical movements of planktonic crustaces in Lake Michigan, *U.S. Dept. Interior Fishery Bull.*, **60**(172): 343–369.

Went, F. W.
1955 The ecology of desert plants, *Sci. Am.*, **192**: 68–75.

West, D. A.
1962 Hybridization in grosbeaks (*Pheucticus*) of the Great Plains, *Auk*, **79**:399–424.

Westlake, D. F.
1959 The effects of organisms on pollution, *Proc. Linn. Soc.* (London), **170**:171–172.

Whitaker, L. M.
1957 A resume of anting, with particular reference to a captive oriole, *Wilson Bull.*, **69**: 195–262.

White, G. F. (ed.)
1956 "The future of arid lands," *Amer. Assoc. Adv. Sci. Publ. No.* 43, Washington, D.C.

Whittaker, R. H.
1951 A criticism of the plant association and climatic climax concept, *Northwest Sci.*, **25**:17–31.
1952 A study of summer foliage insect communities in the Great Smoky Mountains, *Ecol. Monographs*, **22**:1–44.
1953 A consideration of the climax theory: the climax as a population and pattern, *Ecol. Monographs*, **23**:41–78.
1956 Vegetation of the Great Smoky Mountains, *Ecol. Monographs*, **26**:1–80.

1961 Estimation of net primary production of forest and shrub communities, *Ecology*, **42**:177–183.

1962 Classification of natural communities, *Botan. Rev.*, **28**:1–239.

1963 Net production of heath balds and forest heaths in the Great Smoky Mountains, *Ecology*, **44**:176–182.

1965 Dominance and diversity in land plant communities, *Science*, **147**:250–260.

Wiggins, I. L., and J. H. Thomas
1962 A flora of the Alaskan arctic slope, *Publ. Arctic Inst. North America No. 4*, University of Toronto Press, Toronto.

Wilcomb, M. J.
1954 A study of prairie dog burrow systems and the ecology of their arthropod inhabitants in central Oklahoma, PhD thesis, University of Oklahoma, Norman, Okla.

Willard, W. K.
1963 Relative sensitivity of nestlings of wild passerine birds to gamma radiation, in Schultz and Klement (eds.), 1963, "Radioecology," pp. 345–349.

Williams, E. C.
1941 An ecological study of the floor fauna of the Panama rain forest, *Bull. Chicago Acad. Sci.*, **6**:63–124.

Willson, M. F., and G. H. Orians
1963 Comparative ecology of red-winged and yellow-headed blackbirds during the breeding season, *Proc. XVI Inter. Zool. Congress*, **3**:342–346.

Winn, H. E.
1958a Comparative reproductive behavior and ecology of fourteen species of darters (Pisces-Percidae), *Ecol. Monographs*, **28**:155–191.

1958b Observations on the reproductive habits of darters (Pisces-Percidae), *Am. Midland Naturalist*, **59**:190–212.

Winn, H., and J. Stout
1960 Sound production by the satinfin shiner, *Notropis analostanus,* and related fishes, *Science*, **132**:222–223.

Winston, F. W.
1956 The acorn microsere with special reference to arthropods, *Ecology*, **37**:120–132.

Withers, J. D., and A. Benson
1962 Evaluation of a modified Surber bottom fauna sampler. *Proc. West Virginia Acad. Sci.*, **37**:16–20.

Witherspoon, J. P., S. I. Averbach, and J. S. Olson
1962 Cycling of Cesium-134 in white oak trees on sites of contrasting soil type and moisture, *Oak Ridge Natl. Lab.*, **3328**:1–143.

Withrow, R. B. (ed.)
1959 Photoperiodism and related phenomena in plants and animals, *Publ. No. 55*, Amer. As-

soc. Adv. Science, Washington, D.C.

Wolfson, A.
1955 "Recent Studies on Avian Biology," University of Illinois Press, Urbana.

1959 The role of light and darkness in the regulation of spring migration and reproductive cycles in birds, in Withrow (ed.), 1959, "Photoperiodism and Related Phenomena," pp. 679–716.

1960 Regulation of annual periodicity in the migration and reproduction of birds, *Cold Spring Harbor Symp. Quant. Biol.*, **25**:507–514.

Wolcott, G. N.
1937 An animal census of two pastures and a meadow in northern New York, *Ecol. Monographs*, **7**:1–90.

Wolfe, J. N., R. T. Wareham, and H. T. Scofield
1949 Microclimates and macroclimates of Neotoma, a small valley in central Ohio, *Ohio Biol. Survey Bull.*, 41.

Wood, O. M.
1937 The interception of precipitation in an oak-pine-forest, *Ecology*, **18**:251–254.

Wood-Gush, D. G. M.
1955 The behaviour of the domestic chicken: a review, *Brit. J. Animal Behaviour*, **3**:81–110.

Woodwell, G. M.
1962 Effects of ionizing radiation on terrestrial ecosystems, *Science*, **138**:572–577.

1963 The ecological effects of radiation, *Sci. Am.*, **208**(6):40–49.

Wright, S.
1931 Statistical theory of evolution, *Amer. Statistical J. March Supp.*, pp. 201–208.

1935 Evolution in populations in approximate equilibrium *J. Genetics*, **30**:243–256.

1943 Evolution in Mendelian populations, *Genetics*, **16**:97–159.

1955 Classification of the factors of evolution, *Cold Spring Harbor Symp. Quant. Biol.*, **20**:16–24.

1964 Stochastic processes in evolution, in J. Gurland (ed.), 1964, "Stochastic Models in Medicine and Biology," University of Wisconsin Press, Madison, Wisc., pp. 199–241.

Wynne-Edwards, V. C.
1962 "Animal Dispersion in Relation to Social Behavior," Hafner, New York.

1963 Intergroup selection in the evolution of social systems, *Nature*, **200**:623–628.

1965 Self-regulating systems in populations of animals, *Science*, **147**:1543–1548.

Yeatter, R. E., and D. H. Thompson
1952 Tularemia, weather and rabbit populations, *Illinois Nat. Hist. Surv. Bull. No. 25*, pp. 351–382.

Yonge, C. M.
1949 "The Sea Shore," Collins, London.

Suggested readings
for chapters 1–27

In this list of suggested readings I have aimed chiefly at books. Articles and papers are included only when I feel that they have some significance and are not included in the bibliography.

Frankly the best source for additional material is the bibliography, the list of the papers and books cited throughout the text. This was the source material sifted from thousands of references. Any point stressed in the text is elaborated in the original sources. Admittedly these are harder to read—often deadly dull—and some, unless one has access to a well-stocked university library, may be hard to locate.

The listing here goes by chapters or by subjects, depending upon the material. The notation (PB) means the volume is available in paperback. I have not included the paperback publishers where they differ from the original publisher, nor do I claim that the listings of paperbacks is complete. New reprints are constantly appearing on bookstore shelves, so it might pay to check on the publication "Paperbacks in Print" to see if the title is so available.

Chapter 1

This chapter is largely an introductory discussion, but some ideas are further expanded in the following books. They should be read for their philosophical approach to ecology.

Bates, Marston: 1960, "The Forest and the Sea," Random House, New York (PB). Probably the finest general approach to ecology ever written.
Bates, Marston: 1961, rev. ed., "The Nature of Natural History," Scribner, New York (PB). Excellent. A well-written thought-provoking humanistic approach to ecology.
Leopold, Aldo: 1949, "A Sand County Almanac," Oxford, Fair Lawn, N.J. A classic in ecological writing. Contains the famous essay on an ecological conscience.
Sears, Paul B.: 1962, "Where There Is Life," Dell New York (PB). An introduction to the living landscape written for the general reader.

Chapter 2

Ashby, M.: 1961, "Introduction to Plant Ecology," St. Martin's, New York. An elementary text that is both interesting and stimulating. Examples are European.
Bucksbaum, R., and Mildred Bucksbaum: 1957, "Basic Ecology," Boxwood Press, Pittsburgh, Pa. An elementary introduction to community ecology.
Cole, L. C.: 1952, The Ecosphere, *Sci. Am.,* April, pp. 83–92.
Dice, L. C.: 1952, "Natural Communities," University of Michigan Press, Ann Arbor, Mich. A

good book that has never been fully appreciated.
Elton, C. E.: 1927, "Animal Ecology," Sidwick & Jackson, London.
Elton, C. E.: 1958, "The Ecology of Invasion by Plants and Animals," Wiley, New York. These two books, both classics in the best sense of the word, are excellent introductions to community ecology. Short, clearly written without textbook dullness, both should be required reading for everybody.
Evans, F. C.: 1956, Ecosystem as the basic unit in ecology, *Science,* **123**:1127–1128.
Farb, Peter: 1964, "Ecology," Life Nature Library, Time-Life Books, New York. One in the series of Life's Nature Library. An enjoyable and concise introduction to ecology, heavily illustrated with outstanding color photographs.
Hanson, H. C., and E. D. Churchill: 1961, "The Plant Community," Reinhold, New York. A short general introduction to the ecology of plants.
Hutchinson, G. E.: 1959, Homage to Santa Rosalia, or why are there so many kinds of animals? *Am. Naturalist,* **93**:145–159. A paper on community structure that is a treat to read. Its contents are also applicable to Chap. 3.
Margalef, R.: 1963, On certain unifying principles in ecology, *Am. Naturalist,* **97**:357–374.
Oosting, H. S.: 1956, "The Study of Plant Communities," Freeman, San Francisco. A general introduction to plant ecology.
Storer, J. W.: 1953, "The Web of Life," Devin-Adair, New York (PB). A short popular introduction to community ecology.

In addition to these, one should also refer to Odum's "Fundamentals of Ecology" and to Allee et al., "Animal Ecology," both listed in the bibliography.

Chapter 3

The best sources of information here are the papers in the bibliography. The best introduction to the subject of energy is contained in Chaps. 2 and 3 of Odum's "Fundamentals of Ecology."

Davis, D. E., and F. B. Golley: 1963, "Principles in Mammalogy," Reinhold, New York. See Chap. 9, Metabolism of Populations. Considers energy flow at the consumer level.
Kleiber, M.: 1961, "The Fire of Life, an Introduction to Animal Energetics," Wiley, New York. Energy metabolism in animals considered, but lacks inclusion of the latest research.
Lindeman, R. L.: 1942, The trophic-dynamic aspect of ecology, *Ecology,* **23**:399–418. A classic paper that is a milestone in the study of the functioning of the ecosystem.

Odum, E. P.: 1963, "Ecology," Modern Biology Series, Holt, New York (PB). A small volume written from the energy viewpoint.

Odum, H. T.: 1956, Primary production in flowing water, *Limnol. Oceanog.*, 1:102–117. Another paper that has had a great impact on the study of community energetics.

Raymont, J. E. C.: 1963, "Plankton and Productivity in the Oceans," Macmillan, New York. Primary production well covered in a readable fashion in Chaps. 6 through 10.

Ryther, J. H.: 1959, Potential productivity of the sea, *Science,* **130**:602–608. A good general discussion of primary production with special reference to the sea.

Slobodkin, L. B.: 1960, Ecological energy relationships at the population level, *Am. Naturalist,* **94**:213–236. A good reference paper, but rather rough going in places. For the advanced student.

Slobodkin, L. B.: 1962, Energy in animal ecology, in "Advances in Ecological Research," Academic New York. A well-balanced introduction to the subject.

Yentsch, C. S.: 1963, Primary production, in "Oceanography and Marine Biology, Annual Review," G. Allen, London. A short review paper.

Geiger, R.: 1957, "The Climate Near the Ground," 2d ed., Harvard, Cambridge, Mass. The book on climatology for the ecologist for whom the microclimate is much more significant than the macroclimate.

Henderson, L. J.: 1913 "The Fitness of the Environment," Beacon Press, Boston (1958 PB reprint). An old book, but still important. An explanation of the biological significance of the properties of matter.

Kramer, P. J., and T. T. Kozlowski: 1960, Physiology of Trees, McGraw-Hill, New York. A sound text on tree physiology; of interest to the ecologist.

Schultz, V., and A. W. Klement: 1963, "Radioecology," Reinhold, New York. At the time of publication the latest word on the subject. Thorough review of present knowledge and current research.

Shilling, C. W. (ed.): 1964, "Atomic Energy Encyclopedia in the Life Sciences," Saunders, Philadelphia. A concise reference.

Chapter 4

This is a wide-ranging chapter, and the selected references are likewise. The following represent only a few of the many books to which one can turn.

Bartholomew, G. A., T. R. Howell, and T. S. Cade: 1959, Torpidity in the white-throated swift, Anna hummingbird, and poorwill, *Condor,* **59**: 145–155. A paper that pretty well summarizes the information on torpidity in birds

Caldecott, R. S., and L. A. Snyder: 1960, "Radioisotopes in the Biosphere," Center for Continuation Study, University of Minnesota, Minneapolis.

Clarke, G. L.: 1954, "Elements of Ecology," Wiley, New York. A text particularly strong on environmental influences.

Daubenmire, R. F.: 1959, "Plants and Environment," 2d ed., Wiley, New York. A basic reference. (Some of the same material also covered in Oosting's "Plant Communities" listed under readings for Chap. 2.)

Eisenbud, M.: 1963, "Environmental Radioactivity," McGraw-Hill, New York. A sound reference. It includes reference material found only in government reports.

Gates, D. M.: 1962, "Energy Exchange in the Biosphere," Harper & Row, New York (PB). Read in particular Chap. 1, Energy Environment in Which We Live. See also his paper of the same title in *Am. Scientist,* **51**:327–348 (1963).

Chapter 5

The two major reference works on photoperiodism are "Photoperiodism and Related Phenomena" and *The Cold Spring Harbor Symposia on Quantitative Biology,* vol. 25, Biological clocks. The latter volume contains a large number of papers which, taken as a whole, virtually summarize the field.

In addition to the books and the papers in the bibliography the following several publications are excellent introductory material.

Beck, S. D.: 1963, "Animal Photoperiodism," Holt, New York. A short introduction to the subject.

Bunning, Erwin: 1964, "The Physiological Clock," 2d ed., Academic, New York. A short book by an authority in the field of periodicity.

Calhoun, J. B.: 1944–1946, Twenty-four hour periodicities in the animal kingdom, *J. Tennessee Acad. Sci.,* **19**:179–200, 252–262; **20**:228–232, 291–308, 373–378; **21**:208–216, 281. Although written a score of years ago, these pioneer papers are still an important reference.

Farner, D. S.: 1964, The photoperiodic control of reproductive cycles in birds, *Am. Scientist,* **52**: 137–156. A good summary.

Hendricks, S. B.: 1956, Control of growth and reproduction by light and darkness, *Am. Scientist,* **44**:229–247. A readable introduction to the subject of photoperiodism.

Sollberger, A.: 1965, "Biological Rhythm Research," Elsevier, Amsterdam. An exhaustive survey of the literature on biological rhythms in plants, animals and man. A superb bibliography.

Chapter 6

The best bet here is to refer to the papers listed in the bibliography. I recommend especially Cowles' paper on sand dune succession and Olson's later paper on the same subject, both cited in the bibliography. Also be sure to read Thoreau's essay on successsion. Standard textbooks on ecology also have much to say on succession.

Ager, D. V.: 1963, "Principles of Paleoecology," McGraw-Hill, New York. A survey of the subject of communities in the past.

Buechner, H. K., and H. C. Dawkins: 1961, Vegetation changes induced by elephants and fire in Murchison Falls National Park, Uganda, *Ecology*, **42**:752–766. An excellent study in the combined effects of animals and fire on natural vegetation.

Davis, K. P.: 1959, "Forest Fire—Control and Use," McGraw-Hill, New York. An authorative work on the use and misuse of fire in the forest.

Graham, E. H.: 1944, "Natural Principles of Land Use," Oxford, Fair Lawn, N.J. An excellent book stressing the importance of biological concepts to the wise use and management of the land. Should be required reading for all. Contains photos of the Harvard College Forest Models, dioramas illustrating forest succession in mid New England.

Thomas, W. L., Jr. (ed.): 1956, "Man's Role in Changing the Face of the Earth," University of Chicago Press, Chicago. A symposium volume which presents a thorough discussion of the impact of man on the biosphere.

Thoreau, H. D.: 1860, Succession of forest trees. An address to the Middlesex Agricultural Society, September, 1860, in "Excursions" Houghton Mifflin, Boston, (1891). A little-known essay that should appeal to ecologists.

U.S. Department of Agriculture: 1958, Land, Yearbook of Agriculture, Supt. of Documents, Washington, D.C. A survey of the American land, past and present, and the problems of the future.

Chapters 7 to 11

These chapters all deal with the fresh-water habitat and the estuary. Since there is so much overlap in the reference material, all are considered as a group.

Bennett, G. W.: 1962, "Management of Artificial Lakes and Ponds," Reinhold, New York. Limnology and fishery biology from a practical approach. Deals only with artificial impoundments, especially small ponds, popular in ecology laboratory work.

Carpenter, K. E.: 1928, "Life in Inland Waters," Sidgwick & Jackson, London. Old, but still one of the best.

Coker, R. E.: 1954, "Streams, Lakes and Ponds," University of North Carolina Press, Chapel Hill, N.C. An account for the general reader.

Frey, D. G. (ed.): 1963, "Limnology in North America," University of Wisconsin Press, Madison, Wisc. A thorough account of limnology in North America. It summarizes the work to date by regions. See in particular Neel, Impact of reservoirs, pp. 575–593.

Hutchinson, G. E.: 1957, "A Treatise on Limnology," vol 1, "Geography, Physics, and Chemistry," Wiley, New York. An invaluable reference on the physical aspects of limnology.

Hynes, H. B. N.: 1960, "The Biology of Polluted Waters," Liverpool University Press, Liverpool, England. The effects of pollution on fresh water ecosystems.

Macan, T. T.: 1963, "Fresh Water Ecology," Longmans, London. A revised edition of a major work on aquatic life.

Macan, T. T., and E. B. Worthington, 1951, "Life in Lakes and Rivers," Collins, London. Excellent limnology; the finest general book on the subject.

Needham, P. R.: 1940, "Trout Streams," Comstock, Ithaca, N.Y. This book is concerned chiefly with the management of trout streams, but it contains a general account of stream limnology.

Popham, E. J.: 1961, "Life in Fresh Water," Harvard, Cambridge, Mass. An excellent introduction to fresh-water ecology. It contains an account of a long-term survey of an actual pond that can serve as a model for practical field work.

Reid, G. K.: 1961, "Ecology of Inland Waters and Estuaries," Reinhold, New York. Pedantic writing but a good summary of fundamentals.

Ruttner, F.: 1963, "Fundamentals of Limnology," rev. ed., University of Toronto Press, Toronto. A basic reference; one of the finest limnology books available. Draws on European literature.

Tryon, C. A., and R. T. Hartman: 1960, The Ecology of algae, *University of Pittsburg Pymatuning Laboratory of Field Biology Special Publ. No.* 2. Contains excellent papers on the ecology of fresh water algae.

Welch, P. S.: 1952, "Limnology," McGraw-Hill, New York. First North American book on limnology, but the second edition contains relatively few advances.

The following papers deal with the estuary. The titles themselves are largely self-explanatory.

Filice, F. P.: 1958, Invertebrates from the estuarine portion of San Francisco Bay and some factors influencing their distribution, *Wasman J. Biol.*, **16**:159–211.

Hinde, H. P.: 1954, The vertical distribution of salt marsh phanerograms in relation to tide levels, *Ecol. Monographs*, **24**:209–225.

Ingle, R. M.: 1954, The life of an estuary, *Sci. Am.*, **190**(5):64–68.

Ketchum, B. H.: 1951, The exchanges of fresh and salt water in tidal estuaries, *J. Marine Res.*, **10**:18–38.

King, C. A. M., and W. W. Williams: 1949, The formation and movement of sand bars by wave action, *Geogr. Journal*, **113**:69–85.

Nelson, T.: 1947, Some contributions from the land in determining conditions of life in the sea, *Ecol. Monographs*, **17**:337–346. A discussion of the role of tidal flats to the nutrient cycle in coastal waters.

Pearse, A. S.: 1936, Estuarine animals at Beaufort, North Carolina, *J. Elisha Mitchell Scientific Soc.*, **52**:174–222.

Chapter 12

Publications on the sea are numerous. This is reflected in the rather large selection offered here, presented to compensate for the inadequate treatment given to the open sea in this book.

Berrill, N. J.: 1951, "The Living Tide," Dodd, Mead, New York (PB). A popular book on life in the tidal zone.

Carson, Rachael: 1955, "The Edge of the Sea," Houghton Mifflin, Boston (PB). A beautifully written book that deals with marine life along the eastern coast of North America.

Carson, Rachael: 1961, "The Sea Around Us," rev. ed., Oxford, Fair Lawn, N.J. (PB). A classic; the best popular account of the sea.

Coker, R. E.: 1947, "This Great and Wide Sea," University of North Carolina Press, Chapel Hill, N.C. (PB). A brief but comprehensive book on the ocean; one of the best.

Defant, A.: 1958, "Ebb and Flow: The Tides of Earth, Air and Water," University of Michigan Press, Ann Arbor, Mich. (PB). A definitive work on tides.

Dexter, R. W.: 1947, The marine communities of a tidal inlet at Cape Ann, Massachusetts, a study in bio-ecology, *Ecol. Monographs*, **17**:261–294. A study of the organization and dynamics of marine communities of a tidal flat. An important and valuable paper.

Ekman, S.: 1953, "Zoogeography of the Sea," Sidwick & Jackson, London. An indispensible reference on the "shelf fauna" around the world.

Engel, L.: 1961, "The Sea," Life Nature Library, Time-Life Books, New York. A brief introduction to the sea with an excellent collection of illustrations.

Flattely, F. W., and C. L. Walton: 1922, "The Biology of the Sea Shore," Macmillan, New York. Old, but still an important basic text.

Galtsoff, P. (ed): 1954, Gulf of Mexico: Its origins, water and marine life, *U.S. Fish Wildlife Ser. Fishery Bull. No. 89*. A compilation that contains more information about the Gulf of Mexico in one place than ever available before.

Glynne-Williams, J., and H. J. Williams: 1952, Studies on the crevice fauna of a selected shore in Anglesey, *Proc. Zool. Soc. London*, **122**:797–824. This paper discusses zonation, feeding habits of cryptofauna, and development of the crevice community.

Hardy, Alister: 1956–1959, "The Open Sea," vol. 1. "A World of Plankton"; vol. 2, "Fish and Fisheries," Collins, London. One of the great writings on the sea. Beautifully illustrated.

Hedgpeth, J. W. (ed.): 1957, Treatise on marine Ecology and paleoecology, vol. 1, Ecology, *Geol. Soc. of Am. Mem. 67*, New York. A book immense in scope—a bible for the marine ecologist. Covers the open sea, the sea shore, estuaries, etc.

Hill, M. N. (ed.): 1962–1964, "The Seas: Ideas and Observations on Progress in the Study of the Seas," 3 vols., Wiley, New York. The three volumes cover physical oceanography, composition of sea water, comparative and descriptive oceanography; the earth beneath the sea; history. The major reference on the sea. Technical and expensive, but invaluable.

Kuenen, P. H.: 1950, "Marine Geology," Wiley, New York. Contains chapters on the coral reef and marine sedimentation.

MacGinitie, G. E., and Nettie MacGinitie: 1949, "Natural History of Marine Animals," McGraw-Hill, New York. Contains many significant observations on marine invertebrates.

Moore, H. B.: 1958, "Marine Ecology," Wiley, New York. The only text on marine ecology as such.

Nicol, J. A. C.: 1960, "The Biology of Marine Animals," Wiley, New York. Concerned with the functioning of marine animals and their physiological relationships with the environment.

Ricketts, E. F., and J. Calvin: 1962, rev. by J. Hedgpeth, "Between Pacific Tides," 3d ed., Stanford, Stanford, Calif. Contains a wealth of information on Pacific coast intertidal life and an array of illustrations. A must.

Sears, Mary (ed.): 1961, "Oceanography," American Association for Advance of Science, Washington, D.C. A symposium volume.

Sverdrup, H. V., M. W. Johnson, and R. H. Fleming: 1942, "The Oceans: Their Physics, Chemistry, and General Biology," Prentice-Hall, Englewood Cliffs, N.J. Outdated, but still good in spots. Replaced by Hill (see above).

Weins, H. J.: 1962, "Atoll Environment and Ecology," Yale, New Haven, Conn. An excellent and complete book on the ecology of coral reefs.

Wilson, D. P.: 1951, "Life of the Shore and Shallow Sea," Nicholson & Watson, London. One of the finest of all seashore books.

Yonge, C. M.: 1949, "The Sea Shore," Collins, London (PB). Probably the best book on intertidal life in print.

Chapters 13 and 14

Brady, N. C., and H. O. Buckman: 1960, "The Nature and Properties of Soil," 6th ed., Macmillan, New York. A classic college textbook that covers most aspects of soil science.

Cloudsley-Thompson, J. L.: 1958, "Spiders, Scorpions, Centipedes and Mites: The Ecology and Natural History of Woodlice, 'Myrapods' and Arachnids," Academic, New York. The title well describes the contents. A general work.

Farb, P.: 1959, "The Living Soil," Harper & Row, New York (PB). A popular account of life in the soil; scientifically sound and beautifully written.

Jacks, G. V.: 1954, "Soil," Nelson, London. A short, excellent introduction to soil.

Kevan, D. K. McE. (ed.): 1955, "Soil Zoology," Butterworth, Washington, D.C. Proceedings of a symposium on soil zoology. Excellent; notable are the keys to soil invertebrates.

Kevan, D. K. McE.: 1962, "Soil Animals," Philosophical Library, New York. Simplified introduction to life in the soil. Good on the ecology of soils.

Laverach, M. S.: 1963, "The Physiology of Earthworms," Macmillan, New York. Work on earthworms summarized to date.

Lutz, H. J., and R. F. Chandler: 1946, "Forest Soils," Wiley, New York. An old text in need of revision, but still a basic reference on the subject.

Pramer, D.: 1964, Nematode-trapping fungi, *Science,* **144**:382–388. A valuable review.

Russell, E. J.: 1950, "Soil Conditions and Plant Growth," Longmans, London.

Russell, E. J.: 1957, "The World of the Soil," Collins, London. Two great and basic books on the soil.

U.S. Department of Agriculture: 1938, *Soils and Men,* Yearbook of Agriculture, out-of-print. A classic that was devoted largely to the classification of soils, technical aspects of soil science, and the use of the land.

U.S. Department of Agriculture: 1951, "Soil survey manual," *U.S. Dept. Agr., Agricultural Handbook* 18, plus supplement, 1962, Supt. of Documents, Washington, D.C. Identification and nomenclature of soil horizons and soils.

U.S. Department of Agriculture: 1957, *Soils,* Yearbook of Agriculture, Supt. of Documents, Washington, D.C. Principles of soils, soil fertility, and soil management.

Waksman, S. A.: 1952, "Soil Microbiology," Wiley, New York. Technical; the authorative treatment of soil microbiology by a Nobel Prize winner.

Wilde, S. A.: 1958, "Forest Soils, Their Properties and Relation to Silviculture," Ronald, New York. Forest soils with a strong practical approach.

Chapter 15

The best suggested readings appear in the bibliography. Among these I recommend the following (plus a few others tossed in).

Carpenter, J. R.: 1940, The grassland biome, *Ecol. Monographs,* **10**:617–684. An excellent review of the North American grasslands.

Curtis, J. T.: 1955, A prairie continuum in Wisconsin, *Ecology,* **36**:558–566. Applies the continuum concept to grasslands.

Ellison, L.: 1960, Influence of grazing on plant succession of rangelands, *Botan. Rev.,* **26**:1–78. A good review.

Humphrey, R. R.: 1962, "Range Ecology," Ronald, New York. An ecology text with a grassland orientation. A good chapter on fire and grasslands.

Sprague, H. E. (ed.): 1959, "Grasslands," American Association for Advancement of Science, Washington, D.C. A symposium volume with a number of papers on grassland ecology.

Weaver, J. E.: 1954, "North American Prairie," Johnsen, Lincoln, Neb. A detailed description of the original prairie.

Weaver, J. E., and F. W. Albertson: 1956, "Grasslands of the Great Plains," Johnsen, Lincoln, Neb. A sound reference on the grasslands of the mid-continent.

Weaver, J. E., and G. W. Tomanek: 1951, Ecological studies on a midwestern range: the vegetation and effects of cattle on its composition and distribution, *Nebraska Conserv. Bull.,* **31**:1–82. Effects of grazing on the prairie.

Chapter 16

Buxton, P. A.: 1923, "Animal Life in Deserts," E. Arnold, London. An old book on animals in the desert that still has its interest.

Cloudsley-Thompson, J. L.: 1954, "Biology of the Deserts," Hafner, New York. A general book on desert life.

Friedlander, C. P.: 1961, "Heathland Ecology," Harvard, Cambridge, Mass. A good introduction to the ecology of shrub communities, although orientated to the British heathland.

Hodge, C., and P. C. Duisberg: 1963, "Aridity and man," American Association for Advancement of Science, Washington, D.C. Man and the desert, with emphasis on the arid zones of the United States.

Howes, P. G.: 1954, "The Giant Cactus Forest and Its World," Duell, Sloan and Pierce, New York. A pleasant introduction to the southwestern desert.

Jaeger, E. C.: 1957, "The North American Deserts," Stanford, Stanford, Calif. A general survey; excellent reference.

Kirmiz, J. P.: 1962, "Adaptation to Desert Environment; A Study On the Jerboa, Rat and Man," Butterworth, Washington, D.C. A detailed treatment of the adaptations of mammalian life in the desert.

Krutch, J. W.: 1952, "The Desert Year," Sloane, New York (PB). A classic on the desert that should be read for both the description and the philosophy.

Leopold, A. Starker: 1961, "The Desert," Life Nature Library, Time-Life Books, New York. An excellent general account of the desert. Well illustrated.

Shreve, F., and I. L. Wiggins: 1963, "Vegetation and Flora of the Sonoran Desert," Stanford, Stanford, Calif. This two-volume work is a monumental study of the desert vegetation of the Southwest.

Went, F. W.: 1955, The ecology of desert plants, Sci. Am., **192**:68–75. An excellent summary of the ecology of desert plants.

White, G. F. (ed.): 1956, "Future of Arid Lands," American Association for Advancement of Science, Washington, D.C. A symposium volume that discusses the future of deserts in human affairs.

Chapter 17

Aubert, de la Rue, E. F. Bourliere, and J. Harroy: 1957, "The Tropics," Knopf, New York. A good introduction to the tropical world.

Braun, E. Lucy: 1950, "Deciduous Forests of Eastern North America," McGraw-Hill–Blakison, New York. The ecology of the forests of eastern North America, their development, composition, and distribution.

Curtis, J. T.: 1959, "The Forest of Wisconsin," University of Wisconsin Press, Madison, Wisc. A sound regional ecology of forests that should be a model for future studies.

Farb, P.: 1961, "The Forest," Life Nature Library, Time-Life Books, New York. An excellent introduction to forest ecology; beautifully written and illustrated.

McCormick, J.: 1959, "The Living Forest," Harper & Row, New York. A short introduction to the forest—ecology, disease, insects, harvesting, types.

Neal, E.: 1958, "Woodland Ecology," Harvard, Cambridge, Mass. A gem; written with the British woodland in mind, but overall presentation applicable to all temperate forests.

Richards, P. W.: 1952, "The Tropical Rain Forest," Cambridge, London. The book on the tropical rain forest.

Spurr, S. H.: 1964, "Forest Ecology," Ronald, New York. Deals with the ecological foundations of silviculture. Considers the forest environment, the forest community and phytogeography.

U.S. Department of Agriculture: 1949, "Trees," Yearbook of Agriculture, Supt. of Documents, Washington, D.C. An overall view of the forest—the trees, forest regions, forest management.

Chapter 18

Britton, M. E.: 1957, Vegetation of the arctic tundra, *18th Biol. Colloq. Oregon State Chapter Phi Kappa Phi*, Oregon State College, Corvallis, pp. 26–61. A detailed summary.

Byron, K.: 1946, Cryopedology: the study of frozen ground and intensive frost action with suggestions on nomenclature, *Am. J. Sci.*, **244**: 622–642. A basic reference on frozen ground and frost action.

Freuchen, P., and F. Salomonsen: 1958, "The Arctic Year," Putnam, New York. Excellent reading, scientifically sound.

Hayward, C. L.: 1952, Alpine biotic communities of the Uinta Mountains, Utah, *Ecol. Monographs*, **22**:93–120.

Ley, Willy: 1962, "The Poles," Life Nature Library, Time-Life Books, New York. A description of life and exploration in the polar regions. Well illustrated.

Milne, L., and Margery Milne: 1962, "The Mountains," Life Nature Library, Time-Life Books, New York. An account of alpine life.

Pearsall, W. H.: 1960, "Mountains and Moorlands," Collins, London. European mountains and moorlands well described; emphasis on Britain.

Polunin, N.: 1948, "Botany of the Canadian Eastern Arctic; III, Vegetation and ecology," *Buletin 104, National Museum of Canada*, Ottawa. A basic reference by an authority of the tundra.

Washburn, A. L.: 1956, Classification of patterned ground and review of suggested origins, *Geol. Soc. Am. Bull.* 67, pp. 823–865. A detailed discussion of patterned ground in the arctic.

Chapter 19

The best treatment of biogeography for the student and lay reader alike can be found in the six-volume series on land and wildlife, a part of the Life Nature Library. They deal with the major biogeographic regions of the world.

Bates, Marston: 1964, "Land and Wildlife of South America," Life Nature Library, Time-Life Books, New York.

Bergamini, David: 1964, "Land and Wildlife of Australia," Life Nature Library, Time-Life Books, New York.

Bourliere, Francois: 1964, "Land and Wildlife of Eurasia," Life Nature Library, Time-Life Books, New York.

Carr, Archie: 1964, "Land and Wildlife of Africa," Life Nature Library, Time-Life Books, New York.

Farb, Peter: 1964, "Land and Wildlife of North America," Life Nature Library, Time-Life Books, New York.

Ripley, S. Dillon: 1964. "Land and Wildlife of Tropical Asia," Life Nature Library, Time-Life Books, New York.

In addition the two books below should serve as standard references:

Cain, S. A.: 1944, "The Foundations of Plant Geography," Harper & Row, New York.

Darlington, P. J., Jr.: 1957, "Zoogeography: the Geographical Distribution of Animals," Wiley, New York.

Chapters 20 and 21

Andrewartha, H. G.: 1961, "Introduction to the Study of Animal Populations," University of Chicago Press, Chicago (PB). Basically a summary of the volume below. A book that belongs in every ecologists library.

Andrewartha, H. G., and L. C. Birch: 1954, "The Distribution and Abundance of Animals," University of Chicago Press, Chicago. A stimulating and controversial text. The authors divide the environment into four components: food, weather, other animals, a place to live.

Blair, W. F.: 1953, Population dynamics of rodents and other small mammals, in "Advances in Genetics," vol. 5, pp. 1–41, Academic, New York. A review paper.

Browning, T. O.: 1963, "Animal Populations," Harper & Row, New York. A study somewhat along the philosophical lines of Andrewartha and Birch.

Burnet, F. MacF.: 1962, "Natural History of Infectious Diseases," 3d ed., Cambridge University Press, London.

Cheng, T. C.: 1964, "The Biology of Animal Parasites," Saunders, Philadelphia. A sound introduction to animal parasitology without overemphasis on the medical approach.

Dales, R. P.: 1957, Interrelations of organisms: A, Commensalism, in Hedgpeth, "Treatise on marine ecology," pp. 391–412 (see readings, Chapter 12). Excellent summary.

Davis, D. E.: 1957, The existence of cycles, *Ecology*, **38**:163–164. A short discussion.

Davis, D. E., and F. B. Golley: 1963, "Principles in Mammalogy," Reinhold, New York. Chapter 8 is an excellent summary of population ecology.

Dogiel, V. A., G. K. Petrushevski, and Y. I. Polyanski (eds.): 1961, "Parasitology of Fishes," Oliver and Boyd, Edinburgh and London. Comprehensive survey of the subject.

Dorst, J.: 1963, "The Migration of Birds," Houghton Mifflin, Boston. A survey of bird migration the world over.

Dowdeswell, W. H.: 1959, "Animal Ecology," 2d ed., Methuen, London (PB). An elementary but engaging introduction to animal ecology.

Elton, C.: Voles, Mice and Lemmings, Clarendon Press, Oxford. A classic book on animal populations.

Errington, P. L.: 1946, Predation and vertebrate populations, *Quart. Rev. Biol.*, **21**:144–177; 221–245. A time-honored paper that elaborates on compensatory relationships between predator and prey population.

Errington, P. L.: 1963, "Muskrat Populations," Iowa State University Press, Ames, Iowa. The result of a 20-year study of muskrats. A model of field investigation.

Fenner, F., and F. M. Ratchiffe: 1965, "Myxomatosis" Cambridge University Press, New York. The story of myxomatosis, rabbit populations, and the adaptations of host and parasite.

Gibb, J. A.: 1960, Population of tits and goldcrests and their food supply in pine plantations, *Ibid*, **102**:163–208. A study on the interrelations of food supply and populations.

Hopkins, S. H.: 1957, Interrelations of organisms: B, Parasitism, in Hedgpeth, Treatise on marine ecology, pp. 413–428 (see readings Chapter 12). An excellent summary.

Kendeigh, S. C.: 1961, "Animal Ecology," Prentice-Hall, Englewood Cliffs, N.J. An excellent reference text; weighted down in places by terminology. Good bibliography.

Lack, D.: 1954, "The Natural Regulation of Animal Numbers," Oxford, Fair Lawn, N.J. Emphasizes the role of food.

Le Cren, E. D., and M. W. Holdgate (eds.): 1962, "The Exploitation of Natural Animal Populations," Wiley, New York. A symposium volume which explores the scientific basis of the response of natural animal populations to exploitation.

Macfadyen, A.: 1963, "Animal Ecology," 2d ed., Pitman, London. A more technical introduction with emphasis on soil organisms.

Rothschild, Miriam, and Teresa Clay: 1953, "Fleas, Flukes and Cuckoos," Collins, London. Parasitology with special reference to birds.

Slobodkin, L. B.: 1962, "Growth and Regulation of Animal Populations," Holt, New York. A valuable publication on population dynamics, but laboratory populations rather than field populations dominate the text.

Williams, C. B.: 1959, "Insect Migration," Macmillan, New York. The definitive account of insect migrations.

Yonge, C. M.: 1957, Interrelations of organisms: C, Symbiosis, in Hedgpeth, Treatise on marine ecology, pp. 429–442 (see readings, Chapter 12). An excellent summary with marine examples.

Chapters 22 to 24

Auerbach, Charlotte: 1961, "The Science of Genetics," Harper & Row, New York (PB). An elementary introduction to genetics.

Bailey, L. B.: 1933, "How Plants Get Their Name," reprint ed., Dover, New York. A basic introduction to botanical nomenclature.

Blair, W. F. (ed.): 1961, "Vertebrate Speciation," University of Texas Press, Austin, Tex. A symposium volume that contains a tremendous amount of compressed information.

Brown, W. L., and E. O. Wilson: 1956, Character displacement, *Systematic Zool.*, **5**:49–65. An important reference.

Cain, A. J.: 1954, "Animal Species and Their Evolution," Hutchinson, London (PB). A lucid and valuable introduction to the principles of taxonomy and the nature and evolution of species.

Cold Spring Harbor Symposia on Quantitative Biology No. 20: 1955, Population genetics: The nature and causes of genetic variability in populations, The Biological Laboratory, Cold Spring Harbor, N.Y. A symposium that pretty well summarizes the field.

Cott, H. B.: 1940, "Adaptive Coloration in Animals," Oxford, Fair Lawn, N.J. A thorough review (to 1940) of concealing and warning coloration and mimicry.

Darwin, C.: 1859, "On the Origin of Species by Natural Selection, or the Preservation of Favoured Races in the Struggle for Life," J. Murray, London (PB). This is the book that opened the era of modern evolutionary studies. Available in a number of paperback editions.

Dobzhansky, T.: 1951, "Genetics and the Origin of Species," 3d ed., Columbia, New York (PB). Hard reading in places, but one of the most important books on evolution. A must for every serious student.

Dowdeswell, W. H.: 1958, "The Mechanism of Evolution," 2d ed., William Heinemann, London (PB). Variation and natural selection from the field biologists point of view.

Eiseley, L.: 1958, "Darwin's Century: Evolution and the Men Who Discovered It," Doubleday, New York (PB). A perspective of evolutionary studies.

Fisher, R. A.: 1930, "The Genetical Theory of Natural Selection," Clarendon Press, Oxford (PB). Technical, for the advanced student.

Ford, E. B.: 1964, "Ecological Genetics," Methuen, London. The ecological aspects of genetics are well developed here—polymorphism, mimicry.

Huxley, Julian: 1942, "Evolution, the Modern Synthesis," Harper & Row, New York (PB). A survey of contemporary biological thought on evolution.

Huxley, Julian (ed.): 1940, "The New Systematics," Oxford, Fair Lawn, N.J. A symposium volume on speciation and the new concept of the species.

Lack, D.: 1947, "Darwin's Finches: An Essay on the General Biological Theory of Evolution," Cambridge, London (PB). A well-written book; probably the best introduction to the actual origin of new species. Another classic of biology.

Levine, R. P.: 1962, "Genetics," Modern Biology Series, Holt, New York (PB). A concise introduction to genetics.

Li, C. C.: 1955, "Population Genetics," University of Chicago Press, Chicago. A clear and concise exposition of population genetics.

Mayr, E.: 1942, "Systematics and the Origin of Species," Columbia, New York. The famous early book on the mechanisms of speciation, especially geological speciation.

Mayr, E.: 1963, "Animal Species and Evolution," Harvard, Cambridge, Mass. An important book that might well stand as a milestone in the progress of the study of animal evolution.

Moore, Ruth: 1962, "Evolution," Life Nature Library, Time-Life Books, New York. A highly readable, popular introduction to the principles of evolution and natural selection. Beautifully illustrated.

Rensch, B.: 1960, "Evolution Above the Species Level," Columbia, New York. An analysis of evolutionary patterns, primarily in animals, with emphasis on trends in evolution.

Ross, H. H.: 1962, "A Synthesis of Evolutionary Theory," Prentice-Hall, Englewood Cliffs, N.J. An interesting overview of the evolutionary process from the prestellar state to development of biomes.

Savory, T.: 1963, "Naming the Living World," Wiley, New York. An introduction to principles of biological nomenclature.

Sheppard, P. M.: 1959, "Natural Selection and Heredity," rev. ed., Hutchinson, London (PB). A well-written account of natural selection in the light of genetical research.

Simpson, G. G.: 1949, "The Meaning of Evolution," Yale, New Haven, Conn. (PB). A discussion of the philosophical and ethical implications of evolution.

Stebbins, G. L.: 1950, "Variation and Evolution in Plants," Columbia, New York. Does for plants what Mayr's book, "Systematics and the Origin of Species," did for animals. An important reference.

Tax, S. (ed.): 1960, "Evolution After Darwin," vol. 1, "The Evolution of Life"; vol. 2, "The Evolution of Man"; vol. 3, "Issues in Evolution"; University of Chicago Press, Chicago. A symposium in which authorities assess the present state of evolutionary knowledge, including the scientific and religious.

Chapters 25 to 27

Allee, W. C.: 1938, "The Social Life of Animals," Norton, New York (PB). A stimulating introduction to the social life of animals. General; easy to read.

American Zoologist: 1964, Behavior genetics, vol. 4, no. 2. A series of review papers summarizing this field.

Armitage, K. B.: 1963, Social behavior of a colony of the yellow-bellied marmot, *Animal Behaviour,* **10**:319–331. An example of a well-planned field study in animal behavior.

Armstrong, E. A.: 1947, "Bird Display and Behavior," Oxford, Fair Lawn, N.J. (PB). Somewhat dater in places, but a nice overall survey of the whole area of bird behavior. Excellent bibliography.

Darling, F. F.: 1937, "A Herd of Red Deer: A Study in Animal Behavior," Oxford, Fair Lawn, N.J. (PB). A classic in the study of animal behavior that is a treat to read.

Ektin, W. (ed.): 1964, "Social Behavior and Organization Among Vertebrates," University of Chicago Press, Chicago. A rather good summary of the field by a variety of contributors.

Evans, H. E.: 1963, "Wasp Farm," Natural History Press, New York. An engaging account of the comparative behavior of wasps.

Frisch, K. von: 1955, "The Dancing Bees," Harcourt, Brace, & World, New York (PB). An authority's account of communication in honeybees.

Griffin, D. R.: 1958, "Listening in the Dark," Yale, New Haven, Conn. Studies of echolocation in bats.

Hafez, E. S. (ed.): 1962, "The Behavior of Domestic Animals," William & Wilkins, Baltimore. A thorough reading of this volume would be a valuable beginning for the study of big game animals.

Johnsgard, P. A.: 1965, "Handbook of Waterfowl Behavior," Cornell University Press, Ithaca, N.Y. Excellent descriptions of waterfowl displays.

Kendeigh, S. C.: 1952, Parental care and its evolution in birds, *Illinois University Biological Monographs* 22, University of Illinois Press, Urbana, Ill. Summarizes parental care with special reference to the house wren.

Klopfer, P. H.: 1962, "Behavioral Aspects of Ecology," Prentice-Hall, Englewood Cliffs, N.J. A behavioral approach to ecology. Highly speculative in places, but a refreshing point of view.

Lanyon, W. E., and W. N. Tavolga (eds.): 1960, "Animal Sounds and Communication," American Institute of Biological Sciences, Washington, D.C. A selection of papers on bio-acoustics, including two on methods of study.

Lin, N.: 1963, Territorial behavior in the cicada killer wasp, *Sphecius speciosus,* Drury (Hymenoptera: Sphecidae), *Behaviour,* **20**:115–133. An example of how a valuable behavior study can be done near to home.

Lindauer, M.: 1961, "Communication Among Social Bees," Harvard, Cambridge, Mass. Takes up where von Frisch left off. An invaluable summary of communication and orientation among bees.

Lorenz, K.: 1952, "King Solomon's Ring," Crowell, New York (PB). A highly popular book in which this great ethologist describes his experiences in studying animal behavior.

Michener, C. D., and Mary Michener: 1951, "American Social Insects," Van Nostrand, Princeton, N.J. A good introduction.

Moynihan, M.: 1962, Hostile and sexual behaviour patterns of South American and Pacific Laridae, *Behaviour Supplement* VIII, Brill, Leiden. An excellent comparative study of gull behavior.

Rheingold, Harriet: 1963, "Maternal Behavior in Mammals," Wiley, New York. The first general review of maternal behavior in mammals. An important book.

Suggested readings

Roe, Anne, and G. G. Simpson (eds.): 1958, "Behavior and Evolution," Yale, New Haven, Conn. A symposium volume with a number of excellent articles related both to behavior and evolution.

Roeder, K. D.: 1963, "Nerve Cells and Instinctive Behavior," Harvard, Cambridge, Mass. A detailed discussion on the relationship between nerve mechanisms and behavior in invertebrates.

Savory, T.: 1959, "Instinctive Living: A Study of Invertebrate Behavior," Permagon Press, New York. An interesting introduction to invertebrate behavior.

Scott, J. P.: 1958, "Animal Behavior," University of Chicago Press, Chicago (PB). An introductory survey of animal behavior. One of the books to be read first by students of animal behavior.

Thorpe, W. H.: 1961, "Bird Song: The Biology of Vocal Communication and Expression in Birds," Cambridge, London. An important work on vocal communication in birds.

Thorpe, W. H.: 1963, "Learning and Instinct in Animals," rev. ed., Methuen, London. A basic work in the field of ethology. Excellent critical review of learning in animals.

Tinbergen, N.: 1951, "The Study of Instinct," Oxford, Fair Lawn, N.J. A major work on the comparative study of behavior. A necessity for all students of behavior.

Tinbergen, N.: 1960, "The Herring Gull's World," Basic Books, New York. Tinbergen's finest book; an excellent example of how basic research can be presented as good literature.

Tinbergen, N.: 1965, "Animal Behavior," Life Nature Library, Time-Life Books, New York. A highly readable and richly illustrated introduction to ethology.

General references

Aids to identification

The following is a list of recommended guides to various groups of organisms. The list is not complete, but the volumes represent one man's opinion about what are the best and most acceptable guides to plants and animals. The regional works included are those applicable to a wider region than the state borne in the title. Except in rare instances, technical monographs are not included.

Lower Plants

Bodenberg, E. T.: 1954, "Mosses: A New Approach to the Identification of Common Species," Burgess, Minneapolis.

Cobb, B.: 1956, "A Field Guide to the Ferns," Houghton Mifflin, Boston.

Conard, H. J.: 1956, "How to Know the Mosses and Liverworts," William C. Brown, Dubuque, Iowa.

Fink, B.: 1935, "The Lichen Flora of the United States," University of Michigan Press, Ann Arbor, Mich.

Frye, T., and Lois Clark: 1937–1947, "Hepaticae of North America," 2 vols., University of Washington Press, Seattle, Wash.

Groot, A. J.: 1947, "Mosses With a Hand Lens," 4th ed., published by the author, 1 Vine Street, New Brighton, Staten Island, N.Y.

Johnston, J., A. Scott, and H. C. Chadwick: 1924. "The Marine Plankton," Liverpool University Press, Liverpool, England.

Krieger, L. C. C.: 1947, "The Mushroom Handbook," Macmillan, New York.

McVaugh, R., and J. H. Pyron: 1951, "The Ferns of Georgia," University of Georgia Press, Athens, Ga.

Prescott, G. W.: 1954, "How to Know the Algae," William C. Brown, Dubuque, Iowa.

Smith, A. H.: 1951, "Puffballs and Their Allies in Michigan," University of Michigan Press, Ann Arbor, Mich.

Smith, A. H.: 1963, "The Mushroom Hunter's Field Guide," rev. ed., University of Michigan Press, Ann Arbor, Mich.

Smith, G.: 1950, "The Fresh Water Algae of the United States," McGraw-Hill, New York.

Smith, G.: 1951, "Manual of Phycology; an Introduction to the Algae and Their Biology," Chronica Botanica, Waltham, Mass.

Taylor, W. R.: 1937, "Marine Algae of the Northeastern Coast of North America," University of Michigan Science Series 13, University of Michigan Press, Ann Arbor, Mich.

Taylor, W. R.: 1960, "Marine Algae of the Eastern Tropical and Subtropical Coasts of the Americas," University of Michigan Press, Ann Arbor, Mich.

Thomas, W. C.: 1936, "Field Book of Common Mushrooms," Putman, New York.

Watson, E. V.: 1955, "British Mosses and Liverworts," Cambridge, London. (Most species treated also occur in northeastern North America.)

Wherry, E. T.: 1942, "Guide to Eastern Ferns," 2d ed., Science Press, Lancaster, Pa.

Grasses and Wildflowers

Armstrong, Margaret: 1915, "Fieldbook of Western Wildflowers," Putman, New York.

Craighead, J., F. C. Craighead, and R. J. Davis: 1963, "Field Guide to Rocky Mountain Wildflowers," Houghton Mifflin, Boston.

Cuthbert, Mabel: 1943, 1948, "How to Know the Spring Wildflowers; How to Know the Fall Wildflowers," William C. Brown, Dubuque, Iowa.

Dana, Mrs. Wm. Starr: 1962, "How to Know the Wildflowers," rev. modernized ed. of 1900 volume, Dover, New York (PB).

Degener, O.: 1946–1957, "New Illustrated Flora of the Hawaiian Islands," published by the author, Makuleia Beach, Waialua, Oahu, Hawaii.

Dayton, W. A.: 1960, Notes on western range forbs, U.S. Dept. Agri. *Handbook,* 161, Supt. of Documents, Washington, D.C.

Fassett, N. C.: 1940, "A Manual of Aquatic Plants," McGraw-Hill, New York.

Fernald, M. L.: 1950, "Gray's Manual of Botany," 8th ed., American Book, New York.

Gleason, H. A.: 1952, "The New Britton and Brown Illustrated Flora of the Northeastern United States and Adjacent Canada," 3 vols., New York Botanical Garden, New York.

Hitchcock, A. S.: 1950, rev. by Agnes Chase, "Manual of Grasses of the United States," Supt. of Documents, Washington, D.C.

Hulten, E.: 1960, "Flora of the Aleutian Islands," 2d ed., J. Cramer (available from Hafner, New York).

Jaques, H. E.: 1941, "Plant Families, How to Know Them," William C. Brown, Dubuque, Iowa.

Kummer, Anne P.: 1951, "Weed Seedlings," University of Chicago Press, Chicago.

Martin, A. C., H. S. Zin, and A. L. Nelson: 1951, "American Wildlife and Food Plants," Mc-

Graw-Hill, New York. (New paperback 1961 edition, Dover, New York.)

Matthews, F. S.: 1955, ed. by Norman Taylor, "Field Book of American Wildflowers," rev. ed., Putman, New York.

Muenscher, W. C.: 1944, "Aquatic Plants of the United States," Comstock, Ithaca, N.Y.

Muenscher, W. C.: 1955, "Weeds," Macmillan, New York.

Pohl, R. W.: 1954, "How to Know the Grasses," William C. Brown, Dubuque, Iowa.

Porsild, A. E.: 1957, Illustrated flora of the Canadian Arctic Archipelago, *Bulletin 146, National Museum of Canada,* Ottawa.

Steyermark, J. A.: 1963, "Flora of Missouri," Iowa State University Press, Ames, Iowa.

Thomas, J. H.: 1961, "Flora of the Santa Cruz Mountains of California," Stanford, Stanford, Calif.

Wherry, E. T.: 1948, "The Wildflower Guide," Doubleday, New York.

Wiggans, I. L., and J. H. Thomas: 1962, "Flora of the Alaskan Arctic Slope," University of Toronto Press, Toronto.

Trees and Shrubs

Baers, H.: 1955, "How to Know the Western Trees," William C. Brown, Dubuque, Iowa.

Benson, L. D., and R. A. Darrow: 1945, "A Manual of Southwestern Desert Trees and Shrubs," University of Arizona Press, Tucson, Ariz.

Canadian Department of Resources and Development: 1949, "Native Trees of Canada," Canadian Dept. of Resources and Development, Ottawa.

Graves, A. H.: 1956, "Illustrated Guide to Trees and Shrubs," Harper & Row, New York.

Harlow, W. M.: 1957, "Trees of Eastern and Central United States and Canada; Fruit Key and Twig Key to Trees and Shrubs," reprint ed., Dover, New York (PBS).

Harrar, E. S., and J. G. Harrar: 1946, "Guide to Southern Trees," reprint ed., Dover, New York (PB).

Hayes, Doris W.: 1960, Key to important woody plants of eastern Oregon and Washington, *U.S. Dept. Agr. Handbook* 148, Supt. of Documents, Washington, D.C.

Jaques, H. E.: 1946, "How to Know the Trees," rev. ed., William C. Brown, Dubuque, Iowa.

McMinn, H. E., and E. Maino: 1946, "An Illustrated Manual of Pacific Coast Trees," University of California Press, Berkeley, Calif.

Peattie, D. C.: 1953, "Natural History of Western Trees," Houghton Mifflin, Boston.

Sargent, C. S.: 1922, "Manual of Trees of North America," reprint ed., 2 vols., Dover, New York (PB).

Vines, R. A.: 1963, "Trees, Shrubs and Woody Vines of the Southwest," University of Texas Press, Austin, Texas.

Invertebrates

General

Davis, C. C.: 1955, "The Marine and Fresh Water Plankton," Michigan State University Press, Lansing, Mich.

Edmondson, W. T. (ed.): 1959, "Fresh-water Biology," 2d ed., Wiley, New York.

Light, S. F., R. I. Smith, F. A. Pitelka, D. P. Abbot, and Frances M. Neesner: 1957, "Intertidal Invertebrates of the Central California Coast," University of California Press, Berkeley, Calif.

Miner, R. W.: 1950, "Field Book of Seashore Life," Putman, New York.

Needham, J. G., and P. R. Needham: 1962, "A Guide to the Study of Fresh Water Biology," Holden-Day, San Francisco, Calif.

Pennak, R.: 1953, "Fresh Water Invertebrates of the United States," Ronald, New York.

Pratt, H. S.: 1953, "Manual of the Common Invertebrate Animals," McGraw-Hill–Blakiston, New York.

Protozoa

Jahn, T. L.: 1949, "How to Know the Protozoa," William C. Brown, Dubuque, Iowa.

Colenterata

Smith, F. G. W.: 1948, "Atlantic Reef Corals," University of Miami Press, Coral Gables, Fla.

Earthworms

Eaton, T. H., Jr.: 1942, Earthworms of the northeastern United States, *J. Wash. Acad. Sci.,* **32**: 242–249.

Olson, H. W.: 1928, The earthworms of Ohio, *Ohio Biol. Survey,* **4**:45–90.

Mollusca

Abbot, R. T.: 1954, "American Seashells," Van Nostrand, Princeton, N.J.

Baker, F. C.: 1939, Field book of Illinois Land snails, *Manual 2, Illinois Natural History Survey,* Urbana, Ill.

Keen, A. Myra: 1963, "Marine Molluscan Genera of Western North America," Stanford, Stanford, Calif.

Keep, J.: 1935, rev. by J. L. Bailey, Jr., "West Coast Shells," Stanford, Stanford, Calif.

Morris, P.: 1951, "Field Guide to the Shells of our Atlantic and Gulf Coast," Houghton Mifflin, Boston.

Morris, P.: 1952, "Field Guide to the Shells of the Pacific Coast and Hawaii," Houghton Mifflin, Boston.

Pilsbry, H. A.: 1939–1948, Land mollusca of North America, *Academy of Natural Sciences Monograph No. 3*, Philadelphia, Pa.

Insects

Chu, H. F.: 1949, "How to Know the Immature Insects," William C. Brown, Dubuque, Iowa.

Dillon, Elizabeth, and L. S. Dillon: 1961, "A Manual of Common Beetles of Eastern North America, Harper & Row, New York.

Essig, E. O.: 1958, "Insects and Mites of Western North America," Macmillan, New York.

Holland, W. J.: 1934, "The Moth Book," Doubleday, Garden City, N.Y. Out of print.

Holland, W. J.: 1949, "The Butterfly Book," Doubleday, Garden City, N.Y.

Jaques, H. E.: 1947, "How to Know the Insects," William C. Brown, Dubuque, Iowa.

Jaques, H. E.: 1951, "How to Know the Beetles," William C. Brown, Dubuque, Iowa.

Klots, A. K.: 1951, "Field Guide to the Butterflies," Houghton Mifflin, Boston.

Lutz, F. E.: 1935, "Field Book of Insects," 3d rev. ed., Putman, New York.

Needham, J. G., and M. J. Westfall, Jr.: 1955, "A Manual of the Dragonflies of North America," University of California Press, Berkeley, Calif.

Swain, R. B.: 1948, "The Insect Guide," Doubleday, Garden City, N.Y.

Usinger, R. I. (ed.): 1956, "Aquatic Insects of California, with Keys to North American Genera and California Species," University of California Press, Berkeley, Calif.

Spiders

Comstock, J. H.: 1940, ed. by W. J. Gertsch, "The Spider Book," 2d rev. ed., Doubleday, Garden City, N.Y.

Emerton, J. H.: 1961, "The Common Spiders of the United States," reprint ed., Dover, New York (PB).

Katson, B. J., and E. Katson: 1953, "How to Know the Spiders," William C. Brown, Dubuque, Iowa.

Vertebrates

General

Blair, W. F., A. P. Blair, P. Brodkrob, F. R. Cagle, and G. A. Moore: 1957, "Vertebrates of the United States," McGraw-Hill, New York.

Fishes

Bigelow, H. B., and W. C. Schroder: 1953, Fishes of the gulf coast of Maine, *U.S. Fish and Wildlife Service Fishery Bull. No. 74.*

Breder, C. M.: 1948, "Field Book of Marine Fishes," Putman, New York.

Eddy, S.: 1957, "How to Know the Freshwater Fishes," William C. Brown, Dubuque, Iowa.

Harlan, J. R., and E. B. Speaker: 1956, "Iowa Fish and Fishing," 3d ed., Iowa Conservation Commission, Des Moines, Iowa.

Hubbs, C., and K. Lagler: 1958, Fishes of the Great Lakes region, *Cranbrook Institute of Science Bulletin* 26, Bloomfield, Ill.

Perlmutter, A.: 1961, "Guide to Marine Fishes," New York University Press, New York.

Trautman, M. B.: 1957, "The Fishes of Ohio," Ohio State University Press, Columbus, Ohio.

Amphibians and Reptiles

Bishop, S.: 1943, "Handbook of Salamanders," Comstock, Ithaca, N.Y.

Carr, A.: 1952, "Handbook of Turtles," Comstock, Ithaca, N.Y.

Conant, R.: 1958, "A Field Guide to the Reptiles and Amphibians of the United States and Canada East of the 100 Meridian," Houghton Mifflin, Boston.

Ditmars, R.: 1949, "Fieldbook of North American Snakes," Doubleday, Garden City, N.Y.

Pope, C.: 1939, "Turtles of the United States and Canada," Knopf, New York.

Schmidt, K., and D. D. Davis: 1941, "Field Book of Snakes of the United States and Canada," Putman, New York.

Smith, H. M.: 1946, "Handbook of Lizards of the United States and Canada," Comstock, Ithaca, N.Y.

Stebbins, R. C.: 1954, "Amphibians and Reptiles of Western North America," McGraw-Hill, New York.

Wright, A. H., and Anna A. Wright: 1949, "Handbook of Frogs and Toads," 3d ed., Comstock, Ithaca, N.Y.

Wright, A. H., and Anna A. Wright: 1957, "Handbook of Snakes of the United States and Canada," vol. I–II, Comstock, Ithaca, N.Y.

Birds

Blake, E. R.: 1953, "Birds of Mexico," University of Chicago Press, Chicago.

Kortright, F. H.: 1942, "Ducks, Geese and Swans of North America," Stackpole, Harrisburg, Pa.

Jaques, H. E.: 1947, "How to Know the Land Birds," William C. Brown, Dubuque, Iowa.

Palmer, R.: 1962, "Handbook of North American Birds," vol. I, Yale, New Haven, Conn.

Peterson, R. T.: 1947, "A Field Guide to the Birds," Houghton Mifflin, Boston.

Peterson, R. T.: 1961, "A Field Guide to Western Birds," Houghton Mifflin, Boston.

Pough, R. H.: 1946–1951, "Audubon Bird Guides," vol. 1, "Eastern Land Birds"; vol. 2, "Water Birds." Doubleday, Garden City, N.Y.

General references

Pough, R. H.: 1957, "Audubon Western Bird Guide," Doubleday, Garden City, N.Y.

Saunders, A. A.: 1959, "A Guide to Bird Songs," Doubleday, New York.

Mammals

Booth, E. S.: 1961, "How to Know the Mammals," William C. Brown, Dubuque, Iowa.

Burt, W. H., and R. P. Grossenheider: 1963, "A Field Guide to the Mammals," 2d ed., Houghton Mifflin, Boston.

Burt, W. H.: 1957, "Mammals of the Great Lakes Region," University of Michigan Press, Ann Arbor, Mich.

Hamilton, W. J., Jr.: 1943, "The Mammals of Eastern United States," Comstock, Ithaca, N.Y.

Jackson, H. H. T.: 1961, "The Mammals of Wisconsin," University of Wisconsin Press, Madison, Wisc.

Leopold, A. S.: 1959, "Wildlife in Mexico," University of California Press, Berkeley, Calif.

Murie, O. J.: 1954, "A Field Guide to Animal Tracks," Houghton Mifflin, Boston.

Palmer, R. S.: 1954, "The Mammal Guide," Doubleday, Garden City, N.Y.

Schwartz, C. W., and Elizabeth R. Schwartz: 1960, "The Wild Mammals of Missouri," University of Missouri Press, Columbia, Mo.

Journals of interest to field biologists

The following is a list of journals, by no means complete, of interest to field biologists. The scope is international but limited to the English-language publications. There are a number of excellent journals in foreign languages which also publish occasionally in English or have English abstracts.

American Journal of Botany. 1914 on. Botanical Society of America. Technical, of interest chiefly to the professional.

American Midland Naturalist. 1909 on. University of Notre Dame, Notre Dame, Ind. Specializes in papers in field natural history.

American Naturalist. 1867 on. American Society of Naturalists. Concerned largely with morphology evolution, physiology, but of late ecology creeping in.

American Scientist. Society of Sigma Xi. Contains in every volume several papers of importance to ecologists.

American Zoologist. Quarterly Publication of American Society of Zoologists. Most of papers published originate in symposia of society and its annual refresher course.

Animal Behavior. 1952 on. Baillière, London. Contains a wide range of papers on animal behavior.

Annals of the Entomological Society of America. 1908 on. Entomological Society of America. The major entomological journal in America. Strong on taxonomy and morphology.

Audubon Field Notes. 1946 on. National Audubon Society. Devoted to reporting of distribution, migration and abundance of birds. Important information on continental trends in bird populations.

The Auk. 1884 on. American Ornithologists Union. Leading American ornithological journal.

Behaviour. 1947 on. Brill, Leiden, Netherlands. The journal of animal behavior strongly ethological in viewpoint.

Biological Bulletin. 1927 on. Marine Biological Laboratory, Woods Hole, Mass. General papers with emphasis on marine biology.

Bird-Banding. 1930 on. Bird Banding Organizations. A small quarterly. Noted for its excellent coverage of current literature.

Botanical Gazette. 1862 on. University of Chicago Press, Chicago. Covers all departments of botanical science including plant ecology.

Botanical Review. 1935 on. New York Botanical Garden. Excellent review papers, often on plant ecology.

British Birds. H. F. and G. Witherby, London. An important ornithological journal issued monthly. Contains some first-rate papers on the ecology of birds.

California Fish and Game. 1914 on. State of California, Department of Fish and Game. Papers largely devoted to fish and game management. Contains many important papers on western wildlife.

Cambridge Philosophical Society. Biological Reviews, Cambridge University Press. General review papers many of importance to ecology and behavior.

Canadian Entomologist. 1868 on. Entomological Society of Ontario. A major entomological journal devoted to insects of Canada.

Canadian Field Naturalist. 1887 on. Ottawa Field-Naturalist's Club. Papers on all phases of natural history; of strong interest to the field biologist.

Canadian Journal of Zoology. 1923 on. National Research Council of Canada, Ottawa. General zoological papers by many of ecological interest.

Chesapeake Science. State of Maryland, Department of Research and Education, Chesapeake Biological Laboratory, Solomons. A regional publication, but papers of wide interest.

Condor. 1899 on. Cooper Ornithological Society. A western ornithological journal with excellent scientific papers.

Copeia. 1913 on. American Society of Ichthyologists and Herpetologists. Papers on fishes, amphibians, and reptiles.

Ecological Monographs. 1930 on. Ecological Society of America. Contains papers too long for *Ecology.*

Ecology. 1920 on. Ecological Society of America. Indispensable to the field biologist.

Evolution. 1947 on. Society for the Study of Evolution. Papers on evolution and natural selection; worldwide.

Forest Science. 1955 on. Society of American Foresters. Technical, but occasionally contains papers of interest to field biologists.

Ibis. British Ornithological Society. The leading British ornithological journal.

Journal of Animal Ecology. 1933 on. British Ecological Society, Blackwell Scientific Publishions, Oxford. A journal devoted exclusively to animal ecology. Contains many valuable papers.

Journal of Ecology. 1912 on. British Ecological Society. Papers on general ecology but with major emphasis on plants. An important reference journal.

Journal of the Fisheries Research Board of Canada. 1943 on. Fisheries Research Board of Canada, Ottawa. A very valuable source of papers on fish, fish management, and ecology.

Journal of Forestry. Society of American Foresters. Papers on general forestry. Some of interest to ecologists.

Journal of Mammalogy. 1919 on. American Society of Mammalogists. Only journal in English devoted to mammals.

Journal of the Marine Biological Association of the United Kingdom. 1920 on. Marine Biological Association of the United Kingdom. Contains papers on marine biology.

Journal of Marine Research. Sears Foundation for Marine Research. Bingham Oceanographic Laboratory, Yale University, New Haven, Conn. A major source of papers on oceanography, heavy on the physical side.

Journal of Parasitology. 1914 on. American Society of Parasitology. All aspects of animal parasitism.

Journal of Range Management. 1947 on. American Society of Range Management. Advances in the science and art of grazing land management, understanding of practical and scientific range and pasture problems.

Journal of Wildlife Management. 1937 on. The Wildlife Society. Devoted to wildlife research and management. Contains excellent material for the field biologist.

Limnology and Oceanography. 1956 on. American Society of Limnology and Oceanography. The major journal in the field. All papers of strong interest to ecologists.

Nature. Macmillan, London. A weekly journal of science since 1869. Contains a number of important papers of interest to ecologists and field biologists.

New York Fish and Game Journal. 1953 on. State of New York, Conservation Department. An important regional publication with a number of major papers in fish and wildlife field.

Oikos, Acta Oecologica Scandinavica. Munksgaard, Copenhagen. For ecologists in Denmark, Finland, Iceland, Norway, Sweden. A major ecological journal. Papers are in English.

Pedobiologica. Gustav Fisher, Verlag Jena, Villengang. A new journal, international in scope, covering the field of soil biology. Papers in German, Russian, and English.

Physiological Zoology. 1927 on. University of Chicago Press, Chicago. Contains many papers on physiological ecology.

Proceedings of the Zoological Society of London. 1822 on. Zoological Society of London. Contains a number of major papers on ecology and behavior of animals.

Quarterly Review of Biology. American Institute of Biological Sciences. A review journal occasionally publishing papers of interest to field biologists. Excellent book reviews.

Science. 1833 on. American Association for the Advancement of Science. Covers whole field of science, but some papers of interest to field biologist. Good book reviews.

Transactions of the American Fisheries Society. American Fisheries Society. Began as a quarterly in 1959. Contains a number of excellent papers on fish and fresh-water ecology.

Wilson Bulletin. 1888 on. Wilson Ornithological Society. A midwestern ornithological journal that is especially orientated to the field.

General Bibliographies

This list again is incomplete and confined to current bibliographies. These are excellent gateways to literature.

Bibliography of Agriculture. 1942– . U.S. Department of Agriculture. Monthly; covers wide variety of biological subjects. Especially useful for coverage of publications of state agricultural experiment stations.

Biological Abstracts. 1926– . Philadelphia. Most comprehensive biological abstracting journal in North America. A primary reference, it includes brief abstracts available in groups on microfilm.

Forestry Abstracts. 1940– . Commonwealth Agricultural Bureau, Oxford, England. Abstracts of forestry subjects compiled from world literature. Covers all phases of forestry including ecology, soils, general and systematic zoology, animal ecology, general botany, etc. A major bibliography for the ecologist.

Sport Fishery Abstracts. 1956– . U.S. Fish and Wildlife Service. Covers sport fishery research and management, limnology, ecology, and natural history of fishes. Indispensable to the fishery biologist, ecologist, and limnologist. Contains short abstracts of each paper.

Strong, R. M. 1939, 1946, 1959. A bibliography of birds, 4 parts, *Zool. Sci. Bull. No. 25, Field Museum of Natural History,* Chicago. Indispensible to the ornithologist.

Wildlife Abstracts. 1935–1951; 1952–1955; 1956–1960. An annotated bibliography of the publications abstracted in Wildlife Review. A major reference source.

Wildlife Review. 1935– . U.S. Fish and Wildlife Service. Coverage much wider than title indicates. Invaluable to field biologists; a necessity for those in wildlife management.

Zoological Record. 1864– . Zoological Society of London. The major reference for zoologists. World-wide coverage; essential.

Appendixes

An annotated bibliography of statistical methods

$\mathbf{A}$n ecologist friend of mine once described ecology as quantified natural history. In many respects this is an acceptable definition of ecology. It does emphasize that modern studies of plant and animal life must be quantified, in contrast to the purely descriptive studies of an earlier day. Even most elementary studies demand a quantified approach. Since much of the work involves sampling of one sort or another, statistics are involved. But in the hands of those who know little about it, statistics can be dangerous things. They are often abused rather than used, and misapplied to the problems at hand. Too often data are collected and forced to fit some statistical procedure; instead the research should be planned with a particular statistical approach in mind. In spite of the smattering of cookbook statistics given in some ecology texts, none are given here. Rather the reader is referred to a selected list of statistics references. Especially recommended are Schultz, Stearman, and Steele and Torrie, as well as Grieg-Smith and Simpson, Roe and Lewontin.

Andrewartha, H. G.: 1961, "Introduction to the Study of Animal Behavior," University of Chicago Press, Chicago. Parts of this book contain helpful and easily understood discussions on the use and application of statistics to the study of animal populations: sampling, tests for nonrandomness, analysis of variance, etc.

Bailey, N. T.: 1959, "Statistical Methods in Biology," Wiley, New York. A good readable elementary book on statistics, but limited in scope. Treats variation, statistical significance tests, testing methods for homogeneity, correlation, regression, factorial experiments, random sampling, handling a calculating machine, and a summary of statistical formulas.

Batschelet, E.: 1965, "Statistical Methods for the Analysis of Problems in Animal Orientation and Certain Biological Problems," American Institute Biological Sciences, Washington, D.C. Prepared for the use of biologists working in the area of animal migration and homing, biological clocks and periodic activity. Contains solved examples.

Cochran, W. G., and G. M. Cox: 1957, "Experimental Designs," Wiley, New York. Application and interpretation of experimental design. Requires a background of statistics. Should be consulted if the problem requires some experimental design.

Cox, D. R.: 1958, "Planning of Experiments," Wiley, New York. Describes basic ideas underlying statistical aspects of experimental design. Emphasis is on planning. Probably the best general introduction to the design of experiments now available to nonstatisticians.

Donn, O. J.: 1964, "Basic Statistics: A Primer for the Biomedical Sciences," Wiley, New York. A very elementary introduction to statistics that requires only high school algebra as a background. Good for a starter.

Finney, D. J.: 1955, "Experimental Design and Its Statistical Basis," University of Chicago Press, Chicago. Elementary and readable. Does not require a sophisticated background in statistics.

Goldstein, A.: 1964, "Biostatistics: An Introductory Text," Macmillan, New York. An introductory text written from an applied point of view. Discusses and illustrates quantitative data, enumeration data, and linear regression. Some simple nonparametric techniques are treated briefly.

Grieg-Smith, P.: 1964, "Quantitative Plant Ecology," Butterworth, Washington, D.C. A statistical approach to plant ecology. This book is a must for all ecologists concerned with vegetation studies.

Hogg, R. V., and A. T. Craig: 1960, "An Introduction to Mathematical Statistics." A clear mathematical exposition of statistics. Treats binomial and Poisson distributions, density functions, etc.

Kempthorne, O., T. A. Bancroft, J. W. Gowen, and J. L. Lush (eds.): 1954, "Statistics and Mathematics in Biology," Iowa State College Press, Ames, Iowa. Selected papers from a symposium; some deal with sampling and general biometric principles and procedures, estimation of population, etc.

Kershaw, K. A.: 1964, "Quantitative and Dynamic Ecology," American Elsevier Publishing Co., New York. Oriented toward plant ecology, this book considers simpler statistical procedures and their application to vegetation studies. Strong on correlation of positive and negative association between species, Poisson series, and the detection of nonrandomness and natural groupings.

Pearce, S. C.: 1963, "Biological Statistics: An Introduction," McGraw-Hill, New York. Presents statistical methods to biologists who have a minimum of mathematical background, but need to use the techniques. Discusses statistical analysis, experimental design, and interpretation of data.

Schultz, V.: 1961, An annotated bibliography on the uses of statistics in ecology—A Search of 31 periodicals, Publ. TID 3908, *U.S. Atomic Energy Commission*, Office of Technical Information, Environmental Science Branch, Division of Biology and Medicine, Washington, D.C. An extremely useful compendium. Summarizes the uses of statistics in ecology.

Siegel, S.: 1956, "Nonparametric Statistics for the Behavioral Sciences," McGraw-Hill, New York. A collection of nonparametric tests in common use. Procedures are explained and illustrated by mathematical examples.

Simpson, G. G., Anne Roe, and R. C. Lewontin: 1960, "Quantitative Zoology," rev. ed., Harcourt, Brace, & World, New York. As the title implies, this book discusses zoology quantified. Statistical concepts and procedures are applied to taxonomy, distribution, populations, etc. Invaluable for the ecologist involved with animals and animal populations.

Snedecor, G. W.: 1957, "Statistical Methods," Iowa State College Press, Ames, Iowa. Excellent reference for those with some familiarity with statistics.

Stearman, R. L.: 1955, Statistical concepts in microbiology, *Bacteriol. Rev.*, **19**:160–215. An excellent source of information for a biologist interested in reviewing or developing a knowledge of statistical concepts. Discusses those concepts underlying elementary methods involving three basic distributions in statistics: normal, binomial, and Poisson. Pitfalls to be avoided are pointed out. Although dealing with microbiological examples, the discussion is applicable to biological problems in general.

Steel, R. D. G., and J. H. Torrie: 1960, "Principles and Procedures of Statistics," McGraw-Hill, New York. An outstanding "cookbook" approach to statistics slanted toward the needs of the biologist. Includes nonparametric statistics. One of the very best statistics textbooks on the market.

Abstracts of current biometrical literature useful to the ecologist appear in *Wildlife Reviews* (see General Bibliography).

APPENDIX **B**

Environmental measurements

The methods suggested here to measure the chemical and physical aspects of the environment are for the most part the simplest and least expensive for the field student to use. Some of them have a little of the "home-made" quality about them. They may not give the precise results that techniques using more refined instrumentation will do, but if performed carefully, these methods will give results accurate enough for most studies.

Collecting water samples

Collecting samples of water from various depths of lakes, ponds, and estuaries can be a difficult task. Water samplers designed to collect waters from various depths can be purchased from scientific apparatus companies or they can be made by assembling a Meyer sampler. This latter apparatus consists of a heavy bottle fitted with a weight heavy enough to sink it when full of air and attached to a wire harness. A stopper with an eyebolt attached is loosely inserted. A cord is attached both to the eyebolt and to the wire harness. When the bottle is lowered to the desired depth (indicated by a marked line), the cord is jerked to remove the cork. As soon as the bottle fills, pull the bottle to the surface.

Oxygen determination

Water samples must be obtained in 200-ml or 250-cc glass bottles with tight-fitting glass stoppers and taken so that no bubbling or splashing occurs. Be sure that the sample bottle is completely filled, so that there is no air space between the neck and the stopper. Special water samplers are available that make it possible to secure water without introducing atmospheric oxygen. If a sampler is used, then when the water is transferred to the bottle, it should be allowed to overflow the container two or three times to eliminate atmospheric oxygen. The water is then ready for analysis in the field by the rapid Winkler method.

Reagents needed

The following reagents are needed:

1. Alkaline sodium iodine solution. Dissolve 400 grams NaOH and 900 grams NaI to make one liter.

2. Manganous sulfate. Dissolve 480 grams $MnSO_4 \cdot 4H_2O$ in one liter of distilled water.

3. Sodium thiosulfate. Prepare a solution (compute first) of $0.025N$ $Na_2S_2O_3 \cdot 5H_2O$. When dissolved, add a good drop of chloroform to act as a stabilizer, or add 3 grams borax per liter, since this solution does not store. Next standardize a 250-ml sample by adding 25 ml of $0.025N$ potassium dichromate, $K_2Cr_2O_7$. Then add 1 ml of the alkaline NaI solution and 5 ml of concentrated hydrochloric acid (HCl). Titrate this solution with the thiosulfate until the solution turns a faint yellow. Add 10 drops of starch solution (see next paragraph) and continue titration until the blue color disappears. The solution is now ready for use; it should be stored in a brown bottle.

4. Starch reagent. Into 350 ml of water stir 2 grams of powdered potato starch. To this add 30 ml of 20 per cent NaOH, mix, and let stand one hour. Neutralize with HCl, using litmus as an indicator. Then add 1 ml of glacial acetic acid.

Oxygen determination

To determine oxygen follow this procedure:

1. Add 1 ml of the manganous sulfate solution so that it sinks to the bottom. (Slowly and carefully add all reagents deep into the sample with a narrow pipette. When all reagents have been added, the bottle will overflow.) Then with a clean pipette add 1 ml of alkaline sodium iodine solution. Close the bottle, quickly upend, and shake for 20 sec. A glass bead added to the bottle speeds up mixing. A yellow precipitate will form and settle to the bottom.

2. Add 2 ml of concentrated sulfuric acid (H_2SO_4) against the side of the neck, close to the bottle, and invert several times to mix the acid with the solution. This will dissolve the precipitate (maganic hydroxide, in which is fixed the oxygen in the solution) and leave a yellowish-brown color, the deepness of which is proportional to the amount of dissolved oxygen in the sample.

3. After inverting the bottle several times, place the sample into a 400-ml beaker and titrate with the $0.025N$ sodium thiosulfate solution until a pale

straw yellow is reached. Before doing this, *be sure* to read the level of the sodium thiosulfate in the burette and record.

4. Place a white background against the beaker. Then add 10 drops of the starch indicator. Continue titration until the blue color disappears. Read the new level of the sodium thiosulfate in the burette. Record and then calculate the amount used in titration. The number of milliliters used represents the quantity of dissolved oxygen in parts per million.

Free carbon dioxide concentration

In general the amount of carbon dioxide varies inversely with the dissolved oxygen content. Free carbon dioxide occurs only in acid waters.

1. Obtain a water sample and from it fill a Nessler tube to the 100-cc mark. Do not agitate or splash, since CO_2 will easily diffuse into the air.

2. Add 10 drops of phenolphthalein solution. This can be made by dissolving 5 grams of phenolphthalein in 1 liter of 50 per cent alcohol, then neutralized with $0.02N$ NaOH.

3. Titrate this with NaOH, but be sure to record the level of the solution in the burette before starting. When a pink color appears for a few seconds under agitation, quit. Read the new level and record the amount of NaOH used. Multiply amount used by 10. The answer equals the amount of CO_2 in parts per million in the sample.

Temporary hardness

Temporary hardness of water is caused by the carbonates of calcium and magnesium. Since any carbon dioxide present in alkaline and neutral waters will be in the form of bicarbonate, the determination of temporary hardness and the determination of combined carbon dioxide are one and the same.

Reagents needed

1. Hydrochloric acid, $0.01N$.
2. Indicator solution consisting of a mixture of 0.02 per cent methyl red and 0.1 per cent brome cresol green mixed in 95 per cent alcohol.

Determination

1. To the water sample (100 ml) add a couple of drops of indicator.
2. Titrate the HCl into solution until the first appearance of pink.
3. Record the amount in cubic centimeters of HCl needed per 100 ml of water.
4. Multiply this by 5 and the answer will be the amount of CO_2 expressed as parts per million of $CaCO_3$.

Total hardness

Total hardness or permanent hardness generally is caused by the chlorides and sulfates of calcium and magnesium.

There are several ways of determining total hardness, an old-fashioned way, with the soap method, and a colorimetric method. The latter is the most accurate and once the stock solution is mixed, the easiest. The colorimetric method is based on the ability of sodium versenate (sodium diethylenediamine tetracetate, $Na_2C_{10}H_{14}O_8N_2 \cdot 2H_2O$) to form un-ionized complexes with calcium and magnesium. If eriochrome black T, a dark blue dye, is added to this solution containing Ca^{++} and Mg^{++} ions, a complex, pink in color, is formed. By adding sodium versenate solution to this complex, the solution can be turned back to blue again by removing Ca^{++} and Mg^{++} from the dye complex to the versenate complex again. The end point—when the pink changes back to blue—can be used as a measure of total hardness.

Reagents needed

1. Standard calcium chloride solution. Dissolve 55 grams $CaCl_2 \cdot 6H_2O$ in distilled water; then add enough to make 1 liter of solution.
2. Sodium versenate solution. This can be purchased as a standard solution or it can be mixed as follows: Dissolve 2.5 grams of sodium versenate in 2 liters of distilled water. To this add 13.5 cc of N NaOH solution, prepared by mixing 40 grams in 1 liter of water, and make up to 2500 cc. This solution must be adjusted against the standard chloride solution so that 1 cc equals 0.1 mg of Ca^{++}. Use eriochrome black T as the indicator.
3. Indicator. Eriochrome black T. To 30 cc of distilled water add 1 gram of the eriochrome black T and 1 cc of N Na_2CO_3. Mix and make up to 100 cc with isopropyl alcohol.
4. Buffer solution. Dissolve 40 grams of borax in 800 cc of water and 10 grams of NaOH and 5 grams of sodium sulfide ($Na_2S_2 \cdot 9H_2O$) in 100 cc of distilled water. Mix the two solutions together and dilute to 1 liter. This is used to control pH at the 8 to 10 level and to eliminate the effects of copper, iron, and manganese ions.

Determination

1. Take a 100-cc sample of water and slightly acidify with 0.1N HCl; boil for a few minutes.
2. Add 0.5 cc of the buffer solution.
3. Add 5 drops of eriochrome black T indicator solution.
4. Titrate with the standard sodium versenate, the end point being reached when the blue color appears. Each cubic centimeter of sodium versenate needed to titrate the 100-cc sample equals 1 part per million of Ca^{++} and Mg^{++}.

Chlorides: salinity

Salinity of coastal waters varies little, but in the estuary it varies considerably, both vertically and horizontally. Because of its biological importance, the determination of chlorides is nesessary in any estuarine study. The most accurate method is titration.

Determination

1. Add a few drops of potassium chromate solution to a 100-cc sample of water.
2. Titrate with 0.01N silver nitrate solution, stirring constantly. When a faint red color of silver chromate appears, the end point has been reached. Determine the number of cubic centimeters of 0.01N silver nitrate used and multiply this by 0.000355. The answer equals chlorides in parts per million.

599

Acidity

Colorimetric determination of pH is the quickest and simplest method in the field and fairly accurate. For aquatic work there are the narrow-range pH papers. For soils work there are a number of soil-acidity test kits on the market that use color indicators. But be sure to obtain a kit with a selection of narrow-range indicators.

For more sophisticated measurement and research, the electronic pH meter should be used. Most of these are expensive, although moderately priced pocket meters are available.

Current

Estimates of stream flow are necessary in any study of the flowing water community. Fortunately a short, accurate method for estimating the volume of flow is available without resorting to current meters (Robins and Crawford, 1954). It works very well for most stream studies.

Choose a cross section of the stream where the current and depth are most uniform and measure the width. Then divide this width into three equal segments, marked or separated by pushing sticks into the bottom, coloring the surface of stones, and so on. Next record the depth at the midpoint of each segment and determine the velocity of the surface current. The velocity can be found by dropping a fisherman's float (without projecting arms) attached to five feet of limp, monofilament nylon fishing line (0.005–0.01-inch diameter). Record with a stop watch the time required for the float to travel the five feet. This should be done several times and the average figure recorded and converted into feet per second.

Next determine the volume of flow R for each segment of the cross section by the following formula:

$$R = WDaV$$

where
- a = a bottom factor constant (0.8 for rocks and coarse gravel; 0.9 for mud, sand, hardpan, bedrock)
- W = width of the segment
- D = depth at the midpoint of the segment
- V = surface current velocity taken at the midpoint of the segment

Total flow is determined by adding the flows for the three segments.

Estuary

The study of currents in the estuary is more complicated because of the flow of fresh water to the sea and the incoming flow of sea water at high tide. A knowledge of the circulation set up by the incoming and outgoing flow is of major importance in the study of both the physical and biological aspects of the estuary.

A rapid technique for obtaining current profiles in estuarine waters has been developed by Prichard and Burt (1951). It involves the use of a current indicator consisting of a submerged biplane-shaped drag and a device for reading the angle made by the suspending wire with the verticle. The device is made from two half-inch (five ply) fir plywood panels 4 feet long and 3 feet high, assembled so that each panel bisects the other. This gives four planes 2 by 3 feet. To this is added a 30-pound weight, and the entire biplane is attached to hydrographic wire and suspended into the water from a block extending as far as possible out from the anchored ship. The current will swing this drag out in the direction of the current, whose speed of flow is then computed by the angle of the wire from the vertical. Since the velocity of flow is proportional to the square root of the tangent of the angle made by the supporting line with the vertical, the current velocity can be solved by the following formula:

$$v = k\sqrt{\tan \theta}$$

The value of k, a proportionality factor to take care of the opposing forces of frictional drag of water flowing past the drag and the restoring force of gravity, for this device is 1.04. For those interested, the formula for k can be found in the original paper. This method works well for the determination of current velocity down to 50 feet, even where the velocity is as low as 1 cm/sec (less than 0.02 knot).

Light

Aquatic

A commonly employed method of estimating the depth of light penetration into a body of water is the Secchi disk, which is easily constructed. Take a firm metal disk about 8 inches in diameter, paint it with several coats of white enamel. Then divide the disk into several quadrants and paint the alternate sectors black or red. Attach the disk by the center to a rod, cord, or chain calibrated for depth. Be sure the disk is fitted to ride level when it is lowered into the water. To read, lower the disk over the side of the boat and note the depth at which the disk disappears. Sink the disk several more feet, then raise it, noting the depth at which the disk reappears. The average of the two observations gives a single light-penetration reading. This method gives an *estimate* of the compensation level.

For precision readings of light in aquatic environments photometers adapted for underwater work are necessary.

Terrestrial

The usual method of obtaining light-intensity data in terrestrial communities is the use of a photometer, a wide variety of which are available today. Preferable are ones that are calibrated in foot-candles.

While the photometer works satisfactorily in open situations, its use in the forest community leaves a good deal to be desired. Since the photometer measures light intensity at a given spot at a given minute, it fails to yield information on the changing intensity of light on the forest floor. The only alternative with this instrument is to take a large number of readings over a period of time, which

601

is time consuming, inaccurate, and even impossible when more than a few locations are involved.

Superior to the exposure meter is the chemical light meter described briefly in a paper by W. G. Dore (1958). It offers several advantages: (1) it measures the cumulative amount of light reaching a particular location during a period of time; (2) it is comparatively inexpensive: (3) a great number of locations can be sampled at the same time; (4) the measurement can be made in almost any location where a small vial of the light-sensitive chemical can be placed.

The principle of the method is based on the fact that anthracene ($C_{14}H_{10}$) in benzene will polymerize into insoluble dianthracene ($C_{14}H_{10})_2$ upon exposure to light. This property can be used to measure the amount of light that enters an environment over a period of time. In use, vials of the anthracene-benzene solution are exposed to the light of a particular environment for a period of time, then are analyzed to determine the amount of unconverted anthracene remaining in solution. The analysis is made with a spectrophotometer. A standardization curve that relates the per cent transmittance from the spectrophotometer to concentration of anthracene, and a calibration curve that relates the concentration of anthracene to light exposure are required to convert the chemical reaction into standard units of light.

Details of the procedure are too lengthy to describe here, but they are given in step-by-step pictorial detail by Marquis and Yelenosky, 1962, in a U.S. Forest Service publication, *A Chemical Light Meter for Forest Research*.

Temperature

The temperature of air and water at any one given time can be recorded with a standard mercury thermometer or with a dial thermometer. The latter are preferable for ecological work. The cost is moderate, they are not easily broken, and they can be used to take temperatures of streams, of crevices in bark, etc, underneath litter and in the soil.

A semirecording instrument is the maximum-minimum thermometer. It consists of two thermometers, each with a metallic float that in the one thermometer lodges at the highest temperature, in the other at the lowest. For new readings the floats are reset at the top of the mercury columns, preferably with a small magnet. Temperatures usually are recorded on a 24-hour basis. For ecological purposes any time for resetting can be chosen, preferably at some time away from the extremes. In terrestrial communities, maximum-minimum thermometers should be protected in slotted wooden shelters and should be placed at several levels, including the ground level. In animal studies the ground level is best.

The maximum-minimum thermometer can be used to record the water temperatures at different depths in lakes and ponds. Attach one end of the thermometer to a measured line and to the other end attach a weight. Take readings vertically from the surface to the bottom at 0.5- or 1.0-meter intervals.

In the absence of a maximum-minimum thermometer, the temperatures of deep water can be taken as soon as the water samples are raised to the surface.

Electronic temperature-recording devices with battery power and with a sensing probe or lead especially designed to read instantaneously the temperature of water at various depths are now available at reasonable cost. Even some mail-order houses have them available as fish-finding devices.

Highly accurate temperature measurements of microlocations—soil, leaf litter, tree wood, bark, leaf, etc., can be taken with resistance thermometers or thermistors and microprobes that are buried in the material or object. The thermistors have leads projecting above the surface. To take a reading, the wires are attached to the terminals of a potentiometer, on which temperatures are read directly. Compact sensory units are available with which one can take simultaneous readings of both the soil-moisture content and the soil temperature.

Available for continuous recording of temperatures are recording thermographs. A number of types are available, but all work with a simple clock within a cylinder drum upon which temperatures are recorded in graph form by pen and ink.

Humidity

The usual method of determining atmospheric moisture involves the use of the sling psychrometer. This can be purchased rather reasonably from scientific supply houses. When readings are to be taken, the fabric over the wet bulb must be soaked in distilled water. Then the instrument is rapidly swung so that the evaporation cools the wet bulb. When the readings of the two bulbs, wet and dry, are constant, the temperatures on both are recorded. Relative humidity is obtained from the dry-bulb reading and the difference between the dry-bulb reading and the wet-bulb reading. To convert these readings to relative humidity, a conversion table prepared for this purpose must be consulted. Vapor-pressure deficits can also be obtained from the original readings with the aid of suitable tables.

Atmometer

For certain studies the natural rates of evaporation may mean more than the relative humidity.

A useful instrument for measuring total evaporative power is the atmometer, or more specifically the Livingston (or James) atmometer, a standardized and calibrated wet surface constant in size, shape, and texture. It consists of a hollow unglazed sphere connected to a reservoir or graduated cylinder.

For long time measurements, over a period of hours or days, the atmometer is connected to a large reservoir of water (about 500 ml in a flask or bottle) by ordinary glass tubing sealed at the end but with a small hole in the end about 1 inch from the top. This in turn is covered with a tightly fitting rubber tubing, which acts as a valve to allow the water to pass from the reservoir into the porous chamber but not back again. The tube is then inserted into the reservoir through one hole in a two-hole stopper. The bottom of the tube should reach nearly to the bottom of the reservoir. In the other hole, place a hooked vent pipe with the external opening pointing downward. Comparisons are made by weighing the whole apparatus and then determining the loss of weight over a period of time. Multiply the raw data by the conversion factor on the glazed neck of each atmometer. Use distilled water at all times.

603

A simple short-term atmometer can be assembled by filling an inverted atmometer with distilled water and inserting a one-hole rubber stopper in the neck. Then carefully insert a 1-ml graduated pipette through the stopper and into the atmometer far enough to cause the water to rise in the graduated pipette. Expose the atmometer for a constant period of time in the habitat under study and note the amount of water evaporated.

Humidity also can be recorded continuously with the use of a recording hygrograph, which plots the humidity on a graph attached to a revolving drum. In fact the thermograph and hygrograph are often combined into one instrument (rather expensive), the hygrothermograph.

Soil moisture

Soil moisture is best determined through the use of moisture blocks, thermistors, and a potentiometer. This has been discussed briefly already under Temperature. The whole setup can be purchased from agricultural and forestry supply houses.

An alternate but less accurate method is to collect soil samples in the field, place them in plastic bags, and bring them back to the laboratory. Here they should be allowed to drain and air dry for 24 hours. Then weigh out 10 grams of each, place on evaporating dish, and put in an oven at 105° C until the weight is constant. Cool in the dessicator and weigh. The loss in weight expressed as a percentage represents the moisture contained in hygroscopic water and in some of the capillary water. If all samples are handled in the same way, the final figures will provide a valid comparison of the humidity of different soils.

Soil atmosphere

The soil atmosphere, its fluctuations in composition between oxygen and carbon dioxide, and its influence on animal distribution in the soil has received little attention. It is a fertile field for investigation, although its study requires some equipment and is rather time consuming. The collection of the soil gases is relatively simple. An ingenious procedure for obtaining samples of soil atmosphere from the litter has been devised by Haley and Brierley (1953). This procedure might be modified to study atmosphere of deeper soil layers. The apparatus used (Fig. B-1) consists of polyvinal plastic tubing 30 cm long and 3 cm in diameter. Each end is fitted with a rubber stopper. One is fitted with a small piece of glass capillary tubing, which in turn is fitted with a stopper made by fitting a piece of glass rod inside a short rubber tube. The other stopper is fitted with wider glass tubing, to which is attached a short piece of rubber tubing with a screw clamp attached. A length of wire is soldered to the clamping screw.

These tubes, which will hold two 25-cc gas samples are then buried in the surface soil or the litter with location wire projecting upward. Leave the nozzles of the tubes closed in location for several days until the disturbed soil conditions have returned to normal. Then open the tubes by turning the wire handles on the screw clamps. Gaseous diffusion between the tubes and the soil atmosphere will take place until equilibrium is established, usually in about 24 hours. For best results, however, wait a week, return, close the nozzle, and remove the tubes.

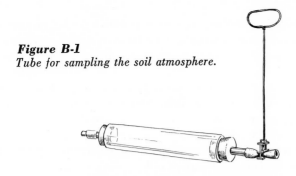

Figure B-1
Tube for sampling the soil atmosphere.

The gases within the tube are then tested in the laboratory for oxygen and carbon dioxide. Analysis procedure can be obtained in analytical chemistry books. A required piece of equipment is the Bancroft-Haldane or Haldane-Gutherie gas-analysis apparatus, obtainable from scientific supply houses. A more accurate field method involving more equipment is described by Wallis and Wilde, 1957.

Soil organic matter

Accurate estimate of soil organic matter is difficult without special techniques, but a reasonable estimate can be obtained by loss of weight on ignition. Take about 5 grams of oven-dried soil, weigh carefully, and then heat red hot in a crucible for about one-half hour. Cool in a dessicator, reweigh, and heat again. Continue this until weight becomes constant. The loss in weight, expressed as a percentage, will represent the amount of oxidizable organic matter present. Correction for the accompanying decomposition of carbonates can be made by adding some ammonia carbonate to the cooled sample, then heating in the oven to 105°C to drive off the excess solution. Cool and reweigh. The gain of weight indicates the amount of CO_2 lost by the carbonates during the previous heating. This gain in weight can then be subtracted from the initial weight loss, before percentage of organic matter is determined.

Soil texture and composition

Examine samples of sand, silt, clay, and gravel with a hand lens. Moisten each of these samples and feel them between your fingers. Note the difference between the four, both as to their feel and the way they behave when moist.

Collect samples of soils from various areas—forests, fields, and gardens. Rub a sample of each between your fingers. If gritty, sand particles are present. If some or all of the soil feels like flour or talcum powder, then it is silty. Clay soils have enough clay particles to give them a harsh feeling when dry. Dampen the samples by sprinkling them with water until they have the consistency of workable putty. From this sample make a ball about half an inch in diameter. Hold the ball between thumb and forefinger. Gradually press your thumb forward, forming the soil into a ribbon. If the ribbon forms easily and remains long and flexible, the soil is probably a clay or silty clay; if its breaks easily under its own weight, it probably is a clay loam or a silty clay loam. If a ribbon is not formed, the soil is probably a silt loam, sandy loam, or sand.

Soil textures are best determined in the laboratory by passing a known weight of oven-dry soil from several layers through various-size sieves (U.S. Department of Agriculture standard sieves with decreasing aperture sizes), separating the various components. By determining the proportion of each, the soil texture can be classified. A similar though less accurate method can be used to demonstrate soil texture. Collect samples of various soils, enough to fill a pint jar about one-half full of each sample. Add water to fill the jar to the shoulder. Put the cap on and shake the jar. Then let the soil settle out; allow plenty of time, for small particles will be slow in settling. The heavier particles will settle out first, the silt next, and the clay last. These components will build up several layers. Hold up a card or heavy piece of paper against the side of the jar and draw a diagram showing the different layers. Label each layer. The relative amounts of each will help you determine the texture of the soil. Since the ecologist is more concerned with combined effects than with detailed particle analysis, this rough estimate may be sufficient.

Sampling the soil

The most efficient device for sampling the soil is a soil augur, which enables you to extract soil from known depths and horizons. After extraction the soil is laid out to dry before determining its composition.

Mapping the study area

In some studies an accurate map is desirable and often necessary. It may be needed to show the location of sample plots, animal concentrations and movements, vegetative cover, and the like. The details of the map, what it should show, all depend upon the nature of the study.

The simplest method of mapping is with the use of aerial photographs. If the area to be mapped is located within the center of the photograph and the terrain is not too rough, then the major vegetational units and features of the landscape can be traced directly from a photograph enlarged to a scale of 660 feet to the inch. (Photographs of most areas are available from the Agricultural Stabilization and Conservation Service, U.S. Department of Agriculture, Washington, D.C.). Scale can be corrected by pacing a given distance along a road, field boundary, or other straight-line feature and comparing it with the distance scale of the photograph. Make any necessary adjustments. For rough or hilly country, or for areas requiring several photographs, the map should be prepared by radial triangulation. For details see the aerial photo references at the end of this appendix.

The area can also be mapped by tape and compass. This will give accurate enough maps for most work. More precise surveying instruments require knowledge of land-surveying techniques.

The compass

The box-type compass is the most satisfactory for mapping work. It requires the use of a tripod, so that the compass can be leveled at each survey point.

The face of the compass is graduated into four quadrats of 90 degrees each. The graduations at the North and South Poles are 0 and increase through 90 degrees from each pole to east and west. The greater the number of degrees, the more the bearing approaches east or west. The bearing is always read from north or south to east or west. For example, S50E means a point 50 degrees away from south towards the east. If the needle points directly east or west, it is read so. Or the compass may be graduated into 360 degrees. North is 0 and the degrees increase clockwise. East is 90, south 180, west 270, and north 360. Both 0 and 360 are the same, north.

The compass needle on a central pivot always points to magnetic north. The angle this line makes with a line pointing to true north is known as the angle of declination. This declination varies in different parts of the country. The degrees of declination are usually indicated on geologic survey topographic maps. If the survey lines are to be changed to true north, they must be corrected by degrees of declination. This is best done by adjusting the dial of the compass to true north before mapping.

The east and west directions on the box-type compass are printed on opposite sides. In other words, east is where one normally would expect to find west and vice versa. There is a reason for this. The direction is indicated by means of a sight or line on the compass lid. The bearing is always read on the graduated dial at the point where the north end of the needle comes to rest. If the sighting is to the magnetic north, the needle will rest at north; if the compass is shifted to the west, the needle will still point north, but the dial is shifted so that west is at the tip of the needle.

Distance by pacing

Distance can be measured in two ways: (1) by the use of a steel tape, marked in meters, feet, or chains, or (2) by pacing. Pacing is faster but not as accurate, and it is more difficult to correct for slope. However, it will suffice for most mapping, if the terrain is fairly level. First one must know the distance of one's average step or pace. Distance by pacing is measured by counting the steps and multiplying the number of steps by the distance covered in each step. Usually only one foot, the left, is counted. Thus the pace is the average distance taken in two steps. Pacing should be practiced by stepping off measured distances in different terrains and dividing the distance by the number of paces or steps taken.

The survey traverse

A traverse is connected by a series of survey lines. Each line is determined by its bearing and distance. A traverse begins at some established point, follows all exterior limits of the area, and closes at the starting point. Traverses that follow roads and streams will not close and their direction will be determined by the route the road or stream takes.

1. The compass is set up at the starting point, *A*, and a sight is taken on the next station, *B*. The bearing is read and entered in the notebook. The distance

between *A* and *B* is then measured or paced and the distance recorded. When the line *AB* is completed, the compass is set up at *B*, a bearing taken on *C*, recorded, and the distance to *C* is then measured. The work progresses in this matter until completed. Accurate and complete notes must be taken as the survey progresses. From these notes the map will be drawn. Notes must be entered so they can be interpreted accurately.

After the exterior lines have been surveyed, interior details can be determined by meandering traverses, as the course of a road or stream. The starting point is located at the exact point on the exterior boundary where the road or stream enters the area. The course will be determined by plotting the bearings and distances. The point where the traverse leaves the area should be determined on the opposite boundary traverse.

Plotting the traverse

A map is plotted from the traverse notes. A protractor, a ruler or engineer's scale, and a straight edge are needed. Before transferring the notes to the map paper, the scale must be determined. The scale will depend upon the extent to which the area can be reduced to fit the size of the map paper. For small areas, the scale of one inch on the paper to equal 660 feet on the ground is satisfactory. For larger areas the scale can be reduced; for smaller areas it can be increased.

The protractor is used to transfer the bearings of the individual lines of the map. The protractor is graduated in degrees, used in plotting the angles.

Drawing the map. Select a point on the map to represent the starting point of the survey. Through this point draw a straight line for the meridian, or north-south line. The protractor is centered over the initial point and carefully aligned to the meridian. The bearing of the initial line is marked by a pencil dot according to the number of degrees it bears east or west from north or south. A line is drawn between the two points, *A*, the starting station and the point located by the protractor. The appropriate distance is then scaled off on this line. The protractor is then centered at *B* and the same operation repeated to locate station *C*. The plotting is continued until all stations and lines are located on the map.

Adjusting the errors. More often than not, the error in plotting the bearings and distance will be great enough so that the map will not close. The error of closure is determined by measuring the distance connecting the last point plotted with the starting point. If the length of line or error of closure is 0.5 per cent of the total length of the perimeter, the error is not excessive and will not seriously affect area determinations. If the error is larger than this, the field work should be checked.

Small errors must be corrected if the map is to close. This can be done as follows:

1. The line representing the closing error is drawn and measured.
2. Through each angle, lines parallel to the closing error are drawn.
3. The length of each line between stations is divided by the total perimeter and the results multiplied by the length of the closing error.
4. On the parallel lines the respective amounts of closing error are marked off, increasing cumulatively at each successive corner.
5. The newly located points are connected and the adjusted boundary to the map is completed.

Interior details. Interior details are now added from the notes to the outline. Care must be taken to have the traverse of vegetation boundaries, roads, etc., end on or leave the area at a point on the map that corresponds to the measured distance in the field notes.

Area determination. If a planimeter is not available, the area can be determined as follows:

1. Divide the map into triangles.
2. Compute in square inches, square feet, or square meters the areas of each triangle by the formula—Area = base × one-half altitude. If the calculations are made in feet, divide by 43,560 to obtain the area in acres; if in chains, divide by 10; if in meters, divide by 10,000 to obtain the area in hectares.

REFERENCES

General

Anonymous
1955 "Standard Methods for the Examination of Water, Sewage and Industrial Wastes," American Public Health Association (1790 Broadway, New York 19, N.Y.).

Barnes, H.
1963 "Oceanography and Marine Biology: A Book of Techniques," Macmillan, New York.

Jackson, M. L.
1958 "Soil Chemical Analysis," Prentice-Hall, Englewood Cliffs, N.J.

Platt, R. B., and J. F. Griffiths
1964 "Environmental Measurement and Interpretation," Reinhold, New York.

Soil Survey Staff
1951 Soil survey manual, *U.S. Dept. Agriculture Handbook No. 18* (Supplement, May 1962, pp. 173–185).

Welch, P. S.
1948 "Limnological Methods," McGraw-Hill–Blakiston, New York.

Other

Avery, G.
1957 Foresters' guide to aerial photo interpretation, *Southern Forest Exp. Sta. Occ. Paper 156.*
1962 "Interpretation of Aerial Photographs," Burgess, Minneapolis.

Dore, W. G.
1958 A simple chemical light meter, *Ecology,* **39**:151–152.

Gerking, S. D.
1959 A method of sampling the littoral macrofauna and its application, *Ecology,* **38**:219–226.

Haley, J. L., and J. K. Brierley
1953 A method of estimation of oxygen and carbon dioxide concentrations in the litter layer of beech woods, *J. Ecology,* **41**:385–387.

Johnston, R.
1964 Recent advances in the estimation of salinity, in H. Barnes (ed.), "Oceanography and Marine Biology," ann. rev. no. 2, G. Allen, London, pp. 97–120.

Marquis, D. A., and G. Yelenosky
1962 A chemical light meter for forest research, *Northeast Forest Exp. Sta. Paper 165.*

Pritchard, D. W., and W. V. Burt
1951 An inexpensive and rapid technique for obtaining current profiles in estuarine waters, *J. Marine Res.,* **10**:180–189.

Robins, C. R., and R. W. Crawford
1954 A short, accurate method for estimating the volume of stream flow, *J. Wildlife Mangement,* **18**:366–369.

Spurr, S. H.
1960 "Photogrammetry and Photo-interpretation," 2d ed., Ronald, New York

Wallis, G. W., and S. A. Wilde
1957 Rapid method for the determination of carbon dioxide evolved from forest soils, *Ecology,* **38**:359–361.

APPENDIX **C**

Study
of
the plant community

The plant community can be approached in several ways. One is the descriptive approach, which involves an analysis of the vegetation in the stand and its ordination with other stands. Some analysis of the stand is necessary in many studies of animals, in wildlife management problems, and in the study of plant distribution. Plant-distribution data, as commonly given in taxonomic works and guides, rarely have been gathered on a sound ecological basis.

A second approach is historical. One method is the study of tree rings, which are related to climate and the past history of the stand. Such studies can result in important information. The other is based on the study of pollen profiles of lake bottoms and bogs. Such studies give clues to community development and replacement in the past.

A third approach, quite popular and promising today, is the functional approach (Chap. 3). Here emphasis is given to the flow of energy and material through the ecosystem, including the plant community. Studies are concentrated on gross and primary production. Such studies are basic to the understanding of community functions and the role of organisms in the economy of nature.

Ideally the study of the community should involve all three, but nothing this ambitious has been attempted, to the author's knowledge.

Vegetation analysis

Methods of analyzing the vegetation occupying a given site are numerous and the literature discussing them, the underlying philosophies, and the statistical treatments are extensive. Basic references are given at the end of this appendix and they should be consulted. Since a major decision in ecological studies involves the methods to be used, a number of ways of handling the vegetation are given here with some comments on their advantages and disadvantages. Again these are simply personal selections, based on experience, and they are not complete by any means.

Quadrats or sample plots

Strictly speaking, the quadrat applies to a square sample unit or plot. It may be a single sample unit or it may be divided into subplots. Quadrats may vary in size, shape, number, and arrangement, depending upon the nature of the vegetation and the objectives of the study.

The size of the quadrat must be adapted to the characteristics of the community. The richer the flora, the larger or more numerous the quadrats must be. In the forests, quadrats of one-fifth acre are established to include the trees, while smaller nested quadrats can be used to study shrubs and understory. For the latter as well as grass cover, quadrats of one square meter are the usual size. The shape of the quadrat is usually square, but rectangular or even circular ones may work better. In fact rectangular plots often give the best results. These are usually 1:2, 1:4, or 1:8.

The number of sample units to be employed always presents some problems. The number will vary with the characteristics of the community, objectives of the investigation, degree of precision, and so on. The final number more often than not is arbitrary, but by using statistical methods the reliability of the sample and the number of samples needed for any desired degree of accuracy can be determined, once a normal distribution around a mean has been established.

Species-area curves. A second approach to this problem is through the species-area curve (Fig. C-1). If the number of species found in plots of different sizes (vertical axis) are plotted against the sample-area size (the horizontal axis), the resulting sigmoid curve will be the species-area curve. Such a curve is obtained because, as the size of the sample plot is increased, it includes at first a considerably larger number of species; then later the number of new species added declines to a point of diminishing returns, where there is little to be gained by increasing the sample area. This curve can be plotted on an arithmetic or a logarithmic base (see Vestal, 1949). The method can be employed to determine the largest size of a single plot (minimal area) needed to survey the community adequately. In this case the sampling should be done by using a geometric system of nested plots (Fig. C-2). Or the curve can be used to determine the minimum number of small multiple plots needed for a satisfactory sample. In addition the species-area curve can be used to compare one community with another (Fig. C-3).

Kinds of quadrats. Quadrats are often labeled according to the uses of or data derived from them.

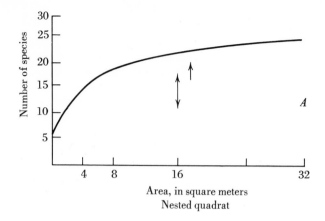

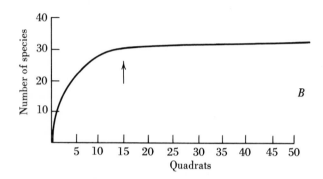

Figure C-1 *Species-area curves. (A) For minimal area of quadrat; (B) for minimal number of quadrats. Arrows indicate minimal areas.*

1. List quadrat. The organisms found are listed by name. A series of list quadrats gives a floristic analysis of the community and allows an assignment of a frequency index, but nothing else.

2. Count quadrats. The numbers as well as the names of each species encountered is recorded. This method is widely used in forest survey work; but here additional information, such as height, volume, basal area, etc., also is taken. Quadrats used in deer-browse studies also fall into this category.

3. Cover quadrat. The actual or relative coverage is recorded, usually as a percentage of the area of the ground surface covered or shaded by vegetation.

4. Chart quadrat. A quadrat that is mapped to scale to show the location of individual plants. This is a tedious job, but where long-range studies of vegetation changes are being made, this method provides the "big picture."

Location of plots. For statistically reliable estimates, the plots must be randomized. This is rather easily done. On an area photo or map of the study area, lay out a series of grid lines. Number the lines on a horizontal and vertical axis. Write the numbers of the vertical and horizontal grid lines on small squares of paper, place in two separate bowls, mix, and draw out pairs of numbers. Then locate the position of each plot by plotting the point given by the paired numbers.

Advantages and Disadvantages. The quadrat method has its advantages and disadvantages. It is a popular method, easily employed. If the individual organisms are randomly distributed, then the accuracy of the sample and the estimate of the density depend upon the size of the sample. But since individuals seldom are randomly dispersed, the accuracy of quadrat sampling may be low, unless a great number of plots are involved. The quadrat method is tedious and time consuming.

Transects

The transect is a cross section of an area used as a sample for recording, mapping, or studying vegetation. It may be a belt, a strip, or only a line on which intercepts by types of vegetation are marked off. Because of its continuity through the study area, the transect can be used to relate changes in vegetation along the line or strip with changes in the environment. As a sample unit, the measurements within a transect are pooled, and each transect is treated as a single observation in the sample.

The Belt Transect. The belt transect can be set up as follows:

1. Determine the total area of the site to be sampled; then divide by 5 or 10 to obtain the total sample area.

2. Lay out a series of belt transects of a predetermined width and length, sufficient to embrace the area to be sampled. Then divide the belts into equal-sized segments. These are sometimes called quadrats or plots, but they differ from true quadrats in that each represents an observational unit rather than a sampling unit.

3. The vegetation in each unit is measured for some attribute, depending upon the problem at hand: abundance, sociability, frequency, stem counts, etc.

A variation of the segmented-belt transect consists of taking observations only on alternate segments. The precision seems to be affected very little (Oosting, 1956). For example 10 quadrats alternately spaced on a 20-foot belt are nearly twice as efficient statistically as 10 quadrats on a 10-foot belt.

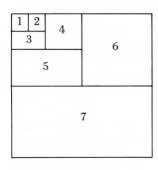

Figure C-2 *An example of nested quadrats.*

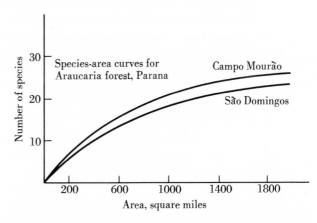

Figure C-3 *Species-area curve for a stand of* Araucaria *forest on different sites near Campo Mourao, Parana, showing the use of species-area curves to compare one community with another.* (From Cain and Castro, *Manual of Vegetation Analysis*, Harper and Row, New York, 1959.)

The belt transect is well adapted to estimate abundance, frequency, and distribution. But for estimating the frequency index, it has the disadvantage that frequency by classes is related to the size of the plot. If one wishes to compare one area with another, the segment size used in sampling must be the same for both areas.

The line-intercept method. The line transect is one-dimensional. It consists of taking observations on a line or lines laid out randomly or systematically over the study area.

1. Stretch a metric steel tape or steel chain between two stakes 33.5 meters, or one chain, apart.

2. Consider the line to be a belt one cm wide extending along one side of the tape.

3. Move along the line and record for each plant species found the distance it covers along the line transect:

  (*a*) For grasses, rosettes, and dicot herbs, measure the distance along the line at ground level.

  (*b*) For shrubs and tall dicot herbs, measure the "shadow," or distance covered by a downward projection of the foliage above.

4. Twenty to 30 such lines are usually sufficient.

The data can be summarized as follows.

1. The number of times each individual species appears along the line.

2. The percentage of occurrence for each species in relation to the total.

3. Total linear distance in centimeters of each species along the belt.

4. The total distance of intercept by all species per 30-meter line.

The advantages and disadvantages can be summarized as follows. This method is rapid, objective, and relatively accurate. The area may be determined directly from recorded observations. The lines can be randomly placed and replicated to obtain the desired precision. The method is well adapted for measuring changes in vegetation if the ends of the lines are well marked. Generally it is more accurate in mixed plant communities than quadrat sampling and is especially well suited for measuring low vegetation. On the debit side, the method is not well adapted for estimating frequency or abundance, since the probability of an individual being sampled is proportional to its size. Nor is it suited where vegetation types are intermingled and the boundaries indistinct.

The loop method

The loop technique is a modification of the Parker three-step method for measuring the condition and trend of forest range. It is useful for determining community composition, species frequency, and range condition. Small circles located along a stretched line as observation points replace the line transect. This method takes little time, and 20 to 25 transects under most conditions adequately sample the community. Since 100 points are used in each transect, the subtotals are read as percentages with suitable adjustments for the number of transects. From these figures the species composition and cover are easily computed.

Briefly the procedure is as follows.

1. Construct from a coat hanger a small wire loop 2 cm in diameter.

2. Locate at random a point in the community, and from this stretch a tape out 33.5 meters. The observation points are located in each meter at the 33-, 66-, and 100-cm mark.

3. At each point drop the loop to the right of the tape and record the species encountered in the loop.

4. Near the end of the line at the 33.33-meter mark make an additional point to bring the total to 100.

This method is simple, accurate, and yields concrete measurements as well as sound observational evidence of trends and changes in ground vegetation. Its use, however, is limited to grass and low herbaceous vegetation.

The variable-plot method

The variable-radius method of forest sampling was developed first in Germany by Bitterlich, who used it to determine timber volume without establishing plot boundaries. The method was introduced into the United States by L. Grosenbaugh (1952, 1958).

The variable-plot method requires no actual measurement in the field; no plots or lines are laid out on the ground; no dimension of any plant is taken. Basically the variable plot (sometimes called point sampling, but this can be confused with another technique of the same name) is a means of selecting trees, shrubs, or grass clumps to be counted on the basis of size rather than on frequency of occurrence. The usual plots or lines are replaced by a series of sampling points distributed at random over the area to be surveyed. At each sampling point the observer uses an angle gauge or prism that subtends a fixed angle of view to sight in each tree dbh or crown diameter of a shrub. Tree boles and shrub crowns that are close enough to the observation point to completely fill the defined angle are tallied; otherwise they are ignored.

The most commonly used sighting angle or "critical angle" is 104.81 minutes. Since this angle can be defined by a one-inch intercept on a sighting base of 33 inches, then all trees located no further than 33 times their diameter from the sampling point will be tallied. Thus a one-inch tree (dbh) must be within 33 inches to be counted, a 10-inch dbh tree up to 330 inches, and a three-foot tree as far as 99 feet.

This angle of 104.81 minutes gives a basal factor of 10, which means that the average number of trees per point multiplied by 10 gives the basal area in square feet per acre.

For shrubs, the angle is somewhat different. A recommended one is 9°25′ (Cooper, 1957, 1963). If one holds an angle gauge with an over-all length of 30 inches and with a crossbar of 3 inches to the eye, the angle includes a circle 10 times its diameter from the observer.

The angle gauge is easily made from a strip of hardwood and scrap metal. Aluminum angles 1 and one-fourth inches on a side (sold as do-it-yourself aluminum products) are excellent for the eyepiece and the crossarm. The eyepiece should have a peephole about three-eighths inch in diameter. For shrubs an instrument length of 30 inches is satisfactory, and 33 inches for forest trees. The crossarm for forest survey should be 1 inch, for shrubs 3 inches.

615

To calibrate the instrument for shrubs, support it firmly and then measure a distance 100 feet from the eyepiece. At this point lay out a target 10 feet in diameter at right angles to the sight. Return, sight through the peep hole, and adjust the crossarm backwards and forwards on the base until the target is exactly covered. Then fasten.

Each shrub tallied with such an angle gauge represents one per cent of the shrub cover at that point. The total number of shrubs counted represents the per cent of ground cover at that point. The average coverage of each species of shrub must be divided by a constant that varies with the dimension of the crossbar. For a 3-inch crossbar on a 30-inch stick, the factor is 4.

If one prefers not to make one's own instrument, one may purchase calibrated prisms from forestry supply houses. These prisms are rather expensive, but uncalibrated ones can be obtained for about one dollar and then calibrated by the user.

The variable-plot method has a number of advantages. It is rapid, simple to apply objectively, and easy to evaluate. It is especially well suited for sampling plant populations consisting of such discrete compact individuals as trees. It is not well suited for measuring crown cover in the forest. And if the plots are large, it may be difficult to count and record the various species accurately.

Random-pairs method

There have been several variations of the variable-plot or "plotless" method developed for ecological work. One is the random-pairs method. In this method the observation points or stations are distributed along grid lines or randomized route of travel. If a grid is used, arrange it so that the lines are evenly spaced parallel to the long axis of the tract. Advance on the first line of sampling 10 or 20 meters, but the distance must be standardized.

At the station, face the closest tree that is 4 or more inches dbh. Raise the arms straight from the sides to establish an imaginary line dividing the field into two parts. Record the tree species and measure its dbh; then return to the reference point (Fig. C-4). Next find the tree closest to the first tree but in back of the imaginary line. Record the species, the dbh, and the distance between the two trees, center to center. Continue to the next station and repeat the same procedure.

Compilation. Once the data has been collected, it can be handled as follows.

1. Add distances between trees at all sets of random pairs.
2. Divide by the number of observation points to obtain an average of distances.
3. Multiply the figure from (2) by a correction constant 0.8.
4. Square this answer to give the average area occupied by one tree.
5. Divide this into the area of an acre to estimate the number of trees per acre.
6. Other calculations include the percentage of each tree species, average basal area for each species, total basal area for the acre, etc. Basal-area tables are available in several textbooks on forest mensuration.

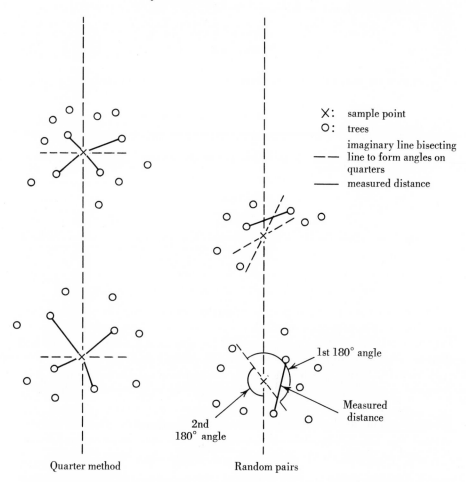

Figure C-4 *The random-pairs method and the quarter method of sampling forest stands. See text for details.*

The quarter method

The quarter method is a variation of the random-pairs method. Four measurements are taken instead of two at each point. Points can be mechanically spaced along a straight line, or preferably they can be located at random.

1. At each station make a point in the ground.
2. Divide the working area into four quarters or quadrants by visualizing a grid line (predetermined by compass bearing) and a line crossing it at right angles, both passing through the point (Fig. C-4).
3. Select the closest tree to the point in each of the four quarters, measure and record the distance of each, obtain the dbh, and record the species. *Four* measurements are taken.
4. Tally at least 50 such points.

617

The computations are as follows.

1. Add all distances in the samples and divide this figure by total number of distances. This gives the mean distance, used to determine the mean area and the density per unit area.

2. Square the mean distance to obtain the average area sampled.

3. Divide this into 43,560 ft^2 to obtain the total number of trees per acre.

4. Relative density $= \dfrac{\text{number of individuals of species}}{\text{number of individuals of all species}} \times 100$

5. Relative dominance $= \dfrac{\text{total basal area of the species}}{\text{total basal area of all species}} \times 100$

6. Basal area per tree $= \dfrac{\text{total basal area}}{\text{number of trees}}$

7. Absolute values for the number of trees per unit area of any species and the basal area per unit area of any species are determined by multiplying the relative figures for density and dominance by the total trees per acre to determine density and by the total basal area per acre to determine dominance.

Of the two, the random-pairs and the quarter method, the latter is the better, since the random-pairs method often is inaccurate. It is also preferred over the variable-plot, since this method is unsuited for obtaining data on frequency and density. The large trees are favored by the sampling gauge.

A variation of the quarter method is the wandering quarter method. It is designed to estimate the density and distribution of individuals and clumps of individuals without bias in aggregations and to permit the computation of sampling error. This method involves more detailed computations than the quarter method and will not be discussed here. Full details may be found in Catana, 1963, and in "Range Research Methods," U.S. Dept. Agr. Misc. Publ. 940.

Analysis of the data

Abundance. If the number of individuals in the plant community is estimated, but not counted, the data are referred to as abundance. This is usually expressed by assigning species to one of a limited number of abundance classes, an example of which is Table C-1.

Density, on the other hand, implies an actual count. Such counts are often used in the study of forest reproduction. The samples are broken down into such classes as 1 foot high, 1–12 feet, or 1–3 inches, 4–9 inches, and so on.

Cover. Abundance implies a number of individuals, but number and density do not necessarily reflect dominance or cover. Cover is the result of both numbers and massiveness. In the field, each species can be assigned to some degree of cover, expressed as a percentage or class, according to the area or volume of the community it occupies. From a practical standpoint, the area of coverage is used to express dominance. This is usually done by estimating the area covered by the foliage of a species projected on the ground. In complex communities, such as the forest, coverage class values are assigned to the various species in each stratum. Species occurring in a single stratum will have one value. Those occupying several strata, such as forest trees (canopy, understory,

TABLE C-1.   ABUNDANCE CLASSES

	STALKS PER SQUARE METER QUADRAT
Rare	1 to 4
Occasional	5 to 14
Frequent	15 to 29
Abundant	30 to 99
Very abundant	100 +

seedling), will have separate values for each layer in which they are found. Each layer then will have its own dominant. For example, the upper stratum or crown of a forest may be dominated by oaks, the shrub layer by blueberry. The dominants of the upper stratum, because they receive the full impact of the climate, are also the community dominants.

For most field surveys, foliage cover estimated by the system devised by Braun-Blanquet (1951) is adequate (Table C-2). In forest communities, basal area (cross section of the tree 4.5 feet above the ground) by species, estimated by plotless sampling, is the most efficient and accurate method. In grasslands estimates of the total spread of foliage has little meaning, especially for comparative studies, because of differences in grazing pressure, weather, etc. Coverage should be expressed as basal area, but here the meaning is different from that of forestry. Basal area in grassland ecology refers to the area of a grass clump about one inch above the ground, the point of normal utilization through grazing (Fig. C-5). Changes in basal area have more meaning than total foliar spread. The information can be obtained by the quadrat method or by the line-transect method.

Total estimate.   Although abundance and coverage are separate and distinct, they can be combined in a community description as the total estimate,

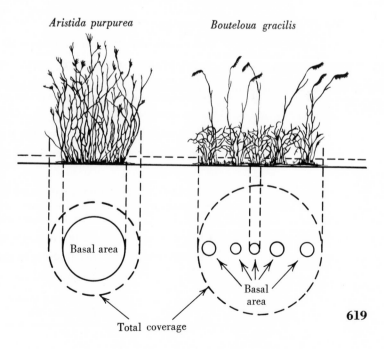

Aristida purpurea   *Bouteloua gracilis*

Figure C-5 *Differences between foliage cover and basal area of grasses. Greatest difference shows up when several small clumps occur together. (From Cain and Castro, Manual of Vegetation Analysis, Harper and Row, New York, 1959.)*

Basal area

Basal area

Total coverage

619

TABLE C-2. COVERAGE CLASSES

CLASS	COVERAGE, IN PER CENT
+	Less than 1
1	1–5
2	6–25
3	26–50
4	51–75
5	76–100

suggested by Braun-Blanquet. For most field studies, it works very well, and although difficult to handle statistically, it is probably the best method by which to obtain a good general picture of the plant community. The scales are given in Table C-3.

Sociability.   Along with total estimates should go an estimate of the sociability of each species (Table C-4)—whether the plant grows singly, in clumps, mats, etc.

By determining both the total estimate and the sociability, each species has paired values. These are usually written as: plant species *A,* 4.3, in which the first figure is the total estimate, the second the sociability. Once a number of stands have been surveyed, the community characteristics can be combined in a sort of an association table. The plant species usually are listed on the basis of fidelity or presence, the characteristic species of the community often heading the list. Examples are given in Table C-5. It is far from being complete and is given here only as an example of how such tables are constructed.

TABLE C-3. TOTAL ESTIMATE SCALE (ABUNDANCE PLUS COVERAGE)

+	Individuals of a species very sparsely present in the stand; coverage very small
1	Individuals plentiful, but coverage small
2	Individuals very numerous if small; if large, covering at least 5 per cent of area
3	Individuals few or many, collectively covering 25 to 50 per cent of the area
4	Plants cover 50 to 75 per cent of the area
5	Plant species cover 75–100 per cent of the area

TABLE C-4. SOCIABILITY CLASSES OF BRAUN-BLANQUET

Class 1	Shoots growing singly
Class 2	Scattered groups or tufts of plants
Class 3	Small, scattered patches or cushions
Class 4	Large patches or broken mats
Class 5	Very large mats of stands or nearly pure populations that almost blanket the area

TABLE C-5*A*. STAND COMPOSITION, CUMBERLAND PLATEAU, WEST VIRGINIA (selected species only, to illustrate table construction)

HERBACEOUS SPECIES	1	2	3	4	5	6	7	8	9	10	FREQUENCY, PER CENT
Polystichum aerostichoides	2.2	+.1	1.2	1.2	2.2	2.2	2.2	2.2	2.1	1.1	100
Cimicifuga racemosa	3.2	2.2			2.2	3.2	2.2	1.2	2.2	2.2	80
Geranium maculatum		+.1	+.1	+.1	1.2	2.2	2.2	+.2	1.1	+.1	90
Disporum lanquinosium	3.2	3.3		3.3	1.1	2.2	1.1	+.1	+.2	2.2	90
Galium circaezans	+.2	+.2			1.2	+.1	2.2	+.1			60
Thalictrum dioicum		+.2			1.2	1.1	2.1			+.2	50
Sanicula canadensis	+.1	2.2	1.1		+.1						40

Importance values. In regions where the plant communities are highly heterogeneous, the classification of communities on the basis of dominants or codominants becomes impractical. Therefore, Curtis and McIntosh (1951) came up with the index "importance value" to develop a logical arrangement of the stands. This index is based on the fact that most species do not normally reach a high level of importance in the community, but those that do serve as an index, or guiding species. Once importance values have been obtained for species within a stand, the stands can then be grouped by their leading dominants according to importance values, and the groups are then placed in a logical order based on the relationships of several predominant species. In Table C-6, for example, are four species that were the leading dominants in 80 of 95 forest stands in southern Wisconsin. Note that the dominants are arranged in order of decreasing importance value, from stands dominated by black oak to those dominated by sugar maple. Such an arrangement also shows increasing values for sugar maple. Trees intermediate in dominance can be handled in the same way.

The importance value is the sum of relative density (the proportion of a density of a species to that of the stand as a whole), relative dominance (the proportion

TABLE C-5*B*. COMMUNITY STANDS, NORTH SLOPES, APPALACHIAN MOUNTAINS, WEST VIRGINIA (selected species only, to illustrate table construction)

HERBACEOUS SPECIES	1	2	3	4	5	PRESENCE CLASS
Polystichum aerostichoides	X	X	X	X	X	5
Cimicifuga racemosa	X	X	X	X	X	5
Galium triflorum		X	X	X	X	4
Medeola virginiana	X	X		X	X	4
Trillium erectum		X		X	X	3
Sanquinaria canadensis	X	X			X	3
Monarda fistulosa	X	X				2
Arabis canadensis			X			1

621

of the basal area of a species to the stand as a whole), and relative frequency. These values can be computed as follows:

1. Relative density of species A in stand X $= \dfrac{\text{Stand density of species } A \text{ in stand } X}{\text{Total stand density of all species in stand } X} \times 100$

2. Relative dominance of species A in stand X $= \dfrac{\text{Basal area of species } A \text{ in stand X}}{\text{Total basal area of all species in stand X}} \times 100$

3. Relative frequency of species A in stand X $= \dfrac{\text{Frequency of species } A \text{ in stand } X}{\text{Sum of frequencies for all species in stand } X} \times 100$

Frequency (used above) $= \dfrac{\text{Total number of plots or points in stand } X \text{ in which species } A \text{ occurs}}{\text{Total number of plots or points sampled}} \times 100$

The maximum value for an importance index is 300 (100 + 100 + 100).

Continuum index. The importance value can be expanded further into a continuum index, a composite figure that can be used to compare a large number of stands. Curtis and others in Wisconsin found in their study of importance values that each species reaches its best development in stands whose position bears a definite relationship to that of other species. In other words the stands varied continuously along a gradient; thus the word "continuum." The continuum

TABLE C-6. THE AVERAGE IMPORTANCE-VALUE INDEX OF TREES IN STANDS WITH FOUR SPECIES AS THE LEADING DOMINANTS

| SPECIES | LEADING DOMINANT IN STAND | | | | ECOLOGICAL SEQUENCE NUMBER |
	Quercus velutina	*Quercus alba*	*Quercus rubra*	*Acer saccharum*	
Black oak *Quercus velutina*	165.1	39.6	13.6	0	2
Shagbark hickory *Carya ovata*	0.3	8.8	5.2	5.9	3.5
White oak *Quercus alba*	69.9	126.8	52.7	13.7	4
Black walnut *Juglans nigra*	1.5	1.2	2.2	1.9	5
Red oak *Quercus rubra*	3.6	39.2	152.3	37.2	6
American basswood *Tilia americana*	0.3	5.9	19.0	33.0	8
Sugar maple *Acer saccharum*	0	0.8	11.7	127.0	10

Adapted from Curtis and McIntosh, 1951.

index is extremely useful, since it can be employed to investigate environmental relationships of component communities, to designate the position of a stand on a gradient, to provide a background for studies of other organisms.

The continuum index for a stand is obtained by first assigning a climax adaptation number to the various tree species involved. Curtis and McIntosh (1951) established a 10-part scale for Wisconsin, in which the highly tolerant sugar maple was given a value of 10, since it was best adapted to maintain itself in a stand. The intolerant bur oak and trembling aspen were given a value of 1, since they are early successional species. Cain and Castro (1959) suggest that the term ecological sequence number be used in place of the climax adaptation number to get rid of that questionable term climax. Next the importance value of each species is multiplied by its ecological sequence number, and the values for all the species in the stand are added. The sum is the stand continuum index. This is used to place that stand on a continuum scale that runs from 300 to 3000. After the stand indices have been calculated, the position of the individual species can be plotted in relation to the position of the stand on the index (Fig. C-6).

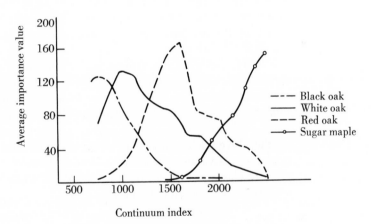

Figure C-6 Distribution of four forest-tree species on a continuum index. (From Curtis and McIntosh, 1951.)

Actually the continuum is not a single linear gradient. Rather it is multidimensional. To place a plant community in a multidimensional matrix where it will fit its proper relationship both to other communities and to environmental gradients is complicated and difficult. The multidimensional arrangement, termed ordination, will not be discussed here. Those interested should refer to Bray and Curtis (1957).

Presence, constancy, and fidelity. Three other attributes widely used in plant ecology are presence, constancy, and fidelity.

Presence refers to the degree of regularity with which a species recurs in different examples of a community type. It is commonly expressed as a percentage that can be assigned to one of a limited number of presence classes, as given in Table C-7. Presence is determined by dividing the total number of stands in which the species is found by the total number of stands investigated. Species that have a high percentage of presence or which fall within presence class 5 often are regarded as more or less characteristic of that community. Presence can

TABLE C-7. Presence Classes

PRESENCE CLASS	PER CENT OF STANDS OF ONE COMMUNITY TYPE STUDIED IN WHICH SPECIES OCCUR
1	1–20
2	21–40
3	41–60
4	61–80
5	81–100

be used as a quick method to compare stands of a community type or of related types.

Constancy is essentially the same as presence, with one major difference. It is based on sample areas of equal size in each of the stands investigated, while with presence this is not true. Equal-sized sample areas reduce the variability introduced by mixed-sized sample areas. The larger plots will have a larger list of species, the smaller sample areas will have smaller ones. The constancy classes are identical with those for presence; only the names are changed.

Fidelity, widely used in Europe, is an expression of the exclusiveness of a plant species to a community type. At one extreme are those species found only in one particular community; at the other are those that flourish in several communities. Fidelity of a species is always expressed in relation to a particular community. Thus a species may have a high fidelity for one community and a low fidelity for another. Five fidelity classes are recognized; these are summarized in Table C-8. Species of class 1 are considered *accidentals;* those of class 2 as *companions;* while those of classes 3 to 5 are regarded as *characteristic species.* These are the key species of the community, especially class 5.

TABLE C-8. Fidelity Classes of Braun-Blanquet

CLASS	DESCRIPTION
1	Strange species: plant species rare or accidental in the vegetational units sampled. They are either intruders from other plant communities or relics from earlier successional stages.
2	Indifferent species: species without pronounced preferences or affinities for any community.
3	Preferential species: species often present in several communities, but with their optimum definitely in one certain community.
4	Selective species: plant species with a strong affinity for a certain community; it occurs sparingly, infrequently, or rarely in other communities.
5	Exclusive species: plant species exclusively or almost exclusively restricted to one community.

Phytoplankton and periphyton

In aquatic communities, algae are the dominant vegetation. There are two kinds of growth involved: the plankton suspended on the water and the periphyton growing attached to some substrate.

Phytoplankton. The phytoplankton can be obtained by drawing water samples from several depths (see Appendix B). Cell counts of algae present in each sample, either normal or concentrated, can be made with a Sedgwich-Rafter counting chamber and a Whipple ocular (see zooplankton, Appendix D). If necessary, the samples can be concentrated by centrifugation in a Foerst plankton centrifuge. The centrifuged samples are then diluted to a suitable volume (100 to 200 ml) in a volumetric flask.

When counting the cells, a separate tally should be kept for each species. This will permit an analysis of community structure at each station. Record the number of cells for single-celled forms, and the number of colonies for colonial forms. The latter should then be multiplied by an appropriate factor for each species to convert the colonies into cells. These factors will have to be predetermined by averaging the cell counts from a large number of typical colonies from the area in question.

Another method of handling the phytoplankton is by filtration (see McNabb, 1960; Clark and Sigler, 1963). The organisms in the sample are first fixed by the addition of four parts 40 per cent aqueous solution of formaldehyde to each 100 parts of the sample. The analysis is as follows.

1. Thoroughly agitate the sample; withdraw a fraction with a pipette large enough to hold a sample that will provide an optimum quantity of suspended matter on the filter.

2. This sample is placed in the tube of a filter apparatus designed to accommodate a one-inch-diameter membrane filter. The water is drawn through the filter with a vacuum pump.

3. Remove the filter and place it on a glass slide. Put two or three drops of immersion oil over the residue, and store the slide in the dark to dry (about 24 hours). The oil replaces the water in the pores of the filter and makes it transparent.

4. Place a cover slip over the transparent filter.

5. Determine the most abundant species by scanning and then choose a quadrat size that will contain individuals of this species approximately 80 per cent of the time.

6. Move the mechanical stage so that approximately 30 random quadrats are viewed. The presence or absence of individual species is noted. There is no need to count.

7. When 30 quadrats have been surveyed, the percentage frequency can be calculated by:

$$\text{Frequency } (\%) = \frac{\text{Total number of occurrences of a species}}{\text{Total number of quadrats examined}} \times 100$$

Periphyton. The periphyton has not received quite the same attention from ecologists as the phytoplankton, particularly in a quantitative way. Methods for studying the periphyton are given in detail by Sladeckova, 1962.

Epiphyton, the periphyton growing on living plants and animals, can be observed in place on the organism if the substrate is thin or transparent enough to allow the transmission of light. If the leaves are thin and transparent, the task is relatively easy, but the growth on one side must be scraped away. If the leaf is opaque, the chlorophyll can be extracted by dipping the leaf in chloral hydrate. Small leaves can be examined over the whole area. Large leaves can be sampled in strips marked by grids on a slide or by an ocular micrometer. With large aquatic plants a square will have to be cut from the leaf or stem. If the leaf is too thick to handle under the microscope, scrape off the periphyton quantatively and mount in a counting cell for examination. The results can be related back to the total surface area.

Algae growing on such aquatic animals as turtles, mollusks, etc., and on stones must be removed for study. The quantitative scraping and transfer is difficult, but there are several techniques available.

One method employs a simple hollow square instrument with a sharpened edge, which is pressed closely or driven into the substrate. This separates out a small area of given size around which the periphyton is washed away. The instrument is then raised and the periphyton remaining in the sample square is scraped into a collecting bottle.

If the stones can be picked up from the bottom, then the periphyton can be removed with an apparatus consisting of a polyethylene bottle with the bottom cut out and a brush with nylon bristles. A section of the stone is delimited by the neck of the bottle held tightly on the surface. The periphyton is scraped loose by the brush and then washed into a collecting bottle with a fine-jet pipette.

The periphyton can be counted in a Sedgwich-Rafter cell recording a predetermined number, usually 100 to 1000, as they appear in the field of view. The results can be expressed as a percentage; or the algae can be checked for frequency in the field of view, using the Braun-Blanquet scale of total estimate.

Some of the difficulties can be avoided by growing the periphyton on an artificial substrate, usually glass or transparent plastic slides. These are attached in the water in a variety of ways. In lentic situations they can be placed on sand or stones in the water. Or they can be placed in saw-cuts on boards, in holes in bricks, clipped to a rope, attached to a wooden frame, or tucked into rubber corks, if the aquatic habitat is lotic.

In fresh water, the glass slides are placed in a vertical or horizontal position. In shallow water the plates are usually laid horizontally, directly on the bottom, especially if the influence of light on the composition of periphyton is one of the objectives of a study. Or they can be hung vertically in the water; in this case both sides will be covered with periphyton. Plates placed horizontally collect true periphyton, detritus, etc., on the upper surface, while the bottom will be colonized by heterotrophic organisms. In running water the vertical position with plates parallel to the current is best since the surfaces will not become too badly filled with mud and debris.

For algae and protozoa, the plates should be exposed for one to two weeks, and for hydras, sponges, and the like, about one month. At the end of this time the slides are collected and placed in wide-mouthed jars filled with water from the locality. In the lab, the periphyton can be observed directly on the slides under the microscope. For counting, the slides should be marked in a grid. To do this one can use a Whipple ocular micrometer, or clean the bottom of the slide and place it on an auxiliary slide marked off in a grid. If the growth is very dense, it can be scraped off and examined in a Sedgwich-Rafter cell.

Biomass and production of periphyton can be determined by methods described below: dry weight, loss through ignition to determine organic carbon, pigment extraction, light and dark bottle containing pieces of plant with and without periphyton attached.

Dendrochronology

Dendrochronology is the science that treats the accurate dating of past events through the aging of trees. As such it is a valuable tool for the ecologist. It has been used in a number of studies—to age trees for management information, to establish dates of past forest fires, insect outbreaks, glaze, periods of suppression and release in the life history of forest trees. It has been involved in hydrological and archaeological studies and even in legal cases involving boundary disputes in which specimens are taken from fence posts and witness trees. An outstanding example of growth-ring analysis in an ecological investigation is Spencer's study (1958) of porcupine fluctuations in the Mesa Verde National Park.

Dendrochronology is based on the variation of growth rings. Growth rings, despite popular belief, are not regular, nor are they all necessarily laid down annually. Because of the failure of the cambium to form a sheath of xylem the entire length of the bole, rings may be omitted, especially near the base. This may be caused by the lack of food manufacture in the crown, by drought, fire, extreme cold, insects, and so on. At the other extreme are multiple rings produced by multiple waves of cambial activity during the growing season. These are caused by temporary interruptions in the normal growth, such as a late spring frost, or by regrowth taking place after normal seasonal growth has ended. At any rate the growth rings reflect the interaction of woody plants and their environment.

The fundamental principle of dendrochronology is crossdating, the correlation of distinctive patterns of growth between trees for a given sequence of years. Since no two plants have exactly the same growing conditions and life history, although the broad features are common to all trees involved, the similarities are relative rather than quantitative. The relative widths of corresponding rings are the same in relation to adjoining rings. By lining up these similarities, the investigator can establish the relative identity of any rings in sequence and aberrant rings in the individual specimen. A great number of specimens must be cross-dated before each ring with a sequence can be dated.

Collection of material

A recently logged-over area can provide an abundance of material, but new sections must be cut from the stump. Sections cut at a 30° angle, clean and sharp, may be ready for examination. Or the stump section can be smoothed with a carpenter's plane or by machine sanding. If the study involves shrubs, sample stems should be cut close to the ground and the entire cross section used.

Increment boring. The usual method of obtaining samples from forest trees is with the increment borer, available from forestry supply houses. This is an instrument designed to bore a core from a tree. It consists of a T handle, a hollow bit, and an extractor. Increment borers are fairly easy to use, but without care they can be damaged or broken. Here are a few hints.

1. For growth and age studies, remove the core as near to the base of the tree as the instrument handle will allow.

2. Coat the screw with heavy-grade oil.

3. To start the borer, combine a strong pushing and twisting motion until the borer is engaged in the wood.

4. Line the borer on the radius, keep the borer straight, and attempt to reach the center of the trunk.

5. When the core is drilled, insert the extractor and press firmly to cut the core from the trunk.

6. Remove the borer with reverse rotation.

7. Paint the wound with tree paint; a small cork can be inserted.

8. Store the cores in soda straws or polyethylene tubing.

Personally I find the large-diameter soda straws very satisfactory. Be sure to label each sample fully, including the directional side of the tree from which it was removed.

To obtain a freshly cut edge for examination, the core is held firmly in a core holder. The groove in a plastic foot ruler is fine if the ruler is clamped to a table and the end is stopped. With a razor blade make a transverse cut the length of the top of the core. It can then be brushed with water or kerosene to make the rings stand out better. When the core is ready, clip it to the stage of a microscope for examination. One-hundred-power magnification usually is sufficient.

With the use of a graduated mechanical stage, a stage micrometer, or a dial micrometer, measure the distance of each ring. The total distance included in the layers observed can be measured and then compared with the accumulated individual measurements. Any error should be distributed over the individual measurements. For serious research a dendrochronometer, a special device with a microscope and precise measuring devices, should be used.

Cross-dating

Although the more involved methods and problems of cross-dating cannot be described in detail here, the basic procedure is as follows.

1. On graph paper write down a series of numbers horizontally from left to right to represent growth layers. You can begin with one or with the years, the first number being the season preceding. This gives a series of numbers starting with the present and leading backward through the tree's life. A number of such blanks should be made up.

2. Set up a scale on the graph in thousands-of-an-inch so that the largest bars represent the *narrowest* widths.

3. Make a small bar graph for each year of the tree's life.

4. Make such a coded summary of all wood samples available.

5. Compare these visually, two at a time, sliding them along each other. Keep looking for corresponding groups of years with the same pattern of ring sequences. By such a technique, multiple rings can be checked, or extremely narrow growth rings previously missed can be picked up.

A simpler method but lacking the quantitative precision is to place an underline beneath the year that has a ring slightly less than the rings adjacent to it. If the decrease is more pronounced, draw two lines, and if very narrow three lines. For very wide rings, draw two lines above the year.

Statistical analysis

The data can be reduced to average values, and then compared to weather data covering the principle growing season for the species involved. Comparisons can be made between rainfall and the current year's growth, rainfall and the previous year's growth, monthly evapotranspiration deficits and growth, with frost-free periods and so on.

Data will have to be analyzed by simple or multiple regression, depending upon the variables, using partial correlations and standard errors for tests of significance. For sample analysis and interpretations, see Fritts, 1962.

Palynology

Palynology is the study of past plant communities by the analysis of pollen profiles. These studies are especially enlightening if they are coupled with carbon-14 dating.

Peat collection

Peat cores are bored at one to several stations in the bog. They are taken with a peat borer, available commercially. (A Hiller-type borer is manufactured by the Deans Manufacturing Company, Deans, New Jersey.) At each station two separate borings should be drilled, several feet apart. Then by taking successive samples from alternate borings (Example: first foot sample in core number one; second foot sample from core number two) contamination of one sample with another can be prevented. Collect two six-inch samples, one from the lower part of the cylinder, the other from the upper, at each boring; then place the samples in glass vials. If the vials are completely filled and tightly sealed, no preservative should be needed (Walker and Hartman, 1960).

Treatment of samples

Back in the laboratory, the samples can be treated as follows.

1. Thoroughly mix each six-inch sample and remove a pea-size lump for deflocculation.

2. Boil the peat for a few minutes in a dilute solution of NaOH, gently breaking it apart with a wooden cocktail stirrer. Use only one stirrer for each sample to avoid contamination.

3. While boiling add several drops of gentian-violet stain.

4. Stir vigorously and strain through fine wire mesh. Then stir again and draw up a 0.5-ml sample into a pipette.

5. Mix with a very small amount of warm glycerine jelly added to this sample.

6. Mount several drops on a slide and add cover slip.

629

Examination

The samples, now transferred to slides, should be examined under a microscope equipped with a mechanical stage.

1. Tally 100 or 200 pollen grains as they are encountered by systematically moving the slide.

2. Each kind of pollen grain must be identified, if only by code, and tallied separately. Identification should be made as far as possible from a reference pollen collection made up beforehand.

3. Record the results from each slide directly as a percentage for each kind of pollen.

Plotting the pollen profile

The pollen profile can be constructed by plotting a graph for each species or kind of pollen. The vertical scale is set up for depth in feet or meters; the horizontal scale is percentage, based on counts of 100 or 200 pollen grains for each spectrum level.

Measuring primary production

The methods of measuring primary production have been discussed in a general way back in Chap. 3. It should be reread as a sort of an introduction to the following. The methods discussed below are the ones commonly employed in determining primary production.

Harvest method

For terrestrial communities the harvest method is the most practical means of obtaining an estimate of primary production. In old-field and grassland communities and on the forest floor, plant growth on a series of one-meter-square quadrats can be removed at monthly intervals. In sampling annuals, take the entire plant, including the roots; for perennials, collect the new growth only; the old growth belongs to previous years. Separate out and bag each species, but keep the material from each quadrat together. After oven drying the material determine the dry weight for each species. The total weight for each species is recorded and tabulated for the season. Thus annual net production will be greater than the standing crop at any one time.

Estimating wood production is more difficult. There are two approaches: (1) weighing and measuring the foliage and current twig growth; and (2) determining the radial increment of trees and larger shrubs. The methods employed are too lengthy to be discussed in detail here, but they are explained in a paper by Whittaker (1961) and in another by Ovington et al. (1963). These should be consulted.

In brief, the method (Whittaker, 1961) is as follows (applicable only in climates with strong seasonal fluctuations where bud-scale scars and wood rings mark the current year's growth).

1. Field measurement of community production by clipping current twigs and leaves of smaller shrubs, and stand counts of larger shrubs and trees together with increment borings and height determinations.

2. Compute estimated volume increment for trees.

3. Analyze major species to determine production ratios (total production to clipping production; and stem wood and total production to estimated volume increment).

4. Estimate net production by woody plants in the community from the field measurements times the correction ratios to total production.

A harvest method of a sort can be used with phytoplankton. Centrifuge liter samples of natural water in a Foerst centrifuge. Remove the residue from the centrifuge cups, dry in preweighed silicon crucibles to a constant weight, weigh, and then ash in a muffle furnace. The difference between the total weight and the ash weight represents the organic weight, a rough approximation of the biomass of phytoplankton. The biomass should be expressed grams per square meter dry weight.

Light and dark bottle

This method, commonly employed in aquatic environments, is based on the assumption that the amount of oxygen produced by plants is proportional to gross production. Two bottles containing a given concentration of phytoplankton are suspended at the level from which the samples were obtained. One bottle is covered with aluminum foil or black tape to keep out the light; the other is clear. In the light bottle, oxygen is produced by photosynthesis, but a quantity is used in respiration. In the second bottle only respiration is taking place. After a given period of time, the oxygen content of the two bottles is determined by the Winkler method (Appendix B). The amount of oxygen produced in the light bottle is added to that used in the dark bottle to give total oxygen produced.

Pratt and Berkson (1959) point out two sources of error in this method. At a temperature range of 11 to 21°C, bacteria are responsible for 40 to 60 per cent of the total respiration customarily attributed to the phytoplankton. Failure to adjust gives a low estimate of production by plants. Then in a two-day experiment large changes in the plankton population occurred in the light bottle. Thus a difference existed in the concentration of phytoplankton inside and outside the bottle. The increase in the plankton inside the bottle was caused by an accelerated regeneration of nutrients by bacteria attached to the bottle walls.

A modification of this method involves the whole aquatic ecosystem, which becomes the light and dark bottle, the daytime representing the light bottle, the nighttime the dark. The oxygen content of the water is taken every two to three hours during a 24-hour period. The rise and fall of the oxygen during the day and night can be plotted as a diurnal curve. To obtain a correct estimate for the oxygen production of plants, the oxygen exchanged between air and water and between the water and bottom must be estimated and deducted. Details for this method, adaptable to the study of flowing waters, can be found in Odum, 1956.

Fixation of carbon-14

The most sensitive method for determining net production is the addition of radioactive carbon-14 (0.5 ml of $NaC^{14}O_3$ to sample bottle) tracer to paired bottles containing a natural phytoplankton population. After allowing photosynthesis to proceed for a suitable period, the plankton is filtered through a membrane filter, washed with 10 ml of 0.001N HCl, dried; and its activity measured by standard counting methods with detection devices. To translate C^{14} into total uptake of CO_2 by photosynthesis, the quantity of available carbon in the water must be calculated from the initial pH (see below).

This technique is based on the assumption that the following relationship is true:

$$\frac{\text{Activity of phytoplankton}}{\text{Activity of } C^{14}O_3^{=} \text{ added}} (k) = \frac{\text{Total C assimilation}}{\text{Total C available}}$$

where k is a constant that corrects for the isotope effect.

Carbon dioxide assimilation

Since the uptake of carbon dioxide, mole for mole, is equivalent to the production of organic carbon, its determination is one of the most direct approaches to the measurement of primary production. As already discussed in Chap. 4, a close relationship exists between the CO_2 in the water and the pH. In alkaline situations, the CO_2 is in equilibrium with HCO_3^- and $CO_3^=$. In acid waters there is more free CO_2. By following the pH change and relating this to CO_2 present, one can measure carbon assimilation.

However, a relatively large uptake of CO_2 is necessary to register a change in pH. To measure it one needs a sensitive piece of equipment such as a Beckman pH meter that will detect a change of 0.1 pH units. The pH reading taken periodically over a 24-hour period can be related back to a titration curve for CO_2, which must be constructed for each body of water being investigated. Once such a curve is constructed, changes in pH can be related to corresponding changes in the CO_2 content of the water.

A method to accomplish this is described by Beyers and Odum, 1959, as follows:

1. Distilled water is allowed to come into equilibrium with a pure CO_2 atmosphere by bubbling the gas through the water. The water is assumed to be at equilibrium with the CO_2 at one atmosphere pressure and at the measured temperature.

2. From tables of CO_2 saturation, compute the moles of total dissolved CO_2 per milliliter.

3. The CO_2 water is now introduced under the surface of a 100-ml sample of natural water with a pipette. The pH is measured against the added CO_2.

4. To avoid the unknown effects of particulate matter, the natural waters can be filtered.

5. From this data of known quantity of carbon dioxide, pH curves can be constructed.

6. Once this has been done, then the CO_2 in the water can be read directly from the curve for any given pH.

Chlorophyll method

Another promising method that can be used to estimate both production and biomass is the quantitative determination of chlorophyll *a*. Since the total quantity of chlorophyll in aquatic (and terrestrial) communities tends to increase or decrease with the amount of photosynthesis (which varies at different light intensities), the chlorophyll per square meter indicates the food manufacturing potential at the time. This photosynthesis : chlorophyll ratio remains rather constant even in cells whose chlorophyll content varies widely because of nutrition or the duration of the intensity of light to which they were previously exposed.

Chlorophyll *a* can be extracted by filtering natural water through a membrane filter and then extracting the pigments with acetone. The light absorption of the acetone extract is measured at selected wave lengths in the spectrophotometer, the chlorophyll *a* content is computed from this information and expressed in grams per square meter. Nomographs for converting the plankton pigment into chlorophyll biomass can be found in a paper "Plankton pigment nomographs" by A. C. Duxbury and C. S. Yentsch, *Journal of Marine Research,* **15:** 92–101 (1956).

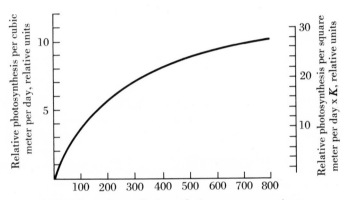

Figure C-7 *Relation between total daily surface radiation and daily relative photosynthesis (R) beneath a unit of sea surface.* (Adapted from Ryther and Yentsch, 1957.)

To estimate production, one must know in addition to the chlorophyll content of the water, the total daily solar radiation reaching the water's surface and the extinction coefficient of light. The following expression is used to determine daily photosynthesis:

$$P = \frac{R}{k} \times C \times p(\text{sat})$$

where

P = the photosynthesis of the phytoplankton population in grams of carbon per square meter per day.

R = relative photosynthesis determined from curve in Fig. C-7 for the appropriate value of surface radiation.

k = extinction coefficient, per meter, as measured.

$p(\text{sat})$ = photosynthesis of a sample of the population at 2000 footcandles, as measured, in grams of carbon per cubic meter per hour. A rough value for this is 3.7.

C = grams of chlorophyll per cubic meter in a sample of a homogeneously distributed population.

REFERENCES

Vegetation analysis

The following are major general references.

Braun-Blanquet, J.
1951 "Pflanzensoziologie: Grundzuge der Vegetationskunde," 2d ed., Springer-Verlag, Vienna.
1932 "Plant Sociology," McGraw-Hill, New York. (An English translation of the 1st edition of above.)

Cain, S. A., and G. M. DeO. Castro
1959 "Manual of Vegetation Analysis," Harper & Row, New York.

Greig-Smith, P.
1964 "Quantitative Plant Ecology," 2d ed., Academic, New York.

Oosting, H. J.
1956 "The Study of Plant Communities," Freeman, San Francisco, Calif.

Methodology

The following papers, including the ones cited, are excellent sources for methodology.

Bray, R., and J. T. Curtis
1957 An ordination of the upland forest communities of southern Wisconsin, *Ecol. Monographs,* **27:**325–349.

Catana, A. J., Jr.
1963 The wandering quarter method of estimating population density, *Ecology,* **44:**349–360.

Cooper, C. F.
1957 The variable plot method for estimating shrub density, *J. Range Management,* **10:**111–115.
1963 An evaluation of variable plot sampling in shrub and herbaceous vegetation, *Ecology,* **44:** 565–569.

Cottam, G., and J. T. Curtis
1956 The use of distance measures in phytosociological sampling, *Ecology,* **37:**451–460.

Curtis, J. T., and R. P. McIntosh
1951 The upland forest continuum in the prairie-forest border region of Wisconsin, *Ecology,* **32:**476–496.

Grosenbaugh, L. R.
1952 Plotless timber estimates—new, fast, easy, *J. Forestry,* **50:**32–37.
1958 Point-sampling and line-sampling: probability theory, geometric implications, synthesis, *U.S. Forest Serv., Southern Forest Expt. Sta. Occ. Paper 160.*

Hyder, D. N., and F. A. Sneva
1960 Bitterlich's plotless method for sampling basal ground cover of bunch grasses, *J. Range Management,* **13:**6–9.

Penfound, W. T.
1963 A modification of the point-centered quarter method for grassland analysis, *Ecology,* **44:**175–176.

U.S. Forest Service
1958 Techniques and methods of measuring understory vegetation, a symposium, *Southern Forest Expt. Station.*
1962 Range research methods; a symposium, *U.S. Dept. Agr. Misc. Publ. 940.*

Vestal, A. G.
1949 Minimum areas for different vegetations, *Illinois Biol. Monographs,* **20:**1–129.

Phytoplankton

Clark, W. J., and W. F. Sigler
1963 Method of concentrating phytoplankton samples using membrane filters, *Limnol. Oceanog.,* **8:**127–129.

Hartman, R. T.
1958 Studies of plankton centrifuge efficiency, *Ecology,* **39:**374–376.

Lund, J. W. G., and J. F. Talling
1957 Botanical limnological methods with special reference to algae, *Botan. Rev.* **23:**489–583.

NcNabb, C. D.
1960 Enumeration of fresh water phytoplankton concentrated on the membrane filter, *Limnol. Oceanog.* **5:**57–61.

Sladeckova, Alena
1962 Limnological investigation methods for the periphyton (aufwuchs) community, *Botan. Rev.,* **28:**286–350.

Welch, P. S.
1948 "Limnological Methods," McGraw-Hill–Blakiston, New York.

Wood, E. J. F.
1962 A method for phytoplankton study, *Limnol. Oceanog.,* **7:**32–35.

Dendrochronology

Fritts, H. C.
1960 Multiple regression analysis of radial growth in individual trees, *Forest Sci.,* **6:**334–349.
1962 An approach to dendrochronology—screening by means of multiple regression techniques, *J. Geophys. Res.*

Roughton, R. D.
1962 A review of literature on dendrochronology and age determination of woody plants, *Tech. Bull. 15, Colorado Dept. Fish Game,* Denver.

Spencer, D. A.
1958 Porcupine population fluctuations in past centuries revealed by dendrochronology, PhD thesis, University of Colorado, Boulder, Colo.

Taylor, R. F.
1936 An inexpensive increment core holder, *J. Forestry*, **34**:814–815.

Palynology

Brown, C. A.
1960 "Palynological Techniques," published by author, 1180 Stanford Ave., Baton Rouge 8, La.
Erdtmann, G.
1954 "An Introduction to Pollen Analysis," Ronald, New York.
Faegri, K., and J. Iverson
1950 "Textbook of Modern Pollen Analysis," Ejar Munksgaard, Copenhagen.
Felix, C. F.
1961 An introduction to palynology, in H. N. Andrews, "Studies in Paleobotany," Wiley, New York.
Walker, P. C., and R. T. Hartman
1960 The forest sequence of the Hartstown bog area in western Pennsylvania, *Ecology*, **41**:461–474.
Wodehouse, R. P.
1935 "Pollen Grains," Mc-Graw-Hill, New York.

Measuring primary production

Beyers, R. J., and H. T. Odum
1959 Use of carbon dioxide to construct pH curves for the measurement of productivity, *Limnol. Oceanog.*, **4**:499–503.
Creitz, G. I., and F. A. Richards
1955 The estimation and characterization of plankton populations by pigment analysis: III, A note on the use of "millipore" membrane filters in the estimation of plankton pigments, *J. Marine Res.*, **14**:211–216.
Odum, H. T.
1956 Primary production in flowing waters, *Limnol. Oceanog.*, **1**:102–117.
Ovington, J. D., D. Heitkamp, and D. B. Lawrence
1963 Plant biomass and productivity of prairie, savanna, oakwood and maize fields ecosystems in central Minnesota, *Ecology*, **44**:52–63.
Pratt, D. M., and H. Berkson
1959 Two sources of error in the oxygen light and dark bottle method, *Limnol. Oceanog.*, **4**:328–334.
Richards, F. A., with T. G. Thompson
1952 The estimation and characterization of plankton populations by pigment analysis: II, A spectrophotometric method for the estimation of plankton pigments, *J. Marine Res.*, **11**:156–172.
Ryther, J. H.
1956 The measurement of primary production, *Limnol. Oceanog.*, **1**:72–84.
Ryther, J. H., and R. F. Vaccaro
1954 A comparison of the oxygen and C14 methods of measuring marine photosynthethesis, *J. Cons. Internat. Explor. Mer.*, **20**:25–37.
Ryther, J. H., and C. S. Yentsch
1957 The estimation of phytoplankton production in the ocean from chlorophyll and light data, *Limnol. Oceanog.*, **2**:281–286.
Steemann-Nielsen, E.
1952 The use of radioactive carbon (C14) for measuring organic production in the sea, *J. Cons. Internat. Explor. Mer.*, **43**:117–140.
U.S. Forest Service
1962 Range research methods; a symposium. *U.S. Dept. Agr. Misc. Publ.* 940. (Harvest methods for low vegetation fully discussed.)
Whittaker, R. H.
1961 Estimation of net primary production of forest and shrub communities, *Ecology*, **42**:177–180.
1963 Net production of heath balds and forest heaths in the Great Smoky Mountains, *Ecology* **44**:176–182.
Yentsch, C. S., and J. H. Ryther
1957 Short term variations in phytoplankton chlorophyll and their significance, *Limnol. Oceanog.*, **2**:140–142.

APPENDIX D

Studying animal populations

The study of animals involves considerably more problems than the study of plants. Animals are harder to see and most are not stationary—they are here one minute and gone the next. When it comes to sampling, the animals have something to say about getting caught, and they are more liable to mortality than plants. The following methods of estimating animal numbers, determining age structure, mortality, home range, and so on will enable the field biologist to make some measurements, however rough, of animal populations in the ecosystem.

Trapping and collecting

The sampling of an animal population involves collecting animals, either alive for marking and release, or dead. Since so much information on collecting and trapping is available in other publications (see references at the end of this appendix), I will deal with this topic very briefly.

Flying insects

For diurnal insects, use aerial nets and heavy-duty sweep nets designed to withstand the hard wear encountered when put through grass and woody vegetation. For nocturnal insects, use traps containing ultraviolet light or a mercury-vapor light, or use an old sheet fitted on a slant against some support with a strong light above it. Insects can then be picked off the sheet. If the insects are to be killed, place them in a killing jar containing a layer, either on the bottom or in a deep lid, of plaster of paris and potassium cyanide. Insert thin layers of tissue or light cloth in the jar to prevent damage to moths and butterflies.

Aquatic organisms

For aquatic organisms use dip nets for organisms in the water, bottom nets for scraping along the bottom of ponds, wire-basket scraper nets, and plankton towing nets. For aquatic collecting from the shore, aquatic throw nets are useful. To collect bottom organisms in deep water, use a bottom dredge lowered from a boat. Fish, tadpoles, and large crustaceans can be collected with seines. A set of assorted widths will be necessary.

Soil organisms

The standard method of collecting small organisms is with the use of a Berlese funnel. Litter samples are placed in the funnel, and the animals are driven out by heat from a light bulb into a collecting bottle below. For details, see suggested activities for the soil community. For larger soil animals such as spiders and beetles, traps made from funnels and cans set in the soil to ground level can be used. Boards placed on the ground may attract millipedes, centipedes, and slugs. Meat bait in small wire traps will attract scavenger insects.

Small animals in vegetation

Sweep nets with stout frames to withstand sweeps close to the ground and in woody growth are useful for collecting many types of insects and even some arboreal amphibians and reptiles. Drag nets consisting of light tubular frames, to which are attached canvas bags, are useful on flat ground. Overhead vegetation can be sampled by beating the limbs with sticks to dislodge the animals, which should fall into canvas collecting trays beneath.

Birds and mammals

Birds can be trapped for banding in specially constructed traps, cannon nets for larger game birds (Fig. D-1), and mist nets. Both Federal and state permits are required for such work. Once a permit is granted, the operator of the banding station will be furnished plans for suitable traps. For mammals, live traps of wood or wire and snap traps are used. Both are available commercially, but live traps are easily constructed (see references). Traps can be baited with natural foods, dripping water, etc. For small mammals, a mixture of peanut butter and oatmeal works well. Also useful are grain, apple, meat, and appropriate scents.

Figure D-1 (above) *Wild turkey being captured by the use of a cannon net. The net is attached to several heavy weights which are fired from pipe mortars.* (left) *This method is very effective if the net is properly placed and camouflaged at a bait area. This method has enabled game biologists to reintroduce wild stock into vacant habitats.* (Photos by G. H. Harrison, courtesy Pennsylvania Game Commission.)

Marking animals

Marking individuals in an animal population is necessary if you wish to distinguish certain members of a population at some future date, to recognize individuals from their neighbors, to study movements, or to estimate populations by the mark-recapture method.

Arthropods and snails are best marked with a quick-drying cellulose paint. It is easily applied with any pointed object. Marking butterflies is a two-man operation. One has to hold the wings together with a pair of forceps; the other does the marking on the side of the wing exposed at rest. For aquatic mollusks and insects, better results are obtained through the use of ship-fouling paint, since the acetate paints do not hold up well in water.

Fish are usually marked by tagging in several ways. Strap tags of monel metal may be attached to the jaw, the preopercle, or the operculum. Streamer or pennant tags attached to various parts of the body, usually at the base of the dorsal fin, are used in some studies. Another method is to insert a plastic tag into the body cavity. To place the tag, a narrow incision is made in the side of the abdominal wall. Once the incision heals, which it does quickly, the fish carries the tag for life. Tags can be recovered only when the fish is cleaned. Fish can also be marked by clipping the fins, but this does not permit the individual recognition of a very large number of fish.

Frogs, toads, salamanders, and most lizards can be marked by some system of toe clipping, which involves the removal of the distal part of one or more toes. One method worked out by Martof (1953) is as follows: Number the toes on the left hind foot one to five, the toes on the right foot 10 to 50. Up front, the left forefoot toes are numbered 100 to 400, and the toes on the right forefoot 800, 1600, 2400, 3200. Thus one can mark up to 6399 individuals by clipping no more than two toes per foot.

Snakes and lizards can be marked by removing scales or patches of scales in certain combinations.

Birds are usually marked by serially numbered aluminum bands (Fig. D-2) and by cellulose and aluminum colored bands. The latter are necessary for individual recognition in the field. In some specialized studies, the plumage is dyed a conspicuous or contrasting color.

Small mammals may be marked by toe clipping in combinations similar to those given for amphibians, or by notching the ear.

A number of other methods have been devised for marking mammals. Fur

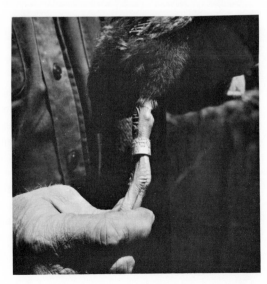

Figure D-2 *The use of aluminum leg bands has permitted the study of migration, longevity, and survival in birds.* (Photo courtesy Pennsylvania Game Commission.)

clipping and tattooing may be employed. Bear, deer, elk, moose, rabbits, and hares can be marked with strap tags or plastic disks attached to the ear. Aluminum bands similar to those used on birds can be attached to the forearm of bats. Dyes can be used to mark both large and small mammals.

Radioactive tracers

The use of radioactive tracers is a particularly useful method for studying animals that are secretive in habits, live in dense cover, spend part or all of their lives underground, or that have radically different phases in their life cycle, such as the moths and butterflies.

If animals are fed small traces of gamma-emitting radioactive material, then the radioactive materials are metabolically incorporated into the tissue. The tracer becomes a part of the animal and is passed along to egg or offspring. Radioactive larvae remain so as they transform to adults, and the material is passed on to the egg. The same is true for birds. This technique is useful for studying dispersal, for the identification of specific broods or litters, for obtaining data on population dynamics and natural selection.

Another method involves the application of a radioactive tracer in or on an animal in such a way that the animal is not seriously injured and behaves in a normal way. This is usually done by fastening a radioactive wire to the animal or inserting it under the skin of the abdomen with a hypodermic needle. The movements of the tagged individual are then followed with a Geiger counter.

Although these techniques have their merits, they also have their disadvantages. The greatest is the potential radioactive hazard to the investigator himself, to other humans, and to the ecosystem. Another disadvantage is the impossibility of separating one animal from another.

Since most work with radioactive tracers requires an AEC license, details are not given here. Specific techniques can be reviewed in Tester, 1962; Godfrey, 1954; Kaye, 1960; and Pendleton, 1956.

Aging techniques

Information on the age structure of wild populations is not easily obtained. During the past several decades, a number of aging techniques have been developed, mostly for game and fish. Fish aging began first when Hoffbauer (1898) published his studies on the scale markings of known-age carp. Since then the technique has been developed further and refined. It is based on the fact that a fish scale starts as a tiny plate and grows as the fish grows. A number of microscopic ridges, the circuli (Fig. D-3), are laid down about the center of the scale each year. When the fish is growing well in summer, the ridges are spaced wide apart. During winter, when growth slows down, the ridges are close together. This annual check on growth enables the biologist to determine the age of a fish by counting the number of areas of closed rings, the annuli (Fig. D-3). Salmon and some species of trout spend one or two years of life in streams before migrating out to sea or into lakes. Since stream growth is slower than lake or sea growth, the scales show when the fish migrated. When salmonid fish spawn, reabsorption of scales occurs, eroding the margins of the scales and interrupting the pattern of circular ridges. This erosion leaves a mark that can be detected in later years (Fig. D-3). Since the growth of a scale continues throughout the life of a fish, it also provides information on the growth rate. This is obtained by measuring the total radius of the scale, the radius to each year's growth ring, and the total body length of the fish. Then by simple proportion, the yearly growth rate can be determined.

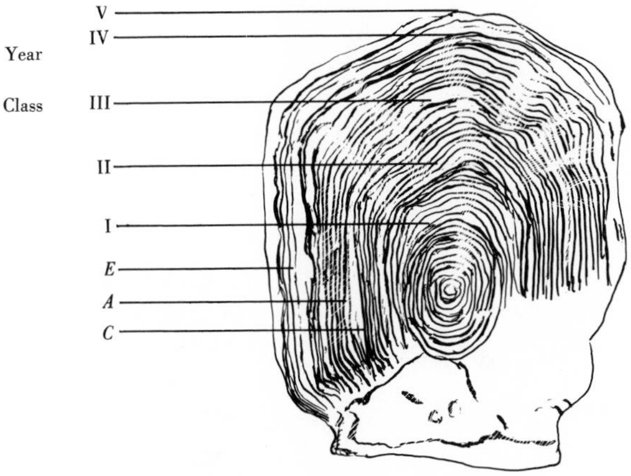

Figure D-3   The age of fish can be determined by the growth rings on the scale. C is the circuli; A, the annuli; E, the erosion of the scale from spawning.

Other techniques in aging fish include the length-frequency distribution, vertebral development, and rings or growth layer in the otolith or ear stone.

Because of the large number of year classes (animals born in a population during a particular year) that can be identified, one can determine dominant year classes, learn the age when fish reach sexual maturity, estimate production mortality, and the effects of fish harvest.

Aging techniques for mammals and birds have developed more slowly and are not as refined as those for fish, but a number of methods are in common use. These involve handling all or a part of the animal. Among birds, plumage development is frequently used. Until molted, the tail feathers of juvenile waterfowl are notched at the tip, in contrast with the normally contoured feather of the winter plumage (Fig. D-4). The shape of the primary wing feather (numbers 9 and 10) separates adults from young among many gallinaceous game birds. When the whole bird is available, the presence or depth of the bursa of Fabricus, a blind pouch lying dorsal to the caecum and opening into the cloaca (Fig. D-4) indicates juvenile birds.

Among mammals the examination of reproductive organs is useful, since the majority do not breed until the second year. This method can be used only during the breeding season. The presence of the epiphyseal cartilage in rabbits and squirrels identifies juveniles up to 6 or 7 months (Fig. D-4). Black bars on the pelage of the underside of the tail of juvenile gray squirrels separate the young from the adults (Fig. D-4). Primeness of pelt on the inside of

641

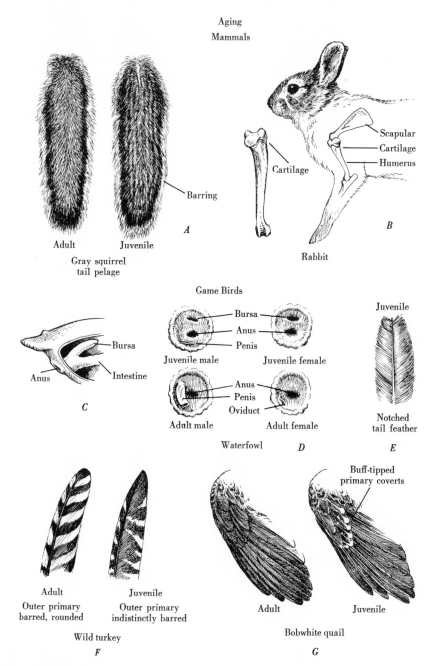

Aging
Mammals

Barring

Adult   Juvenile

Gray squirrel
tail pelage

A

Scapular
Cartilage
Humerus

Cartilage

Rabbit

B

Game Birds

Bursa
Anus
Penis

Juvenile male   Juvenile female

Anus
Penis
Oviduct

Adult male   Adult female

Waterfowl   *D*

Bursa

Anus   Intestine

C

Juvenile

Notched
tail feather

E

Adult
Outer primary
barred, rounded

Juvenile
Outer primary
indistinctly barred

Wild turkey

F

Buff-tipped
primary coverts

Adult   Juvenile

Bobwhite quail

G

Figure D-4   *Age determination in some game birds and mammals.* (A) *Regular barring on the underside of the tail distinguishes the juvenile gray squirrel from the adult.* (B) *Presence of the epiphyseal cartilage on the humerus of the juvenile cottontail rabbit separates that age class from the adult. This method is useful when the biologist wishes to collect data from a wide area by requesting that successful rabbit hunters turn in these bones.* (C) *The bursa of Fabricus (enlarged). Its presence or greater depth indicates a juvenile bird. The depths vary with the species. This method is useful in both waterfowl and some gallinaceous game birds.* (D) *A method of sexing and aging waterfowl by examining the cloaca. Note the presence of the bursal opening on juvenile waterfowl, its absence on the adult.* (E) *The* skins is a good means of aging muskrat during the trapping season. Dark pigmentation on the flesh side of the pelt indicates areas of growing hair. This pigmentation in adults appears in irregular, scattered dark areas, while in immature animals it is more or less symmetrical and linear. Skull measurements are useful in beaver and muskrats. Annual growth rings on the roots of canine teeth indicate age for the first few years of life in the fur seal and other pinnipeds and in canids. Growth rings also show up in the horns of mountain sheep. The wear and replacement of teeth in deer and elk permit the determination of different age classes in these mammals (see Fig. D-5).

Lens-weight technique

Since the lens of the eye of most mammals (and possibly birds) grows continuously throughout life and since there is only slight variation between individuals in lens size and growth, the measurement of the lens is a feasible method for aging a number of mammals. It has been done successfully for the cottontail rabbit, the raccoon, the black bear, and the fur seal.

The technique involves the weighing of the dry lens and comparing its weight against a chart of lens weights of known-age individuals (Fig. D-6A,B). This may require the development of such a table by the investigator, who will have to rear young animals in captivity and sacrifice them week by week for their eyes. A table has been prepared for rabbits by Lord (1959, 1963).

The technique is as follows.

1. Remove eyes as soon as possible after the animal is killed and place in a solution of 10 per cent formalin. The formalin will harden the lens so that it can be removed from the vitreous humor.

2. Fix for one week, but the longer the better.

3. After fixing, remove the lens from the eye and roll it a few minutes on a paper towel to remove excess moisture.

4. Place the lens in an oven to dry at 80°C.

5. Lenses are considered dry when repeated weighing after intervals of drying results in no additional loss of weight. This will usually require 24 to 36 hours.

6. Weigh immediately after removal from oven, since the dried lens is hygroscopic and takes on water. Electric scales that read weights rapidly are preferred over other types of balances.

The lens-growth curve permits a rather close approximation of the age of the mammal. For cottontail rabbits, the method permits the determination of the month of birth of young rabbits and the year of birth of rabbits over one year of age.

---

notched tail feather of juvenile waterfowl. (F) The number X (ten) primary in juvenile gallinaceous birds is sharply pointed; in adults it is rounded. The juvenile wild turkey in addition has its outer primary indistinctly barred. (G) The juvenile bobwhite quail, in addition to having a pointed number X primary, also possesses buff-tipped primary coverts. (For a complete discussion on aging and sexing techniques, see Wildlife Investigational Techniques.*)*

Aging deer by dentition and tooth wear

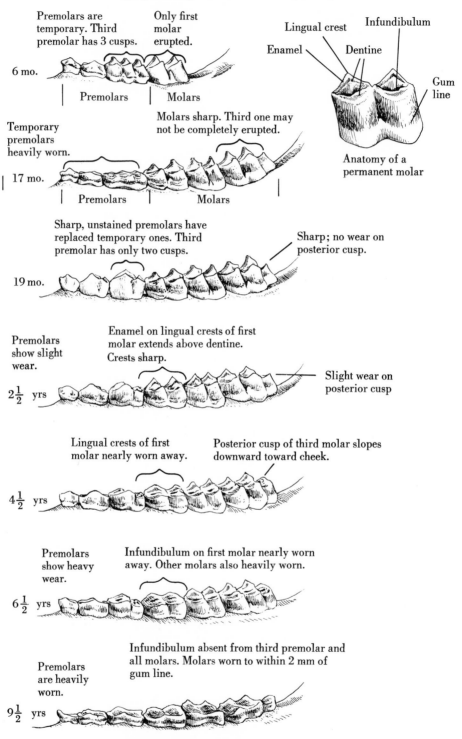

Figure D-5 *Aging deer by dentition and tooth wear.*

DENTITION OUTLINE

Fawn.
Under 5 months: Both deciduous pincers present.
5–6 months: Deciduous pincers lost at this time—one or both absent.
6–10 months: Only first molar erupted. Three temporary premolars, third with three cusps—permanent pincers in place.

1½ years.
17 months: Temporary premolars in place but worn. Note small first premolar and three-cusp third premolar. Permanent third premolar has only two cusps. Part of third molar may not show.

18 months: Usually in some phase of replacement of temporary premolars. Examine both sides as there may be some difference.

19 months: Examine closely, since this age difficult to determine; premolars and second and third molars show no wear. Upper third molar just coming through gum.

2½ years.
Key is normally width of enamel and dentine on first molar. Enamel of lingual crests extends above the dentine and is as wide as dentine. Enamel of buccal crest of second and third molars also extends above dentine. Some slight wear on posterior cusp of third molar.

3½ years.
Lingual crest of first molar is short and not a true crest. Dentine shows as wide or more so than enamel. Dentine begins to assume greater width, particularly on buccal cusps, where it is generally wider than enamel on first and second molars. Balance wear on all teeth and compare width of enamel on boards.

4½ years.
Key is normally the first molar, though there may be exceptions. Lingual crest of first molar almost worn away, dentine almost twice width of enamel. Lingual crests at second molar show same stage as first molar of 3½-year class. Dentine of lingual crests of second molar wider than enamel. On third molar about wide as enamel. Infundibulum beginning to disappear in some first molars, though this is variable and an exception. Wear on first premolar slight, moderate to heavy on third. Compare width of dentine of lingual and buccal crests with 3½- and 5½-year age classes.

5½ years.
Careful comparison usually needed on width of enamel and dentine on all molar teeth. Sometimes the infundibulum of first molar just about gone, but not in all cases. Compare second molar with first molar in 4½-year class; third molar with second molar in 4½-year class. Original lingual crests of first and second molars worn away. Lingual crests of third molar blunt.

6½ years.
In most typical specimens the infundibulum of the first molar has disappeared. Dentine also joined in most specimens. Broadening of dentine in second and third molars continues. Grinding surface of first molar generally smooth. It also helps to note height of teeth above gum and compare with board. On some specimens a difficult age class; so careful comparison on all angles is necessary.

7½ years.
Comparison on height of teeth above gum line is the best key to distinguishing this and the next age class. There appears to be considerable variation in the infundibulum and crests that sometimes remain. First molar usually worn down within two or three millimeters of gum line on buccal side. Infundibulum almost gone from third premolar; gone in first molar, usually shows in second and third molars.

8½–9½ years.
Compare height of teeth above gum. Infundibulum usually entirely worn away from all teeth, though some may show in third molar. Dentine usually joined in all cheek teeth. Wear on all premolars and molar teeth has reduced them to about two or three millimeters of tooth above gum line on cheek side.

10½ or more years.
Since boards do not show this age class, a comparison with 8½–9½ jaw must be made. Look to the height above gum line. Cheek teeth are worn to gum line or within two millimeters on buccal side. All dentine is joined. In some cases pulp cavities may show.

645

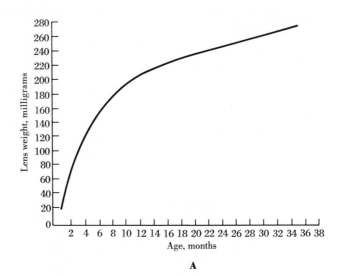

A

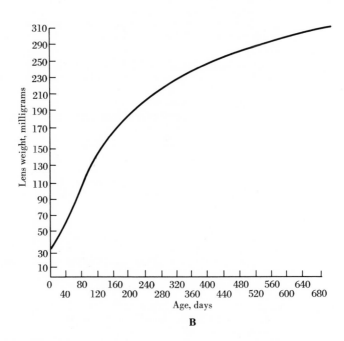

B

Figure D-6 *Growth-rate curves for the lens of* (A) *cottontail rabbit* (after Lord, 1960) *and* (B) *black-tailed jackrabbit.* (After Tiemeier and Plenert, 1964.)

Sex determination

The sex of mammals in most instances can be determined by examining external genitalia, and the sex of birds by plumage differences. For example, the male ruffed grouse can be distinguished from the female by the length of the central tail feather (Fig. D-7); and females of prairie chickens can be distinguished from the males by strong mottling or barring of all the tail feathers (Fig. D-7). Male wild turkeys have body feathers black tipped, while the feathers of the female are brown tipped (Fig. D-7). For detailed information see *Wildlife Investigational Techniques*.

Figure D-7 *Sex determination in game birds. (A) Length of the central tail feather separates male from female ruffed grouse. The male tail feather is five and seven-eighth inches long or more; the female tail feather is under five and seven-eighth inches. (B) The female prairie chicken has heavily barred tail feathers; barring is absent on the outer tail feathers of the male. (C) The breast feathers of the male wild turkey are black tipped; those of the female are brown tipped. (D) Sexual dimorphism distinguishes males from females in many species of birds.*

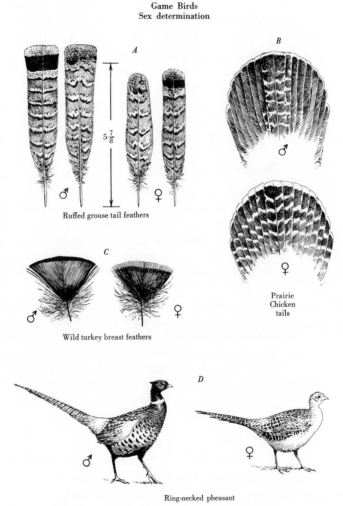

Game Birds
Sex determination

Ruffed grouse tail feathers

Wild turkey breast feathers

Prairie
Chicken
tails

Ring-necked pheasant

Determination of home range and territory

There are a number of methods available for obtaining an approximation of the size of home range. Three methods are offered here.

Calculating home range

On a map, outline and measure the area that includes all the observations made on the movements of individuals. If the observations are obtained by trapping, then one must assume that the animal could have gone halfway toward an adjacent trap, especially if the traps were set in a regular grid.

Center of activity

Arrange the recaptures on a grid and determine the values on an XY axis. An average of these locations will give the center of activity (see Hayne, 1949b). This method has the advantages that the information is relatively easy to summarize and the calculations are not complicated. However a map of the area must be made, and many recaptures of the same individual are required before the extent of the home range can be obtained. As the number of recaptures increase, the area of the known range increases. At least 15 recaptures or more are necessary. This method is unsuited for mammals that follow paths or tunnel underground.

Frequency of recapture

Record the distances between captures in live traps set randomly or in grids. Record the number of captures as a frequency distribution according to the distance between them. Distances between captures are then tallied and proportions calculated for each distance by sex or age categories.

The distances can be measured in two ways. They can be taken from the place where the animal was first marked or observed, or from each successive location.

This method has the advantage that the traps can be set out haphazardly, avoiding the labor of setting them out in grids. The recaptures of all individuals can be used. And information can be obtained during a short period of time since the data from animals captured only two or three times can be used. The disadvantages of this method are that short movements are favored and that no definite boundaries of home ranges can be given. Home range is described as a frequency of distances observed.

Dyed bait

The fact that small mammals come readily to bait can be exploited in a manner that does not involve trapping. Bait boxes are made from quart-size paper milk containers and are set out in a 50-foot grid over the study area. These boxes serve as containers for the bait and as receptacles for the feces. If food at certain stations is stained with a dye, then the visitation by animals that fed on the dyed bait to other bait boxes can be traced through colored droppings. The distance moved by a particular animal from a station with dyed bait can be determined when colored scats are recovered at various stations in the grid. The results with this method compare favorably with those obtained by other methods, and it does not involve the time and work of trapping. Complete details, as well as a list of suitable dyes, can be found in a paper by New, 1958.

Territory

Since territorial boundaries are rather rigidly maintained by birds during the breeding season, territorial boundaries can be mapped by observing the movements of the birds during the day, by plotting singing perches, by observing locations of territorial disputes, and on occasion by chasing the bird. When the bird arrives at the boundary of its territory, it generally will double back.

Radio tracking

The development of transistors and other miniature electronic devices has made possible the construction of small transmitters that can be attached to animals usually by means of a specially designed collar or harness. Mercury cells are used as the source of power. The transmitter is a transistor-crystal-controlled oscillator with the tank coil for the oscillator acting as the magnetic-dipole transmitting antenna. The antenna is constructed of copper or aluminum and has a figure-eight directional pattern. The receiver is a portable battery-powered unit, whose basic components are the receiver, a radio range filter, and two transistorized radio-frequency converters. Positions of stationary animals can be obtained by a single portable direction-finding receiver. Running animals are best located by triangulation, using at least two directional finding receivers.

Details of construction are not given here. They can be found in papers by Cochran and Lord, 1963; Verts, 1963; and Ellis, 1964. Step-by-step construction details are given by Verts, 1963.

Estimating the numbers of animals

Basic to the study of animal populations is the estimation of their numbers, no small task in wild populations. During the past several decades, much work has gone into the development of techniques and statistical methods to arrive at some estimates of animal populations. Basically the methods of estimating the numbers of animals can be put into three categories: a *true census,* a count of all individuals on a given area; *sampling estimates,* derived from counts on sample plots; and *indices,* in which the trends of populations from year to year or from area to area are obtained through roadside counts, animal signs, and the like. In this category everything is relative, and to be meaningful, the data must be compared with those from other areas or other years.

True census

A true census implies a direct count of all individuals in a given area. This is rather difficult to do for most wild populations, but there are situations where a total count can be made.

Many territorial species are easily seen and heard and can be located in their specific area. Such a census is regularly used for birds. The spot-map method is probably the best approach. A sample plot of at least 25 acres (10 hectares) is marked out in a grid with numbered stakes or tree tags placed at intervals of 50 meters. Five or more daily counts are made throughout the breeding season. Each time a bird is observed, it is marked on a map of the plot. At the end of the census period all the spots at which a species is observed are placed on one map. The spots should fall into groups, each group indicating the presence of a breeding pair. Count the groups for each species in order to arrive at the total population for the area. Results are usually expressed as animals per acre or per hectare.

Direct counts can be made in areas of concentration. Deer in open country, herds of elk and caribou, waterfowl on wintering grounds, rookeries, roosts, breeding colonies of birds and mammals permit direct counting usually either from the air or from aerial photographs. Covies of bobwhite quail can be located and counted with the aid of a well-trained bird dog.

Estimates from sampling

Estimations of population from sampling involve two basic assumptions: (1) That mortality and recruitment during the period the data are being taken are negligible or can be accounted for. (2) That all members have an equal probability of being counted—that the members of the population are not trap shy or trap addicted, that they are distributed randomly through the population if marked and released, and that they do not group by age, sex, or some other characteristic.

Sampling also involves one major general consideration. The method employed in taking the sample must be adapted to the particular species, the time, the place, the purpose.

Sample plots. Relatively immobile forms, such as barnacles, mollusks, cicada emergence holes, etc., can be estimated by the quadrat method, similar to that employed for plants. The data can be analyzed for presence, frequency, etc., or the results can be converted to a density per acre, etc. The size and shape of the quadrat will depend upon the density of the population, the diversity of the habitat, the nature of the organism involved. Make a few preliminary surveys before settling on a quadrat size.

Foilage arthropods may be sampled by a number of strokes with a standard sweep net over 10-square-meter area. The number of strokes needed to secure the sample must be predetermined. It will vary with the type of vegetation.

Estimates of zooplankton, obtained by pulling a plankton net through a given distance of water at several depths, can be made by filtering a known volume of sample through a funnel using a filter pump. The filter paper should be marked off in equal squares. With the aid of a hand lens or a binocular microscope, count the organisms in each square. The numbers then can be related back to the total volume of water sampled.

If the organisms are too small to be counted in this manner, a Rafter plankton-counting cell can be used. This consists of a microscope slide base plate ruled into 10-one-centimeter squares. The slides are made from strips of microscope glass slides cemented to the base with Canada balsam. This should hold 1 cc of liquid. After a small volume of water is introduced, cover with a long cover glass, place under the microscope, and count the organisms square by square. Record the number of each form per square until at least 100 observations have been made. The occurrence of individual species can be recorded as percentage frequency. (Note: Plankton-counting cells and eyepiece micrometers can be purchased commercially, but they are expensive).

Strip census.   The strip census, or King method, has been widely used for estimating populations of ruffed grouse and snowshoe hare. First the area must be marked out in a grid, the distances between the lines being one-quarter mile. The observer, or preferably observers, one for each line, walk the grid line, count the animals observed, and record the distance at which they are flushed from the line. The average flushing distance is determined by adding up all the flushing distances and dividing this by the number of flushes made. This figure is then used to calculate the effective width of the strip censused, obtained by multiplying the total length of the line walked by the average flushing distance. The population for the entire area is the number of animals flushed, divided by the area of the strip and multiplied by the total area:

$$P = \frac{F}{2yx}(A) \qquad \text{where} \qquad \begin{aligned} F &= \text{number of flushes} \\ A &= \text{area of study} \\ y &= \text{average flushing distance} \\ x &= \text{length of line} \end{aligned}$$

The flushing distance y is multiplied by 2, since the distance is applicable to both sides of the line walked.

This census method has several drawbacks. For one, the average flushing distance gives an erroneously small sample area and too large a population estimate. However the results of this method are useful as an index used to follow population fluctuations from year to year or from area to area (see Hayne, 1949*a*).

Mark-recapture method.   This method is based on trapping, banding, or marking, and then later recapturing sample individuals. It involves the release of a known number of marked animals turned loose in the original area. Then after an appropriate interval of time (approximately one week for rabbits), a sample of the population is taken. A estimate of the total population is then computed from the ratio of marked to unmarked individuals.

$$N : T :: n : t$$

or

$$N = \frac{T}{t/n} \qquad \text{or} \qquad \frac{nT}{t}$$

where

T = number marked in the precensus period
t = number of marked animals trapped in the census period
n = total animals trapped in the census period
N = the population estimate

651

Suppose that in a precensus period a biologist tags 39 rabbits. Then during the census period he traps 15 tagged rabbits and 19 unmarked ones, a total of 34. The following ratio is set up:

$$N : 39 :: 34 : 15 \quad \text{or} \quad N = \frac{39}{15/34} = 88 \text{ rabbits}$$

The confidence limits at the 95 per cent level may be calculated from

$$S.E. = \sqrt{\frac{T^2 n(n-t)}{t^3}}$$

To determine the limits within which the population lies, add and subtract two standard errors from the estimate. A large standard error and rather wide confidence limits are the result of a small number of recaptures.

For this example the

$$S.E. = \sqrt{\frac{(39)^2 (34)(19)}{15^3}} = 17.06$$

Upper limits:

$$88 + 34 = 122$$

Lower limits:

$$88 - 34 = 54$$

The chances are 95 out of a 100 that the population of rabbits lies between 54 and 122. This wide spread is typical in wildlife studies.

A variation of this procedure is to accumulate the captures and recaptures. There are several ways in which this can be done, but only the Schnabel method will be illustrated here (for others, see *Wildlife Investigational Techniques*). All animals captured are tagged or marked and released daily. A record is kept of the total animals caught each day, the number of recaptures, and the number of animals newly tagged. An example is given in Table D-1. The method of calculating the population is the same as that already given above. However in the Schnabel method, T becomes progressively larger. Population estimates can be calculated daily later in the period, or the season can be divided into periods of, say, a week, and the population computed for each period.

Removal method. The removal method of estimating populations has been widely used in small-mammal studies, although the assumptions on which it is based are open to question. This method assumes (1) that the population is essentially stationary; (2) that the probability of capture during the trapping period is the same for each animal exposed to capture; (3) that the probability of capture remains constant from trapping to trapping (not trap shy, etc.). The trapping program consists of setting the same number of traps for several nights. The number caught the first night is expected to exceed that caught the second, and the second night's catch should exceed the third. In other words the population becomes depleted.

The field procedure is as follows.

1. Set the traps (snap) out in a grid system, three traps to a station; or prefera-bly set the traps in two parallel lines 50 feet apart, 20 stations to a line, 3 traps at each station. The stations are spaced 25 feet or 50 feet apart, depending upon the nature of the vegetation.

TABLE D-1. THE SCHNABEL METHOD OF ESTIMATING POPULATIONS

P PERIOD (DATE)	A NUMBER TRAPPED	NUMBER MARKED	B MARKED ANIMALS IN AREA	$(A) \times (B)$	$(A) \times (B)$ SUM	RECAP-TURES	C SUM OF RECAP-TURES	$\frac{(A) \times (B)}{(C)}$ ESTI-MATED POPU-LATION
1	4	4		00	0			
2	4	4	4	16	16	0	0	
3	2	2	8	16	32	0		
4	6	6	10	60	92	0		
5	10	7	16	160	252	3	3	
6	4	4	23	92	344	0	3	
7	8	6	27	216	560	2	5	
8	4	2	33	132	692	2	7	
9	5	4	35	175	867	1	8	
10	7	6	39	273	1140	1	9	
11	7	6	45	315	1455	1	10	145
12	9	7	51	459	1914	2	12	159
13	6	3	58	348	2262	3	15	150
14	10	6	61	610	2872	4	19	151
15	8	5	67	536	3408	3	22	154
16	6	1	72	432	3840	5	27	142
17	4	2	73	292	4132	2	29	142
18	12	7	75	900	5032	5	34	148
19	8	4	82	656	5688	4	38	149

2. Trap for three nights.

There are several ways of handling the data to obtain the estimate. The most popular is to plot the size of the daily catch against the number of animals previously caught (Fig. D-8). A straight line is drawn through the plotted points to cut the horizontal axis. The point at which the horizontal axis is cut represents the population estimate.

A simpler method of estimating the population based on two captures is suggested by Zippin (1956). The population N equals the number caught the first day (y_1) squared, divided by the difference between the number caught the first day (y_1) and the number caught the second (y_2). Using the same data as on the graph,

$$N = \frac{(y_1)^2}{y_1 - y_2} = \frac{36}{2} = 18$$

The two methods give approximately the same answer.

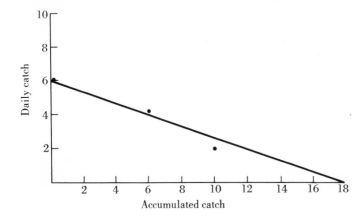

Figure D-8 *Daily catch on a 3-day-removal trap line plotted against accumulated catch to estimate the exposed population.*

There is another variation (Fig. D-9). Instead of setting out parallel lines for three nights, individual lines of 20 stations each are set out in the form of a hexagon and the traps are set for a period of 30 days. The population can be estimated by accumulating the total catch. If graphed, the estimate of the population is taken at the point where the line levels off. The 30-day period seems to give a clearer picture of the species structure of the small-mammal population (Fig. D-10).

The removal method is useful where one desires a relative measure or index figure for small-mammal populations in order to compare one habitat with another. The data will be more valuable if details on vegetation and litter are recorded for each station. Often some association can be obtained between vegetation and trapping success at the various stations.

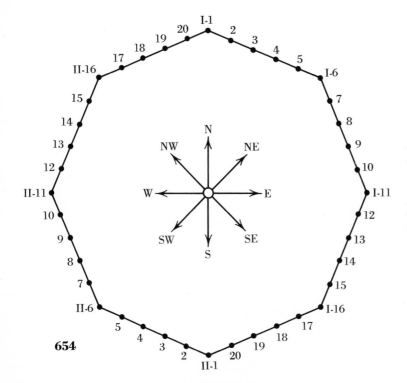

Figure D-9 *Layout for a 30-day-removal trap line. The stations are located 25 or 50 feet apart, three traps to a station. To lay this out in the field, begin at center point O and locate points from there. If stations are 25 feet apart, each segment of the line will be 125 feet.*

Live trapping method. This method employs live traps to estimate absolute populations. Lay out a study area of at least one acre, preferably larger. Arrange the traps in a grid (but place them in favorable locations) so that the traps will be spaced about 42 feet x 42 feet apart, with at least a 20-foot margin around the periphery of the area. Bait with apple, peanut butter, etc., and visit them several times a day. Remove the animals, mark by toe clipping or by ear punching, and release. Record the following:

Date   Line   Station   Species   Sex   Adult or Juvenile

Continue trapping for several days, including at least three nights favorable for small-mammal activity.

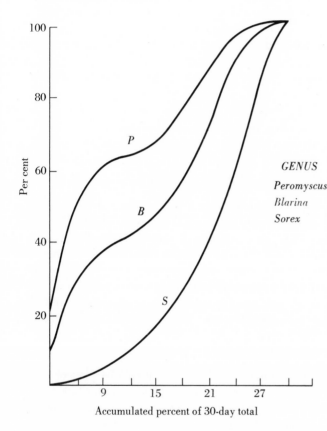

GENUS		*Total Catch*	
		3-day	30-day
Peromyscus	P	12	57
Blarina	B	9	116
Sorex	S	0	48

Accumulated percent of 30-day total

Figure D-10 *As the members of dominant species are trapped off, the inhibitory influences are reduced and members of subordinate species enlarge their home ranges to a point where they are exposed to traps. (Data of Barbehenn, from Calhoun, 1959.)*

The population is calculated as the total number of individuals caught only in the central area plus half of those caught in both the central and the buffer area. Sex and age should be treated separately.

Indices

Indices are estimates of animal populations derived from counts of animal signs, calls, roadside counts, and so on. The results do not give estimates of absolute populations, but they do indicate trends of populations from year to year and from habitat to habitat. Often this type of information is all that is needed.

Call counts. Call counts are used chiefly to obtain population trends of certain game birds such as the mourning dove, bobwhite quail, woodcock, and pheasant. A predetermined route is established along country roads; it should be no longer than can be covered in one hour's time. Stations are located at quarter-, or half-mile intervals, depending upon the terrain and the species involved. The route is run around sunrise for gallinaceous birds and for doves, and around sunset for woodcock. The exact time to start must be determined for each area by the investigator. At each station the vehicle is stopped, the observer listens for a minute or two (standardize), records the calls heard, and goes on to the next station. Routes should be run several times and an average taken. The number of calls divided by the number of stops gives a call-index figure.

Roadside counts. This is similar to a call count, with the exception that the number of animals observed along the route is recorded and the results divided by the number of miles. Other variations include counting of animal tracks, browse, signs, active dens and lodges, and so on.

Pellet counts. Counting pellet or fecal groups is widely used to estimate big-game populations. This method involves the counting of pellet groups in sample plots or transects located in the study area. It may be used for estimating the relative intensity of use of the range by one or more kinds of animals, to determine trends in animal populations, or in rarer cases to estimate the total population. The latter is possible only when an entire herd is known to occupy a given area for a definite period. Intensity of use is usually expressed as the number of pellets or pellet groups per unit area.

The accuracy of estimating populations by this method depends upon some knowledge of the rate of defecation by the animals involved. Herein lies the weakness of the technique, since pellet groups will vary with the diet, season, age, sex, rate of decomposition, and the type of vegetation (that is, the plants can cover the pellet groups). Usually rates will vary with the region; so some preliminary observations will have to be made to arrive at some useful figure. For deer, a pellet-group figure of 15 (per deer) is satisfactory on good range, and 13 for poor range. Rabbits vary too widely in their pellet groups for the technique to have much value with that group.

The field procedure is as follows.

1. On randomly located lines transects, establish several circular plots of one-hundredth acre at fixed (250 to 800 feet) or restricted random (not over 1200 feet) intervals along each transect. Make two counts, one clockwise and the other counterclockwise, to avoid missing pellet groups.

2. Count pellet groups at the most favorable time, when plant growth, leaf fall, etc. is least likely to interfere.

3. Mark the plots permanently and clear or paint the pellet groups at the beginning of the study where age determination of pellets is difficult.

4. For determining the population, use a defecation rate of 13 pellets per deer per day for poor range, 15 per day for adequate range.

5. Sample intensively enough to obtain an acceptable standard error.

6. Calculate the population per square mile by

$$P = \frac{\text{average pellet group per plot} \times \text{area of plots in acres} \times 640 \text{ acres per square mile}}{\text{days since leaf fall, last count, etc.} \times \text{average pellet group per deer per day}}$$

Dropping boards. A modification of the pellet-group method for small mammals is the dropping-board method (see Emlen et al., 1957).

1. Set out four-inch squares of weatherproof plywood (in natural color) in lines or grids. Use at least 100 boards. This will cover 1.2 acres if spaced 25 feet apart, 4.7 acres with a 50-foot spacing, and 18.8 acres with a 100-foot spacing. Be sure the squares are level and placed firmly on the ground.

2. Number each station.

3. The boards may or may not be baited depending upon local conditions.

4. Make a series of at least three visits. The time of day the visits are made and their frequency will depend upon local conditions, such as coprophagous insect activity. Daily visits may be necessary.

5. At each station record the presence of droppings by species and brush the board clean for the next visit. The droppings of small mammals are distinctive and with some experience can be identified. See Murie, *Field Guide to Animal Tracks.*

6. Results can be expressed as incidence of droppings for each species.

Figures obtained from the record of usage are indices of the population useful in comparative studies of interspecific, interseasonal, and interregional abundance. The dropping-board technique can be used in studies of population trends and fluctuations, local distribution, species association, activity rhythms, effects of weather and environmental conditions on activity, and movements if the animal is tagged with a radioactive tracer or with dyed bait.

Measuring mortality

As pointed out in Chap. 21, the measurement of mortality in natural populations is imperative in the analysis of animal populations. Coupled with a knowledge of age structure, mortality data can be used to construct life tables, life equations, survivorship curves, growth curves, and the like. Knowledge of the mortality rate is basic in the management of game and fish populations.

Several methods of determining mortality in wild populations will be discussed here. Further details on these methods and the description of others, including the construction of life tables and the conversion of monthly rates of probability of dying to annual rates and to death rates and estimations of life expectancy can be found in *Wildlife Investigational Techniques*; in Davis, 1960; Davis and Golley, 1963; and Ricker, 1958.

Known deaths

If a number of marked animals are found dead a known time after marking, the percentage dying can be plotted against time and a curve drawn through the points. The probability of dying can be read directly from the chart, or it can be calculated by dividing the number of individuals that die during a period of time by the initial population. At best, however, this is a very rough measurement.

If the animals can be readily aged, as is true with deer, rabbits, mountain sheep, and others, and if sufficient lower jaws, eye lenses, or horns can be obtained, then mortality and the probability of dying can be expressed on an age basis.

657

Change in population

If the size of a population can be determined at two different times, if immigration and emigration are held to a minimum, and if there is no recruitment from births, then the difference in population size between time A and time B is the result of deaths. (Winter deer yards offer an excellent opportunity to determine mortality in this way.) The probability of dying during the period under observation can be calculated by dividing the number dying over the period (population time A — population time B) by the initial population. Davis and Golley (1963) give formulas for changing such data to an annual basis. However since the probability of dying may vary with the season, as it does with deer, an annual probability of dying based on a seasonal figure may be erroneous.

Change in sex or age ratio

This method is most widely used by game biologists. It requires a knowledge of sex or age ratios before the hunting season, in the kill, and after the hunting season. The method can be reversed and the number killed can be calculated from sex and age ratios before and after the hunting season.

The following procedures and formulas are from Selleck and Hart (1957), who give detailed instructions and examples on its use.

Basic formulas. Symbols used in the basic formulas are as follows:

$$B = \text{ratio in population before kill}$$
$$K = \text{ratio in kill}$$
$$A = \text{ratio in population after kill}$$

The population data, which include the numbers of males and females, or adults and young, are considered from two viewpoints, the base population and the ratio population. The *base population* is the one used as a base in expressing the ratios, as the females in the ratio of males per 100 females. The *ratio population* is expressed as a ratio figure, as the males in the ratio of males per 100 females. The total population is the base population plus the ratio population. For example, suppose population ratio consists of 75 males per 100 females. The 100 females represent the base population, the 75 males the ratio population, and 175 the total population.

Using the above symbols and terms, the basic formulas are as follows:

1. $\dfrac{B - A}{K - A} = $ decimal fraction of base population killed

2. $\dfrac{K(B - A)}{B(K - A)} = $ decimal fraction of ratio population killed

To estimate the fraction of the total population killed, the formulas must be adjusted to the number of units in the base population expressed in the ratio.

3. When the ratio is per single unit of base population,

$\dfrac{(K + 1)\,(B - A)}{(B + 1)\,(K - A)} = $ decimal fraction of total population killed

When the ratio is per 100 units of base population,

$$\frac{(K + 100)(B - A)}{(B + 100)(K - A)} = \text{decimal fraction of total population killed}$$

To illustrate how these formulas are used, suppose the following information is known for a population of ring-necked pheasants.

	MALES	FEMALES	TOTAL	MALES/100 FEMALES	
Preseason population	80	100	180	80	(B)
Total known hunting kill	60	20	80	300	(K)
Postseason population	20	80	100	25	(A)

The base population is female, expressed as 100 units.
Using the basic formula 1,

$$\frac{B - A}{K - A} = \text{decimal fraction of base population killed}$$

$$\frac{80 - 25}{300 - 25} = 0.20 \text{ or } 20 \text{ per cent of the base population, females killed}$$

Using basic formula 2,

$$\frac{K(B - A)}{B(K - A)} = \text{decimal fraction of ratio population killed}$$

$$\frac{300(80 - 25)}{80(300 - 25)} = 0.75 \text{ or } 75 \text{ per cent of the ratio population, males, killed.}$$

To determine the decimal fraction of the total population killed, use formula 3 for when the ratio is per 100 units of base population:

$$\frac{(K + 100)(B - A)}{(B + 100)(K - A)} = \frac{(300 + 100)(80 - 25)}{(80 + 100)(300 - 25)} = 0.44 \text{ or } 44 \text{ per cent of}$$

total population killed

This method is useful, for not only can the biologist learn the proportional magnitude of the kill without knowing the actual size of the population, but he can also calculate the size of the population in the field, if he knows the actual number of animals killed.

REFERENCES

General

Andrewartha, H. G.
1961 "An Introduction to the Study of Animal Populations," University of Chicago Press, Chicago.

Davis, D. E. (ed.)
1956 "Manual for Analysis of Rodent Populations," Edwards, Ann Arbor, Mich.

Mosby, H. S. (ed.)
1962 "Wildlife Investigational Techniques," The Wildlife Society, Washington, D.C.

Ricker, W. E.
1958 Handbook of computations for biological statistics of fish populations, *Fishery Res. Board Can. Bull.*, **119**:1–300.

U.S. Department of Agriculture
1962 Range research methods, *U.S. Dept. Agr. Misc. Publ.* 940., Supt. of Documents, Washington, D.C.

Welch, P. S.
1948 "Limnological Methods," McGraw-Hill–Blakiston, New York.

Others

Calhoun, J. B.
1959 Revised sampling procedure for the North American Census of Small Mammals (NACSM), *Population Dynamics of Vertebrates Release No.* 10, Mimeo Administrative Publication, U.S. Dept. Health, Education and Welfare.

Cochran, W. W., and R. D. Lord, Jr.
1963 A radio-tracking system for wild animals, *J. Wildlife Management*, **27**:9–24.

Davis, D. E.
1960 A chart for estimation of life expectancy, *J. Wildlife Management*, **24**:344–348.

Davis, D. E., and F. B. Golley
1963 "Principles in Mammalogy," Reinhold, New York.

Ellis, R. J.
1964 Tracking raccoons by radio, *J. Wildlife Management*, **28**:363–368.

Emlen, J. T., Ruth Hine, W. A. Fuller, and P. Alfonso
1957 Dropping boards for population studies of small mammals, *J. Wildlife Management*, **21**:300–414.

Godfrey, G. K.
1954 Tracing field voles (*Microtus agrestris*) with a Geiger-Muller counter, *Ecology*, **35**:5–10.

Golley, F. B.
1960 Energy dynamics of a food chain in an old field community, *Ecol. Monographs*, **30**:187–206.

1961 Energy values of ecological materials, *Ecology*, **42**:581–584.

Hayne, D. W.
1949a An examination of the strip census method for estimating animal populations, *J. Wildlife Management*, **13**:145–157.
1949b Two methods for estimating populations of mammals from trapping records, *J. Mammal.*, **30**:399–411.

Kaye, S. V.
1960 Gold-198 wires used to study movements of small mammals, *Science*, **13**:824.

Lord, R. D., Jr.
1959 The lens as an indicator of age in cottontail rabbits, *J. Wildlife Management*, **23**:358–360.
1963 The cottontail rabbit in Illinois, *Illinois Dept. Conserv. Tech. Bull.* 3.

MacLulich, D. A.
1951 New techniques of animal census, with examples. *J. Mammal.*, **32**:318–328.

Martof, B. S.
1953 Territoriality in the green frog *Rana clamitans*, *Ecology*, **34**:165–174.

Neville, A. C.
1963 Daily growth layers for determining the age of grasshopper populations, *Oikos*, **14**:1–8.

New, J. G.
1958 Dyes for studying the movements of small mammals, *J. Mammal.*, **39**:416–429.
1959 Additional uses of dyes for studying the movements of small mammals, *J. Wildlife Management*, **23**:348–351.

Pendleton, R. C.
1956 Uses of marking animals in ecological studies: Labelling animals with radioisotopes, *Ecology*, **37**:686–689.

Robinette, W. L., R. B. Ferguson, and J. S. Gashweiler
1958 Problems involved in the use of deer pellet group counts, *Trans. North Am. Wildlife Conf.*, **23**:411–425.

Selleck, D. M., and C. M. Hart
1957 Calculating the percentage of kill from sex and age ratios, *Calif. Fish Game*, **43**:309–316.

Stickel, Lucille F.
1946 Experimental analysis of methods for measuring small mammal populations, *J. Wildlife Management*, **10**:150–158.

Taber, R. D.
1956 Marking of mammals: standard methods and new developments, *Ecology*, **37**:681–685.

Tester, J. R.
1963 Techniques for studying movements of vertebrates in the field, in "Radioecology," pp. 445–450.

Tiemeier, O. W., and M. L. Plenert
1964 A comparison of three methods for determining the age of black-tailed jackrabbits, *J. Mammal.* **45**:409–416.

Verts, B. J.
1963 Equipment and techniques for radio-tracking skunks, *J. Wildlife Management,* **27**:325–339.

Zippin, C.
1958 The removal method of population estimation. *J. Wildlife Management,* **22**:325–339.

Collecting animals

Anderson, R. M.
1948 Methods of collecting and preserving vertebrate animals, *Nat. Museum Can. Bull.* 69, Ottawa.

Needham, J. G. (ed.)
1937 "Culture Methods for Invertebrate Animals," reprint ed., Dover, New York.

Oman, P. W., and A. D. Cushman
1948 Collection and preservation of insects, *U.S. Dept. Agr. Misc. Publ.* 60.

Petersen, A. M.
1953 "A Manual of Entomological Techniques," published by the author, Ohio State University, Columbus, Ohio.

Wagstaffe, R. J., and J. H. Fidler
1955 "The Preservation of Natural History Specimens," vol. I, "The Invertebrates," Philosophical Library, New York.

APPENDIX E

Methods
for studying
animal behavior

Of all the areas of field biology, none offers the student or amateur naturalist greater opportunities than that of animal behavior. The amount of unknown knowledge is tremendous, the equipment needs are small, often requiring little more than a notebook, pen with waterproof ink, a pair of good binoculars, and a stop watch. The main requirements are acute observation, patience, and a willingness to take accurate notes on the spot. Some studies may benefit from the use of motion picture cameras and sound recordings. The collected data should be published or turned over to some interested scientist or research institution.

The following suggestions for study of behavior are based largely on a manuscript, Aspects of Field Ethology, unpublished at the time of this writing, by Robert W. and Millicent Ficken.

Equipment

Binoculars and a notebook are the standard pieces of equipment. The notebook should contain high-grade paper and the pen used in writing should be adaptable to waterproof ink. Data on each species should be kept separately, in chronological order, including date, time, and location; in addition a daily log on ecology, weather, and other conditions should be kept in a separate part of the notebook or in a separate notebook.

Superior to the notebook but more expensive is a pocket tape recorder. These enable one to keep up a running commentary while observing the animal. Choose one that has a long recording time and runs at a constant speed.

For vocalization, sound recordings and analyzing equipment are superior to written descriptions, but very expensive. Although recordings and audiospectrographs should be the ultimate goal, descriptions are adequate in preliminary work and can serve as a "name tag" for each type. When recording vocalizations, data accompanying behavior should be recorded simultaneously. Details for recording sounds in nature can be found in Borrer, 1960, and Kellogg, 1960.

Motion pictures are very valuable, especially since the sequences can be subject to later analysis through reruns and stills. The type of motion picture camera needed will be governed by the kind of study and finances. No attempt will be made here to recommend any type of camera. When taking motion pictures, essential data, especially on vocalizations, must be taken simultaneously on tape. Still photographs and sketches are useful for recording postures.

The stop watch often is a vital piece of equipment. Use the best.

At close range, the blind is a handy aid. The type of blind needed depends upon the situation and the species being studied. Towers, platforms, and tree houses are useful in some situations. Watering holes, feeders, salt licks, and the like will attract higher concentrations of individuals and result in more encounters than would normally be the case.

Traps are a necessity where individual identification, sex, age, and the like must be known. These have already been discussed in Appendix D.

Cages to keep a few specimens in captivity for additional observations will be useful in some studies. No wild animals can be kept in captivity without a state permit. In the case of migratory birds, a scientific collecting permit from the U.S. Fish and Wildlife Service, Bureau of Sport Fisheries and Wildlife, must be obtained.

What to observe

An answer to the question of what behavior to observe is everything. Too often the would-be student of behavior attempts to study some complex form of behavior such as courtship and mating, but fails to spend any time observing such common forms of behavior as maintenance activities.

Maintenance behavior

Not only is maintenance behavior important to the animal, but certain activities also evolve into display components, and thus are essential to the understanding of the evolution of display. Maintenance behavior includes such activities as stretching movements; preening in birds and grooming in mammals; dusting and wallowing; bathing; shaking, rubbing, and scratching; sunbathing; sleeping positions; locomotion; drinking; feeding.

Display

Display, which plays such a significant role in the life of an animal, must be observed and analyzed both for cause and for function.

663

Cause involves internal and external stimuli leading to behavior. It can be assessed in three ways (see Tinbergen, 1960).

1. The form of the movement often suggests which tendencies, attack or escape, are involved.

2. Alternate shifting in behavior patterns between the individual initiating the behavior (actor) and the individual responding to the behavior (reactor) in relation to the particular display studied offers clues.

3. A comparison of situations which evoke pure attack and escape with those evoking agonistic displays. Territorial disputes are examples.

Function can be assessed by observing the reaction of the recipient of the display. Basically, displays involved in agonistic situations and pair formation can be put into two groups: spacing out, or distance-increasing, displays and distance-reducing displays. The latter are important in promoting social bonds between members of a pair, between young and parent, etc.

Song and voice

These are displays; and what has been said above is applicable here. Record and analyze the songs, if possible, for they are important isolating mechanisms. Record in notes the situation under which the songs and calls are given, the reaction of other individuals, where in relationship to aspects of home range or territory the songs are given, etc.

Interspecific contacts

Involved here are the reactions of an animal to predators and nonpredators.

Recording observations

For ease in note taking, some means of rapid recording is necessary.

Codes

Codified descriptions greatly facilitate the rapid recording of long, complicated behavioral sequences. For example, TS–2 could mean a tail spread of medium intensity on a scale of 1–3. The key to the code should be kept in the notebook and perhaps somewhere else in safe keeping. Without them, the notes would be meaningless.

Checklist

These greatly speed the collection of certain types of data. Before such a list can be compiled, extensive observations comprehensive enough to include frequent variants and exceptions must be made.

Time scores

Time scores involve the determination of what behavior patterns alternate in quick succession with the display studied. This is difficult because of the rapid shift from actor to reactor (see Table E-1). It is imperative to record the preceding and following displays of all animals involved. Models or mounted specimens are useful for a constant stimulus. This method gives quantified information on the relative strengths of attack and escape tendencies involved by observing the proportions of attacks and withdrawals associated with each display.

Relative frequency

Information on relative frequency is useful for studies of changes in behavior during the breeding season and of feeding, bedding, comfort movements, and so on. The number of times certain types of behavior occur is recorded and the frequency of each is compared. Information on relative frequency becomes difficult when a common behavior is being compared to a rarer one, because of the number of observations entailed. Certain patterns may be so rare that it is impractical to determine their relative frequency. In fact it is dangerous to say with certainty that a certain behavior pattern is lacking in a species.

TABLE E-1. An Analysis of the Tail-spread Behavior in the American Redstart

ACTS PRECEDING	NUMBER OF OBSERVATIONS
Fight	15
Feeding	14
Chip	13
Chased other	7
Was chased	5
Circling	3
Titi (voice)	2
Pivots	2
Muted Song	2
ACTS FOLLOWING	
(by the displaying bird)	
Approaches other bird	26
Flees	8
Song	8
Chip	7
Fight	5
Muted Song	2
Pivots	2
Titi	1
Head forward	1

From Ficken, 1962, *Auk,* **79:**607–632.

Base line

This is the description and quantification of behavior under one set of conditions for later comparisons under different conditions. Examples are song rates of males when they first arrive on a territory, attentiveness of females under optimal weather conditions, frequency with which one member of a pair or group approaches or joins another when there is no apparent "communication" between them.

Describing behavioral sequences and movements

Since behavior studies (as well as many others) are characterized by inaccuracy of description, the following guide describes some terms and descriptions used in ethology.

Bout

This refers to a period during which certain behavior occurs. It is preceded and followed by periods of other behavior.

Act

A set of observable activities in different effector muscles regularly observed in combination with and recognizably different from other such acts observed in the same species.

Component

A movement or position of a body part that is the result of one or more acts. Example: a head-forward display may include the components of gaping the bill and raising the folded wing to the horizontal. These components are made up of the acts of opening and closing the bill and raising and lowering the wing.

Normal resting position

The characteristic posture, to which all others can be compared. It should be determined when the animal is inactive, undisturbed, and reasonably alert.

Movements of the head

These are best described in birds by the angle of the bill in relation to the longitudinal plane of the body. In mammals this should be described by the position of the head in relation to the neck and to the ground. The angle of orientation of the head (as well as other body parts) to another interacting individual should always be noted.

Movements of the neck

The movements of the neck (extension and withdrawal) are difficult to see in short-necked birds. In long-necked species and in mammals, a description of neck movements, including curvature and angle, are possible.

Movements of the body

These should be related to the horizontal.

Movement of contour feathers

These involve changes in the erectness of contour features. There are four general types.

1. Sleeked. The feathers are full, depressed against the body, giving it a slim appearance.
2. Relaxed. The feathers are either depressed or erected. The body shape is intermediate between slim and rounded. Typical relaxed state of bird.
3. Fluffed. The feathers are erected, but only partially, giving the body a very rounded appearance, with a smooth, unbroken outline.
4. Ruffled. The feathers are fully erected and the body, although rounded, has a very ragged appearance, since the edges of the feathers are not touching.

NOTE: Certain body feathers may be specialized for erection during display: ruffs, beards, throat plumes, crests, rump patches, and so on. These should be described individually, noting the angle of the feathers in relation to the main axis of the head or body, as well as to the form or speed of movement.

Movements of the wing

These are very difficult to describe. Functional anatomical descriptions are best for most wing movement: (a) the maximum and minimum angles that the wing is raised and lowered; (b) the degree of flex on or extension of the humerus, forearm, and hand; (c) the angle of the wing surface (rotation of the humerus).

Movements of the tail

Vertical movements can be classified as:

1. Up-down (U-D). Upstroke followed by equal downstroke.
2. Up-down-up (U-D-U). Small upstroke, larger downstroke, then a second upstroke, returning tail to position between flicks.
3. Down-up (D-U). Down stroke followed by equal upstroke.
4. Wagtail (W). A continuous series of up and down strokes with no pauses.
5. Spread. Tail held in spread position.
6. Fan. Tail continuously opened and closed.
7. Drooped. Tail held below the horizontal.
8. Cocked. Tail held above the horizontal or rotated from horizontal plane.

Position of the ears of mammals

1. Alert. Ears held erect and forward.
2. Back. Ears are laid back tightly against head and neck. Common in both submissive and threat situations.
3. Down. Ears at right angles to sides of head, slightly drooped, often with insides directed forward.

New techniques

Any investigator interested in answering behavorial unknowns should be an innovator and not afraid to experiment with new techiniques. The field is wide open. In the study of the vocalizations of birds and insects, recordings of resident animals can be made, and when a known individual has been studied and recorded, it should be collected and its vocal apparatus preserved. Records of vocalizations and field observations (preferably made with a cheap, portable dictaphone) and the preserved animal should be regarded as one unit and kept in one place, especially in a museum or educational institution that loans such material out to interested scientists.

An example of another new technique is freeze drying, now on demonstration at the United States National Museum. Basically, this technique involves careful drying by freezing. It results in an almost lifelike specimen, with excellent color retention, except in the case of fish. Such specimens are a great improvement over stuffed models, when used to determine aggressive and sexual reaction of an animal to the presence of another of its own kind. To get around the abnormal reaction of an animal to a model, live animals, in the case of birds, albino canaries, or zebra finches, can be dyed with certain "releasers" and tethered or caged in the territory of an appropriate animal.

REFERENCES

Borrer, D. J.
1960 The analysis of animal sounds, in W. E. Lanyon, and W. N. Tavolga (eds.), Animal sounds and communication, *AIBS Publ. no. 7.* Washington, D.C., pp. 26–36.

Ficken, Millicent S.
1962 Agonistic behavior and territory in the American redstart, *Auk,* **79**:607–632.

Kellogg, P. P.
1960 Consideration and techniques in recording sound for bio-acoustics studies, in Animal sounds and communications (see Borrer above).

Tinbergen, N.
1960 Comparative studies of the behavior of gulls (Laridae): a progress report, *Behavior,* **15**:1–70.

For other references applicable here, see the main bibliography.

Index

Page numbers in italics indicate that the word or concept is initially defined or more fully explained at that place.

Abiotic component of ecosystem, *13*

Abundance, *16*
  in vegetational analysis, 618, 619

Acclimatization, 71–73

Acorn, heterotrophic succession in, 141–142

Acquired characters, 438–439

Active surface, 88, 89

Adaptative radiation, 467–470

Adrenal gland, 377, 378, 379

Agamospecies, *454*

Age pyramids, *see* Pyramids

Age ratio, 351–354
  estimation of mortality by, 658–659

Aggregations, 384–385, 524–525

Aging techniques, 640–646

Agnostic behavior, *513–519*
  in courtship display, 528, 529
  display in, 514–516
  expression of, 519–526
  as source of courtship display, 532, 534

  See also Behavior, Territory, Social Dominance

Alarm substances in fish, 509

Algae, sampling of, 625–627
  mutualism with hydra, 398

Alleles, *434*

Allopatry, *451*, 457

Alluvium, *244*

Alpha radiation, *see* Ionizing radiation

Alpine tundra, animal life of, 327–328
  suggested field activities, 328–330
  vegetation of, 319–321, 322–324, 325
  See also Tundra

Alpine zone, 79, 81

Altricial, *504*, 505, 540–541

Aluminum compounds in soil, 244, 250, 251

Amensalism, 398–399

Amphibians, of bogs, 186
  clinal variation in, 442–443
  courtship behavior in, 535, 536

  of deserts, 297
  isolating mechanisms in, 458, 535, 536
  marking for identification, 638
  migration in, 393–394
  moisture problems of, 77
  pesticides, effect of on, 367
  of ponds, 164, 178, 179
  solicitation display in, 535
  subspeciation in, 455
  voice of, in mating activities, 535–536

Anadromous, *391*

Angle gauge, *615*

Animals, collecting and trapping, 636–637

Annual rhythms, *see* Photoperiodicity

Antibiotics, *399*

Anting, *496–497*

Appeasement display, 516–518

Appetitive behavior, *480*, 500

Aquatic habitats, 11–12, 162–242
  determination of current,

Aquatic habitats (*Continued*) 600–601; of light, 601–602; of oxygen, 597–598; of temperature, 602–603
  estimation of primary production, 44–47, 631–633
  suggested readings, 575–576
Aquatic organisms, collecting and trapping, 637
Arctic tundra, animal life of, 326–327
  vegetation of, 319–322
      See also Tundra
Area, determination of from map, 608
Aristotle, 474
Arroyos, *293*
Aspergillosis, 404
Assimilation, *35*, *37*, *38*, *39*
      See also Energy Flow
Atmometer, *603*
Attack and escape, *see* Agonistic behavior
Audubon, 5
Aufwuchs, *174*, 195, 196
Autecology, 5
Autotrophic, *13*, *44*, 45
Azimuth, 110

Bacteria, anaerobic, 173
  in biogeochemical cycles, 50, 56
  cause of disease, 403–404
  in ecosystem, *13*, 32–33
  nitrifying, 50, 247
  nitrogen-fixing, 50, 62
  in sandy beaches, 237
  in soil, 247, 266, 267, 268
  in stomach of ruminents, 31
  in tidal marshes, 217
  in water, 173, 204, 217, 237
Bailey, V., 405
Bajadas, *293*
Batesian mimicry, 445–446
Bauhin, Kaspar, 474
Beagle, Voyage of, 427–428
Behavior, *6*, 485–543
  aggressive behavior, expression of, 519–526
  agonistic, 513–526
  appeasement display, 516–518
  basic considerations of, 485–493
  communal courtship and harems, 537–538
  conflict, expression of, 490–491
  cooperative social groups, 384–385, 524–525
  courtship and reproductive, 526–538

distraction display, 509–510
  egocentric, 494–511
  enemy recognition, 505–506
  escape and defense, 505–511
  feeding, 500–505
  food storage, 117–118
  habitat selection, 497–500
  hierarchial, 373–374, 521–524
  instinct *vs.* learning, 491
  instinctive, 487–491
    as isolating mechanism, 459
    maintenance, 494–497
    parental, 538–543
    reaction-chain, 488–489
    reaction to enemies, 506–511
    regulation of population by, 372–374, 378–379
    shelter seeking, 497–500
    social, 372–377, 513–543
    social aggregations, 384–385, 524–525
    social dominance, 373–374, 521–524
    social dominance and leadership, 525
    sound and scent, 518–519
    source of courtship display, 530–534
    study of, 662–668
    suggested readings on, 581–582
    territorial, 372–375, 519–521
    threat to enemy, 510–511
    voice, role in courtship, 535–537
      See also Behavior, Feeding.
Benthic zone, *169*, 173–174
Benthos, *169*, 173–174
Berlese, Antonio, 269
Berlese funnel, 273
Beta radiation, *see* Ionizing radiation
Bibliographies, general, 590
Bill-raising, 514, 528
Biogeochemical cycles, 48–59
Biogeographical regions, 334–336
Biological clocks, *see* Circadian Rhythms, Periodicity
Biomass, *13*
  periphyton, determination of, 627
  pyramid of, 40
  in relation to numbers and energy flow, 40
Biomes, *13*, 24, 331–333
Biotic potential, *see* Growth curve, Natality, Rate of Increase
Biotic provinces, 339

Birds, acclimatization in, 71–73
  aging of, 641
  agonistic display in, 514–516
  anting in, 496–497
  appeasement display in, 516–518
  attack of enemy in, 511
  banding, 638
  of bogs, 186
  call-count estimation of population, 655–666
  celestial orientation in, 109–110, 392–393
  circadian rhythm in, 103, 106
  clinal variation in, 442, 443
  communal courtship in, 537–538
  courtship and reproductive behavior in, 526–538
  of desert, 297
  direction-finding in, 392–393
  dispersal in, 386–388
  distraction displays in, 509–510
  enemy recognition in, 505–506
  escape and defense behavior in, 505–511
  feeding behavior in, 500, 502–503
  of forest, 311–314
  of grassland, 279, 284–286
  guidance of young in, 542–543
  habitat selection, 497–500
  home range in, 375–377
  hybridization in, 460, 464, 530
  imprinting in, 491–493
  instinctive behavior in, 487–491
  isolating mechanisms in, 458–459
  leadership in, 525–526
  learning in, 491
  light-sensitive period, 120–122
  of mangrove swamps, 220
  mark-recapture of, 342, 651–652
  of marshes, 191
  maturity at hatching, 540–541
  migration of, 389–393; stimulus for, 391
  moisture influence on population, 365
  mortality, 350, 360, 362, 364, 365, 367
  natality in, 346

Birds   (*Continued*)
  parasitism in, 400
  parental behavior in, 538–540, 542
  parental care in, 504–505
  pesticides, effect of on, 366–367
  photoperiodism in, 114–115, 117, 120–121
  polymorphism in, 441
  population growth in, 360
  protective coloration in, 444, 445
  radiation, effect of ionizing on, 87
  reaction to enemy, 505, 509–511
  reciprocal feeding in, 533
  sex determination in, 647
  of shrubland, 290
  social dominance in, 521–524
  social parasitism in, 401–402
  solicitation display in, 532–533, 534–535
  song and calls, 518, 535–536
  strip census method of estimating population, 651
  sunbathing in, 496
  survival in, 351
  of swamps, 192
  symbolic nest building in, 533
  territory in, 372–373, 519–520
  torpidity in, 297
  trapping, 637
  of tropical rain forest, 314
  of tundra, 326, 327
  as vectors of disease, 404
Bitterlich, 615
Body size, relation to energy flow, 39
Bogs, 182–186, 188
Bog-filling, 152, 153
Bog, pollen profile, 153, 154
Boron, 64
Botero, Giovanni, 355–356
Bottom types, streams, 198, 201
  and life in streams, 201
Botulism, 399, 404
Braun-Blanquet, 5
Brewster, 5
Buffer species, 413
Buffon, 356
Bunning model, 118–123
Burrows, John, 4
Bursa of Fabricus, 641
Butterflies, marking of, 638
  chain reaction behavior in, 488–489
  mimicry in, 445, 446
  polymorphism in, 439

Calcification, 250
Calcium, 63, 65
  and aquatic invertebrates, 63
  in relation to strontium, 58
  in soil, 244, 245, 250, 254
  in streams, 194
Caliche, 251
Call counts, 655–666
Calorie, 35
de Candolle, Alfonse, 479
Cannibalism, 31, 416–417
Carbon, 49–50, 245
Carbon cycle, 49–50
Carbon, radioactive, estimation of production by, 46, 47, 631–632
Carbon dioxide, 46, 62, 177
  assimilation as a measure of primary production, 46, 632
  in ecosystem, 62
  and photosynthetic rate, 62
  in soil atmosphere, determination of, 604–605
  in streams, 194–195
  in water, determination of, 598–599
Carbonates, 62, 244, 245, 250, 254
Care of young, 540–543
Carnivores, 31
Carrying capacity, 355
Catadromous, 391
Catena, 256
Census, 342
  removal, 652
  strip, 651
  true, 649–650
Cesalapini, 474
Cesium, radioactive, use in tracing nutrient cycles, 55
Chain-reaction behavior, 488–489, 500–501
Chaparral, 290–291, 333
Characteristic species, 24
Chemical light meter, 602
Chlorides, determination of, 599
Chlorine, 61, 74
      See also Salinity
Chlorophyll, 28
  estimating primary production by, 46, 632–633
Circadian rhythms, 99–110
  in celestial orientation, 109–110
  in cell division, 101
  in constant darkness, 103; flying squirrel, 101, 105; Gonyaulax, 103
  entrainment to light – dark cycles, 105–106; chaffinch, 106; flying squirrel, 105;

Gonyaulax, 105
  entrainment to natural light –dark cycle, 108–109
  entrainment to temperature cycle, 108
  in flying squirrel, 100–101, 105
  function as biological clock, 109
  in *Gonyaulax polyedra*, 102–103, 104–105
  in leaf movements of plants, 99, 102
  light sensitivity in birds, 120–121
  in lizard, 108
  in luminescence, 101
  in man, 125
  in opening of flower, 101–102
  in petal movements, 99, 101–102
  phase drift, in flying squirrel, 103; in flying squirrel, 100, 105–106; in Gonyaulax, 101–103
  phase shift, in Drosophila, 103–104; in flying squirrel, 105; in Gonyaulax, 103–104
  in photosynthesis, 101
  in time memory, 109–110
  Zeitgeber (time cues), 103
Classification, of lakes, productivity, 177
  of maturity in birds, 540–541
  thermal, 166
Classification of organisms, 474–481
  concepts of, 478–481
  hierarchial, 476–477
Clay, 245, 250, 251, 253, 254
Clearcutting of forests, 144
Clements, Frederick, 5, 129, 140, 333
Climate, 66–67, 74–77, 81–82
  of chaparral, 290
  of coast coniferous forest, 303
  of desert, 291–292, 293
  in forest, 307–311
  and forest distribution, 303
  of grassland, 280, 281, 282, 283
  near ground, 87, 88, 89, 90–91, 310
  in rain forest, 303
  of savanna, 314
  of tundra, 318–320; alpine, 322, 323, 324, 325; arctic, 322
Climatograph, 79–80

Climax, concept of, 140–141
economic, *150*
Cline, *442–444*
in amphibians, 442–443, 452
in birds, 443
in plants, 443
Clock, biological, *109*
in navigation of birds and
fish, 392
See also Circadian rhythms
thms
Cobalt, *64*
Codes, nomenclatural, *478–480*
Coloration, animals of arctic,
326
concealing, 444
countershading, 444
deflective, 445
false warning, 445–446
as isolating mechanism, 459
photoperiodic control of, 123
protective, 444–446
Comfort movements, 495
Commensalism, 285, 398
Community, *11–25*
aquatic, described, 11–12
barnacle-blue mussel, 23, 24
characteristic species of, 25
classification of, 23–25
composition, 16–17
concept of, *19*
distribution, of, 331–339
dominance, *14–15*
forest, described, 12
metabolism, 42–45
naming of, *22–25*
oyster bed, 214–215
of past, *151–155*
plant, study of, 610–635
species diversity in, 15
stratification, *18–19;* in forest,
305–313; in grassland,
277–279; in lakes, 163–
165, 171, 172, 173
suggested readings, 573
type, 23
See also Biomes, Habitats
tats
Compass, description and use,
607
Compass, sun, 392
Compensation depth, *169*
determination of, 601
Compensation intensity, 84
Compensatory predation, *411–
415*
Competition, and adaptive radiation, 468–470
in barnacles, 422
in birds, 419–422
in cladocerans, 419
and coexistence, 424

contest type, 370
in fish, 422
in flour beetles, 418–419
for food, 418–420
interspecific, 418–424
intraspecific, 368–372, 406
and natural selection, 423
and niches, 419–420, 422
in paramecium, 418
in plants, 282–283, 423
results of, 370, 422–423
scramble type, 370
space, 421–422
Competitive exclusion principle,
417
Comstock, A., 4
Condensation, 75, 88, 96, 159
Coniferous forest, biome, *331*
compared with deciduous,
305–309
life in, 130, 311–313
Conflict behavior, 490–491
Constancy, 23
determination of, 624
Consumer organisms, 30–33
and ecological pyramids, 40
efficiency of, 38–39
in lakes, 170
in soil, 264–269
in streams, 194, 195
in tidal marshes, 217
Consumer production, 36–39
measurement of, 47–48
Consummatory act, *490, 500*
Contagious distribution, 382,
383
Continuum, *18,* 24
in birds, 18
in forest trees, 17
in grassland, 280
Continuum index, 622
Convergence, 470
Copper, 64
Coral reef, 15
Correns, 430
Courtship behavior, 384, 526–
538
communal, 384, 537–538
voice in, 535–537
See also Behavior, Display, Song
play, Song
Courtship display, hybridization in, 530
tion in, 530
Cover, vegetation, *344–345*
measurement of, 618–619
Cover types, 497
Cowles, 5, 129
Critical temperature, 72
influence on distribution, 73
Crossdating, in dendrochronology, *628*
logy, *628*
Cryoplanation, *319*

Cultivation, and succession,
146–147
Currents, convection, 76
eddy, 169, 171
of estuaries, 210–212; determination of, 600–601
mination of, 600–601
ocean and climate, 292
relation to aquatic life, 198
in streams, 193–194; determination of, 600–601
nation of, 600–601
and stream invertebrates, 201
Cycle, annual in white-tailed
deer, 119
carbon, *49–50*
and intraspecific competition,
370–371
lunar and semilunar, reproductive, 113–114
ductive, 113–114
nitrogen, *50*
nutrient, *53–57*
oxygen, *50–51*
phosphorus, 56–57
population, 379–382
in predator-prey systems, 405,
406
radioactive materials in ecosystem, 57–58
system, 57–58
reproductive in birds, 117
water, *52–53*
Cyclic replacement, *139–140*

Darwin, Charles, 6, 247, 418,
419, 427–430, 439, 449,
450, 486
theory of evolution, 430
DDT and DDD, ecology of,
366–367
and natural selection in flies,
436–437
Decomposers, 32, 247
Decomposition, aerobic, 204
anaerobic, 172, 173, 204,
217, 235
in lakes, 173
in tidal marshes, 217
Defense behavior, 505–511
Delta, *193*
Deme, *431–432*
intergroup selection, 466–
467
Dendrochronology, 627–629
Density, population, 341–345
crude, 342
determination of, 342–345
ecological, 342
and population growth, 360
and predation and parasitism,
407–411
pressure in relation to genetic
feedback, 416
Density-dependent population
regulation, 367–379

Density-independent population regulation, 363–367
Derham, William, 356
Deserts, 291–300
    animal life of, 294, 297–298
    annuals, 294
    climate of, 291–292
    cool, 295
    hot, 295–297
    and mountains, role of in formation of desert, 292
    shrubs, 293
    topography of, 293
    world distribution of, 292
Detritus feeders in food chain, 33
Dew, 88
Dewpoint, 88
Diapause, 67, 78
    photoperiod control of, 116, 120
Dice, L. C., 339
Digestion, cellulose, by ruminents, 31
    by snails and slugs, 266
Dimictic lakes, 166
Disease, 402–404
    bacterial, 404
    fungal, 404
    and population density, 403
    and population regulation, 377–378, 415–416
    virus, 404
Dispersal, population, 385–394
    and population density, 387
    and rate of increase, 387
    by wind, 82
Dispersion, and predator-prey systems, 406–407
Displacement activity, 490, 513
    and courtship, 533–534
    in incubation, 540
    ritualization, 533–534
    and thwarting sexual impulses, 534
Display, courtship, 526–528
    distraction, 509–510
    precopulatory, 532–533
Distance, measurement of by pacing, 607
Distribution, of communities, 331–339
    continuum, 17, 18
    discontinuous, 18
    of plankton in lakes, 171–172
    of populations, 382–385
    and temperature, 73–74
Divergence, 428
Diversity of species, see Species diversity
DNA, 5, 432, 434

Dominance, in community, 14–15, 23
Dominants, animals as, 15
    plants as, 14–15, 17
Dormancy, 78
        See also Hibernation
Dropping boards, 657
Drought, grassland 282–283
Drought evaders, 293–297
Drought resistors, 293
Dyed bait, 648
Dystrophic, 177, 183
        See also Bogs

Earth stripes, 319
Echolocation, in bats, 503–504
    in moths, 509
Ecoclimatology, 6
Ecological efficiencies, 38–39, 43
Ecological equivalents, 14
Ecological importance of eddy currents, 171
Ecological isolating mechanisms, 458–459
Ecological niche, 13, 468
    and species diversity, 470–472
Ecological overlap, 423
Ecological pyramids, 40–41
Ecology, 4
    and behavior, 485–487
    divisions of, 5–6
    and man's future, 7–8
    and molecular biology compared, 4, 7–8
    population, 341–425
    principles of, summarized, 6–7
Economic climax, 150
Ecosystem, 11–25
    abiotic component of, 13
    biotic component of, 13
    cycling of materials, 48–59
    flow of energy, 24–48
    functional divisions of, 13
    gaseous cycles in, 49–53
    nutrient cycles in, 53–57
    nutrients in, 61–66
    structural divisions of, 13
Ecotone, 19, 333
Ecotype, 15
Egg parasitism, see Social parasitism
Elton, Charles, 5, 31
Emigration, 378, 385–389
Encephalitis, 404
Endocrines and population regulation, 377–378
Endogenous rhythm, see Circadian rhythms
Energy, 27–49

    assimilation by consumers, 38–39; determination of, 48
    budget, in animal population, 38–39; in community, 35, 44; in white-tailed deer, 38
    degradation through food chain, 43–44
    in ecosystem, 27–48
    flow of, 27–48; in intertidal salt marsh, 33, 45; through a natural food chain, 42–44; in Scots pine plantation, 33; in soil community, 264; and succession, 129–130
    laws of thermodynamics, 27–28
    pyramids, of, 40–41
    solar, as basic source of, 28–29
    source, sandy beach, 237; streams, 195
    and standing crop, 38–39
Engler, 5
Environmental biology, see Ecology
Environmental discontinuity, 407
        See also Predator-prey systems
Environmental influences, 60–97
    elements and nutrients, 61–66
    interaction of temperature and moisture, 79–81
    light, 82, 84
    microclimates, 87–97
    moisture, 74–78
    radiation, 84–87
    temperature, 67–74
    wind, 81–82, 90, 92, 93
Environmental measurements, 597–609
    references to, 609
Environmental stratification, see Stratification, Forest, Grassland, Habitats, Temperature, Light, etc.
Epilimnion, 163, 167
Epiphyseal cartilage, 641
Equations, exponential growth, 358
    life, 361
    logistic, 359–360
    photosynthesis, 28
    rate of increase, 357
Erosion, 146–149
Estivation, 67, 297
Estuary, 210–215

Estuary   (*Continued*)
  biological importance of, 214
  circulation of nutrients in,
    212
  currents of, 210–212; deter-
    mination of, 600–601
  flushing time, 213
  life in, 213
  salinity of, 211–212
  suggested field activities, 220
  water of, 210–212
Ethology, *see* Behavior
Eutrophic lake, *177*
Evapotranspiration, 52
Evaporation, 52, 75, 90, 159,
    281
  in desert, 293
  determination of natural rate
    of, 603–604
  difference between north and
    south facing slopes, 91
Evolution, convergent, 470
  and species diversity, 470–
    472
Evolution, Darwin's theory of,
    430
Evolutionary studies, 5, 6
Exclusive species, 24
Exemplary display, *514*
Exploitation, *417–418*
  effect on sex ratio, 354

Fallout, problems of, 58
Family, *476–477*
Fast streams, *see* Streams, fast
Feeding behavior, *500–505*
  in canids, 504
  in herons, 502
  in hunting wasps, 501–502
Feeding of young, 542–543
Fell fields, 318, 323
Fidelity, 23, 24, 624
Fields, old, distribution of earth-
    worms in, 271
  succession in, 87, 127, 128,
    136–137, 139, 140
Field capacity, 76
Filter feeders, 57
Fire, *142–143*
  and arid vegetation, 292
  and chaparral, 291
  in forests, 143–144
  in grassland, 143, 278, 279,
    281, 285
  and prairie chickens, 285
  and southern pines, 302
  and succession, 142–143
  tool in land management,
    143
  and trees, effect of intensity
    on, 142, 143
Fish, aging, 640–641

agonostic display in, 514
alarm substances, *509*
annual rhythms in, 114
celestial orientation in, 110
competition in, 422
  of estuary, 213–214
  of lakes and ponds, 172, 177
lunar reproductive cycles in,
    113
mark-recapture method of pop-
    ulation estimation, 651–652
marking, 638
migration in, 391
natality in, 346
parental behavior in, 538,
    539
and pesticides, 365, 366
reaction to enemies, 509
schooling in, 386
social dominance in, 422
sound production in, 536
territory, 372, 373, 520
Flood plain, *193*
Flyways, *391*
    See also Migration
Food, competition for, 418–420
  consumption, estimation of in
    animals, 48
  habits, influenced by photo-
    periodism, 123, 124
  niche, 312, 420
  preference, by African graz-
    ing ungulates, 14; by deer,
    65, 146; by earthworms,
    265; by millipedes, 266
Food, web, *29*, 30
Food chain, 29
  major, 33
  parasitic, 33
  strontium in, 58
  supplementary, 33
Food-seeking behavior, 500–505
Forest, alpine, 303
  animal life in, 311–313
  aspen parkland, 303
  beech-sugar maple, 302
  biomes, 333
  central hardwood, 302
  climate in, 307–310
  community described, 12
  coniferous, 23, 302, 303, 331
  coniferous and deciduous com-
    pared, 306, 307, 312, 313
  cover estimation in, 618, 619
  deciduous, 23, 301, 331
  disease in, 403
  environmental stratification in,
    305–311
  even aged, 305
  frost pockets in clearings, 96–
    97

grazing and browsing in,
    145–146
habitat differences in, 312–
    313
hardwood, 17, 24
humidity and moisture in,
    309
life form spectra, 22
life in the soil, 261–271
and microclimate, 88
mixed mesophytic, 302
net production, 35
northern hardwood, 301
nutrient cycle in, 53–56
oak-chestnut, 302
oak-hickory, 24
organic horizon of forest
    floor, 246–248
precipitation in, 309
primary production estima-
    tion, 630
radiation effects on, 85–87
soil development in, 250–251
southern pine, 302
stratification, *see* Environ-
    mental stratification, above
stratification of life, 311–315
suggested field activities,
    316–317
suggested readings in, 578
temperature stratification in,
    310
tropical deciduous, 333
tropical rain, 303, 313, 333;
    compared to lake, 314
water table relationships,
    144–145
wind velocity in, 92, 93,
    310–311
Fossils, 154
Frequency, 23
  determination of in phyto-
    plankton, 625
  of recapture in determination
    of home range, 648
  relative, in behavior study,
    664
Frequency distribution, 432,
    433
Frogs, distribution influenced
    by temperature, 73
Frost boils, *319*
Frost hummocks, *319, 320*
Frost molding tundra landscape,
    318–319
Frost pockets, *96–97*
Fungi, cause of disease, 403–
    404
  decomposition of forest litter,
    247, 248, 266
  food source for soil fauna,
    266–267

Fungi   (*Continued*)
  mutualism with algae, 397–398
  mycorrhizal, 398
  as parasite, 401
  population control of by soil arthropods, 267
  predacious, 368
  secretion of antibiotics by, 399

Gause, 405
Gauses principle, *see* Competitive exclusion principle
Gene, 43
  frequencies, 434–435
  mutation, 435, 439
  recombination of, 434
Genetic adjustment to parasite-host systems, 415–416
Genetic assimilation, 438–439
Genetic drift, 438
Genetic fixation, 438
Genetic feedback, integration of predator-prey systems, 415–416
  in population regulation, 378–379
Genetic variation, 432–438
  and Hardy-Weinberg Law, 435
  source of, 435, 436
Genus, 476–477
Geographical isolation, 454–456
  breakdown of, 456
Geographical races, 452–453
Geographical speciation, *see* Speciation
Geographical variation, 452–453
  and environmental forces, 542
  polymorphism, 439
Glacial till, succession on, 134–136
Glaciation and past communities, 154
Gleization, *251*
Gradient, *see* Cline, Continuum, Stratification
Grass, bunch, 276
  sod, 276
Grasslands, *275–287*, 333
  animal life in, 283–287
  continuum in, 280
  and drought, 282–283
  estimation of cover, 619
  estimation of primary production, 630
  and fire, 278, 279, 281, 285
  and grazing, 145, 282

and harvester ant, 284
herb growth in, 276
humus in soil, 250
legumes in, 276
litter accumulation in, 278, 279
and mammals, 283–285
and mulch, 278–279
native, 275, 279–283
and prairie dogs, 284–285
production in, 280
root penetration in, 277–278
seral, 275–276, 279
soil development in, 248–250
stratification in, 277–278
succession in, 145, 279, 280, 282, 283
suggested field activities, 287
suggested readings in, 577
types of, desert, 281; eastern, 279; plains, short grass, 281; prairie, mixed, 280–281; prairie, tall, 279–280
Gravel, 253
Gray, 5
Grazing and browsing, 145–146
  on grasslands, 282
Grazing food chain, 33
Grooming activity, 495
Growth curve, 356, 358–360
Growth substances, 385
Guidance of young, 542–543
Gully erosion, *147*

Habitat, 13
  bog, 182–186
  chaparral, 290–291
  desert, 291–298
  estuary, 210–215
  flowing water, 192–206; fast streams, 195–200; slow stream and river, 200–203
  forest, 301–314
  grassland, 275–287
  lakes and ponds, 163–181
  mangrove swamp, 219–220
  marsh, 186–190
  moors, 186
  savanna, 314–315
  seashore, 221–239; loose rocks and boulders, 233–234; rocky shore, 223–232; sandy shore, 235–239; tidal pool, 232–233
  shrubland, 289–290
  soil, 243, 271
  swamp, 190–191
  temporary pond, 177–179
  tidal marsh, 215–219
  tundra, 318–328
Habitat selection, *497–500*
  imprinting in, 498–499

Hardness, total, determination of in water, 598–599
Harems, 537–538
Harvest method, measuring primary production, 46–47, 630–631
Herbivores, *31*, 37, 42, 43
  and cellulose diet, 31, 266
  as energy source for carnivores, 31
Herbivore–plant systems, 406, 407, 415–416
Heterotrophic, *13*
Heterozygous, *434*
Hibernation, 67–70
  in black bear, 70
  in ground squirrel, 68–69
  in skunk, 70
Hierarchy, of behavior, 521–524
  classification, 476–477
Highgrading in forest, *144*
Holotype, 481
Home range, 375–377, 380
  calculation of, 648
  center of activity, 648
  determination of by radio tracking, 649
  dyed bait used to determine, 648
Homeothermal, 66
Homeotherms, acclimatization in, 71–73
Homonomy, 480
Homozygous, *434*
Hooker, J. D., 429
Hormones and agonistic behavior, 519
  and social dominance, 523
Host, *see* Parasites
Humidity, 281
  determination of, 603–604
  in forest, 304, 309
  in grasslands, 281
  relative, 75, 79, 603; determination of, 603; above ground, 90; north and south slopes compared, 94
  See also Climate
Humus, development of on forest floor, 246–248
  formation of, 244
  and fungi, 247
  water retention capacity of, 77
Hybridization, 454, 460–464
  and behavior, 530
  and breakdown of isolating mechanisms, 460-464
  in grosbeaks, 462–464
  in plants, 454, 460, 464
  in prairie chicken, 460, 461, 530, 531

Hybridization   (*Continued*)
  selection against, 456
  as selective force, 460–461
  in sharp-tailed grouse, 460,
    461, 530, 531
  in warblers, 460
Hybrids, selected against, 530
  selective disadvantage of, 459
Hybrid swarms, 460
Hydrogen sulphide, in behthic
    zone, 173
  in bog water, 183
Hygrothermograph, 604
Hypolimnion, *163*, 167, 168,
  169

Identification, aids to, amphib-
    ians and reptiles, 587
  birds, 587–588
  fish, 587
  grass and wildflowers, 585–
    586
  insects, 587
  invertebrates, 586–587
  lower plants, 585
  trees and shrubs, 586
Immigration, 385–389
Importance value, *621*
Imprinting, *491–493*
  and habitat selection, 498–
    499
Increment boring, 627
Incubation behavior, 539–540
Indices, population, 344, *655–*
  657
  call count, 655–666
  dropping board, 657
  pellet count, 656
  roadside counts, 656
Innate behavior, *see* Instinctive
    behavior
Insects, agonistic behavior in,
    518
  circadian rhythms in, 99, 103
  climatic influence on, 356
  competition in, 418–419
  of desert, 248
  diapause in, 116; photo-
    periodic control of, 122
  disruptive selection in, 464
  in fast streams, 198–200
  forest, 311
  grassland, 283–284
  as grazers, 33, 37, 217
  habitat selection in, 498
  industrial melanism in, 439–
    440
  instinctive behavior in, 487–
    491
  isolating mechanisms in, 458–
    459

in lakes, 173, 174
light-sensitive period, 122
migration of, 389
mimicry in, 445–446
moisture effects on, 78
as parasites, 34
parental behavior in, 538
photoperiodism in, 116
in ponds, 178–179
protective coloration in, 444–
  446
radiation effects on, 86
sampling populations of, 650
as scavengers, 34, 141
sibling species, 450
in slow stream and river, 202,
  203
societies in, 384, 524–525
sound in, 518
survival in, 351
time memory in, 109
trapping, 637
of tropical rain forest, 314
as vectors of disease, 404
Instinct *vs.* learning, 491
Instinctive behavior, 487–491
  feeding, 500–503
Insulation in animals, 70–71
Intention movements, 513
Intergroup selection, 466–467
Interstitial fauna of sandy beach,
    239
Invertebrates,   adjustment   to
    winter, 67
  circadian rhythms in, 101
    103, 104, 105, 108
  competition in, 418–419, 422
  distribution   on   north-south
    slope, 96
  dormancy in, 78
  entrainment to tidal rhythms,
    111–113
  of estuary, 213–215
  in fast stream, 198–200
  in forest, 311–314
  of grasslands, 283–284
  in lakes, 170, 173, 174
  lunar and semilunar reproduc-
    tive cycles in, 113–114
  moisture problems of, 77, 78
  and phosphorus cycle, 57
  polymorphism in, 441
  in ponds, 178–179
  predator-prey   systems,   404–
    405
  radiation effects on, 86
  of rocky shore, 223, 225, 227,
    232, 234
  of sandy shore, 236, 237–239
  of slow streams, 202, 203
  of tidal marsh, 217
  of tidal pools, 233

of tropical rain forest, 314
  as vectors of disease, 404
    See also Soil faunal
    community
Ionizing radiation, 84–87
  and invertebrates, 86
  and plant communities, 85–
    87, 151
  types of, 84–85
  and vegetation, 85–87, 151
  and vertebrates, 87
Iron, 64, 250, 251, 254
Irrelevant activity, 490–491
Isolating mechanisms, *456–460*
  behavioral, 459
  ecological, 458–459
  mechanical, 459
  reduction of mating success,
    459
  selective advantages of, 459

Journals, list of, 589–590
Jung, Joachim, 470
"Jungle," 304

Kerner, Anton, 5, 129
Key-industry animals, 31
Krumholtz, 79, 325–326

Lakes and ponds, *162–181*
  classification of, 166
  current in, 167–169
  dystrophic, 177, 183
  life in, 164, 169–177
  mapping of, 180
  origin of, 162
  overturn in, 163–166
  oxbow, 193
  physical   characteristics   of,
    163–169
  production, estimate of, 44–
    47, 631–633
  productivity classes of, 177
  sieches in, 167–169
  stratification in, 163, 166
  suggested field activities, 179–
    181
  thermocline in, 166, 168
  trophic structure, 170
    See also Bogs
Latent heat, *159*
Laterization, *251*
Latosolization, *see* Laterization
Law, Hardy-Weinberg, 435
  Merriams   temperature   con-
    trol, 337
  of the minimum, *60*
  of priority, *480*
  of thermodynamics, 27–28
  of tolerance, 61
Leadership in animals, *525–526*

Learning, *491*
  in food seeking, 503, 505
Lectotype, *481*
Lens weight technique of aging,
  643
Lentic communities, *see* Lakes
  and ponds, Bogs
Leptospirosis, 404
Liebig, Justus von, 60
Life equation, *361–363*
Life expectancy, 347
Life form, classification of, 20
  of plants, 20–21
  spectra, 22
  and radiosensitivity of plants,
  86
Life in the soil, *261–274*
  in relation to soil moisture
  and structure, 263
Life table, 347–349
Life zones, 337–338
Light, 82, 84
  in aquatic habitats, 169; determination in, 601
  influence on plants and animals, 82, 84
  stratification in forest, 307–
  308
  in terrestrial habitats, determination of, 601–602
  and tundra plants, 321, 323
  wave lengths in water, 84
  as **Zeitgeber** in circadian
  rhythms, 103
  and zonation in lakes, 171–
  174
    See also Periodicity and
    Biological clocks
Light and dark bottle method of
  estimating primary production, 44–46, 631
Light-sensitive period, in birds,
  120–122
  in insects, 122
  in mammals, 120
  in plants, 120
Limnetic zone, *169*, 171–172
Lincoln, F. C., 343
Line-intercept, 614
Linnaeus, *see* Linne, Carl von
Linne, Carl von, 448, 475, 478,
  480
Litter, accumulation of in grassland, 278–279
  breakdown by mites and collembola, 267
  and earthworms, 265
  fauna in, 268
  heterotrophic metabolism determination, 287
  injestion by millipedes, 266
  living space in, 263

relationship to animal life in
  grasslands, 285
role in humus formation, 248
in tropical rain forest, 304
Litter feeders, 265–267
Littoral zone, *169*, 174–177
  of rocky shore, 223–229
Live trapping, 655
L'Obell, 470
Loess, 244
Longitudinal succession in
  streams, 201–202
Loop method, vegetation sam-
  pling, 614–615
Lotic communities, *see* Streams,
  Springs
Lotka, 5, 405, 418, 419
Lotka-Volterra model of pred-
  ation, 405
Lumbering and forest succes-
  sion, 143–144
Lunar and semilinar reproduc-
  tive cycles, *113–114*
Lyell, Charles, 429

Macfadyen, A., 5
Macronutrients, 62–63
Magnesium, 64, 244, 250, 254,
  265
"Major life zones," 333
Malthus, Thomas, 5, 6, 355, 428
Mammals, acclimatization in,
  71–73
  aging of, 641
  agonistic display in, 515–516
  appeasement display in, 516–
  518
  and arid regions, 78
  attack of enemy in, 511
  calls in, 507, 508
  cannibalism, 31
  in chaparral, 291–292
  circadian rhythms in, 100–
  101, 105
  coloration in, 123, 326–327,
  444–446
  communal courtship in, 538
  competition in, 420
  courtship and reproductive behavior in, 532
  of desert, 298
  direction finding in, 392
  disease in, 404
  dispersal in, 386–387
  dropping board method of estimating populations, 657
  endocrine balance and populations, 377–378
  food-seeking behavior in,
  503–504
  of forest, 311–314
  of grassland, 279, 283–287

grazing, 31, 282
guidance of young in, 542–
  543
habitat selection in, 497–499
and high altitudes, 328
home range in, 375–377
imprinting in, 491–493
leadership in, 525–526
light-sensitive period in, 120
live-trapping, 655
maintenance behavior in, 495
marking, 639
mark-recapture method of
  population estimation, 342,
  651–652
maturity of young, 541
migration of, 390, 394
moisture, influence on population, 365
natality in, 346
parental behavior in, 539,
  540–543
pellet count method of population estimation, 656
pesticides, effect of on, 366–
  367
photoperiodic control of reproduction, 120
population growth, 360
radiation effect on, 87
reaction to enemies, 506–507,
  510–511
removal method of popula-
  tion estimation, 652
reproduction in, 353–354; influenced by nutrition, 65
as scavengers, 34
sex determination in, 647
sex ratio in, 354–355
of shrubland, 290
social dominance in, 522, 523
sociality in, 524–525
sound and scent in behavior,
  518–519
strip-census of, 651
sunbathing in, 496
survival in, 348, 350–352
territory in, 372–373, 520–
  521
threat of enemy in, 510
trapping, 637, 652, 653, 655
of tropical rain forest, 314
Man, and chaparral, 291
  and desert, 292–293
  and dispersal of plants and
  animals, 389
  and forests, 143, 145
  and grasslands, 279, 285, 286
  and growth of natural populations, 366
  and pollution, 203–205

Man   (*Continued*)
and succession, 142–151
and tidal marshes, 217–218
Mangrove swamps, *219–220*
Maps, 608
Mapping, aerial photographs in, 606
forest floor, 272
lakes, 180
seashore, 240–241
streams, 207
the study area, 606–608
tidal pools, 241–242
Maqui, 290
Mark-recapture method of population estimation, 342, 651–652
Marking animals, 638–640
with radioactive tracers, 640
Marsh, 133, *186–190*, 285
animal life in, 190
classification of, 188–190
depth of, 187
development of, 186
salt, 189
tidal, 189, 215–219
Meadow, alpine, 323
Melanism, industrial, *439–440*
Mendel, Gregor, 6, 427, 450
Metabolic heat loss and large ears of desert animals, 298
Metagea, 334
Metalimnion, *163*
Methods, aging animals, 640–646
analyzing vegetation, 618–624
artificial stream habitat, 209
collecting peat samples, 629
collecting soil samples, 606
collecting water samples, 596
dendrochronology, 627–629
determination of the biomass of periphyton, 627; of carbon dioxide in water, 598–599; of coverage, 343–345; of current, 600–601; of hardness of water, 599; of heterotrophic metabolism in litter, 287; of home range and territory, 648–649; of humidity, 603–604; of light in natural communities, 601–602; of moisture in soil, 604; of organic matter in soil, 605; of oxygen in water, 597–598; of pH, 600; of population density, 342–345, 649–657; of salinity, 599; of soil texture and compo-

sition, 605; of temperature, 602–605
mapping, 606–608
marking animals, 272, 638–640
measuring environmental conditions, 597–609
measuring mortality, 657–659
measuring primary production, 44, 630–634
palynology, 629–630
preserving seashore organisms, 240
sampling drift in streams, 208
sampling earthworm populations, 272–273
sampling periphyton, 626
sampling phytoplankton, 625
sampling stream bottom organisms, 208–209, 626
sampling vegetation, 329, 611–618
sex determination in birds and mammals, 646
studying animal behavior, 662–668
Microclimate, 87–97
as influenced by vegetation, 87–88
of north- and south-facing slopes, 91–96
Microhabitat, *13*
Micronutrients, *63–64*
Migration, *389–394*
celestial orientation in, 110
of soil fauna, 270
stimulus for birds, 391
vertical of plankton, 171
and weather, 389–391
See also Birds, Insects, Mammals
Mimicry in animals, *445–446*
Mineralization in soil, *244*
Moder, *247–248*
Moisture, 74–78
effect of excessive moisture on plants and animals, 78
and germination of desert plants, 294–295
influence on populations, 365–366
interaction with temperature, 79
See also Humidity, Precipitation
Mollusks, as scavengers, 34
Molybdenum, 64
Monoclimax theory, *140*
Monomictic lakes, *166*
Moors, *186*
Mor, *247*
fauna in, 269, 270

Mortality, *347–351*
density-dependent, 370–371
measurement of, 657–659
Motivation, *see* Behavior
Mowing, influence on grasslands, 279
influence on tidal marshes, 217–218
Mulch in grassland, 278–279
Mull, *247*
fauna in, 269, 270
Muller, P. E., 247
Mullerian mimicry, *466*
Muskeg, 139
Mussel, role in phosphorus cycle, 57
Mutation, gene, *435*, 439
See also Gene, Genetic variation
Mutation and agamospecies, 454
Mutualism, *398–399*
Myxomatosis, 415–416

Naming and classifying organisms, 474–481
Natality, *345–347*
maximum, 346
natural selection of, 346
physiological, 346
rate of, 346
realized, 346
Natural history, 4, 5
Natural selection, 14, *427–447*
the basis of, 431–447
and behavior, 486
and competition, 423
and fecundity, 437
and hybridization, 530
an introduction, 427–430
and natality, 346
and nonrandom reproduction, 436–437
and polymorphism, 439–441
and polyploidy, 465–466
and predator-prey, parasite-host and herbivore-plant systems, 415–416
and releasers, 530
and sex ratios, 355
suggested readings in, 580
theory of, 429–430
Navigation in animals, 392–393
Neap tides, 222
Negative estuary, *212*
Nekton, *169*, 172
Neogea, 334
Neotype, *481*
Neutrons, *see* Ionizing radiation
New systematics, 6
Niche, *13*
ecological, *419–468*; and com-

Niche *(Continued)*
petition, 419–422
foraging, of birds in spruce forest, 312
and species diversity, 470–472
Nicholson, A., 405
Nicholson-Bailey model of predation, 405
Nitrogen, 177
accumulation in soil, 134–135
amount in ecosystem, 62, 134, 135, 183, 265
cycle, 50
fixation by bacteria and blue-green algae, 50
Nitrogen-fixing bacteria, 134
Nomenclature, binomial, 475–477
International committee of, 478–479
rules of, 478–479
Notogea, 334
North and south slopes compared, in chaparral, 291
in deciduous forest, 91
Number, pyramid of, 40
Nutrients, and animal life, 64–66
in arctic soils, 322
deficiency symptoms in plants and animals, 63–64
as environmental influence, 61–66
loss of in ecosystem, 56
and production, 66
and reproductive success, 65–66
in streams, 195
transport by current, 193–194
Nutrient cycles, 53–57
through forest soil, 250
in lakes, 172–173
in white oak, 55
Nutrition, and reproductive rates in animals, 65

Ocean currents, *see* Currents
Oligotrophic lakes, 177
Omnivores, 31
place in food chain, 31
Optimum density, 385
Organic matter, accumulation in forest, 250
accumulation in grassland, 248–250
accumulation in succession, 131
in sandy beach, 237
in soil, 244; determination of, 605

Orientation in vertebrates, 392
See also Birds, Fish, Migration
Origin of species, 430
Osmoregulation, 74
Overgrazing, and arid land, 292
and forests, 145–146
and grasslands, 145, 282
Overturn in estuaries, 212
in lakes, 163–164, 167, 172
Oxygen, 62, 177
cycle, 50–51
in lake, 166–167, 172, 173
and productivity measurements, 44–46, 631
in soil atmosphere, determination of, 604–605
stratification, 164–165, 166–167
in streams, 194
in tidal pools, 233
in water, determination of, 597–598
Oyster bed community, 213–215

Pair formation, 532
role of song in, 535–537
Paleoecology, 152
Palynology, 629–630
Pans, salt, 216–217
Parasites, 33
characteristics of, 339
diversity of, 399
as evidence of relationships between organisms, 400
food chains in, 33–34
functional response to host, 407–409
host specificity, 400
life cycle of black grub, 400, 401
numerical response to host, 409–410
Parasitism, 399–402
social, 401
Parasitoid, 33, 405–406
Parental behavior, 542–543
Parental care, 504–505
Parry, Charles, 479
Past communities, 151–152
Pasture as animal habitat, 286
Patterned land forms, 319, 320
Pearl, 5
Peat accumulation in bogs, 185
Peck order, 521–524
Pedon, 254
Pellet counts, 656
Periodicity, daily, 99–110
lunar and semilunar, 113–114
tidal, 111–113

See also Circadian rhythms
Periodicity and biological clocks, 98–125
suggested readings in, 574
Periphyton, and phosphorous cycle, 57
sampling and collecting of, 626–627
See also Aufwuchs
Permafrost, 318–319
Pesticides, density-independent effects of, 366–367
and food chain, 366–369
Petersen, C. G. S., 343
Peterson, R. T., 4
pH, 62
in bogs, 182
determination of, 600
soil, 247, 250, 251, 264
soil fauna, effect on, 264
in streams, 195
Phase shift, *see* Circadian rhythms
Phosphorus, 56, 63, 265
biogeochemical cycle, 56–57
in bog waters, 183
invertebrate role in phosphorus cycle, 57
Phosphorusm radioactive (P^{32}), 47
Photometer, 601
Photoperiodism, in animals and plants, 116–123
Bunning model, 118–123
and control of reproductive cycle, 117
and food of animals, 124
and food storage behavior in squirrel, 117–118
physiological mechanisms of, 118–123
and migration, 117, 391
and tundra plants, 321
See also Periodicity
Photosynthesis, 28
in arctic plants, 321
and CO_2 intake, 62
efficiency of, 35
equation for, 28
in flowing water, 194
and light intensity, 82–83
and nutrient availability, 66
optimum temperature for, 66
rate of, 35, 36
in tidal marshes, 217
and wave length of light, 35
Physical gills, 176–177
Physiological ecology, 6
Physiological mechanisms of photoperiod, 118–122

Phytoplankton, influenced by light, 84, 171
in lakes, 171
and nitrogen cycle, 62
and phosphorus cycle, 50
See also Plankton
Pioneer communities, 133–137
Pioneer communities and ionizing radiation, 85–86
Plankton, 170
in bogs, 185, 186
in lakes, 170, 171, 172
in slow streams and rivers, 203
Plants and aridity, 77–78, 293
circadian rhythms in, 99, 101–102
clines in, 443
competition in, 423; under stress of drought, 282–283
disease in, 403
dispersal in, 387–388
distribution influenced by light, 84
and excessive moisture, 75
growth influenced by wind, 82
hybridization in, 434, 454, 460, 464
and ionizing radiation, 85–87
light tolerance in, 84
long day, 116, 118–119, 122
parasitism in, 400, 401, 402–404
photoperiodism in, 114–116
polyploidy in, 465–466
population distribution of, 382–383
and salinity, 74
short day, 116, 118–119, 120, 122
Plant community, effect of ionizing radiation on, 85–87
study of, 610–635
Plant geography, 5
Playas, 293
Plotless method of sampling vegetation, 615
Pneumatophores, 190, 219
Podzols, 249, 250
Podzolization, 250
Poikilothermal, 66
Poikilotherms, acclimatization in, 71
Point quadrat method of sampling vegetation, 329
Pollen profiles, 153–154
plotting, 630
Pollution, 203–205
Polyclimax theory, 140
Polygons, stone, 319–320
Polymictic lakes, 166

Polymorphism, 439–441
Polyploids, 465
Polyploidy, 465–466
and resistance to radiation damage, 86
Population, 341–425
"crash," 377–379
decline, 360; and disease, 403–404; and dispersal, 387; and predation and parasitism, 407–410
density-dependent regulation, 367–379
density-independent regulation, 363–366
dispersal, 385–394
distribution, 382–385
energy budget of, 38–39
estimation of, 649–657
exploitation, 417–418
fluctuations in, 362–369
growth, 355–363; and age structure, 352–353; concept of, 355–356; curve, 358–359; density, 360; influence by man, 366; life equation, 361–363; rate of increase, 357–358
mortality, 347–351; estimation of, 657–659
natality, 345–346
rate of increase, 357–358
recruitment, 370
regulation of, 363–379
of soil fauna, 264, 269, 270
study of animal, 636–661
Population ecology, 5, 325–341
Population regulation, 363–382
cannibalism, 416–417
cycles, 379–382
density-dependent, 367–379
density-independent, 363–366
deterioration in quality, 378–379, 381
endocrine balance, 377–378
exploitation, 417–418
genetic feedback, 378–379
home range, 375–377
interspecific competition, 368–372
psychological stress, 377–378
social dominance and hierarchy, 373–374
territory, 372–373
Populations, relationships between, 397–425
amensalism, 348–399
disease, 402–404
intraspecific competition, 418–424
mutualism, 397–398
parasitism, 399–402

predation, 404–418
predator-prey systems, 406–407
See also Parasitism, Parasites
Populations, sampling of, 636–637
earthworms, 272–273
large litter fauna, 272
soil arthropods, 274
Ponds, 174–177
life of, 174–177
temporary, 133, 177–179
Pools in streams, 196–197
Potassium, 63, 183, 245, 250
Potholes, 285
Prairie, 79
as ecological barrier, 461–462
mixed, 15, 24, 280–281
short grass, 23, 281
tall grass, 279–280
See also Grassland
Prairie dog, destruction of, 284
effect on grassland, 284–285
social behavior of, 524, 525
Precipitation, in forest, 309
in grassland regions, 281, 282–283
and leaching in soil, 245, 248–251
in nutrient cycles, 53–54, 56
and topography and mass air movements, 52, 74–77
Precipitation-evaporation ratio, and vegetation, 79
Precocial, 540–541
Predation, 404–418
community viewpoint, 413
compensatory, 411, 415
density dependence in, 407–410
functional response in, 407–409
by fungi, 268
numerical response in, 409
regulatory effect of, 413–415
in soil community, 267
theory of, 405
total response, 410–411
types of, 410–411
variables influencing, 411–413
and vertebrate populations, 411–412
Predator, facultative, 413
generalized, 412–413
specialized, 412–413
See also Predation
Predator-prey oscillations, 405–407
Predator-prey systems, 406–407

Predator-prey (*Continued*)
and genetic feedback, 415–416
Preening in birds, 495
in courtship, 534
in displacement activity, 540
in maintenance, 495
Presence, *623*
Prey, alternate, *413*
vulnerability to predation, 411–413
Prey risk, *411–413*, 414
Producer organisms, 29, 33
and ecological pyramids, 40–41
and food chains, 29, 33, 42, 43
Production, 35–39
consumer, *36–39*, 47–48; efficiency of, 38–39; methods of estimating, 48
of grassland, 280
gross primary, 35
in lakes, 172, 173
limitation of by nutrient availability, 66
primary, 35; measurement of, 44–48; variations in plant communities, 36, 37
net primary, *35–36*
standing crop, *39–40*
in stream, 193–194, 197
and succession, 130
in tidal marshes, 217
Productivity classes of lakes, *177*
Psychrometer, sling, 603
Psychological stress, 377–378
Pyramids, age, 352–353
biomass, *40*
energy, *40–41*
numbers, *40*

Quadrats, 343, 611–612
Quarter method of sampling vegetation, 617–618

Rabies, 404
Races, geographical, 5, 452
ring of, 452–453
Radiation, of heat from ground, 88
See also Ionizing radiation, Light
Radio tracking, determination of home range by, 649
Radioactive material in ecosystem, 57–58
Radioactive tracers, estimation of primary production by, 47, 631, 632

in following nutrient cycles, 47, 55
in marking animals, 640
Radioactive wastes, pollution by, 203
Radiosensitivity of animals and plants, 85–87
Rain forest, *see* Forest
Rainfall in forest, 309–310
Rain shadow, 74, 75, 292
Random distribution, 382
Random pairs, sampling vegetation by, 616
Random sample, 342
Rate, birth, crude, 346
specific, 346
Rate, death, 347
Rate, mortality, 370
Rate, population growth, 355
Rate, reproductive, gross, 346
net, *346*
Rate of increase, 357–358
Raunkiaer life forms, 20
Ray, John, 470
Realms of Wallace, 334
Reciprocal feeding, 533
Redirection activity, 491
Reed, C. A., 4
References, behavior study, 668
collecting animals, 661
dendrochronology, 634–635
estimating animal populations, 660–661
palynology, 634
phytoplankton study, 634
primary production, 635
vegetation analysis, 634
Refractory period, *117*
Regolith, *244*
Releasers, 488, 529, 530
in courtship display, 534
in enemy recognition, 505–506
in feeding behavior of young, 504–505
in food begging of young, 505–506
in incubation behavior, 539, 540
Removal method of estimating populations, 652
Reproduction, asexual, 454
gross rate of, 346
in mule deer, 353–354
and natural selection, 437
net rate of, 346
non-random, *436*
periods of, 351
sexual, 454
Reproduction curves, *370–371*
illustrating rates of exploitation, 417

illustrating cannibalism, 416
Reproductive behavior, 526–538
Reptiles, circadian rhythm in, 103, 108
celestial orientation in, 110
of desert, 297–299
marking, 638
navigation in, 393–394
and pesticides, 367
sex ratio in, 354
of swamps, 191
Rhythms, *see* Annual rhythms, Circadian rhythms, Lunar and semilunar rhythms, Periodicity and Biological clocks, Tidal rhythms
Riffle, *195*, 196
Rill erosion, *146*
Rivers, *see* Streams, slow
Roadside counts, 656
Rocks and cliffs, succession on, 133–134
Rocky shore, 232–233
Northeast Atlantic Coast, 223–229
Pacific Coast, 231–232
physical conditions of, 223, 230, 231, 233
Southern Atlantic Coast, 229
zonation of, 223–232
Rodents, and vegetation, 284, 327
Roentgen, 85
Ruminents, *31*
Runoff, surface, 52
See also Erosion
Rules, Allen's, 444
Bergmann's, 444
Gloger's, 444

Saline areas, inland, 189
Salinity, adjustment of plants to, 74
determination of in water, 599
of estuarine water, 211–212
gradient in estuary, 211–212
influence on life in estuary, 213–214
of sea water, 158
of tidal pools, 232
Salt gland in birds, 74
Salt marshes, 189, *215–219*
Sampling, 342–344
Sampling accuracy, 342
Sampling animal populations, 342–344, 650–655
Sampling in dendrochronology, 627
Sampling drift in stream, 208
Sampling earthworm populations, 272–273

Sampling estimate, 342
Sampling, indirect methods, 344, 655–657
Sampling, mark recapture method, 343
Sampling parameter, 342
Sampling peat, 629
Sampling periphyton, 625–627
Sampling phytoplankton, 625
Sampling plots, 343
Sampling precision, 343
Sampling quadrats, 343
Sampling small soil arthropods, 274
Sampling soil, 606
Sampling stream bottom organisms, 208, 209
Sampling vegetation, 342–344, 611–618
Sand, 253
Sand dunes, succession on, 134
  vegetation of, 134
Sandy shore, 234–239
  physical conditions of, 234–235
  zonation of, 237–239
Savanna, 314–315, 333
Saprophytes, 33
  food chains in, 34
Scavengers, 33
  food chain in, 34
Scientific names, 474–477
Sclater, Phillip, 334
Scuba zone, 229
Seashore, 221–242
  loose rocks and boulders, 233–234
  under rock fauna, 233–234
  suggested field activities, 240–242
  suggested readings in, 576
    See also Rocky shore, Sandy shore, Habitats
Secchi disk, 601
Sedgwich-Rafter counter, 625
Sedimentary cycle, 53–57
Selection, direction of, 464
  disruptive, 464–465
  intergroup, 466–467
  stabilizing, 464
Selection cutting, 144
Selective pressure, 416
    See also Natural selection
Seral stages, 127
Sere, 127
Sewage pollution, 204
Sex ratio, 354–355
  estimation of mortality by, 658–659
  and natural selection, 355

Sexual behavior, see Behavior, Courtship Behavior
Sexual dimorphism and display, 530
  as isolating mechanism, 530
Sexual selection, 459
Sheet erosion, 146
Shelford, Victor, 5, 61, 333
Shelter, types of, 497
Shelter seeking, 497–500
Shrub carr community, 290
Shrubland and desert, 289–299
  suggested field activities, 299–300
  suggested readings in, 577–578
Sieves, soil, 606
Sigmoid growth curve, 356, 359
Sign stimulus, 488
Silicon, 244
Silt, 253
Siltation, 205
Site index, 345
Slow streams, see Streams, slow
Smell, in navigation by fishes, 393
Snails, marking, 638
  polymorphism in, 441
Snowbed plant community, 322
Snowbank vegetation, methods of study of, 329
Sociability, 620
Social behavior, 513–543
Social dominance, 521–524
  and leadership, 525–526
Social groups, cooperative, 524–525
Social insects, 524–525
Social parasitism, 401–402
Sodium, 61, 64, 74
Soil, 243–260
  aggregates, 253; influenced by earthworm, 265
  arthropods, role in, 267
  associations, 256
  atmosphere, collecting samples of, 604–605; determination of composition, 604–605
  characteristics as a medium for life, 261–263
  chemical activity in influenced by soil arthropods, 268
  classification, 254–255
  collecting samples of, 606
  color of, 253–254
  conduction of heat by, 91
  development and time, 252–253
  diversity of species in, 263
  earthworm activity in, 265

drainage and soil development, 251–252
  as an environment, 261–264
  faunal community of, 264–271
  formation of, 243–246; as influenced by vegetation, 244
  horizons, 245; characteristics of, 245–246; development of, 245; in forest soils, 250–251; in grassland, 250
  life in, 261–271
  organic horizon on forest floor, 246–248
  organic matter, determination of, 605
  organisms, marking of, 639; trapping and collecting, 272–274, 637
  pathway between organic and mineral world, 243
  pH in, 264; determination of, 600
  pore space in, 263
  predacious fungi in, 268
  profile, 245, 246
  profile differentiation, 248–252
  root penetration in, 277–278
  saline, 251
  structure, 253; influenced by earthworms, 264–265; in relation to fauna, 263
  suggested field activities, 258–260, 328–329
  temperature in, 270; measurement, 260, 603
  termites in tropical soils, 266
  texture, 253; determination of, 605–606
  and topography, 257
  of tundra and instability of, 320, 323
  water retention capacity of, 77
Soil community, ants in, 268
  collembola in, 267–268
  earthworms in, 264–265
  energy source for, 264
  millipedes influence on, 265–266
  mites in, 266–267
  moles in, 268
  prairie dogs in, 268–269
  predation in, 267
Soil fauna, population density of, 269
  in mor, 269, 270
  in mull, 269, 270
  population fluctuations of, 270

Soil fauna   (*Continued*)
  relationship   to   vegetation,
    270–271
  role in humus development,
    247
  study of, 272–274
  vertical migration of, 270
  zonation of, 270
Soil series, 255
Soil types, 256
Soil-water relationships, 251,
    252, 253–254
Solar radiation as energy source
    for ecosystem, 28–29
  and temperature at ground
    level, 88
Solicitation display, 534–535
Solifluction terraces, 319
Song, annual rhythm in, 114
  as isolating mechanism, 536–
    537
Space and social dominance,
    523–524
Speciation, adaptative radiation,
    467–470
  convergence, 470
  geographical, 454–456
  and hybrids, 454
  intergroup selection, 466–467
  isolating mechanisms, 456–
    460; breakdown in, 460–
    464
  non-geographic, disruptive se-
    lection, 464–465
  and reproduction, 454
Species, agamospecies, 454
  allopatric, 451
  biological, 451, 453
  characteristic of community,
    how determined, 25
  concept of, 448–454
  definition of in bisexual or-
    ganisms, 450
  exclusive, 25
  monotypic, 448
  morphological, 448, 450
  opportunistic, 16
  sibling, 450
  and speciation, 448–481
  ubiquitous, 25
Species area curve, 611
Species composition and second-
    ary succession, 136–137
Species diversity, 14, 15–16
  in coniferous and deciduous
    forest, 311–313
  evolution of, 470–472
  in mor, 247
  in mull, 247
  in simple ecosystems, 15
  in small organisms, 16
  in soil, 263

in tropical ecosystems, 15
    See also Abundance
Species problem, 448–454
Species structure in relation to
    succession, 129–131
Species Plantarium, 470, 480
Specific gravity, 158
  and plankton movement, 171
Specific heat, 159
Springs, ecology of, 206
  energy budget of, 44
Spring tides, 222
Sphagnum moss, in bogs, 184
  in moors, 186
Stable polymorphism, 440–441
Stand composition, 620
Standing crop, 39–40
Statistical analysis, in dendro-
    chronology, 629
  in mark-recapture census, 652
  in removal census, 652–653
Statistical methods, annotated
    bibliography of, 593
Stemflow, ecological significance
    of, 309
Stratification, community, 19–
    20
  expression of genetic charac-
    ter of plants, 20
  in forest, 305–311
  in grassland, 277–278
  horizontal, 20–21
  in lakes, 163–167
  of life in forest, 311–314
  of life in grassland, 283,
    284, 285
  of life in lakes, 170–174
  of plankton in lakes, 171–
    172
  in tropical rain forest, 313,
    314
  vertical, 21
    See also Light, Oxygen,
    Temperature
Streams (flowing water), 192–
    209
  collecting periphyton in, 626
  determination of current and
    flow, 600
  drift, index of production,
    200
  food production in, 196
  gradient, 192–193
  longitudinal succession, 201
    202, 206
  physical characteristics of,
    193–195
  pollution in, 203–205
  pools in, 195–196
  riffles in, 195
  sampling bottom organisms,
    208–209

temperature, 194
Streams, fast, 195–200
  adjustment of organisms to,
    198–200
  aufwuchs in, 195
  bottom types, 196–197
  life in, 197–200
  physical conditions in, 195–
    197
Streams, slow, 201–203
  adjustment of life in, 202
  physical characteristics of,
    202
  plankton in, 203
Strip census, 651
Strip mine spoil banks, succes-
    sion on, 137, 138
Strontium-90, cycling in eco-
    system, 58
Subspecies, 452
Succession, 127–155
  aquatic, 131–133
  in bogs, 183–185
  characteristics of, 129–131
  controlled by community,
    137, 142
  climax, 140–141
  cyclic replacement, 139–140
  early history of idea, 129
  effect on prairie chicken habi-
    tat, 285
  gap-phase replacement, 139
  in glacial till, 134–135
  in grassland, 145, 281, 282,
    283
  heterotrophic, 141–142
  influences on succession,
    cultivation, 146–149; fire,
    142–143; grazing and
    browsing, 145–146; indus-
    trialization and urbaniza-
    tion, 149–150; lumbering,
    143–144; radiation, 151
  and ionizing radiation, 86,
    151
  longitudinal in streams, 201–
    202
  marsh succession around pond,
    132
  nature of, 129–131
  in old fields, 128, 139–140
  of past communities, 151–152
  pioneer communities, 131,
    133–136
  in pond, 174–177
  primary, 128, 131–136
  principle of, 6
  on rocks and cliffs, 133–134
  on sand dunes, 134
  on strip mine spoil banks,
    137, 138
  regression of, 138, 185

Succession (*Continued*)
  secondary, *128, 136–140*
  seral stages, *127*
  sere, *127*
  species composition in primary succession, 133–136
  species composition in secondary succession, 136, 137
  suggested readings in, 575
  summarized, 137
  terrestrial, *133–140*
Suggested field activities, bogs and marshes, 191
  estuary, tidal marshes and swamps, 220
  forest, 316–317
  grassland, 287–288
  lakes and ponds, 179–181
  life in soil, 271–274
  seashore, 240–242
  shrubland and desert, 299–300
  soil, 258–260
  streams, 207–209
  tundra, 328–330
Suggested readings, aquatic habitats, 575–576
  behavior, 581–582
  community, 573
  distribution of communities, 579
  ecosystem ecology, 573–574
  energy flow and biogeochemical cycles, 573–574
  environmental influences, 574
  forest, 578
  grasslands, 577
  natural selection, 580
  periodicity and biological clocks, 574
  population ecology, 579–580
  seashore, 576
  shrubland and desert, 577–578
  soil, 577
  succession, 575
  tundra, 578
Sulphur, 63
Sunbathing, 496
Surface tension, 160
Survey traverse, 607
Survival, 347, 351
  See also Mortality
Survivorship curves, *350–351*
Swamps, 186, *190–191*
  anchorage of vegetation, 190
  animal life in, 191
  characteristics of, 190–191
  classification of, 188–189
  mangroves, 189, 219–220
Symbiosis, 398

Symbolic nest building, 533
Sympatry, *451, 452, 453,* 457
Synecology, 5
Synomomy, 480
Syntype, *481*
Systema Naturae, 475, 478, 480

Territory, 372–373, 519, 521
  colonial, 421, 422, 519–520
  competition for, 421–422
  determination of, 649
  in regulation of populations, 372–373
  in relation to predation, 411, 415
  size of, 373
  and social dominance, 523–524
  types of, 519–521
Thermistors, 603
Thermocline, *163,* 167, 168, 169
Thermometers, 602
Thoreau, 129
Threat display, *see* Agonistic display
Tidbitting, 533–534
Tidal creeks, 216
Tidal marsh, *215–219*
  ecological importance of, 217
Tidal overmixing, 212
Tidal rhythms, *111–113*
Tide pools, 232–233
  mapping, 241–242
Tides, 98, *221–222*
Till, glacial, *244*
Time memory, *109–110*
Tansley, 5
Taxonomy, *474–481*
Temperature, 66–74, 79
  adapted races of frogs, 442–443
  air, determination of, 602
  in alpine soil, 323
  critical, 72
  and development of poikilotherms, 66–67
  differences between north and south slopes, 94
  and distribution of Cassins finches, 338
  and distribution of frogs, 73
  and distribution of animals and plants, 73–74
  of estuarine water, 212
  and evaporation, 76
  extremes, effect on poikilotherms, 70–71
  fluctuations, in, 66
  and germination of desert plants, 295

gradient reduced by height of vegetation, 88
  interaction with moisture, 79
  inversion, 96
  Merriams, law of temperature control, 337
  optimal temperature for hibernators, 69
  optimum, 66
  overturn in soil, 270
  and plant growth in tundra regions, 321
  preferred, 66
  profiles in ground and air, 89
  on rocky shore, 67, 223
  on sandy shore, 235
  soil, determination of, 603
  and soil development, 245
  stratification in forest, 310
  stratification in grassland, 88, 90, 278
  stratification in lakes, 163–166
  of streams, 194
  water, determination of, 602
  Zeitgeber, in circadian rhythms, 103
Termites, role in soil, 266
Terrestrial habitats, determination of light in, 601–602
  determination of primary production in, 46–47, 630–632
  determination of temperature, 602–603
Tooth replacement and wear as aging technique, 642
Topography and precipitation, 74–75
Topography and soil development, 251, 252
Topography and tundra vegetation, 321–322
Torpidity in birds, 297
Torry, John, 479
Total estimate, 619–620
Transects, 343
Transformers, 33
Transient polymorphism, *439–440*
Transpiration, 52
  influenced by wind, 82
Trapping and collecting, aquatic organisms, 637
  birds, 637
  insects, flying, 637
  mammals, 637, 652, 653, 655
  small animals in vegetation, 637
  soil organisms, 272–275, 637
Traverse, survey, 607–608
Trophic level, *13,* 29–33
  degradation of energy through, 42–52

Trophic structure of lakes, 170
Trophogenic zone, *169*
Tropholytic zone, *169,* 172
Tropical rain forest, 314–315, 333
Tropical shrub biome, 333
Tschermak, 430
Tundra, 23, *318–330*
  alpine, 318–320, 324, 327
  alpine tundra of Appalachians and Rockies compared, 323–324
  arctic, 318–322, 326–327
  suggested field activities, 328–330
  suggested readings, 578
Types, *480–481*
Type specimen, *481*

Ubiquitous species, *25*
Ultraviolet radiation, 82
Uniform distribution, 382

Vapor pressure deficit, 75
Variable plot method of vegetational sampling, *615–616*
Variation, clinal, *442–443*
  genetic, 432–437
  geographical, 439–442, 452–456
  and mutations, 435–436, 438
  and natural selection, 436–437, 439–440, 454–456
  within population, 432, 433
Vascularization in arctic animals, 72
Vegetation, adaptive differences in arctic and alpine plants, 321
  alpine, 320–321, 322–324
  analysis of sampling data, 618–627; abundance, *618;* constancy, *624;* continuum, *622;* cover, *618–619;* fidelty, *624;* importance value, *621;* presence, *623;* sociability, *620;* stand composition, *620;* total estimate, *619–620*
  arctic, 320–322
  and browsing animals, 145–146
  of chaparral, 290–291
  continuum, 18
  of desert, 293
  discontinuous distribution of, *18*
  and distribution of soil fauna, 270–271
  establishment of, 17
  of grassland, 279–281
  of forest, 301–305

ionizing radiation effects on, 84–87, 151
of lake shore, 174–177
of mangrove swamps, 219–220
moderation of microclimate by, 88
of north-facing slopes, 91–93, 96, 322
of ponds, 174–177
of rocky shore, 223–232
and rodents, 284–285, 327
of salt pans, 217
sampling of, 611–618; loop method, 614–615; point quadrat, 329; quadrats, 611–612; quarter method, 617–618; random pairs, 616; transects, 613–614; variable plot, 615, 616
sampling past communities, 627
sampling phytoplankton and periphyton, 625–626
of sand dunes, 134
of seral shrublands, 289–290
of snowbeds, 322
of south-facing slopes, 91–93, 96, 322
in streams, 195, 200
and temperature gradient near the ground, 88
of tidal marsh, 215–217
of tidal pool, 232–233
and wind, 323
wind deflection by, 90
Velocity of current in streams, 192–193, 195
Velocity of wind in forest, 310
Verhulst, 5, 359
Verhulst-Pearl equation, 359
Vertebrate populations, and predation, 411–415
Virus disease, 403, 415–416
Viscosity, *159–160*
  of water and plankton movements, 171
Vocalization, in amphibians, 536
  in birds, 535–536
  in insects, 536–537
  role in courtship, 536–537
Voice, warning calls, 507
Volterra, 418–419
de Vries, 430

Wallace, Alfred, 334, 429–430, 450, 470
Wallace's Line, 336
Wallacea, 336
Water, *157–161*
  carbon dioxide determination, 598–599

capillary, 76
collecting sample of, 596
current determination, 600–601
and grazing in grassland, 278
ground, 76
hard, 62
hydroscopic, 76
latent heat, *159*
hardness, determination of, 598–599
light penetration of, 84; determination of, 601–602
as medium for life, 157–161
oxygen, determination of, 597–598
pH determination, 600
salinity determination, 599
salinity of sea, 158
soft, 62
specific heat, *159*
structure of, *157–158*
surface tension, *160*
temperature determination, 602
viscosity, *159*

Water balance, maintenance of, 74
Water conservation in desert animals, 298
Water cycle, *52–53*
Water mold, 404
Water table, effect of forest removal on, 144–145
Waves, standing, *167–169*
Webers Line, 336
Weeds, in secondary succession, 136
Wetlands, *186–191*
  classification of, 188–189
Whipple ocular, 625, 626
Wilson, 5
Wind, *81–82*
  effect on alpine vegetation, 323
  and arctic vegetation, 321
  deflection by vegetation, 90
  and evaporation, 76
  in forest, 310
  and insect migration, 389
  movement in dense vegetation, 90
  velocity in coniferous forest, 92
Windthrow, 82
Woodland biome, 333

Zeitgeber, *103, 113*
Zinc, 64
Zonation, altitudinal, 79
  of coraline shores, 230–231

Zonation   (*Continued*)
   on lake shores, 164–165, 169,
      174–177
   of rocky shores, 223–232
   of salinity in estuaries, 212
   of sandy shore, 237–239
   in snowbed community, 322

of tidal marshes, 215–217
of vegetation on east-west
   gradient, 79
      See *also* Stratification,
      and specific names of
      zones
Zones, life, 337–338

Zoological regions, *see* Biogeographical regions
Zooplankton, in lakes, 171
   and phosphorus cycle, 56
   sampling of, 650
   and vertical migration of,
      171

Set in Linotype Fairfield

Format by Frances Torbert Tilley

Composition by The Haddon Craftsman

Printed by The Haddon Craftsman

Manufactured by The Haddon Craftsman